U. S. Geological Survey men using a theodolite to measure angles between mountain tops in **Antarctica**.

THE BOOK OF
POPULAR
SCIENCE

Volume 2

Grolier
INCORPORATED
New York

Distributed in the United States by
THE GROLIER SOCIETY INC.

Distributed in Canada by
THE GROLIER SOCIETY OF CANADA LIMITED

Cover photograph: Eternal
Castle Rock, rising above
Oak Creek Canyon, Arizona.

Ray Manley—Shostal

The Library of Congress Catalog Card Number: 65-10083

15 ✿

CONTENTS OF VOLUME II

(Continued on next page)

CONTENTS OF VOLUME II (Continued)

BASIC UNITS OF LIFE*

The Structure and Functions of Living Cells

PRACTICALLY all living things, from the very smallest to the greatest — from the microscopic ameba and single-celled algae to huge whales and redwood trees — are made up of cells. Many animals and plants consist of one cell, which is the whole individual. Others have passed far beyond this unicellular, or one-celled, stage; they are made up of a great number of cells that are joined together. Such animals or plants are called multicellular (many-celled). The exact significance of "many" in this case can be seen from the fact that more than six million cells may be found in a drop of human blood.

What do we mean by a living cell? Ordinarily, when we speak of a cell, we have in mind a compartment — say a prison cell or the cell of a beehive — which may be empty or not. The walls are the essential factors in compartments of this kind. The prison cell would be just as much of a cell even if there were no prisoner in it; the cell of the honeycomb would still be a cell, even if it were not filled with honey.

When Robert Hooke, an English experimenter of the seventeenth century, examined cork under magnifying lenses, it seemed to him to be made up of just such compartments as those of a bee's hive or the cells of a prison. It is natural, therefore, that he called these plant compartments cells. Later investigators were impressed by the strong and thick walls of the plant cells. They were impressed, too, by the fact that while some of the cells seemed to

* The editors wish to acknowledge the assistance of the Upjohn Company in preparing the illustrative material for this article.

Both photos, National Teaching Aids, Inc.

At the left, above, we show a greatly enlarged view of onion-skin cells. Below: cells from the human cheek.

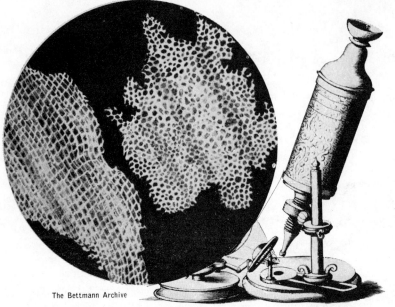

Drawings by Robert Hooke from his book *Micrographia*. At the far left is a very thin longitudinal section of cork as seen under the microscope; next to it is a cross section of cork. We also see here the microscope used by Hooke. He was the first to show that plants consist of cells; but he failed to realize that his instrument revealed only the empty "shells" of dead cork.

be filled with something, others appeared to be empty. They came to the conclusion, therefore, that the cell wall was the important thing. They did not realize that if certain cells appeared to be empty when they were viewed through the microscope, the reason was simply that the contents had oozed out while the cells were being prepared for microscopic investigation.

Still later, it was discovered that cells could be found in animals, too. But the biologists of that period had no idea of the wide distribution and importance of cells.

It was not until the nineteenth century that scientists came to realize the true significance of cells. In 1838–39, two German physiologists, Theodor Schwann and Matthias Jakob Schleiden, working independently, advanced a new and revolutionary cell theory. They held that living things, from the simplest to the most complex, are made up almost entirely of cells and that these cells play an important part in all the activities of life. Later, it was found that not only do the bodies of all the higher animals and plants consist of cells but that each one of these living things has sprung from a single cell.

Modern science has discarded the old idea that the wall *is* the cell and that the contents are mere stuffing, so to speak. We realize now that the important part, the truly living part, of each cell is the contents, to which we give the name "protoplasm." We know that the protoplasm is the scene of the chemical changes that bring about digestion, absorption, muscular activity and all the other activities of life. To be sure, we still use the word "cells" in referring to the units of living organisms. But when specialists in cytology (the study of cells) speak of cells, they have in mind not only the enclosing walls or membranes, but also the living matter inside.

According to the modern conception, the cell is a mass of protoplasm enclosed in a membrane, known as the plasma membrane, and often by a more or less durable wall. The protoplasm is not uniform throughout but shows certain well-defined areas. A nucleus, or core, lies in a more or less central position. (Some cells have more than one nucleus.) The protoplasm that surrounds the nucleus is called the cytoplasm. The nucleus is also enclosed in a membrane. Both the cytoplasm and the nucleus contain various important structures, which we shall discuss later.

The cells of multicellular organisms form tissues — nervous, muscular, connective and the like; tissues combine to form organs such as the heart, intestines and pancreas. The tissues and organs simply co-ordinate the various activities of the individual cells so that the organism as a whole can function properly. We can think of the individual cells as having a life of their own. They absorb various substances; they burn fuels and in so doing release energy for their many activities; they synthesize, or build up, complex substances; they manufacture and secrete hormones and enzymes, which control vital body processes; they eliminate waste products; they reproduce by undergoing division. Thus the activities that engage an organism as a whole are accomplished by the protoplasm contained in an individual cell.

The composition of protoplasm

The composition of protoplasm varies considerably, depending on the particular plant or animal and the kind of tissue. The water content averages roughly 75 per cent. There may be only a small proportion of protein in a cell, or else there may be as much as 30 per cent, as in certain muscle cells. The other constituents of protoplasm, including fatty substances, carbohydrates and minerals, generally make up only a small proportion. In bone, however, the mineral content may be nearly 50 per cent.

Water. Some of the water in protoplasm is bound chemically with the proteins of the cell. The rest of it exists in a free state as the water molecule, H_2O, in which two atoms of hydrogen (H) are combined with one atom of oxygen (O). The free water in protoplasm is a most effective solvent. In it, the inorganic substances called salts ionize: that is, they break up into electrically charged atoms or groups of atoms called ions. Organic substances are either dissolved or dispersed in the water of protoplasm. The result is that chemical reactions are speeded up. The chemical exchanges between dissolved molecules and ions proceed faster than if these substances remained in solid form.

Generally, the greater the water content of cells, the more intense the vital activities that take place. For example, the cells making up fatty tissue have relatively little water, consume little oxygen and release little energy. The cells composing the nervous tissue of the spine and brain contain much more water and consume much more oxygen; they provide the energy necessary for the conduction of nerve impulses.

Proteins. The proteins contained in protoplasm are essential building blocks of this living substance. Among other things, they are important constituents of enzymes — substances that speed up chemical reactions within the body. Associated with proteins in this vital activity are the vitamins. These substances, which are present in minute quantities, serve as coenzymes — that is, as partners in enzyme systems. (See the article The Vitamins, in Volume 5.)

Proteins are formed from varying combinations of chemical substances called amino acids (see Index). There are more than twenty of these acids; each contains an amino group, $-NH_2$ (a compound of nitrogen and hydrogen), and a carboxyl group, $-COOH$ (a compound of carbon, oxygen and hydrogen). Each of the amino acids forms a "link" in the "chain" of which the protein molecule consists; there may be more than a thousand "links." Some proteins are made up entirely of amino acids; they are called simple proteins. Other proteins are more complex. They consist of simple proteins to which are attached various other substances, such as carbohydrates and phosphorus.

Since the amino acids can form all sorts of combinations, the number of entirely different kinds of proteins is exceedingly great. Different cells have different kinds of proteins. The proteins in a man's kidney cells differ from those in his muscle cells and from those in the kidney cells of a dog.*

Fatty substances. The fatty substances in the cell are called lipids (from the Greek word *lipos*, meaning "fat"). They form part of the protoplasmic structure; they also serve as a reserve energy source and com-

---

* It has been found that the cells of corresponding tissues in different animals have a certain affinity for each other. Cells from the kidney tissue of mice and chickens have been grown together in special solutions and have yielded strange hybrid "pseudotissues." See the article "How Cells Associate," in the *Scientific American*, September, 1961, pages 142–62.

ANIMAL CELL

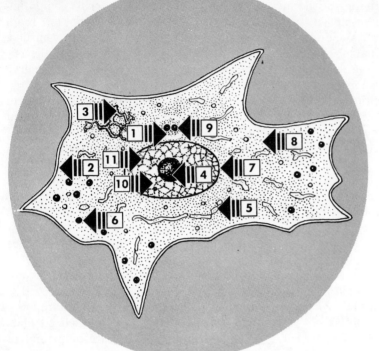

1 CENTROSOME
2 CELL WALL
3 GOLGI SUBSTANCE
4 NUCLEOLUS
5 MITOCHONDRIA
6 FAT DROPLET
7 NUCLEAR MEMBRANE
8 CYTOPLASM
9 CENTRIOLES
10 NUCLEAR SAP
11 CHROMATIN

PLANT CELL

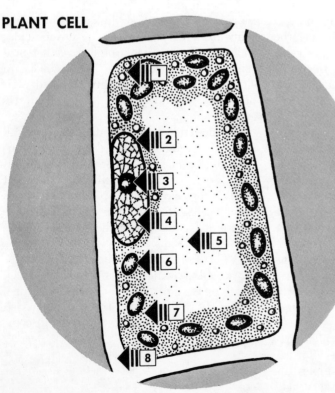

1 MITOCHONDRIA
2 NUCLEAR MEMBRANE
3 NUCLEOLUS
4 CHROMATIN
5 VACUOLE
6 PLASTID
7 CYTOPLASM
8 CELL WALL

Gen. Biol. Supply House, Chicago

pose many of the cell pigments. Some of the lipids are completely insoluble in the water of the protoplasm; they disperse themselves throughout in the form of tiny droplets. In other cases, certain chemical groups attached to the lipids apparently bind these fatty substances to the water molecules.

Lipids may be either simple or complex. The alcohol known as glycerol (glycerine) and the so-called fatty acids are combined to make up the simpler lipids. Weight for weight, the latter release more energy when burned in the cell than do any of the other substances in the protoplasm. However, since they are not so easily burned as are the sugars, the simple lipids are stored in cells as reserve sources of energy. They are found in abundance in the cells of adipose, or fatty, tissues of animals. The simple lipids of plant and animal cells include cocoa butter, olive oil, lard and fish oils.

The complex lipids include the phospholipids, steroids, carotenoids and lipoproteins. Phospholipids are fatty substances containing phosphorus and nitrogen; they occur principally in the cellular structure of nervous tissue. Some steroids are produced by the liver and are a part of the bile. Certain steroids (called sterols) serve as hormones, regulating various activities of the body. (See Index, under Hormones.) The carotenoids are represented by several important cell pigments, including the carotenes, found in carrots and grass. Lipoproteins are lipids linked to protein molecules; they form part of the nucleus and the membranes of the cell.

Carbohydrates. The carbohydrates are made up of the chemical elements carbon, hydrogen and oxygen. The proportion of hydrogen atoms to oxygen atoms in carbohydrates is always 2 to 1, just as it is in the water molecule, H_2O. A carbohydrate, therefore, may be considered as "watered carbon." This accounts for the name "carbohydrates," for "hydrate" is derived from the Greek word *hydor*, meaning "water." *

* The carbohydrates should not be confused with the hydrocarbons. Hydrocarbons are so called because they contain only hydrogen atoms and carbon atoms; "hydro-" in this case is an abbreviation of "hydrogen." Methane (CH_4) and butane (C_4H_{10}) are typical hydrocarbons.

One of the most important of the carbohydrates is the sugar known as glucose. It has the formula $C_6H_{12}O_6$, indicating that the glucose molecule contains 6 carbon (C) atoms, 12 hydrogen (H) atoms and 6 oxygen (O) atoms. It is formed in the cells of plants by the process of photosynthesis, which we describe later in this article, and it is used by these cells as an immediate source of energy. Animal cells, too, burn glucose to provide energy. Glucose is a monosaccharide — the simplest form in which a sugar can exist as such.

When two monosaccharides join together, they form a disaccharide. Lactose, sucrose and maltose are all disaccharides. Lactose is found in animal cells; sucrose and maltose in plant cells. The disaccharides can be broken down to give energy; they readily dissolve in the cell's protoplasm.

When a number of monosaccharides combine chemically, the resulting substance is called a polysaccharide. Starch and cellulose are plant polysaccharides. Starch serves as a food reserve; it exists in the form of granules in the protoplasm. Cellulose goes into the plant cell walls and other supporting structures forming the plant's skeleton. Glycogen, or animal starch, is a polysaccharide found in animal cells. It is an energy source; it occurs, dissolved in the protoplasm, in a variety of cells, but most abundantly in those of the liver and the muscles.

Carbohydrates often unite with protein or mineral elements, such as sulfur and phosphorus. Various important complex substances are formed in this way. Pentoses — sugars whose molecules contain five carbon atoms — link with phosphoric acid and nitrogen-containing groups to form nucleic acids. One of the nucleic acids, called ribonucleic acid, or RNA, is concerned with the building up of proteins in the cell. Another one — deoxyribonucleic acid, or DNA — occurring in the nucleus, is associated with the chromosomes, the hereditary matter of the cell. We discuss nucleic acids elsewhere (see Index).

Inorganic materials. The inorganic substances in protoplasm include various salts and mineral elements. In the watery protoplasm, the salts are broken up into ions; thus common salt, or sodium chloride (NaCl), separates into positive sodium and negative chloride ions. The numerous ions must be present in the right amounts in the cell so that a balance, or equilibrium, may exist among them. For instance, the protoplasm must have calcium ions, in minute quantities, in order to balance sodium, potassium and magnesium ions.

We find about the same relative concentrations of salt ions in the body fluids that circulate around the cells as we do in sea water. It is especially true of the ions mentioned in the preceding paragraph. This is a significant fact, since biologists think that life probably originated in the ocean.

It is important to note that the various ions in protoplasm remain as free ions as long as they are in solution. Thus, instead of referring to the common salt in protoplasm, it is more accurate to refer to the sodium and chloride ions into which the salt is broken up in solution. In the case of the other salts, too, we are particularly interested in the ions they form in protoplasm. These salts exist only in the form of ions as long as the protoplasm retains its water content — that is, as long as the cell is alive.

Sodium ions are more abundant than the other ions of cells. They play an important part in controlling the diffusion of substances into and out of the cell through the plasma membrane. Together with potassium, sodium increases the viscosity, or sticky consistency, of the cell's internal protoplasm.

Potassium ions seem to play an important part in the conduction of nervous impulses by nerve cells and the contraction of muscle cells. Magnesium, which exists in protoplasm in small quantities, forms an essential part of the green plant pigment, chlorophyll. Magnesium and calcium ions tend to make the protoplasm more fluid.

The presence of calcium ions in the cell lowers the permeability of the plasma membrane, so that only small amounts of water and a few dissolved substances can pass through. Calcium ions are vitally important in speeding up the action of various enzymes. They are essential, too, for nerve-cell responses and the contraction of muscle cells.

Iron, copper and zinc occur as part of various enzymes. Sulfur is found in proteins and is an essential constituent of many enzymes. Phosphate forms a bond with lipids, proteins and sugars; this bond is often exceedingly important as a source of energy.

Forms in which the components of protoplasm occur

The components of protoplasm, ranging from relatively simple water molecules and salt ions to the complex molecules of carbohydrates, lipids and proteins, occur in various forms. Salts and some carbohydrates are dissolved in the water of the protoplasm. Other carbohydrates and the proteins and lipids are suspended in water as aggregates (clumps) or as macromolecules (large or long molecules). Though they are too small to be seen through the ordinary microscope, they are too large to pass through membranes that are permeable to ions and small crystalline substances. They belong to the group called the colloids (see Index). The vital chemical activities of the cell take place at the surfaces of the colloidal particles.

The consistency of protoplasm varies in different cells; it even changes in the same cell from a sol, or rather freely flowing liquid, to a fairly firm gel, or jellylike structure. The gel condition is apparently due to the fact that the dispersed colloidal particles are attracted to one another and are linked together to form a three-dimensional network. In the gel condition, water fills the spaces in the network. When the network breaks down, the colloidal particles are dispersed and the protoplasm becomes a sol.

Many colloidal particles, such as various proteins and enzymes, may clump together in crystalline form. There is some evidence that the structure of protoplasm, especially in the gel state, has an inherent crystalline pattern.

The living cell may possess a "skeleton" in the form of complex internal membranes stretching throughout the cytoplasm. These membranes make up what is called the endoplasmic reticulum ("network occurring within the protoplasm"). It may be a continuation of the outer cell (or plasma) membrane. The endoplasmic reticulum is probably involved in the vital process of metabolism.

The cell and
its surroundings

The protoplasm of the cell is usually enclosed by walls or membranes of some sort, to protect it from the environment and to regulate what passes out of and into the cell proper. In plants, each cell is often surrounded by a more or less rigid wall of cellulose, a woody carbohydrate material. The animal cell is contained in a more flexible envelope, called a pellicle, or cuticle, and consisting of protein. Both the cellulose walls of plant cells and the pellicles of animal cells permit water and substances dissolved in water to pass through quite freely.

Just inside the cell wall or pellicle at the surface of the living cytoplasm is the plasma membrane, much thinner than the surrounding cell wall or pellicle. It is known as a semipermeable membrane; it permits certain substances — liquids, gases or dissolved solids — to pass through and restricts or prevents the passage of others. The diffusion of a liquid through such a membrane is known as osmosis.* It involves movement from a region of higher liquid concentration on one side of the membrane to a region of lower liquid concentration on the other side. Suppose that the concentration of water molecules inside a cell is less than that outside. Water will then flow into the cell through the plasma membrane. The cell will increase in size and will become more or less turgid, or swollen. If the water concentration in the inside of the cell is greater than that on the outside, water will flow out of the cell; the cell will shrink.

Water is not the only substance that flows through the plasma membrane; glu-

* Some scientists apply the term osmosis to the passage of any substance — liquid, gas or dissolved solid — that goes through a semipermeable membrane.

cose, amino acids, salt ions, oxygen, carbon dioxide and other substances essential for the proper functioning of the cell also pass through. The passage of materials such as these is not a constant process; it varies with the concentration of these materials inside and outside the cell and with the condition of the plasma membrane.

Biologists are not certain about the structure of the plasma membrane. We know that it is exceedingly thin and slightly elastic, and that it is apparently constructed of lipids and proteins. Lipid molecules are arranged with their long axes perpendicular to the plane formed by the surface of the protoplasm. The proteins form a network at both sides (outer and inner) of the lipid layer; these two networks are parallel to the surface.

It is thought that pores of various sizes perforate these protein-lipid layers and that water and water-soluble substances (such as glucose and amino acids) pass through by way of these pores. Certain pores seem to be electrically charged; salt ions pass into the protoplasm from the outside by being attracted to these pores. Substances that are soluble in lipids get into the cell by being dissolved in the lipid layer.

The plasma membrane, shown in the diagram, is just inside the cell wall of plant cells or the pellicle (flexible envelope) of animal cells. It seems to be constructed of protein and lipid molecules. There is an outer and inner layer of protein molecules, parallel to the surface of the cell. The lipids are arranged with their long axes perpendicular to the two layers of proteins.

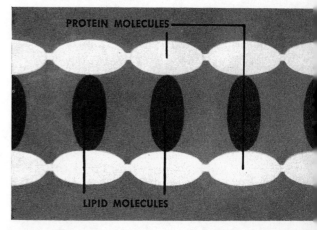

PROTEIN MOLECULES

LIPID MOLECULES

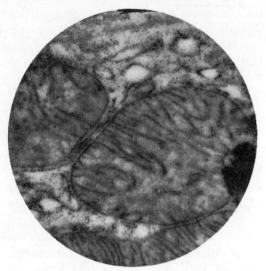

G. E. Palade

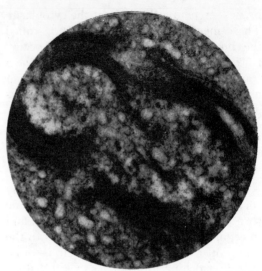

L. E. Roth and O. T. Minick

The photographs on these two pages show details of cell structure as revealed by the electron microscope. Above: mitochondria from the pancreas of a guinea pig.

The Golgi apparatus as seen in developing sperm from the snail *Otala vermiculata*. The Golgi apparatus is also called the Golgi complex and the Golgi substance.

The cell may engulf food and other materials outside itself. The plasma membrane and the cytoplasm wrap themselves about these materials, forming around the latter a clear space called a vacuole. The vacuole ultimately detaches itself from the cell boundary and moves into the cytoplasm, where its contents are absorbed. This phenomenon often occurs in one-celled animals.

**The cytoplasm
    of the cell**

We saw that cytoplasm makes up the bulk of the cell — all of it outside of the nucleus. The cytoplasm contains accumulations of protein and carbohydrate, drops of fat, pigments, small crystals and secretion granules. It also has the specialized structures called organoids, or organelles, which are distinctly visible through the ordinary microscope. The organoids include the mitochondria, lysosomes, ribosomes, Golgi apparatus, cell center and plastids.

The *mitochondria* are small structures in the form of granules, spherical bodies, short rods or filaments. They are made up of protein and lipid material, forming a stable and comparatively rigid gel. Apparently, they can divide. Sometimes, too, the threadlike mitochondria break up into

granules, and the granules unite to form filaments. Mitochondria are vital in respiration, in the breaking down of proteins and fats and in the building up of proteins, fats and glycogen. There may be only fifteen or twenty mitochondria in a cell; there may be as many as several hundred.

The *lysosomes* have much the same functions as the mitochondria. It is believed that they secrete enzymes to digest, or break down, the larger molecules of various food substances.

The *ribosomes* are granular masses associated with the endoplasmic reticulum (the protoplasmic network described above). They are believed to aid the cell in the manufacture of various protein compounds.

The *Golgi apparatus*, or Golgi substance, named after the Italian neurologist Camillo Golgi, is composed of lipids and protein, as far as we know. It occurs in animal cells as an irregular network or as rodlike, globular or granular bodies. Though the shape varies in different cells, it is uniform in cells of the same type. There is a great deal of Golgi substance in gland and nerve cells, but only a little of it in muscle cells. Often it is found around the nucleus of the cell. The exact function of the Golgi apparatus is not known; it may

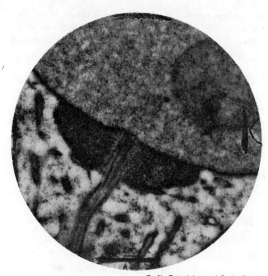

A centrosome (dark area) at the edge of a grasshopper-cell nucleus. The centrosome contains two tiny bodies—the centrioles—which are vital in cell division.

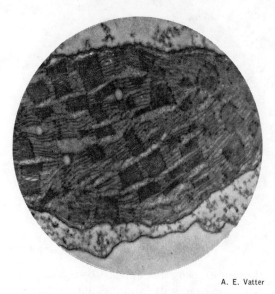

A chloroplast of corn, with the chlorophyll pigment concentrated in the denser regions. Chlorophyll plays a vital part in the manufacture of food by green plants.

play a role in the formation of the endoplasmic reticulum.

The *centrosome,* a rather dense area of protoplasm, lies close to the nucleus. In the middle of the centrosome are two small dotlike, rod-shaped or V-shaped bodies called centrioles. They play an important part in cell division, as we shall see.

The *plastids,* which are found in plant cells, are spherical, egg-shaped, disk-shaped or ribbonlike bodies, made up of lipids and proteins. They are able to synthesize fats, proteins and starch. Some cells have only a single plastid; others may have several dozens. There are at least three different types of plastids—leucoplasts, chromoplasts and chloroplasts. Leucoplasts are colorless plastids found in sex cells and the storage cells of roots and underground stems; they form starch granules. Chromoplasts bear the various pigments that give color, for example, to flower petals. The chlorophyll contained in the chloroplasts is essential for the manufacture of food in the plant, as we shall see; it traps sun energy for the building up of carbohydrate.

Vacuoles, mentioned previously, occur in the cytoplasm of plant cells. (They are uncommon in animal cells, except in the single-celled protozoans.) Each vacuole in a plant cell is separated from the cytoplasm by a membrane, which may or may not be similar to the plasma membrane. The vacuoles are filled with a watery fluid, the cell sap. This contains food substances, cellular secretions and waste products.

The nucleus
of the cell

The cell nucleus is a comparatively large, spherical, egg-shaped or irregularly shaped structure, surrounded by the cell's cytoplasm. There is generally only one nucleus, though some kinds of cells possess two or more. The nuclear membrane encloses a watery fluid, the nuclear sap. Scattered throughout this fluid are filaments, granules or flakes linked by a fine lacy network. These particles form the substance called chromatin, which carries the genes, or determiners of heredity. One or several spherical bodies called nucleoli (singular, nucleolus) are enmeshed in the chromatin network.

The nucleus is composed mainly of nucleoproteins — that is, combinations of proteins and nucleic acids. Many enzymes are present, making the nucleus an active center. From the nucleus, across the nuclear membrane and into the cytoplasm,

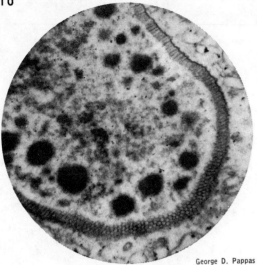

George D. Pappas

The nuclear membrane of an ameba is shown in the photograph. The membrane encloses the watery sap of the nucleus; in this nuclear sap, particles are scattered.

flow substances that appear to be connected with gene activity and protein synthesis. When the cell divides, the nucleus undergoes great changes, as we shall see.

How the
cell functions

One-celled animals and plants can do, in the single cell that forms their bodies, all the things that are necessary to keep alive. Multicelled organisms, such as mammals and trees, also face the problem of remaining alive; they meet it by a division of labor among the cells that compose their bodies. Thus there are plant cells that serve as conductors of food materials, as strengthening units, as food-storage compartments, as centers for absorbing food from the soil. In animals, certain cells are responsible for making bone and cartilage, for shortening in muscle contraction, for carrying nervous impulses, for lining cavities, for engulfing bacteria, for absorbing food from the gut. Yet all cells have certain functions in common.

In the first place, all cells have to obtain essential food elements. Plants absorb water and mineral ions through their root systems and transport these materials by way of conducting vessels to the cells. Carbon dioxide gets into plant cells after it has made its way through the stomata, or pores, of the leaves. In animals, solid foods are broken down, or digested, in a cavity (alimentary canal or intestine) within the body; digestion is speeded up by the action of enzymes. Protein food is broken down into amino acids, carbohydrate into simple sugars, fat into glycerol and fatty acids. These products then pass through the walls of the cavity where digestion has taken place and either enter surrounding cells or are carried to more distant cells by the blood stream.

The simplest way food material gets into cells is by diffusion. Like water mole-

How an ameba moves. The tiny animal is shown here in cross section. Its cytoplasm may be either in the form of a sol, or thin liquid, or of a gel—a substance of jellylike consistency. According to one theory, when the ameba begins to move in a direction that we shall call "forward," it bulges toward that direction. Part of the inner cytoplasm then becomes a sol and streams in the direction of the bulge. On reaching the bulge, it becomes a gel and streams toward the rear, as shown. When it reaches the rear, it turns to a sol again and moves forward.

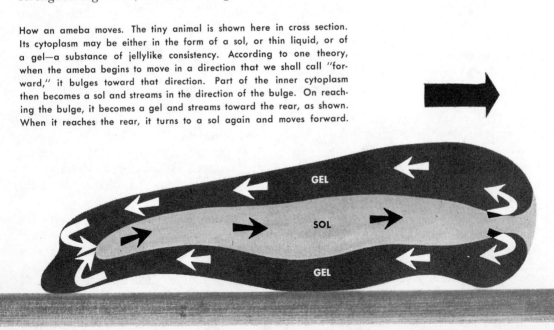

GEL

SOL

GEL

Certain one-celled organisms propel themselves by the whiplike motions of one or more projections, called flagella. 1, below, shows the first position of a flagellum, as it propels the organism in a forward direction (indicated by a broad arrow); 2 is the second position.

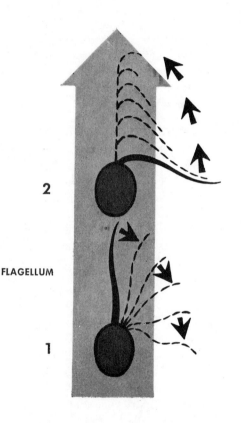

2

FLAGELLUM

1

cules, the molecules or ions of a dissolved substance flow, or diffuse, from a region of higher concentration to one of lower concentration. Amino acids, for example, pass into the cell when there are more amino acids on the outside than on the inside. The concentration of food molecules and ions is usually lower within the cell, because, as soon as these enter, they are built up into more complex compounds or are passed on to other cells. Food molecules and ions, therefore, continue to diffuse into the cell from the greater concentration outside. There is much evidence that protoplasm takes an active part in absorbing food materials. Salt ions from the outside are absorbed into the cell by combining with protein material of the protoplasm; colloids in the protoplasm apparently attract certain ions.

Once food substances get into the cell, they are converted, or assimilated, into a variety of other substances, some of which form the essential parts of protoplasm itself. In the cells of animals, assimilation is the reverse of digestion; the same type of enzymes are involved. Proteins are built up from amino acids, fats from fatty acids and glycerol, carbohydrates from simple sugars. When new protoplasm is made from these substances, it is not stable, but undergoes continuous changes. The nitrogen atoms of proteins, for example, are constantly replaced by new nitrogen coming into the cell; the atoms composing fats also change continually. The simple sugars are sometimes immediately burned to produce energy before they can be built up into more complex carbohydrates.

The cells of green plants can assimilate much simpler materials than animal cells can. Plants, for instance, utilize ammonia and other simple compounds to synthesize the amino acids that form proteins. Carbon dioxide and water are transformed into a sugar by photosynthesis. In this process, the water molecule (H_2O) is split — by sun energy trapped in the pigment chlorophyll — into hydrogen and oxygen. The hydrogen then combines with carbon dioxide, in a series of complicated steps, to produce a simple sugar, glucose. The light energy that was trapped by the chlorophyll now exists as chemical energy in the sugar. Many of the sugar molecules combine with one another to form starch or other polysaccharides, which are stored as reserve material or used in the structure of the plant. Some of the sugar is burned in the process of respiration.

Respiration, or cellular oxidation, is another essential activity of the cell; it causes chemical energy to be released from fuel foods. Carbohydrates are important cellular fuels; fats and proteins are also utilized. The oxygen that serves in respiration is absorbed by diffusion in most plant and animal cells. At one time, it was believed that respiration invariably involved the combination of cellular fuel with oxygen, in the process called oxidation, and the resulting release of energy. We now realize that the loss of hydrogen from food material is also involved in respiration. The substances that give up hydrogen are called hydrogen donors; those that take up hydrogen are known as hydrogen acceptors.

Even in aerobic respiration (respiration in the presence of oxygen), the giving up and taking up of hydrogen play an important part. A chain of reactions is involved. First, a hydrogen donor gives up its hydrogen to a hydrogen acceptor. This hydrogen acceptor, acting now as a donor, hands the hydrogen on to another acceptor and so on through a number of steps. Finally, oxygen, as a hydrogen acceptor standing at the end of this chain of reactions, takes up the hydrogen, and the combination of oxygen atoms and hydrogen atoms yields water (H_2O). A great deal of energy is liberated when hydrogen and oxygen combine. Should this happen at once, the energy would be freed in such great quantity that much would be wasted. In the hydrogen donor-hydrogen acceptor series, only small amounts of energy are conveniently released in steps so that the energy can be fully utilized in the different activities of the cell.

When food material is oxidized in the presence of oxygen, water and carbon dioxide are end products. We have seen that water is formed from the combination of oxygen and hydrogen; but from where does the carbon dioxide come? This is the generally accepted explanation. Starch, glycogen and other carbohydrates are decomposed to the simple sugar glucose, which has six carbon atoms. In a series of complicated reactions, glucose is converted to a three-carbon substance, pyruvic acid, with an accompanying release of energy. The pyruvic acid then enters a cycle, called the citric-acid cycle, in which a chain of reactions keeps repeating itself, releasing energy and throwing off carbon dioxide. Various other reaction systems are connected with the citric-acid cycle. In these systems, proteins, fats and other substances are first built up and then broken down, producing further energy.

In the case of anaerobic respiration (respiration without oxygen), pyruvic acid does not go into a citric-acid cycle but is converted to lactic acid. Energy liberated in anaerobic respiration is rapidly available to the protoplasm, for there is no need of a continuous oxygen supply. Muscle cells take advantage of this quick energy to perform their work. Once they are at rest, the muscle cells use oxygen to oxidize some of the lactic acid; the energy produced by this is used to synthesize the rest of the lactic acid into carbohydrate.

The energy released by respiration is used for the building up of complex materials and, in animals, for muscular work. Protoplasm does work, or exerts energy, when it absorbs certain substances, as we have seen. Energy is also used in several kinds of protoplasmic movements. One of these is cyclosis — the streaming of protoplasm round and round within many plant cells and a few animal cells. Another is the so-called ameboid movement. In this the cell actually changes shape by pushing forth projections, called pseudopodia (false feet), into which protoplasm flows. The cell can move from place to place as a result of this process. The single-celled amebas display ameboid movement; so do white blood cells and various connective-tissue cells. In certain cells, we find another kind of movement — the vibratory lashing or undulating of hairlike processes known as cilia. Cells of this type are called ciliated cells. They line respiratory passages and alimentary canals, are spread over the gills of fishes and various other water-dwellers and may cover the entire outer surface of certain animals.

Some of the chemical energy of cells is converted to heat; some to electricity — especially in the organs of specialized fish, such as the electric eel; some to light, in the luminous cells of fish, worms, insects and certain plants.

Another energy-expending activity is that of secretion, by which substances absorbed into the cell are chemically transformed into new materials and forced out of the cell. Cellular secretions serve to protect the organism, to stimulate or inhibit (check the activity of) other cells or to act chemically on various substances.

THE CELL

The cell is the basis of living structure. Many animals and plants are made up of a single cell; others consist of a great number joined together. Cells are usually microscopic in size. Each is a mass of protoplasm, enclosed by an elastic membrane or (in the case of plants) by a more or less durable wall.

In this color spread, we give several views of the plastic model of a cell, prepared by the Upjohn Company for the American Medical Association meeting at San Francisco in 1958. This is a typical animal cell, and shows the essential parts required for cell functioning. We also include photographs, taken with the electron microscope, of the actual structures that are reproduced in the plastic model.

Over-all view of the Upjohn plastic cell model. It is really hemispherical; but its structures are reflected in the mirror that makes up the flooring of the model, and the illusion of a sphere is created. The model is twenty-four feet in diameter and something like a million times the size of a red blood cell.

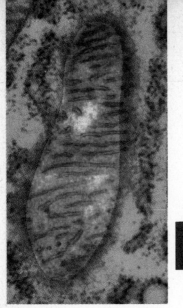

On this page are several electron micrographs (photographs taken with the electron microscope), showing various cell structures. The following page presents details of the plastic cell model; these are based on electron micrographs, such as the ones we show on this page.

The three-dimensional model of a mitochondrion, labeled 1 on the following page, would give a section much like that of the actual mitochondrion in the electron micrograph on the left. Mitochondria may be called the powerhouses of the cell, since many energy-yielding reactions occur in them. The enzymes they contain are arranged in such a way that energy is made available in a continuous flow instead of a series of spurts.

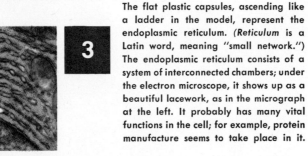

The centrosome, or cell center, labeled 2 in the model, contains a pair of centrioles—cylinders at right angles to one another. (They are clearly shown in the color plate on page 12d.) They play an important part in cell division. The plastic sphere with its radiating projections represents the surrounding area of dense protoplasm. The basic structure of the centrioles is like that of the cilia (hairlike external processes) of the protozoan cell shown in the microphotograph at the left.

The flat plastic capsules, ascending like a ladder in the model, represent the endoplasmic reticulum. (*Reticulum* is a Latin word, meaning "small network.") The endoplasmic reticulum consists of a system of interconnected chambers; under the electron microscope, it shows up as a beautiful lacework, as in the micrograph at the left. It probably has many vital functions in the cell; for example, protein manufacture seems to take place in it.

The nucleus is represented in the cell model by the round structure at the center. The twisted yellow "ropes" it contains are the chromosomes, which are coiling around each other; they transmit the heredity of the cell from one generation to the next. The nucleolus is the small red sphere in the center of the nucleus. Left: electron micrograph of a nucleus, with the nucleolus at its center.

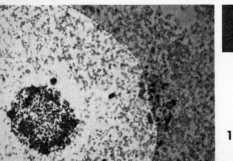

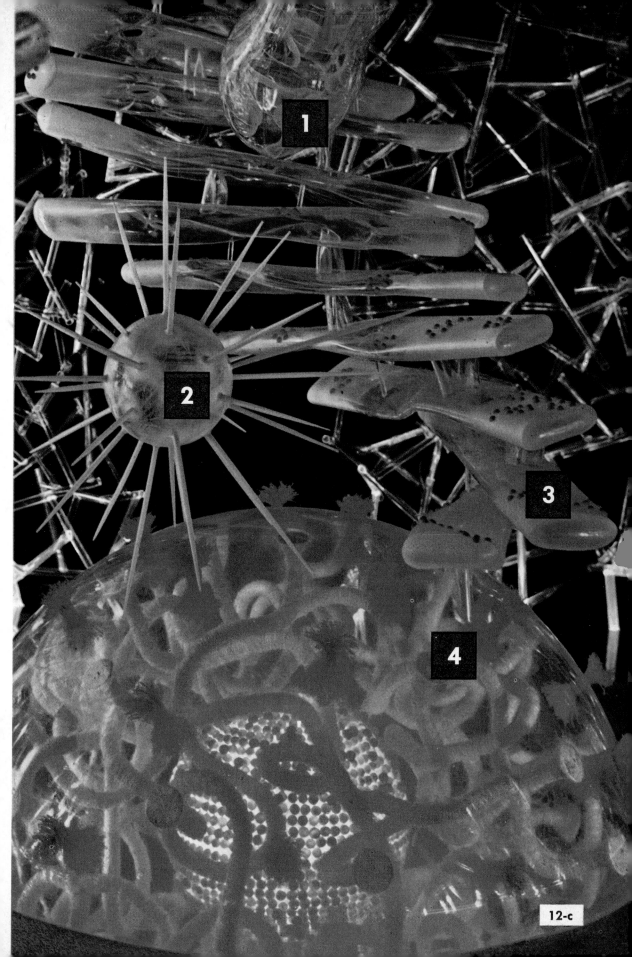

12-c

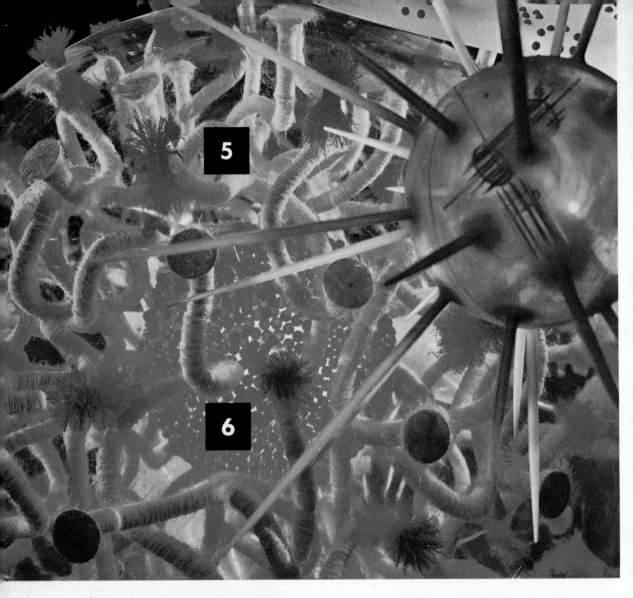

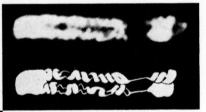

A

B

The nucleolus is represented in the model, above, as a small sphere (actually, a reflected hemisphere) at the center of the nucleus. It consists largely of ribonucleoprotein, which is shown as red in the model. Below is shown an electron micrograph of the nucleus of a cell from an earthworm gland; it contains a nucleolus, which in turn has within it a structure called a formed body. The function of this body has not yet been discovered.

5 The chromosomes—the yellow "ropes" in the model—contain a chemical material called deoxyribonucleic acid (DNA), whose molecules are fibrous and twisted. DNA determines all the characteristics of the species. Above: in dividing cells, the chromosomes shrink greatly as they become coiled. An actual photograph of a single chromosome is shown in A. It is a double coil. This particular detail is brought out much more clearly in the drawing (B) made from the photograph.

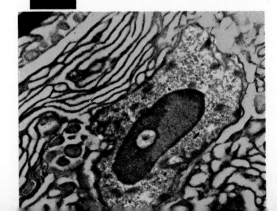

Cell-division stages in the blastula of a whitefish. (The blastula is a form of embryo in a very early stage of development in various animals.) A. Interphase: the resting state between successive cell divisions. B. Prophase: the chromatin material in the nucleus begins to shorten and increase in thickness to form chromosomes. C. Metaphase: the divided chromosomes are arrayed in the equatorial, or central, plane of the spindle that has formed. D. Anaphase: the two sets of daughter chromosomes move toward opposite poles. E. Telophase: the spindle begins to disintegrate; the chromosomes elongate and intertwine. The cytoplasm of the original cell is now divided into two roughly equal parts by a partition that forms at the central plane of the original spindle.

Photos by Norman Drake

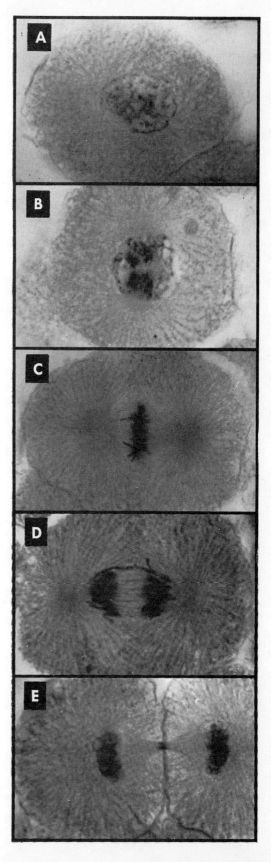

Mucus, cellulose, nacre (mother-of-pearl), hormones, auxins (growth hormones of plants) and digestive enzymes are good examples of these secretions. Substances to be secreted are often visible in the cell in the form of granules, vacuoles or droplets. The cell eliminates its secretions in various ways. It extrudes, or pushes out, solid materials, such as plugs of mucus; it diffuses or actively ejects fluids and dissolved particles.

Various waste products are formed in the cell. Carbon dioxide and water result from the breakdown of fats and carbohydrates. When proteins are broken down, the waste materials may be ammonia, urea, uric acid and other nitrogen-containing compounds. Usually wastes leave the cell through the plasma membrane by diffusion; since the concentration of these products is greater inside the cell, they make their way to the outside. No energy is exerted by the protoplasm, as a general rule, in the process of excretion. In certain special cases, however, energy is expended to excrete water and salts.

The phenomenon of cell division

As the cell synthesizes some of its absorbed food materials into new protoplasm, it grows in volume. But this increase is definitely restricted. After a cell attains a certain size, it generally divides into two cells, which later divide in their turn and so on. As the different cells multiply, the organism as a whole grows and develops. Apparently growth and division bring about a chemical and physical rejuvenation that prevents the protoplasm from growing old and dying. It should be pointed out, however, that certain cells, such as muscle and nerve cells, do not divide after reaching the limit of their growth; and yet they continue to carry on their activities.

The process of cell division is called mitosis. In this process, the nucleus of the cell divides into two daughter nuclei; the cytoplasm also divides, so that in place of one cell there arise two daughter cells, each with its own nucleus. The stage between two successive cell divisions is termed interphase. It is during interphase that the cell performs most of the functions that we have described.

Mitosis is a continuous process; but certain definite stages can be distinguished in it. These are prophase, prometaphase, metaphase, anaphase and telophase.

At prophase, the chromatin material of the nucleus begins to shorten and increase in thickness to form chromosomes. It would be more accurate, perhaps, to say that the chromosomes exist as independent bodies at all times, but that during interphase they are elongated and intertwined, like thread in a tangle of yarn. There is always the same number of chromosomes in the cells of individuals belonging to the same plant or animal species. In the first part of prophase, they become shorter and thicker, acquiring a rodlike shape. Then each chromosome splits lengthwise, so as to form two parts known as chromatids.

We mentioned previously the two small bodies, called centrioles, that lie in the cytoplasm close to the nucleus. At prophase, certain fibers, called asters, or astral rays, radiate from each centriole; their function is unknown. As the chromosomes become distinct, the centrioles migrate in the cytoplasm to opposite ends of the nucleus, so that they are antipodal, or opposite one another. Between the two centrioles arise a bundle of delicate filaments, forming a structure called the spindle. (The cells of most plants lack centrioles; a spindle forms between two points called polar centers.) During prophase, the cell becomes more spherical and turgid.

At prometaphase, the nuclear membrane seems to disintegrate. The spherical body called the nucleolus (as we have seen, there may be more than one) disappears. Some of the nucleolus material attaches itself to the split chromosomes; the rest appears to diffuse into the cytoplasm. The spindle can now be made out more clearly. Some of the filaments stretch from one centriole or polar center to the other; others make contact with the chromosomes.

During metaphase, the divided chromosomes are arrayed for a moment in the equatorial, or central, plane of the spindle. Then the two chromatids of which each chromosome consisted begin to move away from each other. They have become perfectly identical daughter chromosomes.

The cell now enters upon the anaphase stage. Each of the daughter chromosomes formed from a given chromosome migrates to a different centriole or polar center. Finally, they all arrive at their destinations.

At telophase, the daughter chromosomes are bunched at the poles of the spindle, and the spindle begins to disintegrate. The daughter chromosomes begin to elongate and to intertwine; the tangled chromatin network appears. A new nuclear membrane is developed around each clump of chromatin; the nucleoli are reformed. Two daughter nuclei have now developed. Meanwhile, the cytoplasm has been divided into two roughly equal parts by a partition formed at the equatorial region of the spindle. The original cell has given rise to two daughter cells, each with a nucleus. (In plant cells a new rigid cell wall is formed between the two daughter cells.) The organoids and particles contained in the cytoplasm of the old cell have been more or less equally divided, so that each new cell gets its share.

In effect, then, cell division brings about an equal separation of chromosome material and a nearly equal division of cytoplasm and its constituents. Each daughter cell then enters the interphase stage in which it grows until ready to divide again.*

See also Vol. 10, p. 271: "Cell as Basis of Life."
* Sex cells (eggs and sperms) result from another type of cell division, called meiosis. See Index, under Meiosis.

THE SOIL

The Thin Surface Layer

That Supports

Plant Life

THE plants that grow upon the earth's land areas could not exist without the thin, loose surface layer that we call the soil. It provides plants with mechanical support, or anchorage; it offers mineral nutrients for plant growth. Water and air, trapped within it, are made available to the roots. Not only plant life, but animal life as well, is dependent on the soil, for animal foods are derived directly or indirectly from plants.

Weathered rock particles make up a large part of the film of soil; the rest is formed of the decayed products of organic matter (that is, living or formerly living substance). The soil is not an inert, unchanging body; it is constantly being transformed by chemical and physical processes and by the activities of living organisms.

It takes but a moment for you to dig up a spadeful of garden soil; it has taken the processes of nature countless centuries to create it. The first step in soil-building is the weathering of rocks that lie at the earth's surface. The result is a vast accumulation of rock debris above the bedrock. This debris is called the regolith (from two Greek words meaning "stone blanket"); it is not soil itself but rather the forerunner, or parent, of soil.

How the regolith — the forerunner of soil — is formed

The weathering that results in the formation of the regolith is due to many different factors. Among the most important of these are variations in temperature. During the day, an exposed rock is heated by the sun and expands; at night, it cools off and contracts. The rock is composed of different minerals, which expand and contract at different rates. Unequal stresses are built up as a result, and cracks appear. Water gains entrance by way of these cracks and begins its eroding and dissolving action. If freezing occurs, the expansion of the water as it freezes exerts tremendous pressure; this causes the rock mass to break up into smaller pieces. Differences in temperature between the exposed outer part of a rock and the protected inner portion also bring about unequal stresses and cause the surface layers to peel off.

W. Schwarz

The loose material of the regolith is shifted, sorted and transported by rain water beating upon the land and running downhill; water from melting snow has a similar effect. If the running water is carrying a load of debris, it powerfully cuts, or erodes, the bedrock, giving rise to more debris. The sediment may be carried by rivers many miles before it is finally deposited as potential soil in alluvial fans, terraces and deltas. (See the article The Work of Running Water, in Volume 8.) Sometimes debris is laid down in lakes, gulfs and oceans. Here it remains submerged until the elevation of the land or the lowering of the water level exposes it as parent material for a new soil.

Glacial ice is another important agent of transportation, erosion and deposition. As the glacier moves, it picks up the rocks of the regolith and grinds them into fragments against one another. Rock particles imbedded in the lower level and sides of the glacier scour rock powder from the bedrock of the glacier's channel. When the ice melts, the rock fragments and powder are either immediately deposited or carried many miles by the water flowing from the glacial front.

Wind picks up the finer particles of the regolith and, armed with this grit, abrades still more fragments from rocks through the action of sandblasting. The winds carry sand and dust for many miles from one area to another. (See The Winds at Work, in Volume 7.)

Rock is also affected by a variety of chemical changes. Water combines with carbon dioxide to form carbonic acid, which is a powerful solvent and attacks the minerals contained in rock. In the chemical process of oxidation, oxygen combines with various minerals. These are decomposed as a result of the reaction; the rock mass in which they are found is weakened, so that it readily crumbles. In hydration, various minerals take up water molecules. These minerals increase in size and become soft; they are then broken down by weathering and erosion. Hydrolysis is another chemical process that affects rock; it occurs as salts are dissolved in water. The salts undergo ionization: that is, they are converted into electrically charged atoms, or groups of atoms, called ions. The ions then react with certain ions always present in water.*

The formation of true soil

As we have pointed out, the regolith is only the forerunner of soil. The true soil is formed only when living organisms become active in the rock debris. Sooner or later, hardy lichens and mosses gain a foothold on the exposed, weathering surfaces of the regolith. These relatively simple plants catch and hold the finer mineral particles carried by wind and water, and they absorb mineral nutrients. As parts of the plants die, bacteria and molds appear on the scene and feed on the remains. These are broken down and the nutrients they contain are liberated for the use of living plants. The decaying vegetation yields organic acids, which dissolve many of the minerals contained in the regolith. Carbon dioxide, given off by living mosses, lichens and microorganisms, helps dissolve minerals in the presence of water. Eventually a thin film of organic materials combined with mineral matter is built upon the regolith; this represents the beginning of true soil.

Larger and bushier mosses now invade the soil; they trap and hold more minerals and contribute their remains to the growing soil mat. After a time the soil is firmly enough established to provide essential nutrients, water and firm support for grasses, herbaceous plants, shrubs and, perhaps, trees.

As these higher plants gradually establish themselves, a layer of humus develops. Humus represents the very dark material that is usually so noticeable at the surface of most soils. It is the result of complicated chemical reactions carried on by the soil microbes. Part of the humus is a combination of protein and lignin (one of the building blocks of plant-cell walls); part of it, apparently, is composed of the tissues of dead soil microbes.

---

* These "water ions" are hydroxyl ions and hydronium ions. See Index.

The presence of organic humus means the difference between a productive soil and one that is sterile. Humus holds most of the soil's nitrogen and much of its sulfur and phosphorus. It attracts and retains water; it also holds the gases and ions that are needed by plants. It causes soil particles to clump, providing a workable soil. When humus itself is decomposed, heat is produced and the soil is warmed. Under such conditions, the seeds of the higher plants can readily germinate.

The horizons
of the soil

As soil is formed, particularly if water drainage is good, horizontal layers are developed in the regolith. If you dig a trench into the soil down to bedrock or examine any fresh road cut, you can see these layers. They are called horizons by the soil scientist; the horizons taken together make up the soil profile.

There are three major horizons in any soil profile: the A, B and C horizons. The A horizon, or, roughly, the surface soil, is the zone where organic materials have become incorporated within the mineral matter. Often there is a litter of fresh plant remains at the surface and, below this, a layer of very dark humus. Under the humus is a lighter-colored mineral layer. It is the result of leaching — the removal of soluble substances by percolating water. In cultivated soil, the layers of humus and mineral matter are mixed together. A considerable part of the nutrients and water available for plants is to be found in the A horizon. Here we find the most extensive root development.

The B horizon, or subsoil, has little organic material in it, though the mineral matter is noticeably weathered. This horizon contains substances derived from the A horizon above and the C horizon below. Iron and aluminum, and sometimes calcium, compounds accumulate here; so does the clay that is washed down from the surface layers.

The lowest, or C, horizon is composed of the same loose parent material from which the true soil above has developed.

The photograph below shows the horizons (horizontal layers of soil) that make up a typical soil profile. There are three major horizons—the A, B and C horizons—and also a certain number of subdivisions, not given here.

A horizon. This is the surface soil. Organic materials have been incorporated in the mineral matter derived from the original rock.

B horizon. Also called the subsoil, the B horizon has little organic material. Its mineral elements have been heavily weathered.

C horizon. In this, the parent rock material has undergone but little weathering. The C horizon may be absent in certain soils.

N. Y. State Coll. of Agr. at Cornell Univ.

The four upper photos on these two pages show different sizes of rock particles. Above are particles of gravel.

Sand particles, consisting of grains smaller than gravel. These grains are rounded or irregular in shape.

It is more or less weathered, and its upper layers gradually become part of the true soil.

Often the horizons of soil profiles are not distinct; there are zones of transition between the A and B horizons and the B and C horizons. When the soil is mature, its profile does not change much, even though weathering and soil organisms are constantly at work. There is normal erosion at the surface, balanced by the creation of new soil from the C horizon below.

Factors influencing the development of mature soil

The nature of mature soil depends on several factors: the sizes and groupings of the rock fragments of which the regolith is composed; the time it takes for this material to be transformed into soil; the lay of the land; the vegetation; and the climate.

Sizes of soil particles. The regolith consists of particles of various sizes; this variation determines the texture that the soil ultimately develops. The largest particles are stones and gravel, which are irregularly shaped rock fragments having a diameter of more than 2 millimeters. Sand particles range from 2 millimeters to $\frac{1}{16}$ millimeter in diameter. The sand grains are rounded or irregular in shape; they are usually of quartz, though they may also be of feldspar, mica, magnetite and garnet. Silt particles are from $\frac{1}{16}$ millimeter to $\frac{1}{256}$ millimeter in diameter; they are most often composed of quartz and have different shapes. The particles of clay have a diameter of less than

$\frac{1}{256}$ millimeter. They are plate-shaped; they may be of quartz but are more often of complex compounds such as kaolinite, illite and montmorillonite. Clay is sticky and highly plastic (capable of being molded) when wet, and very hard and cloddy when dry.

If sand makes up 70 per cent or more of the soil by weight, the soil is said to be sandy. If the sand grains are not coated with clay, they do not stick together and are not plastic. Sand does not hold water well and has large pore spaces between the grains. Consequently, a sandy soil is exceedingly loose, drains water rapidly and encourages the movement of air through the soil.

Soils with at least 35 to 40 per cent clay are called clay soils. Because clay is made of such finely divided particles, a tremendous surface area is available for the adsorption of water, gases and ions. (Adsorption is the adhesion, in a thin film, of molecules and ions to the surfaces of solids.) A great part of the chemical reactions in soil takes place at the surface of clay particles. The compact clayey soils do not allow rapid movement of air and water through them.

The soils known as loams are a mixture of sand, silt and clay; they combine the desirable properties of both sand and clay. There are various other kinds of soils, depending on the size of the predominating particles; sandy loams, silty loams, clay loams, sandy clays, silty clays and so on.

Upper photos on these two pages by W. Schwarz;
soil materials furnished by M. D. Morris

Silt particles. These are made up of particularly fine-grained erosion products. They will cohere when wet.

Clay particles, shown above, are the smallest of all. When dry, as here, they are very hard and form clods.

Groupings of soil particles. Individual particles of sand, silt and clay are clustered together in a variety of aggregates, or particle groupings; they give the soil its characteristic structure. There may be only one kind of structural pattern in a soil profile; more often, however, the pattern differs from one horizon to the next. The structure of the soil is very important; it influences water drainage, the transfer of heat through the soil, aeration and the degree to which plant roots can penetrate the soil and spread through it.

When thin, flat aggregates, lying horizontally, pile up one on top of another, they form a platy, or platelike, structure. This structure may be found in any part of the soil profile. In semiarid and arid regions, the subsoil often shows a columnar pattern or a prismatic pattern; the aggregates are shaped like pillars. A blocklike or nutlike structure is found in subsoils of humid regions; the aggregates are in the shape of cubes or rounded cubes, lying close together. Small rounded aggregates, loosely combined, make up a granular or crumb soil structure. This formation occurs in many surface soils, especially those rich in organic materials. In some soils, sands are so predominant that there is no structure; the soil is formed of single grains. In other soils, such as those high in clay, the units are quite massive, and they likewise have no distinct structure.

SOIL STRUCTURES

When thin, flat particle groupings are piled on top of one another, they form a platy (platelike) structure. In semiarid and arid regions, the subsoil may show a prismatic pattern, suggesting pillars set side by side. A blocklike structure is found in the subsoils of humid regions. When small rounded aggregates are loosely combined, they make up a granular structure. Below are examples of each type.

Lower photos, Roy W. Simonson

PLATY   **PRISMATIC**   **BLOCKLIKE**   **GRANULAR**

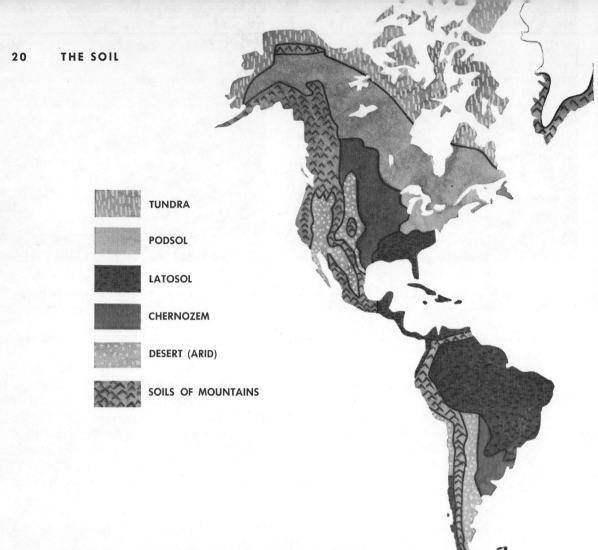

TUNDRA

PODSOL

LATOSOL

CHERNOZEM

DESERT (ARID)

SOILS OF MOUNTAINS

SCHEMATIC MAP OF ZONAL SOIL GROUPS

The time factor in soil formation. The nature of the soil depends to a certain extent on the length of time that the parent materials have been exposed to weathering and have supported vegetation. In areas where debris has been deposited by wind, water, glaciers or volcanic action, there may not have been enough time for the formation of a mature soil.

The lay of the land — its topography — influences soil formation to a certain extent. If the land is hilly, water will be drained off much more rapidly than would be the case if the surface were more or less flat. As the water runs downhill, it takes some of the soil with it. In gently rolling country, a deep soil often develops if the climate is mild and humid. There is enough drainage to bring about important chemical changes, but not enough to remove much soil. On

the other hand, a mature soil cannot be formed if water collects in a level area and stands for most of the year, as in bogs.

Vegetation and soil formation. In its development, the soil is greatly influenced by the plants that grow upon it. Plants take up mineral elements from the soil by their roots; when these plants die, their remains decay, and the mineral nutrients are released to the surface soil. The minerals are leached from this area; again they are taken up by the roots of plants and again they are released to the surface soil when the plants die. This cycle, which varies according to the plants taking part in it, their rooting habits and their mineral needs, has an important bearing on soil development. Plants influence the soil in other ways. The roots hold the soil in place, thwarting the efforts of wind and water to

This schematic map gives some idea of the major zonal soil groups of the world. A detailed description of these groups is given on this page and the following one.

carry it away. Branching roots penetrate and fracture hard soil lumps and layers; they make the soil loose and open for the circulation of air and water.

Climate as a factor in soil formation. Developing soils are influenced most of all, perhaps, by climate. The temperature and amount of moisture control the degree of physical weathering; they also regulate the speed at which chemical decomposition takes place. In an excessively dry climate, for example, temperature changes are extreme. Wind and running-water erosion predominate over chemical weathering, for there is not enough constant moisture to allow vigorous chemical reactions. As a result, the parent soil material tends to be coarse. In humid regions, chemical action is greatly speeded up, and the potential soil material may become exceedingly fine in texture.

The soil organisms that decompose vegetable matter are also affected by moisture conditions and temperature. The climate dictates the kind of vegetation that will live in any given region. As we have seen, this vegetation, in turn, influences the soil in which it grows.

Mature soils produced by different climatic conditions

Mountainous and hilly areas do not show a fixed pattern of zonal soils. In other regions, a definite type of climate will produce a distinct kind of mature soil profile. South of the regions of perpetual snow and ice are the soils of the *tundra*. They are very shallow and are covered with a thick layer of decomposed plant remains. Since the subsoil may remain frozen most of the year, the surface soil is poorly drained and boggy. Mosses, lichens and arctic shrubs grow in these areas.

The soil known as *podsol*, or *podzol* (Russian for "alkaline ashes"), is found south of the tundra, particularly in humid, cool, forested regions, such as the northern part of the Soviet Union, the northeastern United States and the Great Lakes region, extending into Canada. The cone-bearing evergreens and tall grasses that flourish here contribute an abundant amount of litter to the surface of the ground. As all this organic matter slowly decays, it yields a small to moderate amount of humus, which is highly acid in nature. Percolating water, assisted by the acids of decay, dissolves and leaches the soluble calcium carbonate and other salts out of the surface and subsoils. As a result, the lower part of the A horizon is ashy gray in color, highly acid and composed largely of silica. Underneath this, in the B horizon, is a layer of dark humus, which has been leached from the surface. Below this layer is a reddish brown layer of humus mixed with iron and aluminum compounds. Finally, there is a yellowish layer that merges with the C horizon. When first cleared, podsols are not very fertile, but they respond well to careful management.

The gray wooded soils of the cool and somewhat humid western United States and Canada are similar to the podsols but are less leached and less acid. They, too, support evergreen forests. *Gray-brown podsolic soils* occur in the Northern Hemisphere, south of the podsols. They have less plant remains on the surface and are less leached than the podsols; they have a grayish or yellowish brown subsoil. Forests of deciduous trees,* such as ash, hickory and chestnut, prevail. Under careful cultivation, they are adapted to a wide range of crops — vegetables, grains, fruits and grasses. *Red and yellow podsolic soils* are found in a milder climate, such as that of the southeastern United States. These soils are strongly leached and are limited in organic matter. Mixed evergreen and deciduous forests grow on these soils.

Prairie soils represent a transition between forest and grassland soils. The surface soil is a rich black or dark brown, while the subsoil is brown. These soils are very fertile. In the wild state, prairie soils support a dense cover of tall grass; under cultivation, they can be made to yield rich harvests of grain.

Soils called *latosols*, or *laterites*, occur in the tropics and subtropics, where there are high temperatures and a great deal of moisture; they are also found in southern France, Spain, Italy and Greece. Because plant remains quickly decay here, these soils are only slightly acid or not acid at all. The iron in the latosol causes it to have a red or yellow color. Tropical rain forests thrive on latosol soils; when put under cultivation, the soil will grow rubber and banana trees, coffee plants, sugar cane and pineapple.

Where there is relatively little moisture and temperatures are high enough to promote rapid evaporation, calcium carbonate (used in making lime) is not leached away; it accumulates in soils at approximately the depths to which water penetrates. The surface soil is at most only mildly acidic; in most arid regions, it is either neutral or slightly alkaline.* Lime soils of this kind include *chernozem*, *brown* and *desert soils*. Chernozem soils are grass-covered and have abundant organic matter. The upper part of the soil is rich in humus and nearly black in color; this accounts for the name "chernozem," which means "black earth" in Russian. The subsoil has a brown or reddish lime layer. Chernozem soils are found in the United States just west of the prairie soils; they occur also in central Russia. Under cultivation, they are especially adapted to grains, such as wheat. A considerable part of the bread grains of the world comes from chernozem soils or soils similar to them. Brown, or chestnut, soils prevail in drier regions, such as the Great Plains. They have less organic matter than the chernozems, are lighter in color and support only very short grasses. Desert soils are typical of arid regions. Containing little organic matter, they are light-col-

---

* Trees that lose their leaves at the end of each growing season.

* An alkaline substance is also known as a base. We discuss acid, alkaline (basic) and neutral substances in the article Acids, Bases and Salts, in Volume 4.

ored with a yellowish or reddish subsoil of calcium carbonate. Desert shrubs are the predominant plants of these soils.

Local conditions that
cause variations in the soil

The soil variations that are often found within a given region are due to local conditions. For example, where drainage is poor, marshes, swamps and bogs may develop. Mosses, pondweeds, sedges, reeds, shrubs and even trees live and die here. Their remains form thick mats of partially decayed organic matter, eventually producing peaty soils. Where drainage is poor in arid regions, salts accumulate in the surface soil, giving rise to salt and alkali flats. Only a thin surface soil may be present in areas where there are steep slopes. Immature soils occur on steeply sloping glacial drift, on sand dunes, on wind-carried (loess) deposits and on river-carried (alluvial) deposits along river banks and in valley bottoms.

Nutrients provided
for plants by soils

All soils — podsols, chernozems, latosols and the rest — provide the vegetation that flourishes on them with a variety of nutrients. Water, nitrogen, phosphorus, sulfur, potassium, calcium and magnesium are generally present in relatively large amounts. Other vital soil elements — absorbed in smaller quantities and therefore called trace elements — include iron, manganese, boron, zinc and copper. Some plants seem to require still other nutrients, such as sodium, molybdenum, chlorine, fluorine, iodine, silicon, strontium, barium and cobalt.

Nitrogen is among the most essential of all the soil elements required by plants. Most of it is held in plant remains in the form of such compounds as proteins and amino acids. Soil microbes decompose these to ammonium salts. Then certain bacteria oxidize the ammonium (combine it with oxygen) to form nitrite and nitrate salts by the process called nitrification. Plants can use both ammonium and nitrate; they absorb these two substances from the soil solution.

Nitrogen-fixing bacteria live in nodules (more or less globular lumps) on the roots of the peanut plant, shown above. The inset provides a close-up of these nodules.

Bacteria living in the root nodules * of leguminous plants, such as alfalfa, clover, cowpeas, beans and lupines, obtain free nitrogen from the soil air and synthesize, or fix, it in complex forms, which are then used by the legumes. When these plants die they contribute their nitrogen-containing tissues to the soil's organic matter. Other bacteria take nitrogen from the air found in the soil and incorporate it into their bodies. When they die, they decompose, releasing nitrogen compounds for use by higher plants. Small quantities of nitrogen, in the form of ammonium and nitrate, are brought to the soil by rain water. These compounds have been produced through electrical activity in the atmosphere.

Phosphorus occurs in the soil in the mineral apatite and in phosphates of calcium, iron and aluminum; it is also found in various organic compounds. It is released from these materials as various chemical changes occur. Phosphorus is taken up by roots in the form of phosphate ions.

---

* These are more or less globular lumps that form on the roots.

Sulfur is found in the minerals pyrite and gypsum. These minerals are decomposed chemically and the product is acted on by soil bacteria. Sulfates that can be absorbed by plants then become available.

Potassium, calcium and *magnesium* are metals. Potassium is contained in feldspar and mica; calcium in feldspar, amphibole, calcite and dolomite; magnesium in mica, amphibole, dolomite and serpentine. As these minerals react with water or with other substances in the soil, they liberate potassium, calcium and magnesium ions, which all have a positive electric charge. Humus and clay soil particles normally carry a negative electrical charge. They attract the positively charged ions of calcium, potassium and magnesium, which are absorbed on the surface of the particles.

When carbonic acid and other acids in the soil ionize, they free positively charged hydrogen ions. If these are present in quantity, they replace the ions of the metals potassium, calcium and magnesium on the soil particles, since hydrogen ions are more strongly attracted to the particles than are other positively charged ions.

If hydrogen ions are not numerous, the potassium, calcium and magnesium ions remain on the surface of the soil particles. Root hairs now come into intimate contact with the particles; but they cannot at once absorb the metallic ions that have collected on the surface of the particles and are held fast there. A striking phenomenon now takes place. A series of chemical reactions takes place at the boundary where root tissues and soil particles meet, and positively charged hydrogen ions are formed as a result. These positive ions are attracted to the negatively charged soil particles and they drive away the metallic (potassium, calcium and magnesium) ions, which are then absorbed by the root hairs.

The vital nutrients that we have just described are more abundant in some soils than in others. However, the quantity of nutrients is not so important as the ease with which they are made available to plants. This depends to a large extent on how acid or alkaline the soil is. In highly acid soils, for example, phosphorus may become unavailable because it forms compounds with aluminum and iron, and these compounds do not dissolve in soil water. Plants may not obtain enough calcium from soils that are too acid, because it has been leached from the topsoil. Microbes do not flourish in such soils; as a result, organic matter will not be decomposed and such essential nutrients as nitrogen, sulfur and phosphorus will not be released. If the soil is too alkaline, iron, manganese, copper and zinc will become unavailable to plants. However, when the soil reaches an extreme degree of alkalinity, these metals become too readily available and plants may be poisoned by them.

Water and air are vital to the soil and its plant life

The water contained in the soil is essential for the chemical and other activities that take place there, as well as for the functioning of plant life. The abundance or lack of soil water depends on many factors. Among them are the quantity of rain, snow and other forms of precipitation; the ability of soil particles to hold on to moisture; the amount of drainage; the slope of the soil surface; the amount of water removed by plants; the amount lost by evaporation.

Water gains entrance to the soil and circulates through it by way of the innumerable pore spaces between the soil particles. Earthworms, insects, moles, rodents and other burrowing animals provide other paths for water in the soil; so do the roots of plants when they die and decay. After a heavy rain or quick thaw of snow or ice, a great deal of water percolates downward through all these channels under the influence of gravity and is generally lost to the surface soil. This water is unavailable to plants except as it passes over their roots in its passage. If the water moves rapidly, it is likely to wash down plant nutrients, especially nitrate, sulfate, calcium and potassium ions, with it.

A part of the soil water is held in the form of a surface film by the particles of soil. This is called capillary water, since it adheres to the particles through capillary force — surface attraction. Capillary water forms the true soil solution; it is readily absorbed by roots, and in it nutrient substances, available for plants, are dissolved.

The air in the soil also plays an important part. Atmospheric air is a mixture of gases: about 21 per cent oxygen, 78 per cent nitrogen and 1 per cent of other gases, including a small amount of carbon dioxide. These gases are adsorbed on the soil particles, or dispersed through the pore spaces or dissolved in the soil solution.

Roots and soil organisms require oxygen for respiration; roots need it, too, in order to absorb nutrients and water adequately. Oxygen is essential for various activities of the bacteria in the soil, including the important activities of nitrogen fixation and nitrification. Because of these oxygen requirements, the amount of the gas

is usually lower in the soil air than in the outside atmosphere. If the soil is porous, this imbalance may be somewhat lessened, as oxygen diffuses into the soil from the atmosphere. Carbon dioxide is much more concentrated in the soil and tends to diffuse to the outside. As for the nitrogen that forms the principal part of air, it is important in the soil only as it is fixed by bacteria.

In a soil where plants are to flourish, there must be a suitable balance between water and air. If the soil is waterlogged, there is not enough air in it, and as a result roots and soil organisms suffer. If the water supply is inadequate, the essential chemical processes that take place in the soil are slowed up, and food manufacture and growth are impeded.

See also Vol. 10, p. 273: "Soil."

Diagram indicating the complex relationships of water, minerals, organic matter and microorganisms in the soil.

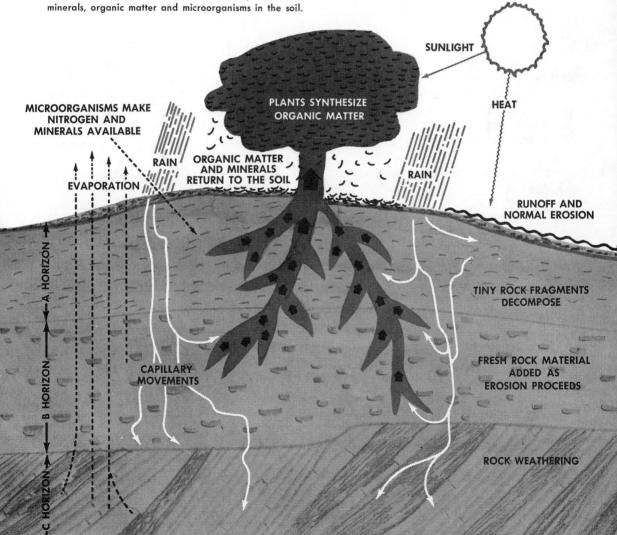

Cats are quite self-sufficient. When this tabby wishes to enter the house, she first jumps up on the step rail.

She skillfully trips the door latch with a paw, pulls the door open, as shown above, and enters with a leap.

ANIMAL INTELLIGENCE
ON DISPLAY

The great seventeenth-century French philosopher René Descartes held that the lower animals were mere automata, who functioned in a purely mechanical way. We know now that he was as wrong as he could be. Careful experimentation by competent investigators has shown that animals have capacity for learning, that they possess memory and that, in certain cases, they can reason from cause to effect. The pictures in this chapter show some striking instances of animal intelligence.

This German shepherd makes an efficient canine valet. He goes to the door each morning and fetches the newspaper.

He walks over to his master who is still asleep, wakes him up gently and then offers him the morning's news.

The well-trained members of this spirited black-horse troupe go through a variety of complicated maneuvers.

These college-bred pigeons at the Psychological Laboratory at Harvard are intent upon a game of Ping-pong.

University of Wisconsin

If his memory stands him in good stead, as usually happens, this monkey will find a raisin under the dish.

Forty seconds have now elapsed since he watched an experimenter putting a raisin under one of the dishes.

Pigeon photos, Harvard University

If either one of them misses the ball, it rolls down into a trough; the other pigeon then collects a food reward.

New York Zoological Society

Testing the memory of an elephant. One of the two panels set on the sawhorse is gray; the other is of a different color. If the elephant blows over the gray panel, she will be given a food reward from the bucket.

FORCES WITHIN LIQUIDS AND GASES

An Analysis of Molecules at Work

Above: LeTourneau-Westinghouse Co.

Right: The De Vilbiss Co.

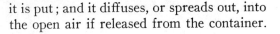

The forces within liquids and gases serve man in a great many ways. Thus the pressure of a liquid lifts the body of the dump truck shown above. Compressed air plays an important part in the action of the sprayer at the right.

EVERY time you turn on the water in your kitchen or your bathroom, or put your foot down on the brake pedal of your car, or run the vacuum cleaner or pump up a bicycle tire, certain powerful forces in liquids or gases are working for you. The safety of deep-sea divers and of submarine crews depends upon a knowledge of how these forces behave. Engineers must calculate them with great accuracy when they build tunnels beneath rivers or construct airplanes that seemingly defy the law of gravity.

Liquids and gases are made up of tiny, constantly moving particles called molecules; the forces in both liquids and gases are transmitted by these molecules as they strike one another and collide with the objects in their path. Both liquids and gases flow freely from a container and have no definite shape.

There are, however, some important differences between them. The molecules of a liquid are held together much more tightly than those of a gas. Again, a liquid will fill a container up to a certain level, and the upper surface of the liquid will be horizontal. A gas, however, will fill uniformly the whole of a container into which

it is put; and it diffuses, or spreads out, into the open air if released from the container.

The density of liquids

In order to measure accurately the forces within a liquid, we must know its density: that is, the mass (amount of material) packed into a given quantity of the liquid. We express density in terms of weight per unit volume; thus we say of a given substance that it has a density of so many pounds per cubic foot.

The density of pure water is about 62.4 pounds per cubic foot when its temperature is 4° centigrade (39⅕° Fahrenheit). Alcohol is less dense than water, and one cubic foot of it weighs only some 50 pounds. Mercury, however, is so dense that it weighs nearly 850 pounds per cubic foot.

We can, therefore, find the density of any liquid — or of any solid — by finding out how much a cubic foot or a cubic centimeter of it weighs. If we compare the density of the liquid or solid with that of the same volume of water, we shall know what is called its specific gravity. Water is usually the basis of this type of comparison;

therefore, we say that the specific gravity of water is 1. A substance half as dense as water would have the specific gravity of 0.5. Mercury is 13.6 times as dense as water; its specific gravity, then, is 13.6.

The pressures
exerted by liquids

A liquid exerts force on any surface with which it is in contact; and the denser

the pressure of the atmosphere upon the surface of the liquid. As we shall see, atmospheric pressure at sea level is about 14.7 pounds per square inch.

We have been considering the pressures within a tank that is a perfect cube. The pressure per square inch at the bottom would be the same in a tank of any size or shape, provided that the depth is the same (Figure 1). The reason is that pressure

1. There is the same amount of pressure per square inch at the bottom of each of these irregularly shaped tanks, containing water, as the depth of the liquid is the same in each.

the liquid, the greater the force that it will exert. The water in a glass aquarium, for instance, presses against both the bottom and the sides of the aquarium, as well as against the fish and any objects that are submerged in the water. We measure a force exerted by a liquid in terms of so many pounds per square foot or square inch; and we speak of it as pressure.

Imagine a cubical tank 10 feet long, 10 feet high and 10 feet wide, and filled with water. Since water weighs 62.4 pounds per cubic foot and since the volume of the tanks is 1,000 cubic feet, the weight of the water in the tank is 62,400 pounds. The thrust of the liquid against the 100-square-foot bottom of the tank is equally distributed; the water will push against every square foot of the bottom with a pressure of 624 pounds per square foot — that is, 62,400 pounds divided by 100. Since there are 144 square inches in one square foot, the pressure of the water in pounds per square inch at the bottom will be 624 pounds divided by 144, or 4.33 pounds per square inch. This figure represents the pressure due to the liquid only. To obtain the total or absolute pressure, you would have to add

within a liquid depends only on the depth and density of the liquid. Suppose a piece of one-inch pipe is placed in a vertical position and filled with liquid to a depth of ten feet. The pressure at its bottom is the same as it would be on a square inch at the bottom of a big tank filled to a depth of ten feet with that same liquid.

Liquids exert pressure not only on the bottom of a container, but in all directions and at all places throughout the liquid. The pressure downward or sideways increases with greater depth below the surface because of the added weight of the water above.

You can easily prove this by a very simple experiment. Punch holes in an empty tin can near the top and near the bottom; then fill the can with water. The water will escape from the holes, thus proving that liquids exert pressure sideways as well as from above and below. Water will spurt from the holes near the bottom much more rapidly than from those near the top. This is because the pressure of the water is greater near the bottom of the can, since the total weight of the liquid above that level is greater than the total weight above the hole near the top. Since pressure in-

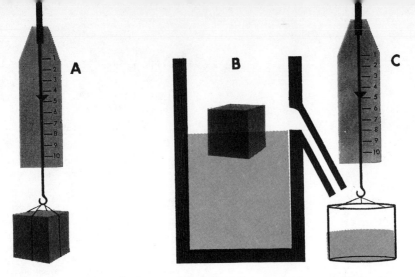

2. A block of wood weighs 5 ounces (A). It is put into an overflow can filled with water up to the spout (B). The displaced water flows into the container at the side of the overflow can (C). The weight of the displaced water equals the weight of the block.

creases with depth, a dam is built so that the thickest and strongest part is at the bottom where the pressure of the water is greatest.

Because of the presence of salt and other impurities, seawater has a density of about 64 pounds per cubic foot instead of 62.4. At a depth of only 600 feet, the pressure is about 267 pounds per square inch. A submarine designed to descend to this depth would have to be well built to withstand the weight of the salt water. At certain places off the coast of Asia, the ocean has been found to have a depth of more than 6 miles. At this depth the pressure is more than 7 tons per square inch!

Liquids possess the property of buoyancy

Everyone knows that some objects float in water and that others do not. An object that floats in water might sink in alcohol, and one that sinks in water might float in glycerin. All liquids possess in varying degrees the property that is called buoyancy — an upward push upon objects that are submerged within them.

If you throw a piece of dry wood into a pond or a pool, the wood floats; the upward push of the water makes this possible. An object that sinks in water — like a piece of iron — weighs less when under water than when in air; this also is because the water exerts an upward pressure upon it. When you are taking a bath in a well-filled tub, you can raise your whole body easily by a slight pressure of your hands on the bottom of the tub. You could not do this so easily if you tried to raise yourself from the living-room floor because, though air is buoyant, it is less buoyant than water.

In the third century B.C., the Greek mathematician and physicist Archimedes discovered the principle of buoyancy which bears his name. Archimedes' Principle states that a body wholly or partly immersed in a fluid is buoyed upward with a force equal to the weight of the volume of liquid it displaces. Let us imagine that in a full pail of water we place an iron ball that weighs ten pounds when weighed in air. We discover, however, that under water this ball weighs only eight pounds — a loss of two pounds. The volume of water that spilled over when the ball was placed in the full pail weighs two pounds, which just equals the ball's loss of weight. In other words, our iron ball, though it sinks, is actually buoyed up by a force equal to the weight of the water it displaces.

A floating body always sinks to such a depth that the weight of the displaced liquid is the same as that of the body itself (Figure 2). A body that weighs more than the liquid that it displaces will sink. A ship having a total weight of 5,000 tons sinks into the water until the weight of the water displaced is 5,000 tons. If a barge floating on a river is given a load of 2,000 tons of coal, the barge will sink farther down until an additional 2,000 tons of water is displaced. On the other hand, a block of iron will not float in water because it weighs more than the water it displaces. Since iron sinks in water, you may wonder why a ship made entirely of steel (an alloy of iron) can float. The reason is that it is not solid but contains much hollow space filled with air; its density is less than that of solid iron.

A solid that is more dense than the liquid in which it is placed will sink; if it is less dense than the liquid it will float. Even a block of lead will float on mercury because mercury is denser than lead. If kerosene and water are poured into the same container, the kerosene will float on the water, since its density is less than that of water. For the same reason, cream rises in milk and floats on the top.

If an oceangoing vessel sails up a river, it sinks deeper in the river than it did in the sea. The reason is that seawater, because of the salts dissolved in it,* is denser than fresh water. It is easy to show how objects are affected by the added buoyancy of salt water. Place an egg in a drinking glass full of water from your tap. The egg will sink to the bottom. Remove the egg and stir about four tablespoonfuls of salt into the glass. If you put the egg in this salt solution, it will float on the surface. Gently add fresh water until the glass is almost full, and then stir. This time the egg will sink about halfway to the bottom of the glass. This is obviously because the fresh water that you add to the drinking glass is less buoyant than salt water.

A submarine is built so that its total weight is a little less than the weight of the same volume of seawater. It has tanks into which seawater is allowed to enter when the craft is about to submerge. With the added weight of the seawater in its tanks, the submarine now weighs more than an equal volume of seawater, and so it sinks. When it is to rise to the surface, the water is forced out of the tanks by means of compressed air.

Pascal's Law
and its applications

Another property of liquids was discovered in the seventeenth century by the great French scientist Blaise Pascal. He

* The average salt content of the sea is a little less than 35 parts of salt for every 1,000 parts of seawater.

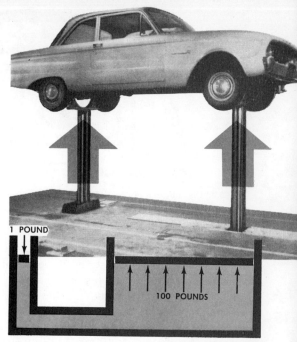

3. A downward force of 1 pound on a small piston exerts an upward force of 100 pounds on a large one. The two-post lift shown in the photograph above is based on the same principle.

showed that pressure applied to any part of a liquid in a closed vessel is transmitted with equal intensity to all parts of the liquid and acts in all directions. This principle is known as Pascal's Law.

Let us see how Pascal's Law works. Suppose we have two cylinders filled with some liquid — oil perhaps — and connected at their bottoms as shown in Figure 3. Each cylinder is fitted with a movable piston. Suppose that a downward force of one pound is exerted on the small piston, which has an area of one square inch. This force applies a downward pressure of one pound per square inch at the top of the liquid in the small piston. Now, according to Pascal's Law, this causes an increase in pressure of one pound per square inch at every point throughout the liquid in both cylinders since they are connected. Suppose the large piston has an area of 100 square inches. The upward force against this piston will be 100 pounds. Therefore, a downward force of one pound against the small piston exerts an upward force of 100 pounds against the large piston.

As we look at Figure 3, it may seem strange that a small force on the small piston can exert such a large force on the

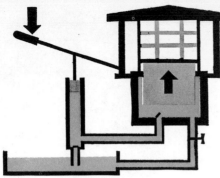

Fred S. Carver Inc.

4. The diagram above shows a hydraulic press compressing a cotton bale. At the right is a hydraulic press that is used in a laboratory.

large one. The fact is that the gain in the force or push upward is at the expense of the distance that the big piston is moved. When the small piston moves downward the entire length of the cylinder, the large piston will actually rise very little. Where the ratio of the areas is 100 to 1, the large piston will be forced upward only one hundredth of an inch when the small one is pushed downward one inch.

The city pumping station can pump water to your house only because of the forces explained by Pascal's Law. If none of the faucets in the water system are open and if the faucets and the pumps are at the same level, the pressure at the pumping station and at your faucet is the same. In other words, the pressure exerted by the pumps at the pumping station, on the body of water there, has spread throughout the water in the system, passing through the pipes, which extend in many directions, perhaps many miles away to your own faucets.

Pascal's Law explains the working of the hydraulic press, shown in Figure 4. ("Hydraulic" comes from a Greek word meaning "water organ.") The small cylinder consists of a pump that forces liquid into the larger cylinder. As the small pump piston is pushed downward, there is an upward force on the large piston.

The principle of the hydraulic press is used in many common appliances. In the hydraulic brake on automobiles, a small force applied to the brake pedal is so magnified on the brake drums as to stop the car. When your barber wishes to raise his barber chair, he works a lever that pumps oil into a cylinder containing the piston that supports the chair. A slight pressure on the lever is magnified so greatly that it raises the weight of the heavy chair. Hy-

draulic pressure operates the wing flaps of many planes; it also compresses cotton bales into comparatively small bundles so that they will take up less shipping space.

Properties of
liquids in motion

Liquids that are in motion, such as water moving through a pipe, do not follow exactly the same rules as liquids at rest. For instance, although the pressure is the same for all points at the same depth below the surface of a liquid at rest, this is not true for liquids in motion. In a stream of water moving through a pipe that has everywhere the same diameter, the pressure decreases uniformly in the direction in which the water is moving. The pressure will be greatest nearest the point where the water enters the pipe. Where water is piped from a spring to a house, the pressure is greatest close to the spring; where the pipe enters the house the pressure is much less. Pumps often have to be used in a case of this kind to step up, or increase, the pressure. One way of showing how the pressure becomes constantly less in the direction in which water is flowing in a pipe is to place vertical glass tubes in the pipe at various points along it, as shown in Figure 5. The pressure at each point will be indicated by the

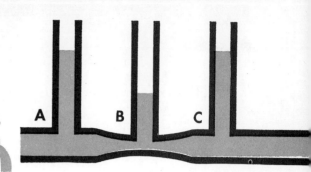

5. The pressure on each of the vertical tubes is indicated by the height to which the water rises.

6. Varying pressure in a horizontal tube. The liquid moves faster at B than at either A or C.

height to which the water rises at that particular point. The height of the liquid in the glass tubes decreases uniformly in the direction in which the liquid is flowing.

Now there is a different and very strange effect which we notice in liquids that are moving through horizontal pipes. You might imagine that the pressure in a liquid would be greatest where its speed is greatest, but this is not true. The pressure is least where the speed is greatest.

In a pipe whose inside passageway, or opening, is smaller at some places than at others, the liquid will flow more rapidly through the smaller sections than through the larger ones. In Figure 6, the liquid is moving faster at B than at either A or C. But the pressure in the wide parts of the pipe at A and C is greater than the pressure in the small part of the pipe at B. When the pressure is greater in the pipe, the speed is less, and when the pressure is less the speed is greater. This law was discovered in the eighteenth century by Daniel Bernoulli; it is called Bernoulli's Principle.

The jet water pump, which is often used to pump water out of basements, works on Bernoulli's Principle (Figure 7). In this type of pump, the tube A is connected to a water faucet. As water from the faucet rushes through this tube, it travels fastest through the narrow part at B. The lessened pressure at B creates suction, which pulls water up from the basement through the tube G. The water from the faucet and the water from the basement flow out at C.

Bernoulli's Principle also explains why two speedboats moving parallel and close to each other are likely to be pulled together and collide (Figure 8). As the boats move forward, water is funneled into the narrow region between them. The relative speed

between the water and the boats is greater in this narrow region than if there were more space between the boats. As a result, there is a decrease in pressure of the water between the boats, and the greater pressure of the water upon the outer sides pushes the boats together.

The gases that surround us

Since we can see and feel liquids, it is comparatively easy to visualize the forces

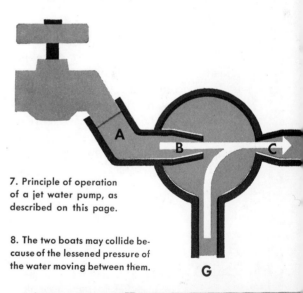

7. Principle of operation of a jet water pump, as described on this page.

8. The two boats may collide because of the lessened pressure of the water moving between them.

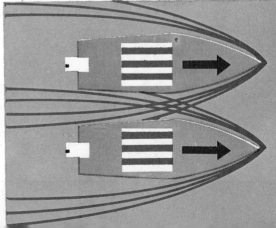

that they exert. The forces at work within gases are apt to seem far more mysterious, because most gases are invisible and many are odorless as well. Yet they surround us on every side. The very breath of life, the air, is a mixture of several gases — a great deal of nitrogen (about 78 per cent), a sizable amount of oxygen (about 21 per cent) and small quantities of carbon dioxide, argon, helium, krypton, neon and xenon.

Many other kinds of gases are common in everyday life. Illuminating gas is piped to your kitchen range and perhaps to your furnace. Ginger ale fizzes because of a gas in it. Your electric refrigerator, the neon lights above your theater, the plumber's blowtorch and hundreds of other familiar devices are operated by gases.

All gases have weight, just as solids and liquids have. A cubic foot of air at average temperature and pressure weighs about $1\frac{1}{4}$ ounces. The air in a room 30 feet long, 20 feet wide and 14 feet high weighs about 655 pounds — more than a quarter of a ton. Gases vary greatly in density. Hydrogen is the lightest gas; helium, which is twice as heavy as hydrogen, is only about $\frac{1}{7}$ as heavy as air.

As we pointed out, the atmosphere is made up of a number of gases. It is really an ocean of air, which surrounds the earth and which extends upward for hundreds of miles. The total weight of the atmosphere is about 5,810 million million tons. It presses down on every square inch of the earth's surface with a force of about 14.7 pounds at sea level.

The force of atmospheric pressure

The existence of atmospheric pressure was demonstrated in a series of experiments in the seventeenth century by the Italian Evangelista Torricelli and the Frenchman Blaise Pascal. Torricelli took a long, slender tube, sealed at one end and containing mercury, and set it, open end down, in a dish containing mercury. He showed that the atmospheric pressure at sea level on the mercury in the dish would keep the column of mercury in the tube at a height of about 30 inches (Figure 9).

The modern mercury barometer, used to measure the pressure of the atmosphere, is based upon Torricelli's model. It consists of an inverted mercury-filled tube in a reservoir of the same liquid. There is another type of barometer that is more sturdy and that can be carried about much more easily — the aneroid barometer (Figure 10). It has no tube and no liquid; as a matter of fact, the word "aneroid" comes from a Greek word meaning "not wet." This type of barometer is an airtight box made of very thin and flexible corrugated metal fastened firmly to a base. Some of the air is removed from the box, and as a result the flexible top becomes very sensitive to changes in air pressure from the outside.

When the pressure of the atmosphere increases, the top of the box is pushed down some distance. When the pressure decreases — pushes with less weight upon the top of the box — the top rises again. The

9. The mercury barometer of Evangelista Torricelli.

MERCURY

ATMOSPHERIC PRESSURE

10. The diagram below gives an idea of the basic parts of the aneroid barometer. At the right is the dial of such a barometer.

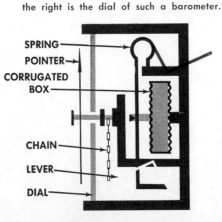

SPRING
POINTER
CORRUGATED BOX
CHAIN
LEVER
DIAL

Taylor Instrument Co.

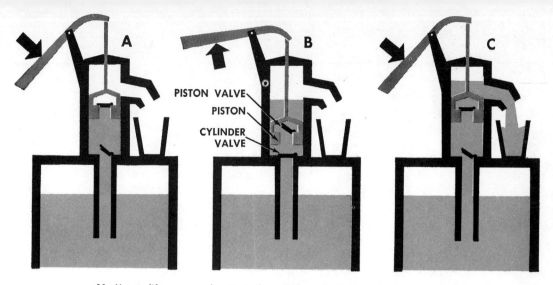

11. How a lift pump works. In *A*, the cylinder valve is open as the water rises. *B* shows the piston descending; the cylinder valve is closed. In *C*, the piston valve is closed as the piston rises; the water above the valve is then forced out.

motion of the box top is transferred by a system of springs, levers and chains to a pointer that moves along a scale. The number on the scale at which the pointer comes to rest indicates the barometric, or atmospheric, pressure.

The ordinary lift pump that raises water from a well or spring works because of atmospheric pressure. The weight of the atmosphere pushes down against the water in the well and forces it up the pipe which connects the well and the pump.

The pump itself consists of a cylinder into which a sliding piston is tightly fitted (Figure 11). This piston is attached to the pump handle, and as the handle is moved up and down, the piston slides down and up inside the pump cylinder. A valve opens upward in the piston, and another valve also opens upward in the bottom of the pump cylinder.

When the pump handle is pushed down, the piston in the cylinder rises, increasing the distance between it and the bottom of the cylinder. In this space a partial vacuum is created. Water from the well, forced upward by the pressure of the atmosphere, then passes through the inlet valve at the bottom of the cylinder and into the cylinder itself.

When the pump handle is pushed up, the piston descends in the cylinder with its valve open; the cylinder valve is closed. When the piston reaches the bottom of the cylinder, its valve closes because of the weight of the water above it. With the next

stroke the piston is raised, bringing with it a load of water, which pours out through the spout of the pump; the cylinder valve remains open while the piston valve is closed. This process is repeated again and again.

Atmospheric pressure can hold up a column of water thirty-four feet high, equivalent to thirty inches of mercury. Usually, however, a pump will lift water only about thirty feet because even in the best pumps of this type there is some leakage.

The pressure of the atmosphere also makes it possible to move water or other liquids by siphon from a higher level to a lower one when it is inconvenient to pour the liquid from one container into another. The siphon is a bent tube, one of whose arms is longer than the other (Figure 12). The tube is filled with liquid, and the shorter arm is immersed in the liquid in the higher

12. A siphon consists of a bent tube.

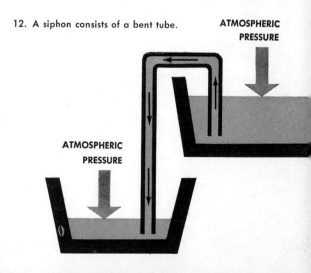

37

vessel. The liquid immediately starts to flow into the container at the lower level.

The pressure of the atmosphere forces the liquid up the shorter arm rather than up the longer one because the weight of the liquid in the shorter arm is less. If the liquid being transferred is water, the bend in the siphon must not be higher than thirty-four feet above the water's surface at sea level.

With a siphon, one can draw off the upper part of the liquid in a container without stirring up the sediment that lies at the bottom. Laboratory workers use siphons to transfer liquids from containers that cannot be tipped. Certain enterprising thieves draw gasoline from the tanks of automobiles with siphons; to prevent such thefts, the cap of a gasoline tank is sometimes provided with a lock. The name "siphon" is often used for a bottle through which charged water may be drawn. This is not a true siphon, however, since the water is driven out by the pressure of the gas inside the bottle and not by the pressure of the atmosphere.

The ordinary atomizer works because of atmospheric pressure. You will remember that, according to Bernoulli's Principle, the pressure in a moving liquid is least where the liquid is flowing most rapidly. The principle holds true not only of liquids but also of gases, including the collection of gases that we call the atmosphere. In the case of the atomizer, a rubber bulb is compressed suddenly to cause a jet of fast-moving air to pass over the top of a tube that extends down into the liquid in a bowl (Figure 13). The pressure above the liquid in the tube is greatly reduced by the air motion over the top of the tube. Atmospheric pressure upon the liquid in the bowl then forces liquid up and out at the end of the tube. The liquid is broken into a fine spray by the air jet and is carried along with it.

Bernoulli's Principle reveals why a baseball or tennis ball can be made to curve. If a baseball is moving forward and spinning around as it moves, some air adheres to the ball and is carried around with it. Because of the ball's forward motion, there is a backward flow of air past the ball. At the top of the ball, the flow of air is opposite in direction to the motion of the air that is dragged around due to the ball's spinning motion. At the bottom of the ball, the two air motions have the same direction. There is, therefore, a greater relative speed past the ball on the underside than on the upper side. Because the pressure is less on the underside the ball will be forced to curve downward.

Anyone can make a ball curve and thus demonstrate Bernoulli's principle, with the help of a simple bit of apparatus. Roll up a sheet of sandpaper, as shown in Figure 14, making the diameter of the roll such that a Ping-Pong ball can pass through it easily. Wrap a string around the roll and tie the ends of the string together. Now put a Ping-Pong ball inside the roll and throw the ball away from you at high speed. Can you explain what happens?

Bernoulli's Principle also explains the lift on an airplane wing. The shape of the wing causes air to rush over the top surface faster than it flows past the under surface (Figure 15). This causes a reduction in pressure above the wing which usually accounts for about two-thirds of the lift. The rest of the lift on the wing is due to the upward push of air against the underside.

You can see how lift is brought about in accordance with Bernoulli's Principle by making your own airplane "wing" as fol-

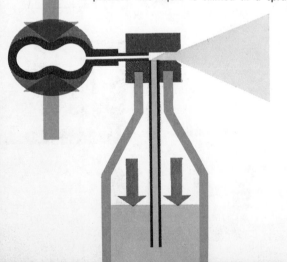

13. Atmospheric pressure within the bowl of the atomizer, below, forces liquid up when the bulb is pressed. The liquid is emitted in a spray.

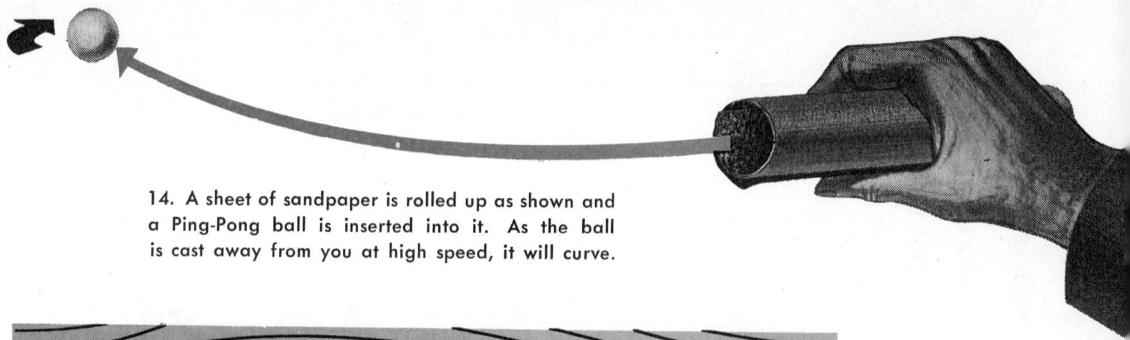

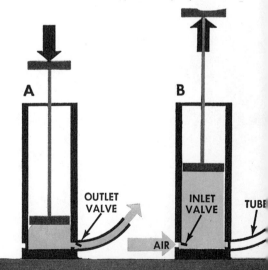

14. A sheet of sandpaper is rolled up as shown and a Ping-Pong ball is inserted into it. As the ball is cast away from you at high speed, it will curve.

15. Reduced pressure on the upper surface of an airplane wing causes most of the lift.

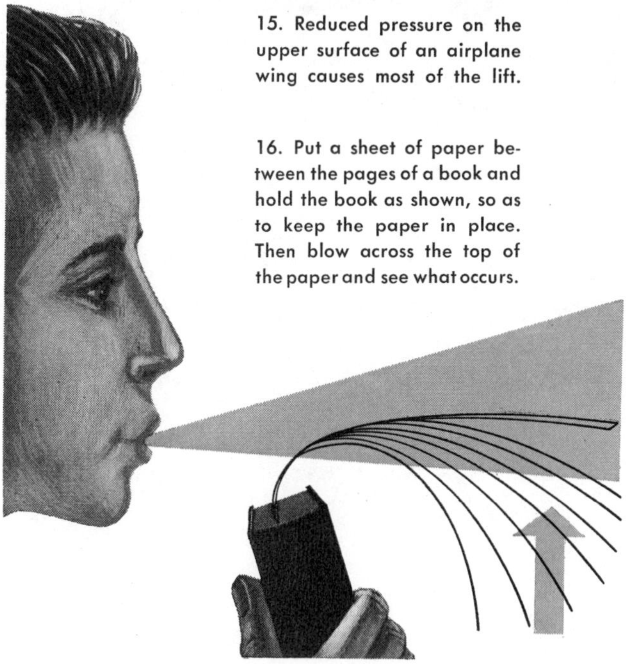

16. Put a sheet of paper between the pages of a book and hold the book as shown, so as to keep the paper in place. Then blow across the top of the paper and see what occurs.

have a flat tire. You must therefore force more air into the tire than it would have under normal atmospheric pressure.

The ordinary air pump is a very simple instrument. In one type (Figure 17), there is a cylinder with a sliding piston that is worked by a handle at the top. On opposite sides at the bottom of the cylinder are two valves, one for taking in air from the outside and the other for transmitting that air into the tube attached to the tire.

As you push the piston down (*A*, Figure 17), the inlet valve closes, and the compressed air is forced through the outlet valve into the tire. As you raise the piston (*B*, Figure 17), a partial vacuum is formed in the cylinder and the atmospheric pressure forces more air through the inlet valve. With the next downstroke of the piston,

lows. Insert a sheet of paper between the pages of a book; hold the latter as shown in Figure 16, in order to keep the "wing" in place. Blow across the top of the "wing" and see what happens to the sheet of paper.

**Pumps that increase
the pressure of the air**

Under normal conditions, as we have seen, the pressure of the atmosphere at sea level is about 14.7 pounds on every square inch. There are times when we need higher air pressures than the pressure of one atmosphere, as 14.7 pounds per square inch is called. For instance, if the pressure within the tires of your automobile were just equal to the pressure of the atmosphere, you would

17. How a familiar type of air pump works.

A   B

OUTLET
VALVE

INLET
VALVE

TUBE

AIR

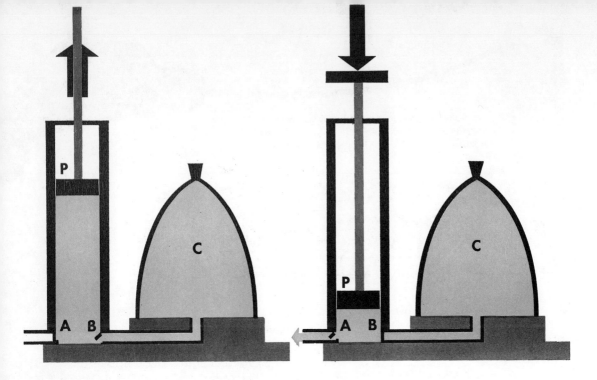

18. The vacuum pump is an air pump in reverse.

pressure is again exerted on this new batch of air, and in its turn it is forced through the outlet valve into the tire. In this way the tire is filled with compressed air.

In another type of pump, the inlet valve is a flexible leather gasket connected to the piston. This gasket allows air to slip past it when the piston is raised, and then expands tightly against the cylinder with the downstroke.

The use of gases under high pressure saves man a great deal of labor. Much heavy work that once was done by hand and with backbreaking effort can now be done easily with the help of compressed air. It works air brakes on trains, riveting machines, various types of drills and blasting machines for cutting stone and metal.

When new bridges are built across bodies of water, the foundations have to be laid under water. For this purpose engineers often sink a caisson, which is a great tank open at the bottom. Air is then forced into the caisson at pressures high enough to hold back the surrounding water. Workmen enter or leave the caisson, and materials are transferred to it, through air locks. The men can work with comfort in the caisson once they have adjusted themselves to the very high pressure there.

Compressed air is also used to keep water from rushing in during the construction of tunnels, and in completed tunnels for ventilation. As we said before, submarines are so built that they submerge by admitting seawater into special compartments, in this way increasing their weight. To bring the submarine back to the surface, compressed air is used to force out this water and lighten the craft.

The vacuum pump forces air out of a container

If it is possible to pump air into a container, it should also be possible to pump air out of it and in this way to leave the vessel empty or, rather, almost empty. We can do this by means of a vacuum pump, which is really an air pump in reverse. A simple type is shown in Figure 18. As the piston P is raised, the pressure in the cylinder below the piston decreases. The valve at A is held firmly closed by the air outside, while the valve B is forced open by the air in C, which expands into the cylinder. At the downward stroke, the valve at B closes, and the air in the cylinder is forced out through A. Each stroke of the piston removes a fraction of the air from C. The pressure in C decreases greatly after many

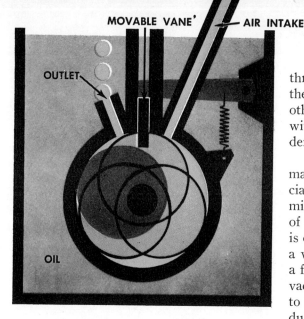

OUTLET

OIL

19. How a rotating vacuum pump works. An inner cylinder rotates off-center within an outer (stationary) one, keeping in contact with the inner wall of the latter and with a movable vane. The turning inner cylinder moves air from the intake and toward the outlet.

strokes, and, therefore, such a pump can never be very efficient. Eventually the pressure becomes too small to operate the valves.

A more efficient type of vacuum pump (Figure 19) uses a rotating inner cylinder that keeps turning in off-center fashion within an outer cylinder. As the inner cylinder rotates, it always makes contact with the inner wall of the outer cylinder and with a movable vane. The mechanism is immersed in oil, which serves as a lubricant and as a seal to prevent leakage. At each revolution of the inner cylinder, some air is drawn in through the intake, from the container to be evacuated, and is forced out through the outlet into the oil. Extremely low pressures can be achieved.

The vacuum plays a constant and practical role in our life today. If the air were not removed from the ordinary electric light bulb you use in your lamp, the oxygen in the air would cause the little filament or wire inside the bulb to burn out very soon. Many of the tubes in your radio are vacuum tubes. In some other types of bulbs and tubes, other gases are pumped in after the air has been pumped out. In neon advertising signs, the air is removed from the glass tubing, and neon gas at low pressure is admitted. As an electric current passes

through the tubing, the neon gas glows with the familiar pinkish red color. If certain other gases are used, the tubes will glow with other colors. The gases must be under low pressure if they are to glow.

In modern dairies, cows are milked by machines that are nothing more than special kinds of vacuum pumps. The necessary mixture of fuel and air enters the cylinders of the automobile engine because a vacuum is created as the piston moves forward. In a vacuum cleaner, an electric motor causes a fan to whirl rapidly and this fan creates a vacuum inside the nozzle. As air rushes in to fill up the vacuum, it carries particles of dust, lint and so on with it.

Gases exert an upward or buoyant force very much as liquids do. A body immersed in a gas is buoyed upward with a force equal to the weight of the gas displaced. This lifting power of air makes it possible for balloons to rise and to carry heavy loads. The buoyant effect becomes less the higher the balloon rises because of the decrease in density of the air. There is a limit to the height to which any balloon can travel. Sooner or later, it will reach an altitude where the buoyant force is not greater than the total weight. The balloon will then go no higher unless its load is reduced.

The earliest balloons were filled with hot air, which is not so dense as cool air. Later practically all balloons were inflated with hydrogen, the density of which is about one-fourteenth that of air. However, hydrogen is a highly inflammable gas, as many balloonists learned to their cost. In the case of dirigibles, too, the use of hydrogen sometimes led to disaster. Helium proved to be far more satisfactory for lighter-than-air craft because it will not burn. It is true that helium is twice as dense as hydrogen. However, since it is only approximately a seventh as dense as air, it still has abundant lifting power.

We can measure the pressure of gases in various ways. The mercury or aneroid barometer, as we have seen, indicates atmospheric pressure. The pressure of a gas in a closed vessel is measured differently. If the pressure of the gas is not too high or too low, a U-shaped glass tube — a manom-

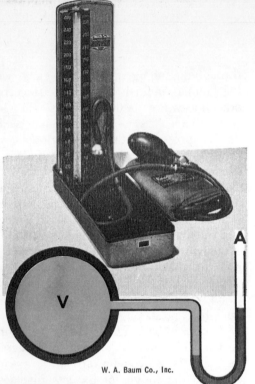

eter — is used (Figure 20). This glass tube is partly filled with mercury and one of its ends is connected to the vessel (V) that contains the gas. The other end is left open to the atmosphere at A. If the pressure in V is greater than the atmospheric pressure, the mercury will be pushed up in the open side of the tube, as shown in the diagram. If the pressure in V is less than the atmospheric pressure, the mercury will stand lower in the open end of the tube. The difference between the height of the mercury in the two sides of the tube will show how the pressure in V compares with the atmospheric pressure.

The small pressures in closed vessels containing very thin gas cannot be measured by ordinary manometers. In such cases, a large volume of the low-pressure gas is tapped and then compressed into a small volume. The pressure in this small volume of gas and the relative change in its volume are then measured. According to Boyle's Law (see Index), where there is no change in temperature the volume of a gas varies inversely as its pressure. By Boyle's Law, the pressure in the low-pressure gas can then be computed.

High pressures, such as the pressure of steam in a boiler and in all cases where compressed air is used, are measured by the Bourdon spring gauge (Figure 21). The instrument consists mainly of a hollow tube bent into a circular arc. One end of this tube is closed and the other is connected to the container of gas. As the gas under pressure enters the curved tube, the tube tends to straighten out. As it does so, a pointer attached to it by a system of levers moves along a scale. The scale is usually so made that it reads zero at atmospheric pressure. Anything above zero, then, gives the pressure in excess of atmospheric pressure. A gauge pressure of 30 pounds per square inch would mean a total pressure of 30 plus 14.7 or 44.7 pounds per square inch.

Today we have definitely harnessed the forces within liquids and gases. We can measure these forces, use them and avoid dangers often inherent in them.

See also Vol. 10, p. 280: "General Works."

W. A. Baum Co., Inc.

20. Diagram of a manometer, which measures the pressures of gases. The photo shows a sphygmomanometer, which contains a built-in manometer, measuring blood pressure. The sphygmomanometer is described elsewhere; see the Index.

21. The Bourdon spring gauge in this diagram measures high gas pressures. Two Bourdon gauges are used in the oxygen tank in the photo. The upper one indicates the amount of pressure in the tank at a certain room temperature. The gauge to the right of and below the first one measures the working pressure of the gas being released from the tank.

Linde Co., Division of Union Carbide

TUNNELING THE EARTH

How Man Burrows through Mountains and under Seas and Cities

THE tunnel builders of today perform many remarkable feats of engineering that attract only passing attention. Because of such achievements, trains bear their passengers under lofty mountains and beneath harbors and rivers; water supplies are brought to cities through aqueducts miles in length. The earth beneath our metropolitan centers is a veritable honeycomb of underground passages that carry traffic or serve as conduits for water, heat, gas and electricity.

Probably the first human tunneling took place when prehistoric men dug through rock in order to enlarge their caves. Stone Age men dug into rock to obtain superior flint for weapons; various relics of these early operations have been found in the chalk districts of southern England. Generally speaking, the tunneling of prehistoric man was restricted to soft rock strata. The ancient Egyptians, however, mastered the art of boring through hard rock in order to construct their subterranean tombs and temples.

In India, too, cave temples were dug out of solid rock. The Assyrians, Medes and Persians built tunnels serving as passageways, aqueducts and drains. The Old Testament describes a water-supply tunnel constructed in Jerusalem about 700 B.C. (II Kings 20:20). The Athenian silver mines in Attica represented the most extensive Greek tunneling operations. Several thousand shafts and galleries were dug.

The Romans were the greatest tunnel builders in antiquity. The greatest of all Roman tunnels, completed in 52 A.D. during the reign of the emperor Claudius I, was dug in order to drain the Fucino Lake. It was about 3½ miles long, with a cross section of 6 by 10 feet and a maximum depth of 400 feet. The aqueduct tunnels of Rome were likewise outstanding; the underground passageway of the aqueduct known as Aqua Antonia Marcia was particularly famous. The Romans built a great number of impressive road tunnels. The passage of Posilipo, near Naples, completed about 36 B.C., is still in use today; it is 3,000 feet long, 75 feet wide at the portals and 25 feet wide at the middle. Visitors still marvel at the Roman catacombs — subterranean burial places with miles of passageways at different levels.

Engineering declined in the early Middle Ages; but when large stone structures began to reappear, tunneling was resumed. Some castles, monasteries and churches had secret tunnels, dug out for various purposes. Agricola's famous treatise CONCERNING METALS, published in 1556 (see Index, under Agricola), shows that the tunneling methods employed by the Romans were still in use during the Middle Ages and in the period of the Renaissance. As a matter of fact, CONCERNING METALS remained a standard handbook on mining and tunneling practices for over three hundred years after the date of its publication!

The great era of modern tunnel building began with the development of the steam railroad in the first half of the nineteenth century. The construction of the early railroad tunnels involved great hardships and difficulties. The men toiled with pick and shovel and hand drills in dim candlelight; they had scant protection against cave-ins, hidden streams of water and foul air. Ill health or violent death was too often their ultimate reward.

The first tunnel through the Alps was at the mountain called Massif du Fréjus, which is one of those separating Italian Piedmont from the French province of Savoie on the other side of the Alps. Travelers going from Paris to Rome in those days could travel by railroad to the Mont Cenis Pass, sixteen miles northeast of Massif du Fréjus; there they were forced to transfer to horse-drawn carriages, which made their way slowly across the Alps.

In 1857 work began, at Massif du Fréjus, on what is called the Mont Cenis Tunnel, though, as we have seen, Mont Cenis is really sixteen miles away. Workers started drilling at both ends of the projected tunnel. At first the drilling was done entirely by hand. Progress was so slow that the men advanced an average distance of only nine inches a day at each end of the tunnel. In 1861 the newly developed compressed-air drill was introduced in the Mont Cenis Tunnel project. Air compressors operated by water power were situated near the mouth of the tunnel; the compressed air was carried through pipes to the drills. Work now advanced much more rapidly; the workers tunneled almost four feet a day at each end using not only drills but

gunpowder for blasting purposes. The original plans called for a tunnel about twenty-five feet in diameter. In constructing this single big-bore tunnel, three small tunnels were first bored, side by side; the rock between the tunnels was then broken through by means of hand tools. The tunnel was completed in 1871 at a cost of about fifteen million dollars; through it runs the double-track Turin-Lyons Railroad.

The site of the next railway line to cross the Alps was the Saint Gotthard Pass in southern Switzerland. When the Saint Gotthard Tunnel was begun in 1872, the engineers used new tunneling methods developed in the light of the experience acquired at Mont Cenis. With these methods it was possible to advance 18 feet each 24 hours. In the course of the construction, a new type of drill was introduced. This new drill was worked by air compressed to 7 atmospheres, or 102.9 pounds to the square inch. Another advance was the use of dynamite instead of gunpowder. The tunnel was completed in February 1880; it lies between the towns of Göschenen and Airolo. The total length is 9.3 miles.

The Arlberg Tunnel was begun in 1880; it lies between Innsbruck and Bludenz in

Ingersoll-Rand Co.

Drifter drill on a column and arm mounting. This efficient tool is a "must" in modern tunnel building.

Austria. Improved drills increased the speed of excavation to 27.2 feet each twenty-four hours. Approximately 900 tons of rocky material had to be removed daily from the tunnel. Eight thousand cubic feet of fresh air per minute was circulated by means of ventilators; this was a great improvement over the method used at Saint Gotthard Tunnel, where air discharged from compressed-air drills served for ventilation purposes. The Arlberg Tunnel was completed in 1884. Its total length is 6¼ miles.

The Simplon Tunnel was begun in 1898 to speed travel from Paris to the center of industrial northern Italy by means of a new rail line northeast of the Simplon Pass, between Switzerland and Italy. Two parallel tunnels were to be built, each carrying a single line of track. The engineers met with serious difficulties in constructing this tunnel. For one thing they tapped large quantities of water, which interfered with tunneling operations. This water was used later to provide power for air compressors and water pumps. Because of the unusual depth reached by the tunnel (the greatest depth was 7,005 feet), the engineers were confronted with extremely high temperatures. They overcame this difficulty by installing ventilation plants, which forced air into the tunnel by means of fans.

With improved rotary drills the work advanced, on the average, 35 feet each 24 hours. The first of the two tunnels was completed in 1905; the second, in the early 1920's. The Simplon Tunnel extends for 12.3 miles; it carries the railroad from Brig, Switzerland, to Iselle, Italy.

In the first half of the nineteenth century, engineers proposed to construct a tunnel through the Hoosac Range as part of a canal system across Massachusetts, from Boston to the Hudson River. The Hoosac Range is part of the Green Mountain chain, between Massachusetts and New York State. When railroads were built throughout the northeast, this project was abandoned. Plans for a tunnel through the Hoosac Range to carry the old Troy and Greenfield Railway were then advanced. Construction work on the tunnel began in 1856.

The project was to be held up and started again many times before it was completed. Nitroglycerine was used in 1866 in place of black powder; this was the first time it served for tunneling in the United States. The powerful explosive was poured into the drill holes for blasting, and electricity was used to set off the blasts. This risky way of handling nitroglycerine caused an appalling number of lives to be lost in the construction of the tunnel.

Compressed air drills were used for the first time in the United States in this project. The drills, mounted on carriages, were able to bore five feet in about one hour. The work of removing the rocky material and properly aligning the tunnel was made easier by vertical shafts sunk from the

The construction of a subway tunnel. A steel or iron framework, called a shield, is transported on the wide track from the shaft to the very end of the tunnel that is being excavated.

Ingersoll-Rand Co.

American Express Co.

Approach to St. Gotthard Tunnel, in the Alps. Torrents of hot water and high temperatures impeded its construction.

mountain top to the tunnel grade. These drills also furnished ventilation during construction. The tunnel was finally completed in 1876. It has a total length of four and three-quarters miles; it is wide enough for two railway tracks to pass through it. The tunnel requires no artificial ventilating system; a vertical shaft 1,028 feet deep, sunk near the center of the tunnel's length, provides adequate air movement.

Loss of life in the building of the Hoosac Tunnel

There is always some loss of life in the construction of any large tunnel. One hundred ninety-five men gave their lives before the Hoosac Tunnel was completed. The worst accident occurred when the central shaft had been sunk to a depth of 583 feet. A fire broke out in the large house that had been built over the shaft's mouth and that had been used as a general storehouse and office.

Thirteen miners were at work at the bottom of the shaft at the time, and an effort was made to rescue them by means of the hoisting bucket, but without success. The fire burned away the cable and dropped the heavy bucket. The landing floor at the top of the shaft, upon which were piled several hundred steel tools, then fell on the miners below; it was followed in a few moments by the roof timbers of the burning building. It was months before the shaft was finally cleared and the bodies of the thirteen miners were found.

A tragedy in the Italian Alps

Tunneling disasters continued to occur through the years with distressing regularity. For example, a more recent tragedy occurred in 1956 in the Italian Alps. A tunnel was being constructed near the city of Trent. The premature explosion of a blasting charge caused five workmen to be blown to bits and buried five others in an avalanche of rock and earth. Still other workers were trapped within the tunnel as a result of the explosion. Fortunately, they were dug out in time.

Men building the Delaware Aqueduct Tunnel for the New York City water supply are protected by the rib-type steel roof supports that shore up the tunnel excavation in poor rock areas.

Modern methods and safety devices have greatly reduced the loss of life. However, tunneling is still a physically wearing, dangerous occupation.

The tunneling methods to be used depend on the type of tunnel to be built and on the nature of the ground to be gone through. When a tunnel is bored, engineers are not always certain about the character of the strata which will be encountered in the course of digging. In general, geologists are able to determine the nature of the types of earth through which the tunnels will have to pass. However, their conclusions are not always infallible. They may make borings to obtain samples of the deep layers of earth which must be penetrated. The borings, however, do not always reveal the presence of the dangers that are subsequently discovered. Loose, sandy materials and underground streams of water are particularly dreaded and have caused most of the disasters that have occurred in tunneling. Ground water becomes a particularly serious problem if it is combined with sand or gravel. It may be encountered at great depths and at very high temperatures. Underground natural gases are also dangerous; they may cause violent explosions. When we consider all these hazards, we can readily understand why engineers must so carefully plan methods which assure the greatest safety for the workers. Ventilating systems must be arranged for and piping systems planned to pump out any ground water which may be encountered. All these plans must be made before work on the tunnel is begun.

Many difficulties were encountered in constructing tunnels in the mountain system of the Alps. Borings could not be taken due to the height of these mountains; however, geologists were able to state approximately the character of the strata which must be met. On the northern side of the St. Gotthard Tunnel, workers excavated 6,000 feet of solid granite without coming upon any water. On the southern side, however, the discharge of water from the yielding and disintegrated rock was 4,000 gallons per minute. Often the drilling-machine frames had to be laid in a torren-tial stream twenty inches deep. The men worked in an incessant tropical rain, which fell from the roof of the tunnel. Frequently solid jets of water as thick as a man's arm burst out from floor or wall. The men also had to work under a high temperature, which was increased by dynamite blastings. Sometimes, as in the Simplon Tunnel, there was an inrush of water from hot springs. The water would knock down the workmen and the air temperature would rise to such an extent that work became impossible. It was then necessary to pipe cold water into the tunnel and to mix it with the hot water, so the temperature would be lowered and work could be resumed.

Many tunnels have been built in the United States, not for railroad transportation, but for drainage purposes or to carry water supplies. Some of these tunnels have involved serious engineering problems. For example, the aqueduct that was to bring the waters of the Catskills to millions of users in the New York City metropolitan area had to be carried across the Hudson River. It was decided to have the aqueduct cross the river at Storm King. Comparative studies were made to determine the respective advantages of bridging, placing steel pipes on the river bed or tunneling. The latter method was finally adopted; the project was completed in 1913.

It was planned to locate the tunnel in bedrock in order to prevent slipping or collapse at some future time. Many exploratory borings were made; it was necessary in some cases to go to extreme depths in order to find bedrock. The final decision was to locate the tunnel about 1,100 feet below the river surface. This was accomplished by first sinking, on both banks, vertical shafts to this depth and then opening up horizontal headings, or passageways. The length of the tunnel is 3,022 feet; the section is circular and has a 14-foot inside diameter.

Both shafts and tunnel were lined with concrete to prevent seepage from the river. At one point, the workmen were driven back by the inrush of water from a water-bearing stratum through the seams of the tunnel. An eighteen-foot wall of concrete was placed across the tunnel heading to hold back the water. Liquid cement (grout), carried through pipes in the concrete wall, was then forced into the leaking seams under a pressure of from 400 to 900 pounds per square inch. When this grout had hardened, the concrete wall was removed. The inrush of water had now been reduced to a slight dampness which showed itself on the tunnel roof. This is just one example of the ingenuity that sand hogs (men who work in tunnels) show in protecting their lives and in getting the job done.

Sand hogs were also threatened by occasional "popping" of rock as the excavation proceeded. Fragments of the solid rock would suddenly shoot from the sides of the tunnel with terrific force, accompanied by a loud explosion. Workmen had to be protected by steel shields placed around the sides of the tunnel. (According to geologists, this popping was due to the relieving of great pressures which had previously existed in the rock.)

City of New York Board of Water Supply

This tunnel, completed in the year 1913, brings water from the Catskills to New York City. Located 1,100 feet below the Hudson River, its construction presented engineers with many challenging problems.

The ever-increasing demands of the New York City water supply system, for which this tunnel was built, and the advances in our knowledge of tunnel building have led to the construction of some of the world's longest tunnels. When it went into operation in 1917, the tunnel called City No. 1 held the record with a length of 17.7 miles. Starting from the Hill View Reservoir, it travels southward beneath the Harlem River, the entire island of Manhattan and the East River and terminates in Brooklyn.

Due to the great network of pipes and conduits that already filled the city's streets, the entire tunnel had to be driven through bedrock, at a depth that varied from 750 to 200 feet below street level. The 25 vertical shafts from which the headings were opened served later to bring the water, under great pressure, to the distributing mains in the street.

City Tunnel No. 2, begun in 1929, was in many ways similar to the first; both had the same terminals and both were located entirely in bedrock. The path of City Tunnel No. 2, however, ran east of the East River, forming a sort of oval with No. 1. It is 20.5 miles long, with an average diameter of 17 feet.

The most recent addition to the city's system, the Delaware River Aqueduct, completed in 1944, includes a continuous true tunnel 85 miles in length, the longest of its kind in the world. Twenty-six shafts were sunk to depths varying from 300 to 1,500 feet; from these, horizontal headings were opened. It is a striking demonstration of progress in tunneling methods and machinery that only one more shaft was required for this tunnel than for the 17.7 miles of City Tunnel No. 1.

When tunnels are bored from opposite ends, as is commonly done, they generally meet with little error at the center. In the construction of the Delaware Tunnel, twenty-four separate meetings took place, and the error of the floor level was never more than two inches; meetings of the walls sometimes missed by as much as two feet. When the Simplon Tunnel was joined, the walls corresponded exactly, and the floors showed a difference of only four inches. In the Hoosac Tunnel, the center lines of the two headings met with a deviation of only five sixteenths of an inch.

This is accomplished in several ways. In the planning of tunnels, as in all construction, the laying of lines is done by the use of the transit. This instrument consists of a telescope in a finely machined and calibrated mounting, set firmly upon a tripod. By means of gears in the mount, the telescope can be rotated vertically and horizontally, and its cross-hairs sighted on an exact point, whose position is given by the calibrated scales. A plumb line and

Tail view of the shield that was used in the construction of New York City's Sixth Avenue Subway. The photograph shows the ring of hydraulic jacks.

Spencer, White & Prentis, Inc.

The inner shell of the two-lane Elizabeth River tunnel at Norfolk, Virginia. In the construction of the tunnel, an 18-inch lining of concrete was built over the ribbing of the walls, and a 22-foot-wide roadway slab was installed. The concrete was piped in through hatches along the top of the tube and it was molded by special traveler forms. When the interior was complete, concrete and welded steel sealed all the hatches, making the tube completely watertight. This fine tunnel should give centuries of service.

bubble level, attached to the transit, exactly determine its own location.

When there is no great obstruction in the line of view between the two ends of the tunnel, a line is established by sighting and marking a number of points along the route. A shaft is sunk at each portal, and plumb lines are dropped to the shaft floor from two points as far apart as possible on the surface line. The lines are protected from disturbing air currents by long tubes of wood or metal, and the oscillation of the weights is damped by immersing them in oil. Two points on the shaft floor are thus obtained; the line between these points represents a segment of the original surface line. We now have two segments, one at each portal. The transit is used to prolong each segment as tunneling proceeds; an exact meeting at the center requires only much care and repeated observations of the reference points.

When a direct portal-to-portal sight is impossible, due to some great obstruction, the line is established indirectly by sighting on a peak between the two portals and visible from both, and then projecting a line, in opposite directions, from this point to landmarks beyond either portal. At each portal, a transit situated on the line is backsighted to these landmarks and then rotated through 180 degrees, thus bringing the line into the headings.

Though tunneling in rock is difficult and often dangerous, it is a simple matter compared to boring through soft material, which carries water in large quantities. Not only must the caving-in of the soft material be prevented, but also the possible seepage of water into the workings.

The caving-in is prevented by means of a steel shield, or compartment (discussed below). It is driven into the heading by powerful hydraulic jacks. The men can work in comparative safety within the shield's confines. The shield also prevents another danger — that of the bottom of the tunnel's boiling up in soft ground — truly a nightmarish experience for those who have witnessed it and lived to tell of it. Seepage of water is overcome by forcing air into the tunnel under a pressure sufficient to hold back the water. This air pressure is a menace to the workmen, but it is safe to say that few of the subaqueous tunnels in existence could have been driven without it. Sometimes weak ground at the tunnel face gives way and permits the compressed air to escape with a rush. This loss of pressure through the top of the tunnel will permit an inrush of water and silt at the bottom. Unless the leak is stopped, there will be a flood.

The shield was invented by Brunel, an English engineer who took out his first patent in 1818. We may think of a shield as a huge steel cylinder placed on its side and having a diameter approximately that of the tunnel which is to be built. It is made of steel plates and angle supports and has a braced diaphragm placed across its face. This diaphragm is of heavy steel plate. It may be divided into a number of pockets with doors to permit the workers to excavate material in front of the shield. There are also platforms on which the workers stand. The forward cutting edge is forced ahead into the material to be excavated. It advances as hydraulic jacks press against the rear end of the shield. The lining of the tunnel is put in place as the shield advances. Because of the shield, no part of the excavation is left unsupported, save at the heading. There is a forward extension which prevents the falling in of the exposed face of the excavation. There is a backward extension several inches below the level of the cutting edge of the shield. It affords space for putting the primary tunnel lining in place. The shield cuts a clean hole a few inches larger in diameter than the inner diameter

British Information Service

Cross section of the Wapping-Rotherhithe Tunnel, under the Thames, showing men at work behind a Brunel shield.

of the finished tunnel; an impervious lining of concrete or iron is then provided. The cycle of operation is: forward thrust, fitting of a new lining, clearing away of muck and another forward thrust.

A heavy airtight bulkhead is built across the tunnel as soon as water is encountered; air under pressure is supplied to the heading. All workmen and all the material excavated must pass through the bulkhead. This requires a device called an "air lock," which is a space or room built into the interior of the bulkhead. It is entered from either side by doors which are capable of being made airtight. When the workman enters the lock, he closes the door behind him and the pressure of the air in the lock is raised slowly until it corresponds to that in the tunnel workings. When he comes out, the process is reversed.

Care has to be taken to see that the men do not come out too quickly. This is to prevent the occurrence of caisson disease, or the "bends," one of the greatest hazards threatening men who work under compression. Sufferers complain of sharp pains in abdomen or joints, uneven gait, paralytic symptoms, swelling and sometimes complete collapse. Permanent disability may result from severe attacks. Caisson disease is caused by a too-rapid change from a higher to a lower atmospheric pressure or vice versa. Nitrogen from the air is dissolved in the blood and absorbed by the body tissues when the atmospheric pressure is high. This nitrogen is released if the pressure is lowered suddenly. It then forms gas bubbles in the body tissues. Not only do the bubbles cause severe pain as they escape from solution in the body fluids, but they are also quite dangerous because they obstruct small veins, capillaries and arteries. Except in cases where the worker has suffered repeated attacks of this malady, it can usually be overcome by lengthening the period of decompression. This prevents the formation of gas bubbles in the body tissues. Another method of prevention is to use a helium-oxygen mixture in the air lock and work chamber.

The first time the shield was used in the United States was in building a tunnel under the Hudson River between New York City and New Jersey. It was the first of four tunnels built under this river by the Hudson River and Manhattan Railroad Company.

Work was begun in 1874 by Dewitt C. Haskins, who sank a shaft on the New Jersey shore and began the tunnel through the silt of the river bed without a shield.

Then financial troubles developed and Haskins had to stop work on the tunnel in 1888. English financiers became interested in it, and work was resumed in 1890. The tunnel was found to be full of silt and mud and there was a hole twelve feet in diameter through its roof up to the bed of the river. It was impossible to get beyond the last bulkhead, or partition, left by Haskins. After trying many methods, a canvas container full of calking material was put into the hole from above the river by means of a large floating crane. The door in the bulkhead was then jacked open and the material allowed to leak into the tunnel. When this material was removed from the tunnel, the hole in its roof was found to be closed and it was possible to get by the bulkhead and build a chamber in which to erect the shield.

Building this shield was very difficult. The plates had to be fitted and riveted, not in a workshop with every appliance available, but in the wet, treacherous end of a 2,000-foot tunnel. When the shield was finished, it began to give a great deal of trouble by tending to turn at right angles and to cut a vertical shaft. Finally, how-

Another view of the Wapping-Rotherhithe Tunnel, showing workers behind the Brunel shield. This invention was a contribution to safety.

British Information Service

He used compressed air and canvas linings to hold back the soft material until a masonry lining could be put in place. A disastrous accident occurred. The canvas lining collapsed and the river bed engulfed the workmen.

Therefore the canvas linings were discarded; iron plating supported by timbers was used instead, and tunneling continued successfully for a distance of 2,000 feet.

ever, it was adjusted so that it went straight ahead. There were no further difficulties until financial troubles again developed in 1891, and it became necessary to suspend the work. The jacks were filled with oil, and everything possible was done to leave the work ready for someone to finish.

Water was let into the tunnel and it remained untouched until 1902, when a new corporation was formed to complete the work. The tunnel was pumped out, and after a few alterations were made in the shield, progress was resumed. However, the workers ran into veins of stone which made tunneling very difficult. Blasting ahead of the shield was dangerous, both to men and shield. Twice the blasts made holes in the tunnel roof through the bed of the river. Only by dumping scow loads of clay in the holes was the tunnel saved.

At one point, the silt above was so soft that it ran like syrup through the shield doors. Nothing could stop it until the engineers decided that it might be possible to bake the claylike silt into a harder substance which would not run. Tanks of kerosene under pressure were brought in and flames from blowpipes were played over the soft clay. Meanwhile, water was trained on the shield to prevent damage from the heat. After eight hours of baking, the silt was found to be hard enough to dig, and work was resumed. The air pressure at this point was thirty-eight pounds per square inch, which made the operation extremely hard on the workers. Seven days later the rock disappeared and sand was reached. After this, good progress was made until finally the shield reached the bulkhead of the short tunnel that had long before been built out from the New York shore. The tunnel was completed in March, 1904, thirty years after the first construction work had started.

The experience gained in building the tunnel just described enabled the work on the others under the Hudson River to proceed with comparative ease as long as silt only was encountered. It was found that the powerful jacks with which the shield was equipped could drive through the silt without removing any of the material through the shield — the earth was simply pushed aside as the shield advanced.

In 1909, the last of the four tunnels was opened and the dream of a half century was realized. Since that time, the Pennsylvania Railroad and other companies have built numerous tunnels under both the Hudson and East rivers in New York City.

There are a number of different methods of building tunnels other than those we have discussed. In railway subways through cities, a "cut and cover" method is often used. That is, an open trench is first built, and the completed subway is constructed in it. All that then remains is to replace the dirt, covering the structure, and the work is done.

A similar method is sometimes followed when it is desired to tunnel under a river. First, cofferdams are built across the river. These are watertight enclosures, from which the water can be pumped to expose the river bottom. A trench is then dug between the cofferdams. The concrete tunnel proper is placed in position, the trench filled and the cofferdam removed.

Another method of constructing a tunnel under a river is that used in Detroit, Michigan. Here twin tunnels were built to carry the Michigan Central Railroad tracks under the Detroit River. The tunnel was built in sections on the shore. These sections were then floated out into their proper positions and sunk to the river bed. A trench had been dug on the bottom by ordinary dredges, and piling had been driven. The ends of the tunnel sections were afterward connected by divers. Then the steel tubes forming the tunnels were embedded in concrete poured through long pipes fed from a floating scow. This project called for the highest type of engineering ingenuity and skill.

The construction of the Holland Tunnel

The Holland Tunnel, under the Hudson River, eclipsed the Hudson and Manhattan railroad tunnels both in size and as an engineering feat. This structure, which was opened in 1927, connects New York City and Jersey City. It was the first tunnel to be built exclusively for the passage of autos, trucks and other motor vehicles. It is named after Clifford Milburn Holland, the engineer who planned and directed the work. When the project was nearing completion, he died, succumbing to the great physical strain involved in directing the huge undertaking.

His successor, Milton H. Freeman, suffered a similar fate. The work was com-

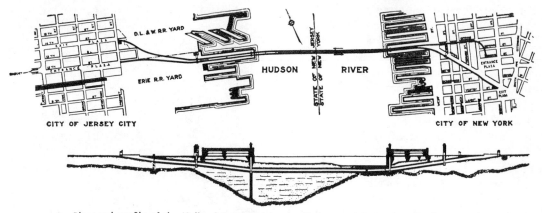

Plan and profile of the Holland Tunnel under the Hudson, connecting New York City and Jersey City.

pleted under the direction of Mr. Ole Singstad.

The Holland Tunnel consists of two cast-iron tubes lying parallel to each other throughout the main part of their length but diverging at the ends where they emerge, in order to avoid congestion due to the immense traffic that pours in and out of them and to take advantage of streets already in existence. The tunnel is used by motor vehicles only, of which more than 60,000 have used the tunnel in one day. Each tube is for one-way traffic, wide enough to accommodate two parallel lines of vehicles, the light, fast-moving taking the left side of the roadway and the slow-moving and the heavy trucks keeping to the right.

The shield method of construction previously described was used for driving the tubes, the method of dredging a trench and laying the tube from a floating plant, as at Detroit, not being considered feasible on account of the heavy river traffic. Storms and ice would also delay progress whereas by the underground method work could be pushed continuously.

The north tunnel is 8557 feet long; the south, 8371; under river part, 5480. Quite obviously such a tunnel could not be ventilated by natural means and as will be seen the problem of ventilation was a great factor in the size and arrangement of the tubes. It should be remembered that the impurities in the atmosphere of a tunnel used by motor cars are the products of combustion of gasoline. If complete combustion can be secured these products

are largely carbon dioxide, which can be tolerated with safety in considerable volume. But complete combustion never takes place either in a coal-burning furnace or an internal-combustion engine. Due to incomplete combustion the exhaust gases from the motor vehicle always contain varying amounts of carbon monoxide, a highly poisonous gas injurious to health, even if breathed in minute quantities for any length of time. The proper ventilation of these tubes therefore required the drawing off of the burnt gases and the forcing in of enough fresh air to dilute the atmosphere to the point where carbon monoxide would be harmless.

It is apparent that if it were attempted to ventilate by simply blowing air in at one end and permitting it to escape at the other its velocity would be very great: at any point where a truck and an automobile were side by side it would be about 72 miles per hour. Other methods were therefore necessary. It so happens that the circular tube is admirably adapted for ventilation if the cross section has been appropriately designed. The Holland Tunnel tubes are $29\frac{1}{2}$ feet in diameter throughout their length, except that the diameter of one is enlarged near the Jersey side to 30 feet 4 inches, which was the largest diameter for tubes of this kind then constructed. They consist of rings made up of 14 sections $2\frac{1}{2}$ feet wide, bolted together with 10-pound bolts. The weight of each ring is about 16,630 pounds. The tubes are lined with concrete $14\frac{1}{4}$ inches thick, and are divided horizontally into three parts by two concrete partitions. The lower one is the 20-foot roadway, with a 2-foot sidewalk for the use of the police who patrol the tunnel. A fresh-air duct is set underneath the roadway. Air flows into the tunnel from this duct through slots just above the curb. Stale air passes through screen openings in the ceiling to an exhaust air duct that leads to the outer air. Fresh air is circulated through the tunnel, at the rate of 3,750,000 cubic feet a minute, by 84 electrically driven fans. These are located in four buildings, two on each side of the Hudson River. It took four years to build the Holland Tunnel; the cost was approximately $50,000,000.

New York City's Queens-Midtown Tunnel, connecting the boroughs of Manhattan and Queens, was opened November 15, 1940. The north tube for westbound traffic extends a distance of 6,414 feet between portals. The south tube for eastbound traffic is 6,272 feet long; the length of the under-river portion is 3,098 feet. Forty-six fans in two ventilation buildings provide forty-two air changes per hour. The air is fresher than out-door city air. The estimated cost of the Queens-Midtown project was more than $58,000,000.

Pictures, Port of New York Authority

A section of New York City's Holland Tunnel.

The three-tube Lincoln Tunnel connects midtown New York with New Jersey. The first tube, which was later called the south tunnel, was opened to traffic in December, 1937. Both eastbound and westbound traffic passed through it until the opening of a second tube — the north tunnel — in February, 1945. After that time, eastbound traffic passed through the south tunnel, westbound traffic through the north tunnel. In May, 1957, the third tube was completed. It runs parallel to and south

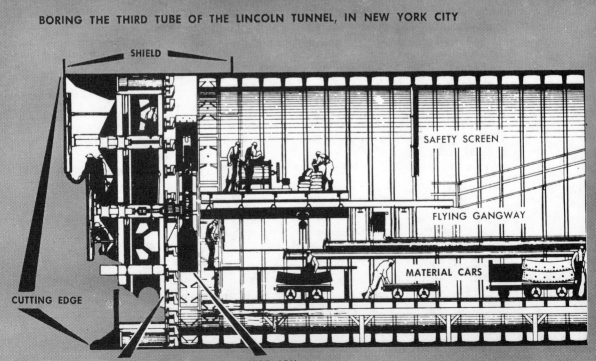

BORING THE THIRD TUBE OF THE LINCOLN TUNNEL, IN NEW YORK CITY

SHIELD

SAFETY SCREEN

FLYING GANGWAY

MATERIAL CARS

CUTTING EDGE

HYDRAULIC JACKS   ERECTOR ARM

of the existing tubes. The middle tube operates in either the eastbound or westbound direction, depending upon the predominating traffic flow.

All three tubes of the Lincoln Tunnel are similar in design and construction. The north tunnel is 7,482 feet long between portals; the middle tunnel, 8,216 feet long and the south tunnel, 8,013 feet long. Each tunnel is thirty-one feet in diameter, with a roadway twenty-one and a half feet wide. The ceiling clearance in the tunnels is thirteen feet. Aeration is provided by seventy-eight fans in five ventilation buildings. The air is changed every one and a half minutes. The total cost of the tunnel and its approaches was $183,000,000.

All three tubes of the Lincoln Tunnel were driven beneath the Hudson River by the shield method. A brilliant record for efficiency and safety was established in the construction of the third tube. A 55-foot vertical shaft was excavated in solid rock at the base of Kings Bluff, in Weehawken, New Jersey. At the base of the shaft a prefabricated steel shield was erected; it was driven under the river by twenty-eight huge jacks. The shield reached its destination at the correct elevation, only three quarters of an inch south of the anticipated point! Not a single casualty resulted among the two hundred sand hogs who worked for months on the project — a truly remarkable record.

The Brooklyn-Battery Tunnel, which connects the lower part of Manhattan with Brooklyn, has two tubes. Because of the great length of the tunnel (9,117 feet between portals), one of its ventilation buildings is located on an island, midway between the portals. There are three other ventilation buildings, which provide a complete change of air every three minutes.

In constructing this tunnel, a shield was driven from each terminal to the midpoint. When the two shields met, the last ring sections were bolted in place. Then the hydraulic jacks and all the working parts of the shields were melted by applying a welding torch. In this way a continuous tube was provided. The tunnel was then finished by concreting, lining the walls and ceilings, laying pavements and installing utilities. The dimensions of the tubes are comparable to those of the other New York tunnels (the Holland and Lincoln Tunnels) described above.

See also Vol. 10, p. 286: "Tunnels."

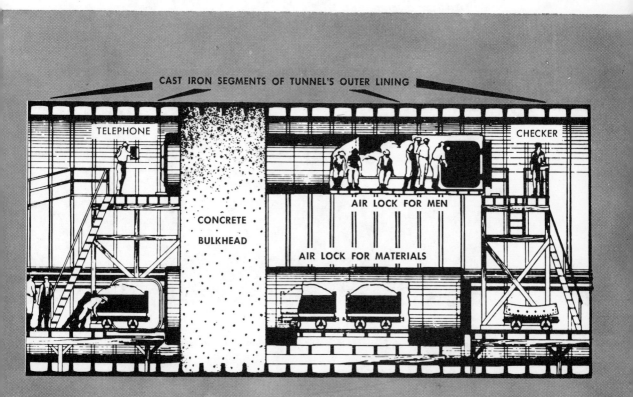

CAST IRON SEGMENTS OF TUNNEL'S OUTER LINING

TELEPHONE

CHECKER

CONCRETE BULKHEAD

AIR LOCK FOR MEN

AIR LOCK FOR MATERIALS

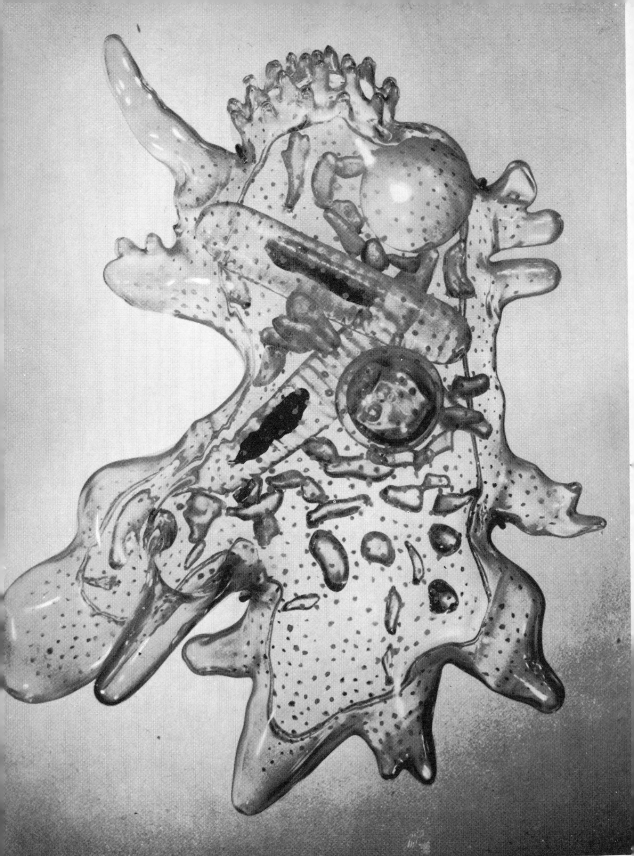

Glass model of *Amoeba proteus*. This protozoan, which is common in fresh water resembles a mass of living jelly. It moves about by extending fingerlike projections of its substance and flowing into them.

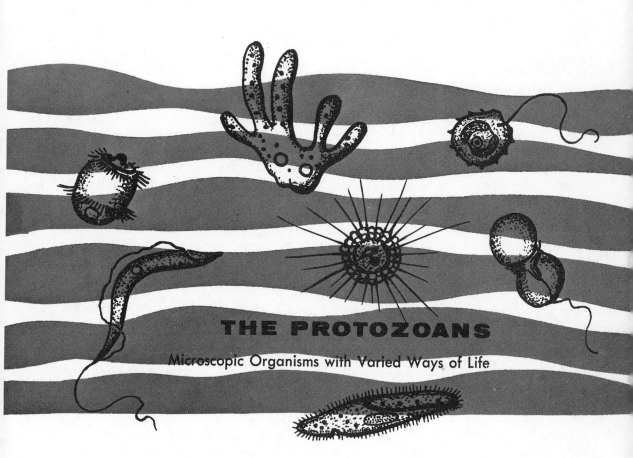

THE PROTOZOANS

Microscopic Organisms with Varied Ways of Life

WHEN a drop or two of pond water is viewed through a microscope, a fascinating world in miniature is revealed — a world peopled by a host of minute organisms. Many of them are the tiny creatures called protozoans, which range in size from several microns * to a few millimeters. The protozoans have often been described as single-celled animals, with a simple organization. This definition is not quite exact.

For one thing, a certain number of protozoan species are plantlike in one important respect. They possess pigments by means of which they can manufacture foods — sugars and other carbohydrates — through the process of photosynthesis

* A micron is equal to 1/1,000 of a millimeter or 1/25,000 of an inch.

(see Index). These species of protozoans are often classified as plants. Yet they are closely related to other protozoan species that lack pigments, cannot manufacture food and must obtain it after the fashion of animals. Perhaps it would be best to consider protozoans, together with the algae, which are generally classified as plants (see Index), as connecting links between the plant and animal kingdoms.

Is the protozoan single-celled? It is true that most protozoans consist of a single unit of protoplasm containing a nucleus and surrounded by a cellular membrane or wall of some kind. But some forms, as we shall see, have a great many nuclei. Others consist of colonies made up of a number of individuals.

The protozoan can hardly be called a simple organism. This becomes evident when we compare it with the specialized cells in the bodies of multicellular, or many-celled animals. Each type of specialized cell forms a different kind of tissue; the tissues make up the different organs by means of which the animals move about, catch and chew and digest food, circulate body fluids, breathe, eliminate wastes, reproduce and so on. In the protozoan, all these activities occur within the tiny blob of protoplasm of which its body consists. The specialized cells have no independent life of their own; the protozoan is completely self-sufficient.

It is because they are comparatively complex that protozoans can adapt themselves to a wide range of environments. They flourish in fresh or stagnant permanent ponds, in semipermanent rain-water ponds, in marshes and in streams. Many inhabit mud, moist soil, brine pools and hot springs, where temperatures range from 100° to 150° F. Protozoans are abundant in the seas, from the open surface waters to the bottom muck. They are found even in snow drifts. Many species live as parasites in the body cavities, tissues and cells of animals and plants.

There are at least 15,000 to 20,000 protozoan species. They have not yet been adequately classified. However, for the sake of convenience we can divide protozoans into five major groups — flagellates, amebalike protozoans, spore-producing protozoans, ciliates and suctorians. The "true" algae and the fungi are quite closely related to some of these forms. The multicellular animals probably evolved from the flagellates or ciliates.

The flagellates (Mastigophora)

The flagellates possess one to several long filaments — the flagella (singular: flagellum) — usually attached to the front end of the body. A flagellum may be used for swimming or for creating water currents that bring in food. It may also serve as a sensitive organelle (special structure) for exploring the environment. In swimming, the flagellum ordinarily makes first a sidewise or backward beat and then a relaxed recovery stroke to the forward position again. This causes the organism to move forward, often in a more or less spiral path. The body of the flagellate usually assumes a definite shape and is covered by a firm pellicle, or "skin." Some species may be encased in a shell, or a cover of plates or some other kind of armor. Often a flagellate will develop pseudopods, or "false feet," which are formed by a flowing of the organism's protoplasm. Such a flagellate moves as its protoplasm streams into the newly formed pseudopods. These "false feet" are only temporary extensions of the protoplasm.

Chromulina pascheri, a comparatively simple plantlike flagellate.

Gonyaulax, a dinoflagellate. Its body has an encircling furrow and also a longitudinal furrow, each containing a flagellum.

Flagellates are divided into plantlike and animallike forms. The plantlike forms possess chromatophores, structures that contain the green pigment chlorophyll. In many species this green color is masked to some extent by red, brown or yellow pigments. The plantlike flagellates manufacture their own food — carbohydrates and protein — from carbon dioxide, water, salts and the energy derived from sunlight — energy absorbed by the chlorophyll.

The flagellates readily form cysts: that is, they become rounded and secrete a more or less impermeable membrane over the body surface. In this stage the organism remains alive even though the cyst may be thoroughly dried and blown about by the wind.*

Besides forming protective cysts, many plantlike flagellates enter upon what is called the palmella stage. In this, the body becomes round and the flagella are lost. The organisms then grow and reproduce by fission (splitting the body in two), forming extensive green scums on ponds and other bodies of water.

The plantlike flagellate called *Chromulina* is quite simple. This animal, commonly found in fresh water, is naked — that is, it has neither pellicle, nor shell nor other such covering — and it is spherical or oval in shape. It has only one flagellum

* Many species of protozoans are widely distributed over the world because they are transported as cysts by the wind and are carried on the feet of wading birds.

and one or two yellow-brown, bandlike chromatophores. Sometimes *Chromulina* occurs in such numbers that the water is colored a golden brown. This flagellate is apparently closely related to certain brown algae and to the diatoms (see Index).

Cryptomonas is a somewhat more complex organism, having two flagella, a single yellowish to brown-green chromatophore and a distinct gullet. Its body is flattened, oval in shape and surrounded by a firm pellicle.

The dinoflagellates are unique among plantlike flagellates in that the body wall is grooved by an encircling furrow, or girdle, and a longitudinal furrow. Each of these furrows contains a flagellum. Usually there are two pink vacuoles * within the body; canals lead from them to the outside. The vacuoles serve to draw in nutritious liquids and possibly solid particles. The chromatophores, when present, range from yellow-brown to blue-green. The body surface may be naked, or covered with a thin cellulose wall or armored with a thick cellulose wall, divided into plates. Most of the dinoflagellates are marine organisms. They form part of the plankton — the passively floating or weakly swimming plant and animal life of a body of water. (See Index, under Plankton.) Many dinoflagellates produce poisons that kill enormous numbers of fish.

* A vacuole is a cavity, filled with a watery fluid, in the protoplasm of a cell. See Index, under Vacuoles.

Eudorina elegans. This flagellate is made up of thirty-two cells, in loosely packed form, near the surface of a jellylike sphere.

Trypanosoma diemyctyli. The single flagellum is attached throughout the body by a thin layer of pellicle, or "skin." One of the *Trypanosoma* species causes African sleeping sickness.

The plantlike flagellate *Chlamydomonas* belongs to a fresh-water group in which the chlorophyll, when present, is not masked by other pigments. These organisms, therefore, are usually grass-green in color. *Chlamydomonas* is small and oval-shaped and has two flagella. A red form of *Chlamydomonas* is found in melting snow, giving it a red color.

Eudorina is an odd-looking flagellate. It is made up of thirty-two individual organisms arranged, in loosely packed form, near the surface of a jellylike sphere. *Eudorina* is closely related to *Volvox,* which is generally considered to be an alga (see Index, under Volvox).

Euglena is another fresh-water green flagellate. There are many species of *Euglena;* they are usually spindle-, cigar- or oval-shaped. One flagellum arises from the wall of a flask-shaped gullet at the front end of the body. In the presence of light *Euglena* uses its chlorophyll to manufacture carbohydrate. Carbon dioxide serves as the source for the carbon in this product. In darkness, or if it loses its chlorophyll, *Euglena* must absorb organic acids or other organic sources of carbon in order to produce its carbohydrate. Some authorities consider *Euglena* to be a plant; it is discussed as such elsewhere in The Book of Popular Science (see Index).

Peranema is very much like *Euglena;* but it is colorless and has a mouth opening.

A pair of rodlike structures extend alongside the gullet and serve to support the mouth while food is being drawn in. This rod apparatus may be used also for piercing *Peranema's* prey.

None of the animallike flagellates have chromatophores and therefore they cannot manufacture their own food. Some forms, especially the parasitic ones, absorb dissolved food materials from the medium in which they live. Most species, however, feed on microorganisms or nutritious particles in the water; this food material is digested in food vacuoles, which form within the flagellate's protoplasm. In general, the body shape of the animallike flagellates is rather plastic; no cellulose wall encloses the body.

Among the most important of the flagellates, as far as man is concerned, are several species belonging to the genus *Trypanosoma*. *Trypanosoma gambiense* is the cause of sleeping sickness. It has a slender, curving body, which tapers at both ends. The single flagellum is attached throughout the length of the body by a thin layer of pellicle. This forms a membrane that undulates when a wave passes down the flagellum. Trypanosomes, as the members of the genus *Trypanosoma* are called, are sucked up with the blood when a tsetse fly bites an infected host. The trypanosomes undergo development first in the gut and then in the salivary glands of

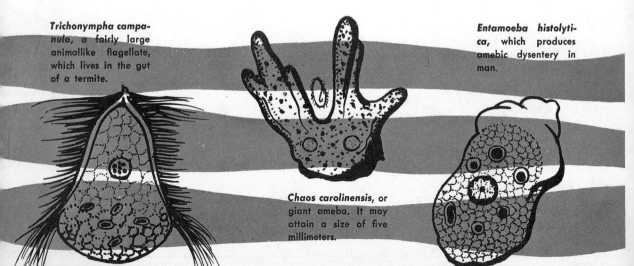

Trichonympha campanula, a fairly large animallike flagellate, which lives in the gut of a termite.

Chaos carolinensis, or giant ameba. It may attain a size of five millimeters.

Entamoeba histolytica, which produces amebic dysentery in man.

the fly. Finally, when the fly bites another victim, the flagellates are introduced into the blood stream of the new host. They invade the lymph nodes and sometimes the cerebrospinal fluid (a fluid in the brain and spinal cord), causing sleeping sickness.

Trypanosoma cruzi is the cause of Chagas' disease, or South American trypanosomiasis, which affects the muscles, heart and nervous system. Other trypanosomes are found in the blood streams of fish, amphibians, reptiles, birds and various mammals. *Bodo,* a somewhat different flagellate, but apparently related to *Trypanosoma,* is a small, oval-shaped organism, inhabiting stagnant fresh water. It has two flagella, one of which is trailed in swimming.

In fresh water we find two strange kinds of flagellates, *Codosiga* and *Protospongia.* These organisms have an oval-shaped body surmounted by a collar which encircles the base of the single flagellum. The collar, a membrane made up of protoplasm, is a device for obtaining food. Food particles or bacteria adhere to the collar and pass down it slowly to the body proper. In *Codosiga,* a number of these transparent collar cells, as they are called, cluster at the end of a simple or branching stalk. *Protospongia* is a colony of from six to sixty organisms, embedded irregularly in a gelatinous mass. The collar cells occur at the surface of the mass; the or-

ganisms on the inside are collarless. The only other animals with collar cells are the sponges (see Index). It may be, therefore, that the sponges evolved from organisms similar to *Protospongia.*

Various flagellate species belonging to the genus *Trichomonas* inhabit the intestines of vertebrates; they feed mostly on the bacteria and yeasts found in this environment. In man, different forms of *Trichomonas* are found in the mouth, colon and vagina. A typical *Trichomonas* is small, oval in shape and has four free flagella; a fifth flagellum is attached to an undulating membrane.

The large animallike flagellate *Trichonympha* lives in the gut of the social insect called the termite (see Index, under Termites). Here it digests the wood fragments swallowed by the termite and makes some of the products of this digestion available to the insect. If the termite loses its flagellates, it will die of starvation, even though it continues to swallow large quantities of wood. *Trichonympha* is a bell-shaped organism, covered with a great number of flagella; it is one of the most complex of the flagellates. Closely related forms inhabit the alimentary canal of cockroaches and woodroaches.

The amebalike protozoans (Sarcodina)

The amebalike protozoans, or Sarcodina, float or creep about in their liquid en-

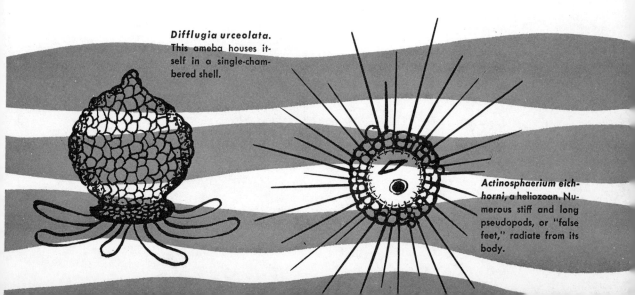

Difflugia urceolata. This ameba houses itself in a single-chambered shell.

Actinosphaerium eichhorni, a heliozoan. Numerous stiff and long pseudopods, or "false feet," radiate from its body.

vironment. A thin membrane surrounds the protoplasm of the body, allowing for the formation of pseudopods; these "false feet" are used both in movement and for capturing food. Some species are plastic, naked organisms; others develop internal or external skeletal structures that protect the body and give it some rigidity. The Sarcodina live almost entirely on small organisms, such as other protozoans, tiny multicellular animals and algae.

Perhaps the best-known of the Sarcodina is *Amoeba,* a fresh-water form. It is quite large, as protozoans go, ranging up to three-fifths of a millimeter in size. *Amoeba* puts forth one to several finger-like pseudopods. The protoplasm of the body contains a nucleus, numerous food vacuoles, granules, crystals and a contractile vacuole.* The giant ameba (*Chaos*) has several hundred small nuclei. This animal may grow to be as much as five millimeters across.

Various amebas are found in man. *Entamoeba histolytica* occurs in the human large intestine and is responsible for the disease known as amebic dysentery. This ameba secretes a substance that dissolves the intestinal lining. The ameba then enters the connective tissue and muscular

---

* The contractile vacuole is a sort of water pump. Since *Amoeba* lives in fresh water, water diffuses into its body from the external environment (see Index, under Osmosis). The contractile vacuole pumps this excess water out, thus preventing *Amoeba* from swelling unduly and perhaps bursting. Contractile vacuoles are found in all fresh-water protozoans.

layers, where it feeds on red and white blood cells and tissue-cell fragments. It may invade the liver, where it does great damage by causing abscesses. Another *Entamoeba* species seems to contribute to pyorrhea, one of the most serious disorders of the teeth.

The slime molds resemble the ameba-like organisms in some respects, though they are not protozoans. At one stage of its life history, the slime mold is a large mass of naked protoplasm, often several inches in diameter and containing thousands of nuclei. It lives and literally flows about in decaying and wet logs, leaves, manure piles and soil, feeding on bacteria and other microorganisms or absorbing liquid nutrients. Eventually the slime mold produces spores, or resistant reproductive bodies. When these germinate, small amebalike organisms are released; eventually another large slime-mold body develops.

Arcella and *Difflugia* are amebas that house themselves in a single-chambered shell. *Arcella* secretes a transparent to yellowish-brown shell that is made of tiny siliceous * prisms, fitted together. The shell is domelike above and concave below, with a central opening through which the pseudopods extend. *Difflugia* fashions a globular or flask-shaped shell out of sand grains, which it "glues" together. Both

---

* Siliceous means "containing silica." Silica (silicon dioxide, SiO_2) occurs as quartz, opal and so on.

Didinium nasutum, a barrel-shaped ciliate. Note the projecting cone at the top of the "barrel." The mouth is at the tip of this cone. *Didinium* preys on *Paramecium.*

Paramecium multimicronucleatum, a slipper-shaped ciliate. It has a long groove leading into the mouth.

of these shelled amebas occur in fresh water and moist soils.

The foraminiferans are shelled amebas that live almost exclusively in the sea. The shells usually contain many chambers, for the young organism starts life with one chamber and adds new chambers as it grows. Many foraminiferans secrete siliceous or calcareous* shells. Others use foreign materials that are picked up by the pseudopods and pulled into the body, where they are held together in the shell wall by a secreted cement. The chambers of the shell may be connected like a string of beads; they may be coiled in a flat or conical spiral like a snail's shell; they may be in two or three alternating rows like a braid; they may be arranged irregularly. The shell is just inside the body of the foraminiferan, so that a layer of protoplasm covers it. The pseudopods form a meshwork, which traps the small organisms the foraminiferan eats. Among the best-known of the foraminiferans are those belonging to the genus *Globigerina*. Their shells form a thick deposit, called globigerina ooze, on the ocean bottom.

Other Sarcodina groups are the heliozoans and the radiolarians. The heliozoans are fresh-water organisms with spherical bodies that are almost frothlike

* Calcareous means "containing calcium carbonate" ($CaCO_3$). This solid occurs in nature as the minerals calcite and aragonite and is also found in shells, bones, plant ashes and so on.

in appearance. Numerous stiff, long and thin pseudopods radiate from the body. The radiolarians are floating marine animals. They differ from the heliozoans in that the body is divided into an inner central capsule and an outer layer, both of protoplasm. They also have radiating and stiff pseudopods. The radiolarians secrete skeletons of silicon or strontium sulfate, which take the form of radiating spines or latticed networks. The skeletons assume the form of spheres, helmets, disks, bells and various other shapes. They form a mud deposit known as radiolarian ooze on the ocean floor.

The spore-forming protozoans (Sporozoa)

The Sporozoa are all parasitic protozoans with a very complicated life cycle; spores are produced at some stage or other of the cycle. The Sporozoa spore is a cell that is usually surrounded by a resistant membrane; it is called a sporozoite. In general the sporozoans are incapable of locomotion; but the young sometimes move by means of pseudopods. These protozoans absorb from their hosts such food materials as dissolved protoplasm, body fluids or tissue fluids.

The most famous sporozoan is *Plasmodium*, the malarial parasite. Naked sporozoites, exceedingly small and spindle-shaped, are inoculated into man's blood stream by the bite of an infected female

The four drawings below show how *Didinium* swallows *Paramecium*. The mouth of *Didinium* attaches itself to the side of its prey and widens. The victim is then sucked inward. After it has been drawn in completely, *Didinium* returns to its former shape.

Epidinium ecaudatum. This is a complex variety of ciliate. It has special structures for moving about, feeding, swallowing, digesting, excreting and contracting. Skeletal plates maintain the form of the body.

Anopheles mosquito; eventually the parasites enter the red blood cells. *Plasmodium* also causes malaria in birds, reptiles, frogs, monkeys, apes, bats, squirrels, buffalo and antelopes. *Babesia bigemina* whose sporozoites are inoculated by the bite of the tick, is responsible for Texas cattle fever (see Index). *Nosema bombycis* brings about pebrine, the fatal disease of silkworms; *Eimeria* infects chickens, causing coccidiosis. Sporozoan parasites, as a matter of fact, are found in almost any animal you can think of.

The ciliates (Ciliophora)

The ciliates are so called because they are provided with hairlike processes called cilia, which serve for locomotion. The cilia are shorter and much more numerous than flagella. They are arranged on the ciliate's body in diagonal or horizontal rows; their action suggests that of the oars in a multi-oar racing hull. The cilia push backward for the power stroke; in the recovery stroke they return to the forward position. Since at any one time some of the cilia are engaged in the power stroke and some in the recovery stroke, the result is a continuous flow of power, and the animal moves ahead smoothly. Though the body of the ciliate may twist or turn to some extent, or lengthen or shorten, it still retains a more or less permanent shape. The ciliates feed on dead organic matter or on various live microorganisms.

Opalina is a very much flattened ciliate possessing many nuclei of the same size. It is found in the intestine of frogs. The rest of the ciliates possess two kinds of nuclei: small ones, or micronuclei, and large ones, or macronuclei. The macronucleus seems to control many of the metabolic activities of the animal; the micronucleus is concerned with the reproductive process. Most of the ciliates possess a mouth; all of the fresh-water species have contractile vacuoles.

Paramecium is a well-known slipper-shaped ciliate found in fresh water. It has a uniform covering of cilia and a long groove leading into the mouth. Some species of *Paramecium* may reach a length of a third of a millimeter. *Paramecium* often falls victim to one of its relatives, *Didinium*. This is a barrel-shaped organism; at the front end there is a projecting cone, with the mouth at the tip.

In one group of ciliates (order Peritrichida) we find a disk-shaped head end, with two or more rows of cilia surrounding the mouth; the beat of the cilia creates water currents that bring food into the mouth. There are few if any cilia on the rest of the body. Most species of this group are fixed to some attachment point or other by means of a stalk. *Vorticella,* a bell-shaped organism, is a common ciliate of this type.

Blepharisma is a typical representative of the ciliate order Spirotricha. Its elongated-oval body is covered with cilia for swimming. Rows of fused cilia surround the mouth and help push food toward it. *Spirostomum,* a common freshwater relative of *Blepharisma,* has an elongated, cylinder-shaped body from one to three millimeters in length; it is a giant among protozoans. *Stylonychia,* another freshwater form, has an oval body, with a flat bottom surface and a convex top surface. This ciliate has cirri — large, stiff bristles composed of fused tufts of cilia; they are moved like legs in walking.

Epidinium, a related form, is found in the digestive tracts of cattle and reindeer. It has special structures for moving about, feeding, swallowing, digesting, excreting and contracting, and nuclei for maintaining metabolism and controlling reproduction. There is a rectum, an anus and skeletal plates for maintaining the body's form.

The suctorians (Suctoria)

The suctorians are common in fresh and salt water. The young are ciliated and free-swimming. Adults have no cilia and are attached by stalks to inanimate objects, or plants or small animals. They lack a mouth. They have tentacles with which they seize their victims — small ciliates, whose protoplasm they suck. Suctorians may be spherical, conical or branched in shape. Some are parasitic.

See also Vol. 10, p. 275: "Invertebrates."

AN INTRODUCTION TO ALGEBRA

The Mathematics of "Any Numbers" or "Variables"

BY HOWARD F. FEHR

IN THE article Of Arithmetic, in Volume 1, we were concerned with particular numbers, which were expressed by symbols. "Sixty-seven" is a particular number. To do arithmetical problems in which sixty-seven plays a part, we use the symbols "6" and "7," combined as 67. We are now going to consider a branch of mathematics in which a symbol, such as a letter — a, or b or c — stands not for a particular number but for a whole class of numbers. This kind of mathematics is called algebra.

We can illustrate the difference between arithmetic and algebra by a very simple example. Let us take the number 4. Multiply it by 5 ($4 \times 5 = 20$); add 4 ($20 + 4 = 24$); double the answer ($24 \times 2 = 48$); subtract 8 ($48 - 8 = 40$); divide by the original number, 4 ($40 \div 4 = 10$). The result of all these operations, as you see, is 10. In arriving at the final result, 10,

we used the method of arithmetic, involving particular numbers, throughout.

Suppose now that we think of *any* number. Let us indicate "any number" by the symbol x and let us go through the same operations as before. We multiply x by 5 ($5 \times x$, written $5x*$); add 4 ($5x + 4$); double the answer ($10x + 8$); subtract 8 ($10x$); divide by the original number, which is x $\left(\dfrac{10x}{x} = 10 \right)$. The answer, then, is 10. Here we have been using the methods of algebra, because x can be replaced by any number. We could substitute for it 2, or 3 or 15, and the final result would be 10.

---

* When a generalized number, represented by a letter (such as a) is multiplied by a particular number (such as 5) or by another generalized number (such as b), we do not use multiplication signs, but indicate multiplication by putting these symbols close to one another. Thus $a \times b = ab$; $5 \times a = 5a$; $5 \times a \times b = 5ab$. We could not indicate the multiplication of two particular numbers in this way. 7×5 could not be given as 75, because 75 really stands for $70 + 5$.

Let us consider another example. In the equation $(2 + 3)^2 = 25$, we are dealing with the particular numbers 2 and 3, and the result is always 25. But suppose that instead of two particular numbers, we used the letter a, standing for any number, and the letter b, standing for any number other than a. We would then have $(a + b)^2 = a^2 + 2ab + b^2$.*

What is significant about $(a + b)^2 = a^2 + 2ab + b^2$ is that it indicates a general relationship that holds true for a great many particular numbers. If we substituted 3 for a and 2 for b, we would have $(3 + 2)^2 = 3^2 + (2 \times 3 \times 2) + 2^2 = 9 + 12 + 4 = 25$. Or we could substitute 5 for a and 6 for b, giving $(5 + 6)^2 = 5^2 + (2 \times 5 \times 6) + 6^2 = 25 + 60 + 36 = 121$.

Algebra, the mathematics of "any numbers" or "variables," goes to the heart of the relationship between numbers. Generally speaking, it is concerned with particular numbers only insofar as they are applications of general principles. It is also used in the solution of certain specific problems in which we start out with one or more unknown quantities whose values are indicated by algebraic symbols.

The study of algebra goes back to antiquity. Recent discoveries have shown that the Babylonians solved problems in algebra, although they had no symbols for variables. They used only words to indicate such numbers, and for that reason their algebra has been referred to as rhetorical algebra. The Ahmes Papyrus, an Egyptian scroll going back to 1600 B.C., has a number of problems in algebra, in which the unknown is referred to as a *hau*, meaning "a heap."

Little further progress was made in algebra until we come to Diophantus, a Greek mathematician, living in the third century A.D. He reduced problems to equations, representing the unknown quantity by a symbol suggesting the Greek letter Σ (sigma). He also introduced an interesting system of abbreviations, in which he used only the initial letters of words and omitted all unnecessary words. If we were to use the method of Diophantus in present-ing the problem: "An unknown squared minus the unknown will give twenty," we would first state the problem as "Unknown squared minus unknown equals twenty." Then we would use initial letters for all the words except the last and we would give the numeral for "twenty," as follows: "USMUE20."

In the sixteenth century, François Vieta, a French mathematician (1540–1603), used the vowels a, e, i, o, u to represent unknown numbers and the consonants b, c, d, f, g and so on to stand for values that remained fixed throughout a given problem. The great French philosopher René Descartes (1596–1650) proposed the system of algebraic symbols now in use. In this system, a, b, c and other letters near the beginning of the alphabet represent the fixed numbers; the last letters of the alphabet — x, y, z and also sometimes w — stand for the unknown numbers in a problem. As soon as this symbolism came into general use, algebra grew quite rapidly into a systematic set of rules and theorems that could be applied to all numbers.

The word "algebra" originated from the title of a work on algebra by a Persian, Mohammed ibn Musa Al-Kwarizmi, who lived in the ninth century A.D. He wrote in Arabic a work called AL-JEBR W'AL MUQABALA, which means "restoration and reduction." By *al-jebr*, or restoration, was meant the transposing of negative terms to the other side of an equation to make them positive. When the Arabs came to Spain, they brought this word with them. In the course of time, *al-jebr* was changed to "algebra," and it came to be applied not to a single operation, but to all algebra.

Three fundamental laws of algebra

Algebra generalizes — that is, expresses in general terms — certain basic laws which govern the addition, multiplication and division of all numbers.

(1) When we add or multiply two integers, the order in which we add or multiply them is immaterial. Thus $2 + 3$ is the same as $3 + 2$, and 4×3 is the same as 3×4. Since this is true for all integers,

---

* We show later how we obtain the product $a^2 + 2ab + b^2$ when we multiply $a + b$ by $a + b$.

we set up the following algebraic formulas:

$$a + b = b + a; \quad ab = ba$$

These are called the commutative laws of addition and multiplication.

(2) When more than two numbers are added or multiplied, we can group them in any order we choose, and the answer will always be the same. If 2 is added to (3 + 6), the result is the same as if we added (2 + 3) to 6. Similarly, 2 times the product of 3×6 is the same as 3 times the product of 6×2. These results are indicated in the formulas:

$$a + (b + c) = (a + b) + c; \quad a(bc) = (ab)c$$

These are the associative laws of addition and multiplication.

(3) If a multiplicand has two or more terms, a multiplier must operate upon each of these terms in turn. Suppose we wish to multiply $3 + 2$ by 5, a problem which we could set down as $5(3 + 2)$. We would first multiply 3 by 5 and then 2 by 5, giving $15 + 10$, or 25. This rule is called the distributive law of multiplication and is given by the following formula:

$$a(b + c) = ab + ac$$

Suppose we want to multiply $a + b$ by $a + b$, which of course would be the same thing as $(a + b)^2$. We would set up the problem as follows:

$$\begin{array}{r} a + b \\ a + b \\ \hline \end{array}$$

In accordance with the distributive laws of multiplication, we first multiply b and a, above the line, by b below the line; then we multiply b and a, above the line, by a below the line; finally we add the results:

$$\begin{array}{r} a + b \\ a + b \\ \hline ab + b^2 \\ a^2 + ab \\ \hline a^2 + 2ab + b^2 \end{array}$$

We use the same distributive law in multiplying 25 by 25. Ordinarily, we would present our calculations as follows:

$$\text{(I)} \quad \begin{array}{r} 25 \\ 25 \\ \hline 125 \\ 50 \\ \hline 625 \end{array}$$

Actually, since the 2 in 25 is really 20, the problem is

$$\begin{array}{r} 20 + 5 \\ 20 + 5 \\ \hline \end{array}$$

Using the distributive law, we multiply 5 in the first line by 5 in the second line and 20 in the first line by 5 in the second line. Then we multiply 5 in the first line by 20 in the second line and 20 in the first line by 20 in the second line. Finally we add the products. We could indicate these operations as follows:

$$\text{(II)} \quad \begin{array}{r} 20 + 5 \\ 20 + 5 \\ \hline 100 + 25 \\ 400 + 100 \\ \hline 400 + 200 + 25 = 625 \end{array}$$

If you carefully compare (I) and (II) above, you will see that basically the same operations are performed in both. Simply bear in mind that, for example, when in (I) we multiply the 2 in the second line by 5 in the first line, the 2 in the second line stands for 20.

Formulas, tables of values and graphs

There are different ways of showing how different quantities are related. We can use a formula, set up a table of values or draw up a graph.

Take the rule: "The area of a square is equal to the square of the length of its side." This is a rather roundabout way of expressing the relationship in question. We could state it much more simply by using the symbol A to represent the number of square units in the area, and the symbol s to represent the number of units in the side. The above rule can then be stated as $A = s^2$. This abbreviated rule is called a formula.*

* This is a Latin word meaning "little form," or "abbreviated form."

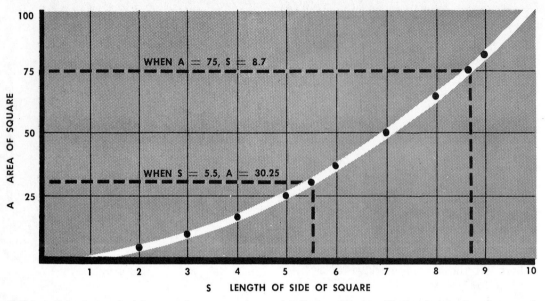

WHEN A = 75, S = 8.7

WHEN S = 5.5, A = 30.25

A — AREA OF SQUARE

S   LENGTH OF SIDE OF SQUARE

1. How to draw the graph of the area of a square, using horizontal and vertical axes, according to the method described on this page. The graph shows how the area of a square increases as the length of the side increases

If the length of the side is 6, we can get *A*, the area, by substituting 6 for *s* in the formula. *A* then becomes 6^2 or 36. As you see, we have put our formula to practical use. Technically speaking, we have evaluated the formula for the value 6.

We can also represent the relationship $A = s^2$ by setting up a table of values. Suppose the side of the square is equal to 1; *A* is then 1^2 or 1. If the side of the square is equal to 2, $A = 2^2$, or 4. Substituting for *s* the values from 1 through 10 in turn, we obtain the following table of values:

s	1	2	3	4	5	6	7	8	9	10
A	1	4	9	16	25	36	49	64	81	100

This table tells us that if $s = 1$, $A = 1$; if $s = 2$, $A = 4$; if $s = 3$, $A = 9$, and so on.

There is still another way of representing the area of a square. We could construct a graph, as in Figure 1. First, we draw two lines, called axes, which are perpendicular to each other. Along the horizontal axis, or base, we mark out a series of numbers at equal intervals, corresponding to the values of *s* in the table. We mark out another series of numbers on the vertical axis; these numbers correspond to the values of *A*. At each of the values of *s* — 1, 2, 3, 4 and so on — we erect a per-

pendicular. Then we mark the appropriate value of *A*, corresponding to a given value of *s*, on the vertical scale. We draw a perpendicular at this point, and mark a point where the two perpendiculars meet. When we have performed the same operation for each of the values of *s* and *A*, we shall have the series of points indicated in Figure 1. A smooth, curved line is then drawn, connecting the different points. This line is called the graph of the area of the square. It shows how the area increases as the length of the side increases.

We can use the graph to find out the area of squares with sides not given in the tables of values. For example, if $s = 5.5$, we erect a perpendicular at this point, extending it until it meets the graph. From the point of meeting, we erect a perpendicular to the vertical axis. The point where this perpendicular meets the vertical axis will represent the area, which is about 30. The correct value is 30.25.

If we know the area of a square, we can find out the approximate length of the side by means of our graph. Suppose the area is 75. From a point corresponding to the number 75 on the vertical axis, we draw a line parallel to the horizontal axis. From the point where this line meets the curve,

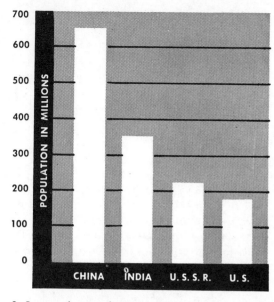

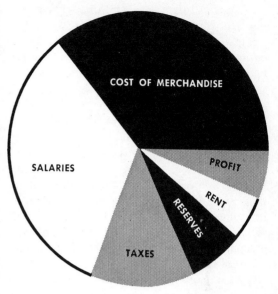

2. Bar graphs: populations, in 1960, of China, India, Union of Soviet Socialist Republics and United States.

3. This circle graph indicates how each part of a dollar received in sales by a department store is spent.

we drop a perpendicular to the horizontal axis. This line will meet the horizontal axis at about 8.7, the length of the side of the square. (Here the correct value, expressed to five decimal places, is 8.66025.)

There are many different kinds of graphs; the most common are the bar graph, the circle graph and the line graph. If, for example, we would like to show how the populations of China, India, Russia and the United States compare, we would draw four bars, as in Figure 2. The lengths of the bars would be proportionate to the populations in question.

If we desired to compare parts of a whole quantity, we would use a circle graph. It could serve to indicate how each part of a dollar received in sales in a department store is spent by the store (Figure 3). Each sector of the circle, as compared to the whole circle, would show the proportion given to a particular service.

4. In a hospital, nurses make line graphs of the temperatures of patients, taking temperature readings at regular intervals. If a nurse took a patient's temperature every four hours, the graph would look like this.

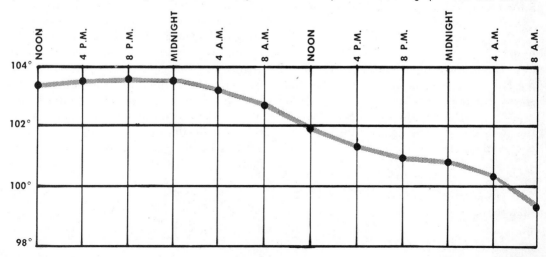

When a quantity is continuously changing, we would use a line graph. In a hospital, the nurse makes a graph of the temperature of each patient (Figure 4). She takes the temperature every four hours, say, locates the temperature reading at a given point, and then connects the point with the preceding point by a straight line. When the doctor consults the chart, he can see at a glance how the patient is responding to treatment.

To repeat, then, we can show how quantities are related by a formula, a table of values or a graph. It is the formula that is basic. If a table of values is worked up, a scientist tries to find the formula that will express the relationship in question. If an engineer plots a graph showing the length of a steel cable under increasing tension, he works out an algebraic formula to sum up his findings.

Formulas are extremely important in many branches of pure and applied science. For example, to indicate the speed of a body having uniform rectilinear motion (see Index, under Rectilinear motion), the physicist uses the formula $v = \dfrac{s}{t}$, where v is the average speed of the body, s is the space or distance covered and t is the time required to travel this distance. We can apply this formula to specific cases by substituting appropriate values for v, s or t. For example, if a car takes 5 hours to travel 200 miles, as indicated by the speedometer, we could find the average speed by substituting 5 for t and 200 for s. The average speed, then, would be $\dfrac{200}{5}$ miles, or 40 miles, per hour.

The chemist often has occasion to use the law of Charles and Guy-Lussac, which states that if the pressure and the mass of a gas are constant, the volume is proportional to the absolute temperature.* This law can be stated very concisely by the formula $\dfrac{V_1}{T_1} = \dfrac{V_2}{T_2}$, in which V_1 is the volume of a gas at temperature T_1, while V_2 is the volume of a gas at temperature T_2.

Perhaps the most famous formula of all is the Einstein Equation, $E = mc^2$ *. With this formula the great physicist Albert Einstein (1879–1955) indicated the amount of energy that appears when matter is transformed into energy. Atomic energy for peace and war would not have been possible without this formula.

How equations are employed

The equation plays an all-important part in algebra. It may be looked upon as a balance, with equal numerical values on each side of the "equal" sign ($=$). To show how an equation is applied, let us consider the formula for the perimeter (the outside boundary) of a rectangle: $P = 2l + 2w$, where P is the perimeter, l is the length and w is the width. Suppose we have 100 feet of wire with which to make a rectangular enclosure, which is to be 20 feet wide. We wish to find out the length of this enclosure. The formula for the perimeter, we saw, is $P = 2l + 2w$. We know that the perimeter is 100 (the 100 feet of wire at our disposal). We also know that the width is to be 20 feet. Substituting 100 for P and 20 for w in the formula, we have $100 = 2l + 2 \times 20 = 2l + 40$. In the equation $100 = 2l + 40$, the 100 on one side of the equal sign is exactly equal to $2l + 40$ on the other side. To find out what l is, we subtract 40 from each side of the equation. That gives $60 = 2l$. l, therefore, is 30; the length of the enclosure is 30 feet.

In solving the equation, we used the rule: "If the same operation is performed on each member of an equality, then the results are equal." If we add the same quantity to each side of the equation or subtract the same quantity, the equality will be maintained. It will be maintained, too, if we multiply or divide each side of the equation by the same quantity.**

Equations may be used to solve problems in which no formula is involved but

---

* That is, temperature reckoned in degrees centigrade from absolute zero ($-273.16°$ C.).

* Here E stands for the amount of energy, m for the amount of mass and c for the speed of light (approximately 186,000 miles per second), measured in appropriate units.

** Of course, if we multiplied each side of the equation by zero, the result would be $0 = 0$, which would get us nowhere in the task of solving the equation. Division by zero is not permitted.

in which certain data are given. Here is a simple problem: "A man is 6 times as old as his son. In 20 years, the father will be only twice as old as his son. How old are the father and son at the present time?"

On the basis of the data, we can write an equation and solve the problem. First, we let x stand for the son's age. Since the father is 6 times as old as his son, his age can be given as 6 times x, or $6x$. In 20 years — that is, when 20 years are added to the son's age — the son will be $x + 20$ years old. In 20 years, the age of the father will be $6x + 20$ years. At that time, the father's age will be twice that of the son, a relationship which we can express by the equation: $6x + 20 = 2(x + 20)$. Applying the distributive law to the right-hand side of the equation, we have $6x + 20 = 2x + 40$. We subtract $2x + 20$ from each side of the equation and get $4x = 20$. If $4x = 20$, $x = 5$. The son's age at the present time, therefore, is 5. Since the father's age at the present time is 6 times that of the son, or $6x$, the father is 30 years old.

Not all problems are as simple as this one, in which the unknown is x. The equation may involve not only an unknown quantity, x, but also higher powers of x. If x^2 is the highest power occurring in an equation, it is called a quadratic equation. $x^2 + 6 = 5x$ is an example of such an equation. In various equations, the highest power of x may be x^3 or x^4; or there may be even higher powers.

Identities
in algebra

When an equation is true for all the replacement values of the variables concerned, it is called an identity. A familiar example of an identity is $(a + b)^2 = a^2 + 2ab + b^2$. As we pointed out before, this equation holds true no matter what values we assign to a and b. It can be used as an aid in mental arithmetic. To square 22, we can think of this number as $(20 + 2)^2$, 20 being substituted for a and 2 for b in the above identity. Mentally we square 20, giving 400; then we double 20×2, giving 80; finally, we square 2, giving 4. $400 + 80 + 4 = 484$. The answer, then, is 484.

Another identity is $(a - b)^2 = a^2 - 2ab + b^2$. You can verify this by performing the multiplication $(a - b)(a - b)$. We would have:

$$\begin{array}{r} a - b \\ a - b \\ \hline -\ ab + b^2 \\ a^2 -\ ab \quad\quad \\ \hline a^2 - 2ab + b^2 \end{array}$$

Still another identity is $(a + b)(a - b) = a^2 - b^2$. This also is useful in certain mental-arithmetic problems. If we wish to multiply 34 by 26 in our heads, we can change the problem to $(30 + 4) \times (30 - 4)$. Solving this in accordance with the identity $(a + b)(a - b) = a^2 - b^2$, we have $900 - 16 = 884$.

Other well-known identities are:

$$(a + b)^3 = (a^3 + 3a^2b + 3ab^2 + b^3)$$
$$(a - b)^3 = (a^3 - 3a^2b + 3ab^2 - b^3)$$
$$(a^3 - b^3) = (a - b)(a^2 + ab + b^2)$$

Exponents in
algebraic expressions

Exponents simplify the writing of algebraic expressions. Thus $aaabbbcc$, which is really a continuous multiplication (a times a times a times b times b times b times c times c), can be written $a^3b^3c^2$. The mathematician has derived a series of rules for combining exponents.

(1) $a^n a^m = a^{n+m}$*. In multiplying powers, we add the exponents of like bases. Thus $2^2 \times 2^3 = 2^{2+3} = 2^5 = 32$.

(2) $a^n \div a^m = a^{n-m}$. In dividing powers, we subtract the exponents of like bases. This means that $2^5 \div 2^2 = 2^{5-2} = 2^3 = 8$.

(3) $(a^n)^m = a^{nm}$. To raise a given power by another power, we multiply the two exponents. For example, $(2^2)^3 = 2^{2\times3} = 2^6 = 64$.

(4) $(ab)^n = a^n b^n$. When a product is raised to a power, each member of the product is raised to that power. Thus $(4 \times 2)^2 = 4^2 \times 2^2 = 16 \times 4 = 64$.

---

* a^n stands for the base a raised to the nth power; a^m, for the same base raised to the mth power.

(5) $\left(\dfrac{a}{b}\right)^n = \dfrac{a^n}{b^n}$. When a quotient is raised to a given power, each member of the quotient must be raised to that power.

$$\left(\frac{2}{3}\right)^3 = \frac{2^3}{3^3} = \frac{8}{27}.$$

We have already noted that a base with the exponent zero is equivalent to 1. Thus $10^0 = 1$; $3^0 = 1$; $1^0 = 1$. The above rules for exponents apply to zero exponents. For example, $a^n a^0 = a^{n+0} = a^n$; $5^3 \times 5^0 = 5^{3+0} = 5^3 = 125$.

Negative exponents* also follow the rules for exponents. Thus $a^{-5}a^3 = a^{-5+3}$ $= a^{-2} = \dfrac{1}{a^2}$; $10^{-7} \times 10^5 = 10^{-7+5} = 10^{-2}$ $= \dfrac{1}{10^2} = \dfrac{1}{100}$.

Exponents can also occur in the form of fractions; thus we have $a^{\frac{1}{2}}$, $a^{\frac{1}{3}}$, $a^{\frac{1}{4}}$ and so on. $a^{\frac{1}{2}}$ means the square root of a ($\sqrt{a}$); $a^{\frac{1}{3}}$ means the cube root of a ($\sqrt[3]{a}$); $a^{\frac{1}{4}}$ means the fourth root of a ($\sqrt[4]{a}$). The numerator in fractional exponents need not necessarily be 1. We frequently deal with exponents such as $\dfrac{2}{3}$ and $\dfrac{3}{5}$. In such cases, the numerator stands for a power of a base and the denominator for the root of a base. $10^{\frac{2}{3}}$, for example, is equal to $\sqrt[3]{10^2}$.

All fractional exponents, whether or not the numerator is 1, follow the rule for exponents. For example, $10^2 \times 10^{\frac{2}{3}} =$ $10^{2+\frac{2}{3}} = 10^{\frac{8}{3}} = \sqrt[3]{10^8}$.

Using exponents to express very large or very small numbers

Exponents provide a convenient way of writing very large or very small numbers. We know that 1,000,000 is 10^6, the exponent 6 representing the number of zeros after 1. We could indicate 5,000,000 as $5 \times 1,000,000$, or 5×10^6. To write 5,270,000, we would multiply 1,000,000 or 10^6 by 5.27; the number would be written

as 5.27×10^6. In other words, we can express a large number as the product of two numbers: the first a number between 1 and 10; the second, a power of 10.

The number 5,270,000 is not too formidable and we can grasp it readily enough. But consider the problems that would arise if, in our calculations, we had to use a number such as 602,000,000,000,000,000,000,-000. It represents the number of molecules in 18 grams of water and it is called Avogadro's number, after the Italian scientist Amedeo Avogadro (1776–1856), who worked out the value. It is used in a great many scientific calculations, but practically never in the form in which we have given it; instead, it is written as 6.02×10^{23}.

The American mathematician Edward Kasner (1878–   ) invented a new system of indicating extremely large numbers. He coined the word "googol" to express the number 10^{100}, which would be equivalent to 1 followed by 100 zeros. He invented another term, the "googolplex," to stand for $10^{10^{100}}$, or the figure 1 followed by a googol of zeros: that is, 10,000 zeros.

Exponents can be used just as effectively to express very small numbers. Since a minus exponent indicates how many times the fraction $\dfrac{1}{\text{base}}$ is repeated as it is multiplied by itself, $10^{-3} = \dfrac{1}{10} \times \dfrac{1}{10} \times \dfrac{1}{10} = .001$. Note that the exponent 3, in 10^{-3}, represents the number of digits after the decimal point in the number .001. .005 could be written as $5 \times .001$, or 5×10^{-3}. Now consider a much smaller number. The wave length of red light is 0.00000077 meters. We can write this number as $7.7 \times .0000001$ meters, or 7.7×10^{-7} meters.

Writing a number as the product of (1) a number between 1 and 10 and (2) a power of 10 is called *scientific notation*. It is widely used by scientists and engineers.

Calculations with logarithms

Exponents have also been put to work to simplify arithmetical calculations. Suppose that we represent numbers as powers of 2. We know that $2^{-2} = \dfrac{1}{2^2} = \dfrac{1}{4}$; 2^{-1}

---

* Let us point out here that a base with a negative exponent is equal to the reciprocal of the base $\left(\dfrac{1}{\text{base}}\right)$ with the corresponding positive exponent. $2^{-2} = \dfrac{1}{2^2}$.

$= \frac{1}{2^1} = \frac{1}{2}$; $2^0 = 1$; $2^1 = 2$; $2^2 = 4$; $2^3 = 8$; $2^4 = 16$; and so on. Expressed as a power of 2, therefore, $\frac{1}{4}$, or .25, is 2^{-2}; $\frac{1}{2}$, or .5, is 2^{-1}; 1 is 2^0; 2 is 2^1; 4 is 2^2; 8 is 2^3; 16 is 2^4. Let us now make a table setting down (1) certain numbers; (2) these numbers expressed as powers of 2; (3) the exponents in question.

NUMBER	NUMBER EXPRESSED AS POWER OF 2	EXPONENT IN PRECEDING COLUMN
.25	2^{-2}	—2
.5	2^{-1}	—1
1	2^0	0
2	2^1	1
4	2^2	2
8	2^3	3
16	2^4	4
32	2^5	5
64	2^6	6
128	2^7	7
256	2^8	8
512	2^9	9
1024	2^{10}	10

Consider the problem .25 × 1024. The table shows that $.25 = 2^{-2}$ and that $1024 = 2^{10}$. The problem then becomes $2^{-2} \times 2^{10}$. Applying the first law of exponents given above, we have $2^{-2} \times 2^{10} = 2^{-2+10} = 2^8$. Consulting the table, we find that $2^8 = 256$. 256, then, is the answer to the problem .25 × 1024. We have changed a problem in multiplication into a problem in addition — a simpler operation.

Let us take another problem: 1024 ÷ 32. Looking at the table, we see that 1024 is 2^{10} and that 32 is 2^5. Applying the second law of exponents, we have $2^{10} \div 2^5 = 2^{10-5} = 2^5$. We now consult the table and find that 2^5 is equal to 32; this is the answer to 1024 ÷ 32. In this case, we have changed a problem in division into a simple problem in subtraction.

Our next problem is to raise 4 to the fifth power; in other words, we want to know what 4^5 would be. The table shows us that 4 is 2^2. From the third law of exponents, we know that $(2^2)^5 = 2^{2 \times 5} = 2^{10}$. 2^{10}, according to the table, is 1024, which is the answer. We have solved our problem by a single multiplication instead of multiplying $4 \times 4 \times 4 \times 4 \times 4$.

Suppose we wish to get the square root of 1024. According to the table, 1024 is 2^{10}. To get the square root of a given power, we divide the exponent indicating that power by 2 *; hence the square root of $2^{10} = 2^{10 \div 2} = 2^5$. The table shows that $2^5 = 32$. 32, then, is the square root of 1024.

When a number is expressed as a power of a given base, in this case the base two, we call the exponent that indicates the power the *logarithm* of the number. All the exponents in the third column of the table are the logarithms, to the base two, of the numbers in the first column. —2 is the logarithm of .25 when the base is two; as a mathematician would put it, $\log_2 .25 = -2$. Also when the base is two, the logarithm of 4 is 2; the logarithm of 64 is 6. To multiply numbers, we add their logarithms; to divide numbers, we subtract their logarithms; to raise a number to a given power, we multiply the logarithm of the number by the power in question; to obtain the root of a number, we divide the logarithm of the number by the desired root. After we have added, or subtracted, or multiplied or divided in this way, we find the number that corresponds to the resulting logarithm.

All the logarithms we gave above were to the base two. Most tables of logarithms are given to the base ten. Let us now prepare another table, giving (1) a series of numbers; (2) the numbers expressed as powers of 10; (3) the logarithms of the numbers — that is, the exponents when the numbers are expressed as powers of 10.

---

* This is really in accordance with the third law of exponents, above. The square root of a number, as we have seen, is equivalent to the same number with the exponent $\frac{1}{2}$. The square root of 2^{10}, therefore, can be expressed as $(2^{10})^{\frac{1}{2}}$. Remember that to multiply a number by $\frac{1}{2}$ is the same thing as to divide it by 2.

NUMBER	NUMBER EXPRESSED AS POWER OF 10	LOGARITHM TO THE BASE TEN (LOG₁₀)
.0001	10^{-4}	-4
.001	10^{-3}	-3
.01	10^{-2}	-2
.1	10^{-1}	-1
1	10^0	0
10	10^1	1
100	10^2	2
1000	10^3	3
10000	10^4	4

To solve the problem $.0001 \times 100$, we consult the table and find the logarithms of .0001 and 100 (-4 and 2, respectively), add the logarithms ($-4 + 2 = -2$) and find the number corresponding to the logarithm -2. This number, as we see from the table, is .01. We can also do such problems as $10,000 \div .0001$, 10^4 and $\sqrt{10,000}$.

Of course, to be serviceable, a table of logarithms would have to include the logarithms of other numbers besides those given above. It would have to give, for example, not only the logarithms of 1 and 10, but also those of 2, 3, 4, 5, 6, 7, 8 and 9. We know that since $1 = 1^0$ and $10 = 10^1$, the logarithm of 2 would be between 0 and 1. Mathematicians have calculated that it is 0.301.* This means that, expressed as a power of 10, the number 2 is $10^{0.301}$. The integer part of the logarithm (0 in this case) is called the characteristic; the decimal part (.301) is called the mantissa.

The logarithms of the other numbers from 3 through 9 have also been worked out, so that now we can set up this table:

NUMBER	LOGARITHM (BASE TEN)
1	0.
2	0.301
3	0.477
4	0.602
5	0.699
6	0.778
7	0.845
8	0.903
9	0.954
10	1.

* We give only three decimal places for the sake of simplicity. Logarithms have been calculated to more than twenty places. Depending upon the accuracy desired, one would use a four-place table, or a five-place table, or a seven-place table and so on.

Using the table, let us multiply 2 by 4. We add 0.301, the logarithm of 2, and 0.602, the logarithm of 4, and we get the logarithm 0.903. Consulting the table, we see that 0.903 is the logarithm of 8.* 8, therefore, is the answer to the problem 2×4. Let us now divide 9 by 3. The logarithm of 9, as we see from the table, is 0.954; the logarithm of 3 is 0.477. Subtracting 0.477 from 0.954, we get 0.477. The table shows that 0.477 is the logarithm of 3. Hence $9 \div 3 = 3$.

Our table of numbers and logarithms to the base ten gives only ten numbers. Mathematicians have prepared tables making it possible to find the logarithm of any number whatsoever. The tables give only the mantissas; we can determine the characteristic in each case by inspection. For example, the logarithm of the number 343 must be between 2 and 3, since $100 = 10^2$ and $1,000 = 10^3$. The logarithm, then, must be 2 and a fraction; the characteristic must be 2. If we look up a five-place table in order to find the mantissa of 343, we observe that it is equal to .53529. Putting together the characteristic 2 and the mantissa .53529, we have the logarithm 2.53529.

In calculations involving arithmetical problems, we can often save a tremendous amount of time by consulting a table of logarithms. Of course we would not use logarithms to get the answer to 4×5 or $72 \div 9$. But suppose we had to perform the various operations in a problem such as:

$$\frac{-2.953 \times 5.913^5 \times \sqrt[5]{5.973}}{49.743 \times 0.35947^3}$$

If the methods of arithmetic were used, this would be a most laborious task. It could be done in a few minutes if we employed logarithms.

Logarithms to the base ten are called common logarithms. Other bases have been used. In the so-called natural logarithms, the base is $2.71828 \ldots$, generally indicated by the letter e. Natural logarithms serve widely in various types of higher analysis because they lead to comparatively simple formulas.

* A mathematician would say that 8 is the antilogarithm, or antilog, of 0.903. An antilogarithm is the number that corresponds to a given logarithm.

Algebraic sequences and series and how they serve

Many events seem to recur in regular sequences. The sun "rises" every day*; the planets revolve in their orbits around the sun so regularly that astronomers can calculate their positions years in advance. Man has analyzed periodic happenings by means of algebraic sequences and series,** and he has sometimes used the results of his analyses to predict future happenings. We shall briefly consider here the arithmetic and geometric sequences and the binomial series.

The arithmetic series. In an arithmetic sequence, each term, after the first one, is formed by adding a constant quantity to the preceding term. An example of such a sequence is 1, 3, 5, 7, 9, 11, 13, 15, in which 2 is added to each succeeding member of the sequence. If a stands for the first number, d for the constantly added number and n for the total number of terms, we can represent the arithmetic sequence algebraically by this formula:

$$a, (a + d), (a + 2d) \ldots [a + (n - 1)d]$$

Here $[a + (n - 1)d]$ is the nth term.

If we add n terms together, the sum of the terms is called a series and can be expressed in the formula

$$s \text{ (sum)} = \frac{n}{2} [2a + (n - 1)d]$$

Let us apply this formula to the sum of the terms in the sequence given above: 1, 3, 5, 7, 9, 11, 13, 15. Here there are eight terms in all; the first term is 1; the quantity that is constantly added is 2. Substituting these values for n, a and d:

$$s = \frac{8}{2} [2 \times 1 + (8 - 1) \times 2]$$

If you work out the arithmetic involved, you will find that the sum of the eight terms is 64. You can verify this by adding the eight terms of the sequence.

* Of course, it only apparently rises, since the earth moves around the sun.
** A sequence is a succession of numbers; a series is a sum of numbers in a sequence.

The arithmetic series is very useful in various types of calculations. It serves, among other things, in finding the total cost of an item that you are buying on the installment plan. Suppose you buy a piano for $1,000. You pay $400 down and agree to pay the other $600 in 20 monthly installments of $30 each, plus the interest at 6 per cent on the unpaid balance. Let us apply the arithmetic series to the problem in order to determine the total interest payments that will be required.

The first of these payments is $\frac{1}{12} \times$ .06* $\times$ $600 (the unpaid balance), or $3.00. Each month the interest is less than in the preceding month, since the unpaid balance is reduced by $30. You would pay $\frac{1}{12} \times$ .06 $\times$ $30, or $.15 less interest than the month before. The interest payments, therefore, would be $3.00 (for the first month), $2.85 (for the second month), $2.70 (for the third month) and so on until the 20 installments would be paid. Going back to the formula for the sum of an arithmetic series, we see that n (the number of terms) is 20 in this case; that a (the first term) is $3.00; that d (the number added to the different terms) is $-.15$. Making the appropriate substitutions in the formula, we have:

$$s = \frac{20}{2} \times [(2 \times 3.00) + (20 - 1) \times -.15]$$

The answer, representing the total interest paid, is $31.50.

The geometric sequence. In a geometric sequence, each term, after the first one, is formed by multiplying the one before it by the same fixed quantity. A typical geometric sequence is 1, 2, 4, 8, 16, in which the fixed term used as the multiplier is 2. Algebraically, any geometric sequence can be represented as:

$$a, ar, ar^2 \ldots ar^{n-1}$$

where a is the first term, r the constant multiplier and n the number of terms. The sum of n terms of a geometric sequence — a sum called a geometric series — is given by the formula:

* The six-per-cent interest means "6 per cent yearly." The installment period is a month, or $\frac{1}{12}$ of a year.

$$s = \frac{ar^n - a}{r - 1}$$

Applying it to the series $1 + 2 + 4 + 8 + 16$, you will find that the sum is 31.

The geometric series plays an important part in the mathematics of finance. It is used, among other things, in figuring compound interest. Suppose that we put $100 in a bank and that the interest is 3 per cent, compounded annually.* At the

* Interest is said to be compounded when it applies, not to the principal alone, but to the principal plus the unpaid interest, periodically added to the principal.

end of the first year, the principal plus interest would come to $100 plus $3.00 (representing the interest), or a total of $103. We could write this as $100 × 1.03. For the next period — that is, for the second year — we would receive interest of 3 per cent on $103; hence the total amount at the end of the second year would be $103 + (0.3 × $103). Expressed somewhat differently, the amount in question would be equal to $100 × 1.03².*

* $103 + (.03 × $103) = $106.09. $100 × 1.03² = $106.09.

5. A binomial series, reading downward. Each member of such a series, after the first member, is formed by multiplying the preceding member by $a + b$. For example, $a + b$, multiplied by $a + b$, is equal to $a^2 + 2ab + b^2$.

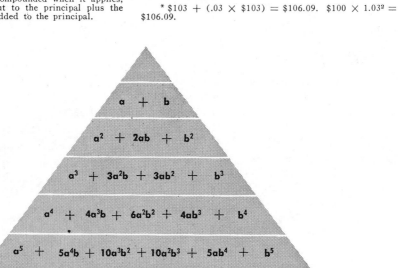

$$a + b$$
$$a^2 + 2ab + b^2$$
$$a^3 + 3a^2b + 3ab^2 + b^3$$
$$a^4 + 4a^3b + 6a^2b^2 + 4ab^3 + b^4$$
$$a^5 + 5a^4b + 10a^3b^2 + 10a^2b^3 + 5ab^4 + b^5$$
$$a^6 + 6a^5b + 15a^4b^2 + 20a^3b^3 + 15a^2b^4 + 6ab^5 + b^6$$

6. Here the coefficients of the different powers of a and b, in a binomial series, are arranged in the same order as indicated in Figure 5. A coefficient is a multiplier. For example, 2 is the coefficient in 2ab.

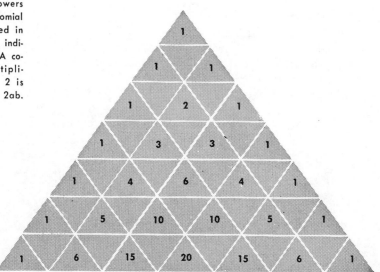

```
            1
         1     1
       1    2     1
     1    3    3     1
   1    4    6    4     1
 1    5   10   10    5     1
1    6   15   20   15    6    1
```

To repeat, then: at the end of the first year, the total amount we would have in the bank would be $100 × 1.03; at the end of the second year, we would have $100 × 1.03². Following the same procedure, we would have $100 × 1.03³ at the end of the third year; $100 × 1.03⁴ at the end of the fourth year and so on. This represents the geometric sequence

$100, $103, $106.09, $109.27, $112.55 . . . .

in which 1.03 is the fixed term that is used as the multiplier.

At the end of n periods, the total amount of money in the bank would be $100 × 1.03^n. For ten interest periods, the sum would come to $100 × 1.03^{10}. Calculating by logarithms, we find that 1.03^{10} = 1.344. 1.344 × $100 = $134.40; $100, at 3-per-cent interest, compounded yearly, would be $134.40 at the end of ten years.

The binomial * *series.* The binomial series is the sum of terms based on the ex-

---

* A binomial consists of two terms connected by a plus or minus sign. $a + b$, $2x + z$ and $x^2 - y^2$ are all binomials.

7. The pegs (a, b, c, d, e, f and so on) in this shallow box are in the exact positions of the numbers in Figure 6. The walls that extend from the bottom pegs form a series of compartments at the bottom of the box.

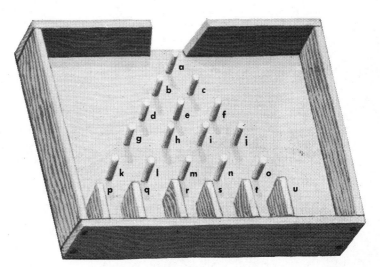

8. If we drop 64 disks, one by one, in the box shown in Figure 7, they will make their way down the pegs about as indicated. The ratios of the disks hitting the pegs in each row (right) reproduce the triangle in Figure 6.

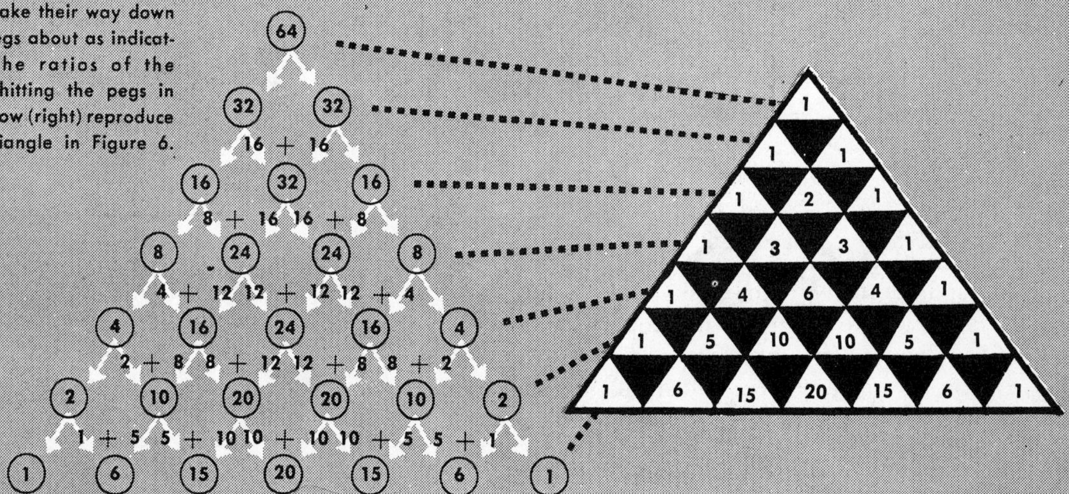

pansion of the power of a binomial. The series for $(a + b)^1$ is $a + b$. For $(a + b)^2$, we obtain the series by multiplying $a + b$ by $a + b$, giving $a^2 + 2ab + b^2$. The series for $(a + b)^3$ is obtained by multiplying $a^2 + 2ab + b^2$ by $a + b$. This gives $a^3 + 3a^2b + 3ab^2 + b^3$. We can arrange these binomial series and also those for $(a + b)^4$, $(a + b)^5$ and $(a + b)^6$ as in Figure 5.

Suppose now that, instead of the different powers of a and b, we give only the coefficients * and reproduce the triangle in this modified form as shown in Figure 6. You will note that we add the number 1 at the peak of the triangle.

Let us now put a series of pegs in a shallow box, in the exact positions of the numbers of the numerical triangle, as shown in Figure 7. The pegs are to be just far enough apart so that a small disk will be able to pass between them. We cut out a small section of one side of the box (which will be the top), as indicated in the figure, and we also build a series of walls extending from each of the bottom pegs, so as to form a series of compartments at the bottom of the box.

We keep the box in a tilted position so that when a disk is dropped through the gap at the top, it will make its way through the maze of pegs to one of the bottom compartments. Now we drop 64 disks one by one into the box through the gap. We can expect that half of the disks that hit a peg will fall to the left of it and the other half to the right. Hence 32 disks should drop to the left of peg a and 32 to the right of the peg. Of the 32 that fall to the left and strike peg b, 16 should fall to the left of b and should strike peg d; 16 should fall to the right of peg b and should hit peg e. Of the 32 disks that hit peg c, 16 should strike peg e and 16 should strike peg f. That means that 32 disks in all will hit peg e. We can indicate how the disks should fall on their way to the bottom compartments by the diagram in Figure 8.

As we have seen, 32 disks should strike peg b in the second row and 32 should strike peg c. 32 and 32 are in the ratio 1-1. In the third row, 16 should strike d; 32 should strike e and 16 should strike f. The ratio between 16, 32 and 16 is 1-2-1. Going down the rows, the ratios of the disks striking the different pegs would be 1-3-3-1 in the fourth row, 1-4-6-4-1 in the fifth row and 1-5-10-10-5-1 in the sixth. The disks in the seventh row would follow the distribution 1-6-15-20-15-6-1. Note that these ratios all correspond exactly to the coefficients of the binomial series in Figure 6.

In an actual experiment, the disks will not fall exactly as we have indicated. Some compartments will have one or two more than the number predicted; others will have one or more less. Yet in every case the result will be nearly that which was forecast. If the experiment is repeated over and over again, in a great number of trials, the number in each compartment will agree more and more closely with the expected number. Thus the coefficients of the binomial series provide an effective means for calculating probabilities when the chances of an event occurring are even.

To determine probabilities when the chances are not even, other algebraic analyses have been made. The results of these analyses have been applied in engineering, science, industry, public-opinion polls and other fields. The subject that deals with such analyses is called statistics.

Insurance companies make extensive use of this kind of algebra. They can predict with fair accuracy how many men out of a given number — say, 1,000 — will be alive each succeeding year. They can also predict that if these 1,000 men take out life insurance, the premiums they pay will grow to a certain amount at compound interest during their lifetimes. To make insurance work, the company must collect enough in premiums and in compounded interest to pay the insurance when their clients die. Probability and compound interest, as developed by algebra, are therefore the bases on which all insurance is built.

Thus algebra, which began by examining the general relations of arithmetical operations, has become an interpreter of our experience and a guide for the future.

---

* A coefficient is a numeral (sometimes a letter) used as a multiplier. 5 is the coefficient in $5ab$.

See also Vol. 10, p. 279: "Mathematics."

TREASURES OF THE QUARRY

How Stone Is Made Available to Man

UP TO modern times, the march of civilization has been generally recorded upon stone. Extensive quarrying was first undertaken by the Egyptians of the Pyramid Age, about 3000 B.C. The earliest architect in stone was Imhotep the Wise, who built the first pyramid for his royal patron. In Egyptian construction the use of limestone as a basic material was customary. The statuary was often carved in diorite, a smooth, granitelike rock. These materials and others employed in the building of temples and tombs were found near the Valley of the Kings — the chief burial site of the Pharaohs.

In later periods, the stone city of Thebes rose beside the Nile to replace the ancient brick and wood capital of decaying Memphis. At Thebes stood the temple of Karnak, perhaps the most massive conception in stone of all time. In the grand colonnade of Karnak towered some 136 huge columns set in 16 rows, the capital of each 69 feet high, with enough room for 100 men to stand upright.

The stone glories of the Egyptians passed to other peoples: the Persians, the Sea Kings of Crete, the Greeks and the Romans. At Hellenistic Alexandria a marvelous lighthouse was erected on the island of Pharos. Over 370 feet high, the beacon of Pharos blazed for almost 1,600 years. From the Hanging Gardens of Babylon to Nero's Golden House, vast enterprises in stone were carried out — of which even the ground plan seems incredible today. Like the Egyptians, later peoples employed stone of the country. In Attica, quarries supplied Greek marble for temples and statuary of the Heroic Period. From Carrara in Tuscany came marble for Roman villas and thermae.

Following the Classical Age, a decline in civilization was reflected in the use of perishable construction materials: rushes, sun-dried brick, soft wood. From the period of barbarian migration in the West, no contemporary building has survived. The values of beauty and permanence continued to be upheld in the imperial East especially at Constantinople with its glorious basilica of St. Sophia.

In the West a new era began under the Normans. Devoted to war, the Norman barons employed stone primarily for military defense. Thick-walled Norman keeps dotted Western Europe. A distinctive buff limestone was quarried at Caen in Normandy and shipped all over the West. In the Tower of London the austere Chapel of St. John was built of Norman stone. Tewkesbury Abbey, the finest Romanesque church in England, had a clerestory tower and sixteen great pillars of Caen stone. The famous Westminster Abbey was largely rebuilt in this Norman material by a succession of Norman-Plantagenet monarchs. From the Romanesque period through the Decorated Gothic and on to Renaissance times, the use of stone became increasingly skillful and imaginative. The Italian baroque style of the Venetian palaces along the Grand Canal and of Wolsey's Hampton Court in England reflected man's awakening vision and his feeling for an ideal of beauty.

During modern history the employment of stone has at times become associated with tyrants who wish to glorify their regimes in the classical manner. The severe "Empire style" of Napoleon I relied on black basalt and red porphyry granite, of which an outstanding example survives in the Emperor's tomb at the Invalides.

As civilization advances, stone must meet the competition of other building materials, such as wood and brick and steel. Wood and brick are now generally preferred in the construction of small houses; steel, frequently combined with concrete, is used extensively for large structures, such as skyscrapers and suspension bridges. However, stone is still highly prized as a building material. It is often used for buildings and other structures in whose construction beauty, dignity and endurance are the main considerations. In the case of buildings whose basic material is steel or brick, architects often specify stone for ornamental purposes. They favor this material for facings, halls, floors and pillars, where they wish to obtain particularly pleasing effects.

Stone provides a
medium for artists

Certain kinds of stone are natural materials for art. The leap from the rough, rock-built huts of primitive peoples to the statuary of the Athenian sculptor Phidias, working in Parian marble, is a long one indeed — almost as long as the range of man's intellectual progress. Yet it all lies within the limits of the fascinating story of stone.

The rocks of the earth serve in other ways, too. As we shall see, broken stone is used for the construction of roads and also for railroad ballast. A large amount of crushed limestone is employed for agricultural purposes. Immense quantities of stone, finely broken or ground, go into the manufacture of glass. The quarry, therefore, supplies materials that are used for the home, for industry, for transportation arteries and for art.

How rocks
are formed

The rocks that are put to these varied uses vary widely in their character and origin. We should have at least some idea of the formation and structure of granite rocks, sandstones, limestones, slates and marbles before we consider how all these materials are used at the present time.

Rocks are divided, geologically, into three main groups. First, there are the rocks that have solidified from a molten mass; these form the igneous group, which includes granite, porphyry and basalt. In certain cases, igneous rocks were broken up into fragments in the course of the ages. Later, these fragments were compacted and cemented to form the rocks of the second group — the sedimentary rocks. Sandstone, mudstone, shale, limestone and dolomite all belong to this group.

The origin of
metamorphic rocks

In the third group, we find rocks that were originally igneous or sedimentary and that were later transformed by temperature, pressure and other factors operating within the crust of the earth. The name metamorphic is given to the rocks of this group; they include marble, slate and schist.

There are various kinds of igneous rocks. Those of the so-called plutonic type (of which granite is an example) solidified and slowly cooled deep down under the surface of the earth, where they were subjected to heavy pressure. In the course of time they were often injected through weaker overlying beds. These afterward weathered away until their plutonic core was left bare. In plutonic rocks, crystallization (chiefly into quartz, feldspar and mica) has been complete.

Certain igneous rocks solidified in small masses from the molten state; they cooled more quickly and their crystallization is less distinct. Porphyry is a good example of these hypabyssal rocks, as they are called. Finally, there are volcanic rocks, which cooled rapidly at the surface of the earth, as in the case of basalt. In this rock crystallization is imperfect and in some cases, as in the natural glasses, it may be entirely absent. Such forms are called amorphous.

The many uses
of igneous rocks

The igneous rocks furnish the stone that is used wherever strength and endurance are required. They are used more extensively than any other kinds of rocks for building purposes; they are crushed for

Charles Phelps Cushing

Under this magnificent granite fountain, in Washington, D. C., is a tremendous underground garage.

road making. Though the metamorphic rock known as marble has been the favorite material of artists working in stone, igneous rocks have also served for art work, particularly with modern methods of dressing and shaping by pneumatic power.

Granites are the most widely used of all the igneous rocks. They are made up chiefly of quartz and feldspar, with a certain admixture of mica (a black variety of mica) and, occasionally, of hornblende. They generally occur in the field in great masses, which cover extensive areas; these masses frequently form the cores of mountain ranges. There are a good many different varieties of granite; the distinctions between these types are based on composition, color and texture.

Other igneous rocks are more or less closely allied to the granites. Thus the rocks that are known as the diorites have much the same texture as the granites; they differ from the latter chiefly because they consist mainly of feldspar and contain little or no quartz. A good many of the igneous rocks, other than granite, have what may be called granitic qualities: that is, they are hard, tough and will take a polish. These rocks are quarried and used much as are the granites.

In the United States granites are quar-

ried in the states along the Appalachian Mountains from Maine to Alabama, and also in Minnesota, Wisconsin, Missouri and California. Vermont is the most important producer of granite; the quarries of New Hampshire, California, Massachusetts and Maine are also very valuable.

Of the Vermont stones, the Barre and the so-called Hardwick granites are particularly well known. The former occurs in several shades of gray and is used largely for monumental purposes; it was employed, for example, in the Calhoun Monument in Lexington, Kentucky. Hardwick granites are either gray or white; the white variety was used in the construction of the Wisconsin State Capitol at Madison. The granite in the Pennsylvania State Capitol at Harrisburg came from Woodbury, Vermont.

Fine building granite is quarried in many areas of New Hampshire; the popular name of this state is the Granite State. California also contains extensive granite areas; this rock makes up the core of the Sierra Nevadas, besides occurring in smaller scattered districts. It is from light to dark gray in color, and it is put to a wide variety of uses. A number of western states, other than California, produce granite only for local use.

Several well-known types of granite are quarried in Massachusetts. Milford is noted for its pink granite and Rockport for its gray and green varieties. Quincy granite, because of the high polish it will take, is widely used in monuments and in ornamental work.

With a few exceptions, such as the quarries in Hallowell and North Jay, Maine's granite quarries are located along the seaboard. General Grant's tomb, on Riverside Drive in New York City, was built of "white granite" from North Jay. Several pink granites are quarried on islands along the coast, especially near Rockland. One quarry in this region supplied sixteen columns measuring six feet in diameter for the Cathedral of St. John the Divine in New York City.

Granites from Westerly, Rhode Island; Stony Creek, Connecticut; Port Deposit, Maryland; and Mt. Airy, North Carolina, are famous. Pink and red types come from Wisconsin, Minnesota and Missouri.

Granite has always been a popular building stone. The red granite of Syene (Aswan) was fashioned by the ancient Egyptians into obelisks, sarcophagi and statues. It was also used in temples, pyramids and palaces. Coarse red granites come from Peterhead, Scotland, and gray granite from Aberdeen. Both gray and red granite are quarried in Canada.

Granite is so tough that it must be blasted loose from the mass. Sometimes it is loosened in enormous quantities — thousands of tons — at one time. Granite is sawed, not by a toothed saw, but by an untoothed steel bar that cuts or abrades the rock by friction on minute steel filings. The groove in the granite, once started, is filled with water and with hard steel particles which furnish the cutting surfaces. The bar is moved back and forth, by machinery, over these steel particles in the gash. The dressing of granite is now done mainly by a process of chipping with chisels worked by pneumatic power.

Polished black granite slabs used on the C.I.T. Financial Corporation Building in New York City. The slabs came from the granite quarry on Peribonca River, Lake St. John, Canada.

Courtesy, George A. Fuller Co., Builder

The granites are valued particularly for their great strength and durability. Certain softer sedimentary rocks, such as sandstones, are also employed extensively in industry and construction.

Sandstone is less durable than granite and differs in composition as well as in origin. This type of rock consists of fine grains of sand or pebbles, which have been cemented together by such substances as calcium carbonate, silicic acid and iron oxide. The element silicon in the form of its oxide, silicon dioxide, is the major constituent of sandstone.

Rocks are classified according to their method of formation. Sandstone is known as sedimentary rock, for it is formed by the deposition of sand or pebbles in sea water. As the sand settles, the skeletons of tiny sea organisms come to rest between the grains. These skeletons are composed mainly of calcium carbonate, which may be dissolved by the sea water and then reprecipitated. Finer crystals, which act as cement, result from this process.

In the geologic past, many continents were covered by shallow inland seas. It is in these submerged areas that most of the sandstone beds were laid down. According to certain estimates, it took 450 years to deposit a formation only one foot thick. As time passed and the seas receded, the sandstone deposits were no longer covered with water. They became part of the continental land mass.

Many grades of sandstones occur, depending upon the fineness of the sand and the amount of pebbles and clay that they contain. There is a good deal of clay in the sandstones called argillaceous. If sandstones are mostly pure sand, they are known as arenaceous. Limy sandstones are ofen called calcareous.

Though most sedimentary rocks can easily be altered in structure by heat and pressure, sandstones are highly resistant to these forces. The reason for this phenomenon is the natural resistance to heat of the silicon dioxide found in the sand and pebbles. If, however, these rocks are subjected to high enough temperatures and pressures, they will eventually fuse to form the crystal-clear mineral, quartzite. In addition to this mineral, sandstones may contain substances which will color them. The calcareous stones are white, due to the presence of calcium carbonate. Varying amounts of iron oxide account for the colors of red, yellow or brown sandstones. Stones with blue-green or gray colors result from the presence of iron-potassium salts called glauconites.

Sandstone is a porous material, for approximately 30 per cent of its volume is made up of interspaces between the sand grains. Because of its porosity, sandstone cannot be polished readily. It is therefore not used extensively for ornamentation and sculptural purposes.

The porosity or consistency may vary with the type of cement present. The stones with silicic acid as cement are heavier, less porous, more lasting and finer grained than other types. They are employed most frequently as building stones. Moderately cemented sandstones are capable of holding water. They serve in the construction of water-storage devices, such as wells and basins. The least firmly cemented sandstones are used for making millstones, grinding stones, pulpstones and abrasives.

The heat-resistant quality of sandstone has already been described. This makes the stone useful in the manufacture of furnace linings, bricks and hearths.

The quarrying of sandstone is not difficult since it is soft and is found at the surface of the earth. If the stone deposit is not too thick, it can be cut with crowbars and wedges without drilling or using dynamite. Gunpowder is employed if an explosive is needed to break up the sandstone into stones of fair size. If broken stone is desired for the preparation of concrete, for road making and for similar purposes, a strong explosive is used.

Some of the most popular sandstones are quarried in the northeastern United States. Amherst, Berea and other quarries in Ohio produce a light brown or gray stone. The Berea sandstone is made into grindstones. The New England states have always been famous for their quarries.

Massachusetts and Connecticut produce the Longmeadow brownstone and the red sandstone. The bluestones or flagstones used as steppingstones come from New York; so do the Medina stone, the Shawangunk grit and the Potsdam red stone. New Jersey also quarries red and brown sandstones.

Perhaps the most ornamental and highly valued of the sedimentary rocks are the limestones. They are in general more durable than sandstones but less resistant to crushing than granite.

Limestones were first formed when the continents were covered with inland seas. Many of the largest conglomerations of limestones were deposited 300,000,000 years ago in the Mississippian period Some were as much as 2,000 feet thick.

Limestones are made up chiefly of calcium carbonate and are formed in various ways. The calcium carbonate dissolved in sea water may be precipitated chemically or by bacterial action or by a drop in the temperature. The finest-grained limestones are formed in this manner. The coarser stones are made up of whole or broken skeletons of marine creatures. These so-called calcareous fragments may be large or microscopic. They are cemented together by the solution and re-precipitation of some of the calcium carbonate they contain. In all of these methods of formation, the limy muds solidify into limestone beds which may be many feet thick.

Today the most extensively quarried stone of North America is the Bedford oölite or Salem limestone. It is found near Bedford, Indiana and in Kentucky. In some instances the bed covers an area of seventy square miles and may be eighty-five feet in thickness. This type of limestone is valued for its softness and uniformity of texture. Salem limestone is easily sculptured and can be cut into blocks and slabs. Its uniformity makes it reliable for use in architecture.

Limestone quarries occur in several states lying between the Rockies and the Appalachians. In Missouri, the principal limestone is a strong, light-gray crystalline rock from Jasper county. It is known as Carthage limestone, and it takes a good polish. Minnesota limestones are usually yellow or yellowish brown. This finely grained limestone is obtained in the south-central portion of the state.

The quarries may be open-surface pits, but frequently they are underground mines. An instance of subterranean quarrying is found at Bath in England, where limestone has been mined for many centuries. The stone is found between 90 and 120 feet below the surface; the principal seams are from twelve to thirty feet thick. The stones are brought to the surface; they are left in the open to harden and weather.

Though the best limestones are used as building stones and for sculpture, they serve many purposes in industry. Crushed limestone is employed in making portland cement. In the steel industry crushed limestone serves as a flux in the blast furnaces. It fuses with various impurities and forms a slag which is removed . It can also serve to neutralize soil acidity in farming. Freshly precipitated limestone is used in making tooth pastes.

When the purest limestone is subjected to intense metamorphic forces, white marble is formed. (See Index, under Metamorphism.) Marbles of different colors exist. Those that are red, yellow or brown owe their color to varying proportions of iron compounds. Gray or black colors are due to the presence of carbon particles. The minerals chlorite and serpentine produce green colors. When marble is examined under a low-powered microscope, it appears to be made up of crysals with a beautiful, fine granular appearance.

Marbles are found in many parts of the world. The marble of Carrara, Italy, is perhaps the most famous. Other fine marbles are found in Greece, North Africa and the Union of South Africa. There are many large deposits in the United States, especially in Vermont, Massachusetts, New York, Pennsylvania, Georgia, Tennessee, Texas, Utah, Colorado and California. In the United States, marble is used for monumental and building stone and also for crushed and broken stone.

Marble is often quarried by machines that cut through the rock. These machines, which are called "channelers," are used in the Vermont marble quarries. A row of long chisels, set in a strong framework that travels with them, moves up and down, cutting out a channel in the marble ledge. The grooves may be cut either vertically or horizontally and they can be made deep enough to surround almost any block, no matter how large, that may be quarried. The blocks of stone are wedged loose and are then lifted by enormous cranes into the railroad cars that will transport them to their destination. The marble may be dressed at the quarry or by the purchaser after receipt of the stone. In some places, marble is blasted by dynamite — in Italy, for example. This method is extremely wasteful and is being replaced by others.

The classical white Parian marble comes today, as it has since the sixth century B.C., from the Greek island of Paros, one of the Cyclades Islands in the Aegean Sea. In Italy and in Greece, whole buildings were built completely of marble. The Parthenon, in Athens, was built of marble from Mount Pentelikon, ten miles northeast of the city. Augustus Caesar boasted truly that he found Rome brick and left it marble. This transformation was made possible only by the relative nearness of the Tuscan quarries of Carrara. Today, travelers between Spezia and Pisa note that the mountains that have long been cutting the eastern sky are scarred with yellow patches, almost from base to summit. Here are the "four hundred" quarries of Carrara and Massa, from which marble is exported to places all over the world.

The beauty of the Hall Auditorium at Oberlin College is greatly enhanced by the marble used in its construction, especially the massive pillars. The auditorium seats about 500 people.

Harrison and Abramovitz, Architects

Slate is another important building material, though it is not used as extensively as marble. It is produced by the compression of clay or shale during volcanic upheavals or mountain-building movements in the earth's crust. The result is a rock that splits readily into thin sheets in a direction at right angles to the direction of the compression. The small particles of which slate is formed overlap like fish scales.

Slates vary within a fairly wide range in their physical characteristics as well as in their color. Rocks with relatively large mineral particles yield coarse slates. A good slate is hard, compact and fine-grained; it splits up into sheets with a clean straight surface. The most common color is some shade of gray. Red slate has an excess of iron, while the sea-green variety is heavy with sulfur; black slate has a high percentage of graphite or lead. Other slate colors are purple and blue.

Slate quarries yield an important roofing material

Slate is widely used as roofing material. Important quarries for roof slates are located in the New England-Appalachian Mountain slate belt, the Ouachita Mountains of Arkansas and in certain parts of the Sierra Nevada. Very good slates come from Wales; they generally have a finer grain than those that are produced in southwestern England.

Excavations often extend to hundreds of feet below surface level before the quarries can be worked. Mills that are located nearby are equipped with specially designed machines for cutting the slate into slabs of the proper size.

An advantage in using slate over other materials is that it is placed on the roof in exactly the same condition as it was when found in the ground hundreds of feet below the surface. A slate roof is very little affected by weather conditions; it may last for hundreds of years.

Gendreau

A slate quarry in Pennsylvania. The heaped-up fragments (top) are crushed to powder for use as a paint filler.

AIR IN MOTION

The Origin and Nature of the Earth's Winds

BY IVAN R. TANNEHILL

EVERYONE realizes that the air circulates in the form of breezes, eddies, variable winds, hurricanes and so on. The importance of this circulation, however, is not so well known. It is not simply a single feature of the weather, such as sunshine, sleet or fog, but it is largely responsible for all weather changes. It may produce clouds that veil from us the sun by day and the stars by night. It may bring snow, or rain or hail; droughts, or floods or tidal waves.

The air in motion affects the distribution of the world's population and the character of its civilization. In regions where the winds are favorable at the proper seasons, agriculture and industry flourish and man prospers. In other areas, where the winds are too cold or too dry, there are frozen or desert wastelands. Thus the circulation of the air (in the form of monsoon winds) brings rain to densely populated regions of China and India, while at approximately the same latitudes it denies moisture to the vast deserts of northern Africa.

Why the air circulates

The circulation of the air is due partly to the effects of solar radiation. The sun's rays do not heat the air very much as they pass through it on their way to the surface of the earth. The air is warmed chiefly by the heat that is radiated back from land and

U. S. Weather Bureau

Hurricanes represent an extreme form of the air in motion. A hurricane is a rotating wind system, with winds of more than 75 miles an hour and a calm area, known as the eye, at the center of the system. Above is a composite photo, taken by the weather satellite *Tiros III*, of the typical whirling cloud formations of two hurricanes—Debbie and Esther—moving over the Atlantic.

sea. Air circulation is also brought about in part through the force of gravitation. The effects of gravitation upon air masses depend upon the degree to which these masses have been heated.

When air is heated, it expands. Since a cubic foot of warm air is less dense than the same bulk of cold air, it exerts less pressure. The warm, low-pressure air at the surface is hemmed in on all sides by colder, denser, high-pressure air. The atmosphere grows less dense, the higher up one goes; the warm air, following the path of least resistance, makes its way upward in the atmosphere. It is to this fact that we owe the formation of the clouds, which in their turn may yield rain, snow, hail or sleet. For the rising air currents carry water vapor, which is a gas, up into the higher levels of the atmosphere. Here the water vapor is converted into droplets and becomes visible in the form of clouds.

The atmosphere is not uniformly heated because the rays of the sun do not strike all parts of the earth's sphere at the same angle. They strike the earth's surface at the equator, on the average, more vertically than in any other region of the earth. Hence the air is heated most effectively in the vicinity of the equator.

Suppose that the earth's surface consisted entirely of water and that the earth did not rotate on its axis nor move around the sun but hung motionless in space. Suppose, too, that the earth and the sun remained forever in the relative position they occupy at the equinoxes (about March 21 and September 23), when the sun's rays strike perpendicularly at the equator. This is roughly what would happen in the regions exposed to the sun *:

   * *Editor's note*: For the sake of simplicity, the cold air on the unlit side of the earth is ignored in this account of the theoretical circulation. Actually, this cold air would complicate matters.

Theoretical circulation of the atmosphere. We assume that the earth's surface consists entirely of water and that the earth neither revolves around the sun nor rotates. Actually, the circulation is complicated by a variety of factors, which are described in this article.

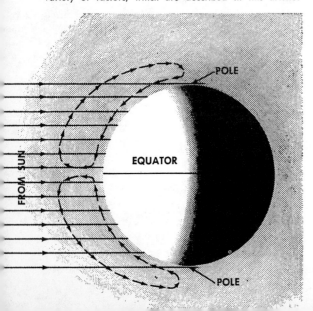

The air would be effectively warmed by the sun at the equator and it would rise. This would bring about a region of low pressure at the lower levels of the atmosphere at the equator. As the air would rise, it would produce greater pressure at the upper levels in the vicinity of the equator, because the weight of the rising air would be added to the weight of the air already in that particular area.

Farther north or south, the sun's rays would strike more obliquely. As a consequence, the surface of the water would not be heated so much and it would not heat the air so thoroughly. Therefore the air would not rise so rapidly, and the pressure in the upper areas would not be so great as at the equator. The air would be heated least of all at the North and South poles and would rise least of all. Naturally the pressure aloft would also be the least of all.

The result of all this would be a kind of pressure slope aloft from the equator to the poles. This slope would be highest at the equator and lowest at the poles. To the upper air at the equator, as we have seen, would be added new supplies of warm air from the surface of the water. The air would then flow down the pressure slope toward the poles and would set up a constant circulation in that direction.

There would normally be a high-pressure area at low atmospheric levels at the poles, since the cold air in that region would tend to hug the surface. To this cold air at the poles would be constantly added the air circulating from the equator. Equatorward from the poles, the pressure of the air at the surface would constantly decrease as more of the air would be warmed and would be carried to higher levels. Hence the accumulated air at the poles would begin making its way to the regions of less resistance in the direction of the equator. There would be a circulation at the surface away from the poles and toward the equator. When the air masses from the poles would reach the equator at last, they would be heated with the rest of the surface air and would rise to higher levels in the atmosphere. They would make their way down the pressure slopes to the poles as before.

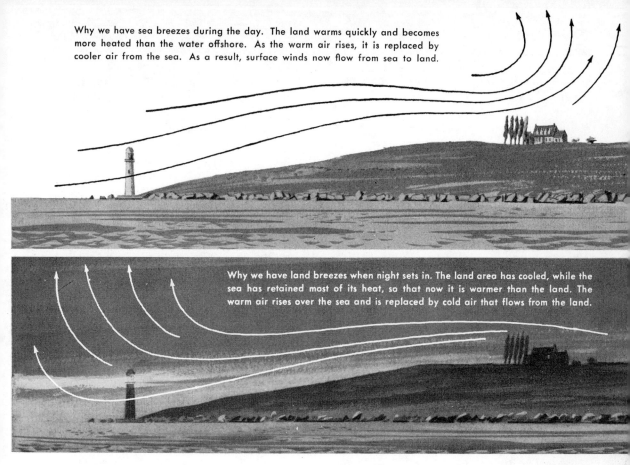

Why we have sea breezes during the day. The land warms quickly and becomes more heated than the water offshore. As the warm air rises, it is replaced by cooler air from the sea. As a result, surface winds now flow from sea to land.

Why we have land breezes when night sets in. The land area has cooled, while the sea has retained most of its heat, so that now it is warmer than the land. The warm air rises over the sea and is replaced by cold air that flows from the land.

Factors that affect the circulation of the air

The actual circulation of the air is not nearly so simple as this description would make it appear. It is true that in many areas there is a general drift toward the poles in the upper air and a general drift toward the equator at the surface. But the circulation is affected by a number of important factors.

For one thing, the surface of the earth is not a continuous expanse of ocean; it is made up of land and sea areas. These are not equally heated by the rays of the sun, and such differences in heating are heightened by the alternation of day and night and of the four seasons.

Water warms more slowly than land; it also cools more slowly. There are several reasons why this is so. The water reflects more of the sun's rays than it absorbs. The rays that are absorbed penetrate the water to a considerable depth and are not concentrated at the surface. The colder water from the lower depths of the sea is constantly being mixed with the warmer water at the surface through the churning action of the waves. Again, evaporation is always taking place at the surface; and evaporation has a cooling effect. (See Index, under Evaporation.) Water is a poor radiator of heat; once it has been warmed, it has a tendency to retain heat for a considerable period of time.

The land does not reflect the rays of the sun to any considerable extent; it absorbs most of them. The rays do not penetrate far beneath the surface. Hence the land surface effectively collects the sun's heat and rapidly becomes warm. It stores very little of this heat, but radiates it away rapidly; therefore it loses heat quickly at night and in the winter. That is why temperatures on land often show striking extremes. The highest and the lowest temperatures on earth are to be found in land areas. In these areas, too, we find the widest temperature range. The average annual range is less than 5° F. over the ocean at the equator; it is about 120° F. in certain regions of Asiatic Russia.

The effects of the varying temperatures of land and sea are clearly seen in the case of sea and land breezes. In the daytime, the land, warming quickly, becomes more heated than the waters offshore. The warm air rises rapidly and is replaced by the colder air flowing in from the sea. Hence the surface winds blow from the sea to the land by day, and we have sea breezes. At night, the land cools quickly, while the sea retains most of its heat, so that now it is warmer than the land. The warm air, therefore, rises over the sea and is replaced by the cooler air from the land. Consequently surface winds blow from the land to the sea at night, and we have land breezes.

We find much the same situation on a grander scale on the continent of Asia and the nearby seas. The interior of the great Asiatic landmass becomes heated in the summer. Its atmosphere expands and flows outward aloft. A great low, or low-pressure area, develops, and moist air flows inland from the comparatively cool oceans to the east and south. This produces the seasonal wind called the summer monsoon. ("Monsoon" comes, by way of the Portuguese, from *mausim,* an Arabic word meaning "season.") In winter, the interior of the Asiatic continent becomes colder than the seas to the east and south, and a vast high, or high-pressure area, develops. The air over the seas, warmer than the land air, rises rapidly and is replaced by air from the land. Therefore dry, cold winds blow seaward, producing the winter monsoon.

In other areas, too, highs and lows of vast extent develop because the oceans differ in temperature from the surrounding landmasses. For example, the northern oceans are relatively warm in winter; hence they are the seats of two great lows, one centered near Iceland and the other near the Aleutian Islands.

Thus the circulation of the air is affected by the relative temperature of the land and water as day alternates with night, and winter with spring, summer and fall. It is also profoundly influenced by the rotation of the earth.

Because of this rotation, the earth acts like a great turntable, sliding from under any air that is moving over its surface. To an observer facing the direction of the equator, the effect of this turntable is such that the wind, whatever the direction of its mo-tion, is turned to the right in the Northern Hemisphere and to the left in the Southern.

The circulation of the air is also affected by mountains, hills, trees, buildings and other irregularities, natural and man-made, upon the earth's surface. On a more or less level plain, where such obstructions are fewest, the winds sweep across the surface of the earth with the greatest regularity. Within a big city, with its innumerable buildings of different heights, the force of the winds is broken and there are many capricious eddies. The higher above the earth's surface the winds are, the less they are affected by the features of the landscape — the topographical features, to use the technical term.

The friction that air motion meets at the earth's surface causes eddies and other irregularities, which are called turbulence. The erratic course of smoke pouring from a chimney may follow a general direction, but it will continually swerve from it. Weather observers ignore turbulence in most calculations. They are interested in the average speed and direction of the wind and not in the innumerable deviations from that speed and direction. In aviation forecasts, however, turbulence is carefully indicated, for it is an important factor. It accounts for the existence of air pockets, which may cause an airplane to suddenly dip or rise, to the great discomfort of the passengers. In fact, if the turbulence is unusually severe, it may be dangerous.

How winds are measured

It is all very well to indicate in a general way, as we have done, the various factors that cause the circulation of the air to be what it is. We would not be able to study the winds effectively, however, unless we could determine accurately their direction and speed and the changes in atmospheric pressure caused by their circulation. Fortunately, a number of devices supply us with this essential information.

At the surface of the earth, the direction of winds is indicated by wind vanes and their direction by anemometers. By following the drift of pilot balloons as they rise

THE BEAUFORT SCALE (for indicating wind velocity)

SCALE NUMBER	MILES PER HOUR	DESCRIPTION OF WIND	INDICATIONS ON LAND
0	0 to 1	Calm	Smoke goes straight up
1	1 to 3	Light air	Smoke drifts
2	4 to 7	Slight breeze	Leaves rustle
3	8 to 12	Gentle breeze	Leaves and small twigs are in motion
4	13 to 18	Moderate breeze	Small branches move; dust and paper fly
5	19 to 24	Fresh breeze	Ripples on water; small trees sway
6	25 to 31	Strong breeze	Large branches move
7	32 to 38	High wind	The trunks of trees bend; walking is difficult
8	39 to 46	Gale	Twigs are broken off
9	47 to 54	Strong gale	Chimneys and shingles are carried away
10	55 to 63	Whole gale	Trees may be uprooted
11	64 to 75	Storm	Damage is widespread
12	Over 75	Hurricane	Any disaster may be expected

Large-scale movements of winds over the earth's surface. The wind belts named here are described in the text.

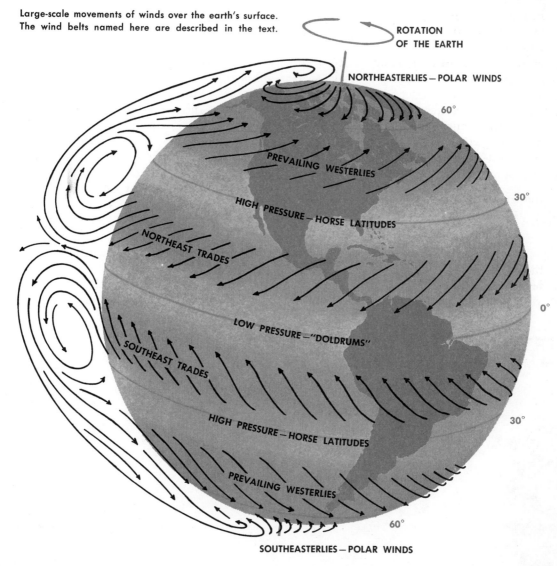

93

in the atmosphere, observers can determine the direction and speed of winds at upper levels. Rawinsondes — pilot balloons carrying radar targets — can be tracked by radar even when they rise above the clouds and are invisible from the earth. The pressure of the air at the earth's surface is indicated by the instrument called the barometer. Pressure in the upper air is measured by a balloon-borne device called the radiosonde. (It also measures temperature and humidity.) All these devices are described in detail in the article on The Weather Problem in Volume 1.

The Beaufort wind scale is often used to indicate wind velocity. This scale was introduced by Sir Francis Beaufort, an English admiral, in the first decade of the nineteenth century. He based it on the force with which the wind blew on the sails of a vessel. He divided winds into thirteen different classes on the basis of their speed and gave a code number — from 0 through 12 — to each. Later this scale was applied to a definite range of wind speeds and it has been used widely ever since. The Beaufort wind scale is given on the preceding page of this article.

The wind belts
of the earth

If we record our observations of the winds over a period of years, we find that there are certain definite large-scale wind belts: areas where the winds follow the same general direction for months at a time.

These belts are the doldrums, the trades and antitrades, the horse latitudes, the westerlies and the polar winds.

The doldrums. You will recall that at the equator the warm air is constantly ascending. This causes an equatorial belt of low pressure, in which calms alternate with variable winds. The name "doldrums" is given to this low-pressure belt. The word is probably akin to the English word "dull," and it means "a state of listlessness or boredom." As applied to the equatorial wind belt, the name goes back to the days of sailing ships, when it was most important to have favoring winds. Ships' captains were "in the doldrums" in this wind belt, where ships might lie becalmed for weeks.

The trades and antitrades. To the north of the doldrums in the Northern Hemisphere and to the south in the Southern Hemisphere we find the trade winds. They represent the surface flow of air from the poles to the equator — a flow which the rotation of the earth deflects to the right in the Northern Hemisphere and to the left in the Southern. In the Northern Hemisphere, the trade winds blow from the northeast to the southwest and therefore are called the northeast trades. (A wind gets its name from the direction from which it is blowing.) In the Southern Hemisphere, the trade winds blow from the southeast to the northwest and therefore are called the southeast trades.

The trades are generally steadier in direction than any other winds. The word

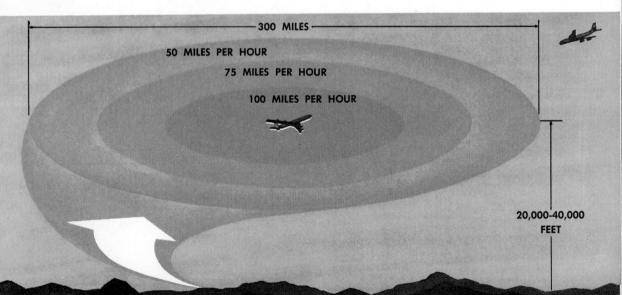

300 MILES

50 MILES PER HOUR

75 MILES PER HOUR

100 MILES PER HOUR

20,000-40,000 FEET

"trade" in this case has nothing to do with business or commerce, but is used in the older meaning of "path" or "course." Trade winds are so called because they keep to a pretty straight course. Yet even these winds are not absolutely reliable; they sometimes shift their direction temporarily. They blow more regularly over the oceans, especially the Atlantic, than over the land.

Since the prefix "anti" means opposite, you might gather that the antitrades blow in the opposite direction from the trades — and that is exactly what happens. The antitrades are winds in higher levels of the atmosphere above the trade winds. They represent the outflow aloft from the equator toward the poles — an outflow that is turned in a general direction toward the east. The antitrades blow from the southwest in the Northern Hemisphere and from the northwest in the Southern Hemisphere.

The horse latitudes. Beyond the trades we find a belt where, as in the doldrums, calms alternate with baffling winds — the horse latitudes, or subtropical high-pressure belts. They are centered about latitudes 30° north and 30° south. Since the air is descending in this high-pressure area, surface winds are often absent; when the wind blows, it is irregular and weak. Various explanations of the name "horse latitudes" have been offered. According to one explanation, vessels carrying horses from Europe to the West Indies in colonial days were sometimes becalmed so long that the horses's feed and water gave out, and the animals had to be thrown overboard. Another theory has it that the horses succumbed because they could not stand the unfavorable conditions in this wind belt.

The westerlies. Still farther removed from the equator we find the winds known as the prevailing westerlies. In this belt the winds tend to blow poleward but are turned by the earth's rotation. In the Northern Hemisphere they become southwest or west winds, and in the Southern Hemisphere, northwest or west winds. They are particularly strong over the ocean. Since there is more ocean area in the Southern Hemisphere than in the Northern, prevailing westerlies in that area are so boisterous that the region over which they blow (between latitudes 40° south and 50° south) is known as the roaring forties.

The polar winds. The belts of the polar winds tend to blow from the usually cold areas at the poles toward the equator, but they are turned by the earth's rotation. They become northeast winds in the Northern Hemisphere and southeast winds in the Southern. They are sometimes called northeasterlies and southeasterlies, respectively.

There are important changes in the wind belts in the course of the year. These changes are due to alternation of the seasons and the resulting differences in the rates of heating and cooling of landmasses and ocean areas.

Jet streams. Meteorologists (weather experts) have discovered that swift westerly winds flow in a band several hundred miles

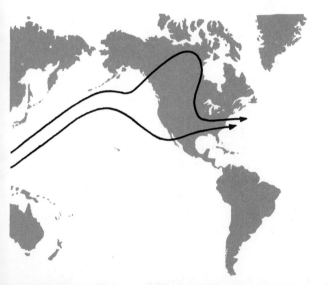

Jet streams are rapid westerly winds flowing in bands several hundred miles wide. At the left is a cross section of a typical jet stream. The figures we give here are only approximate; actually, there are numerous variations in height above the ground and also in wind speed. Eastward-bound planes fly deliberately into jet streams in order to take advantage of the favorable winds. Westward-bound planes dodge the jets so as to avoid the head winds they would encounter in these swift rivers of air.

wide at heights of from 20,000 feet to 40,000 feet above the earth's surface. These currents are aptly called jet streams, or jets; they are really swift jets of air that move faster than the air on either side or above them or below them. The average speed of the air in the core, or central part, is 100 miles or so in the winter and 50 miles in the summer; but speeds of over 250 miles per hour have been observed. The speed of the currents making up a jet stream decreases outward from the core. The number and paths of the jets vary from week to week and sometimes from day to day. The strongest jets, in the Northern Hemisphere, flow across Japan and the United States.

Jet streams tend to move over certain areas at certain times. In winter, for example, they are frequently discovered over the region extending along the coast of the Gulf of Mexico up through the Carolinas. In the summer, they are seldom found over that region but are common over and north of the Great Lakes. Thus they migrate with the seasons — northward in summer, southward in winter.

The jet streams play an important part in weather changes. For example, jets moving northward tend to pull masses of warm air with them; as they flow south, they pull the cold air from the arctic regions into the temperate zones. Meteorologists plot the course of the jet streams, and thus obtain information about prospective movements of invading air masses.

Flying schedules for high-flying planes must take account of jet streams. Pilots of eastward-bound planes deliberately fly into jets in order to take advantage of the favorable winds, which will add greatly to their flying speeds. Westward-bound pilots, however, dodge the jets in order to avoid the head winds they would encounter in these swift currents of air.

Local and
regional winds

The prevailing winds blow over huge areas of the earth's surface. There are also many local winds, which blow fairly steadily for considerable periods of time over comparatively small local areas.

The circulation of air over mountain ranges is responsible for many local winds. The wind crossing the northern side of the Alps from the south in the winter and early spring is called the foehn. It loses most of its water vapor as it ascends the mountain slope; as this vapor is condensed, it may give rain or snow. When the foehn descends the opposite side of the slope, it has become warmer and very dry. The name foehn is applied to similar winds in other areas. The foehn of the Rocky Mountain area is called the chinook; it blows from west to east, warming and drying the prairies that lie east of the Rockies.

In the Adriatic region, we find the dreaded bora, which makes itself felt particularly along the shores of Dalmatia. The bora is a cold northwesterly wind. It is caused by the cold and dense air of the mountains making its way to the sea, where the air is warmer and less dense.

The wind known as the mistral prevails more than a hundred days a year in the lower Rhone Valley. When this wind blows, the skies are generally cloudless, the atmosphere is dry and the cold is biting. Sometimes the mistral is very violent.

The winds blowing from the Sahara Desert have been given different local names. Among the most noted of these winds is the hot and dust-laden simoom, or simoon, which blows in Arabia and Syria and other lands of the eastern Mediterranean area. Another wind from the Sahara is the harmattan, which makes itself felt along the Atlantic coast of Africa. The sirocco, a hot wind from the Libian deserts, blows over Malta, Sicily and Italy.

Air masses
and fronts

The prevailing and local winds that we have just described follow roughly a course that will not vary greatly from one season to the next. But other systems of air circulation are quite erratic. These are movements of cold and warm air masses, which form over different areas of the earth's surface and which travel great distances.

The air masses in question differ according to the source regions — that is, the areas over which they form. The circulation of the atmosphere may cause air to linger over the tropical oceans. As a result, the air mass becomes warm and moist; it is called tropical maritime. An air mass that originates over land in the tropics is known as tropical continental. Polar continental air masses form over the snow-covered lands of the polar regions; polar maritime masses, over the polar oceans. All these masses retain their characteristics for a long time after moving away from their source regions.

The boundaries between air masses are known as fronts. The boundary of relatively cold air of polar origin, advancing into an area occupied by warmer air, usually of tropical origin, is called a cold front. When relatively warm air advances into an area occupied by colder air, it causes a warm front to form. When a cold front overtakes a warm front and displaces it completely at the earth's surface, forcing it upward, the two fronts are combined to form an occluded front. Sometimes two air masses remain in contact for some time without encroaching upon one another. The boundary between two such masses is called a stationary front. On this page, we give the symbols for these fronts as shown on printed weather maps.

Cyclones and anticyclones

When two contrasting air masses meet, the air currents flowing along their front generally move in opposite directions. The

WARM FRONT	
COLD FRONT	
OCCLUDED FRONT	
STATIONARY FRONT	
UPPER WARM FRONT	
UPPER COLD FRONT	

Left: the symbols for the different fronts (that is, boundaries between air masses), as presented in weather maps. Below: how the fronts appeared in a typical weather map prepared by the United States Weather Bureau.

U. S. Weather Bureau

The map at the left, above, shows the day-by-day progress of the hurricane called Donna, from the day it reached the West Indies, September 4, 1960, until it passed over the Maine border into Canada's maritime provinces. Right, above: wreckage of buildings in Humacao, Puerto Rico, after the town had been devastated by Donna.

rotation of the earth will cause these currents to curve. They are then apt to form a gigantic vortex, or whirl, with the winds spiraling toward a low-pressure area at the center. The resulting wind system is known as a cyclone. Some cyclones move, roughly at least, in a circle; others describe an ellipse, while still others form irregular patterns. The winds of a cyclone system turn counterclockwise in the Northern Hemisphere and clockwise in the Southern.

Sometimes the winds flowing outward from a high-pressure area in the center of an air mass are curved by the rotation of the earth so as to form a rotating wind system known as an anticyclone. These winds spin in the opposite direction from those that make up a cyclone: that is, they turn clockwise in the Northern Hemisphere and counterclockwise in the Southern.

In 1857, the Dutch meteorologist Christoph H. D. Buys Ballot gave a rule for determining air pressure, as applied to cyclonic and anticyclonic circulation. Here is the rule, stated in his own words: "Stand with your back to the wind and in the Northern Hemisphere pressure will be lower on your left hand than on your right, while in the Southern Hemisphere the reverse will be true."

Both cyclones and anticyclones are traveling wind systems. They may be compared to spinning tops; they have a rotary motion as they move from place to place. Cyclones are sometimes called lows because their winds move toward a low-pressure area at the center; anticyclones are sometimes called highs because their winds move out from a high-pressure center.

In the normal course of events, when a cyclone moves out of a given area in the middle latitudes, it is followed by an anticyclone; the anticyclone in turn is followed by a cyclone. In the United States, this cycle may be completed in four or five days. The shifts between cyclones and anticyclones bring about various changes in the weather. Cloudiness and rain or snow will be followed by clearing skies and colder weather.

The most violent winds are all of the cyclone type. Among these are the hurri-

Pictures on these two pages, Wide World

Above: the funnel of a tornado approaching the city of Dallas (April 3, 1957). This tornado killed eight persons, injured many others and caused widespread damage. Right: after the passing of the tornado. Note the strips of metal roofing blown and wrapped around the tree.

canes, or tropical cyclones, so called because they arise in tropical or subtropical regions. They are particularly frequent in the Caribbean Sea, the Gulf of Mexico in the western Pacific, off the east and west coasts of India, east of southern Africa and north of Australia. The tropical cyclones of the western Pacific are known as typhoons; those of India are called cyclones.

We have already compared a cyclone to a top, spinning rapidly as it advances slowly. The destructive effect of hurricanes is due chiefly to this spinning motion, which may reach a speed of more than one hundred miles an hour. The forward movement of the hurricane in low latitudes is comparatively slow — usually from ten to fifteen miles an hour.

Sometimes a hurricane causes great damage. Trees may be uprooted and frame houses crushed like matchwood. People who happen to be out of doors during such a storm run great danger of being battered to the ground or of being struck by flying fragments of all kinds. Along the coast, hurricanes often pile up the surface waters and cause disastrous waves, which submerge the land sometimes to a depth of ten feet and more. Hurricanes can severely batter the stoutest ocean liners; they often overwhelm smaller ships.

Despite the destructive force of the outer area of the hurricane, the wind is calm at its eye, or center. That is why a hurricane may seem to strike a double blow in some places. First, there are the raging winds in the van of the hurricane; then the relative calm of the eye; finally, after the eye passes, the violence of the winds that make up the rear guard.

Fortunately, much progress has been made in giving timely warning of a hurricane's approach. Particularly effective warning is provided by hurricane reconnaissance aircraft, equipped with radar and many meteorological instruments. These planes search for hurricanes in suspected areas. When the characteristic whirling cloud formation has been spotted on the radar screen of one of the planes, the craft will fly right into the hurricane. Thus it will be able to obtain exact information about the extent of the hurricane, its course and the speed with which it is advancing. This information will then be radioed to ground stations. An important advance in the spotting of hurricanes has been contributed by the Tiros weather satellites, constructed for the National Aeronautics and Space Administration (NASA). These satellites, orbiting far above the surface of the earth, transmit to earth television pictures of cloud formations over wide areas. Thus they provide warning of hurricanes in their early stages.

The cyclones that occur outside of the tropics — the extratropical (out-of-tropics) cyclones — are usually rather mild wind systems. There are exceptions, however. Sometimes a cyclone, in combination with an anticyclone, develops great force. It may cause a cold wave or a blizzard, a gale with heavy rain or heavy snow or a local storm.

The local type of cyclone known as a tornado, or twister, is particularly destructive. Like all cyclones, it arises along the front of opposing air masses; there are very strong air currents flowing in opposite directions along the front at lower cloud levels. If an updraft of warm air is carried aloft at some place along this wind front, a whirl is formed, drawing its force from the opposite winds and spinning dizzily around the low-pressure area represented by the updraft.

As the winds revolve around the low-pressure center, they may reach speeds of from two hundred to three hundred miles an hour. Finally a spinning, funnel-shaped cloud makes its way to the earth. As the narrow end of the funnel sweeps along the ground, it strews destruction in its wake. Sometimes the funnel narrows so that it assumes the appearance of a dangling rope. At other times it passes by at a height of fifty feet or more above the ground, sparing the objects under it.

The path of destruction is very narrow, compared to that of a hurricane; it ranges from five yards to about a thousand and it averages a few hundred yards. Yet within its path a tornado is even more destructive than a hurricane. The raging winds flatten houses and strip the ground of its vegetation; they drive stones through brick walls; sometimes they carry men and animals aloft as if they were straws. Tornadoes are most frequent in the United States; they occur particularly in the southern and western areas.

A tornado at sea is called a waterspout. As its funnel reaches the surface of the ocean, the water is sucked up, forming a whirling spray fountain which may reach a height of fifty feet or more. Waterspouts are far less destructive than tornadoes for the simple reason that there is less to destroy at sea than on land. Since they can be seen from great distances and travel slowly, it is comparatively easy to avoid them, in daylight at least.

Major changes in the circulation

In addition to all the variations in the circulation of the air that we have considered, certain large-scale changes make themselves felt from year to year and from decade to decade. For several years in succession there is more air in the Northern Hemisphere than in the Southern. Following this period there is a greater-than-average accumulation of air in the Southern Hemisphere. We do not completely understand these changes. They seem to be related to small but widespread temperature differences over the vast ocean surfaces.

Long-term changes in the circulation of the atmosphere seem to be associated with periods of warm and dry years alternating with periods of cold and wet years. Successful weather forecasts for months and seasons are not likely until the weatherman learns more about these cycles.

In the past generation or two, meteorologists have been steadily filling in the gaps in our knowledge of the wind belts of the earth and the day-to-day, seasonal and long-term changes that are so important to mankind. Yet more data must be made available, particularly about conditions in the upper atmosphere, before we can consider ourselves well informed about the different phases of the subject.

See also Vol. 10, p. 271: "Weather and Climate."

SHELL COLLECTING

A Fascinating Hobby Based on the Mollusks

BY WILLIAM D. CLARKE

IF YOU have ever walked along the shore at a beach, it is altogether likely that you have picked up shells that caught your fancy because of their unusual shape or coloring. If your case is typical, you threw away your finds after a few hours, or days or weeks. Some persons, however, have made an interesting and instructive hobby of shell collecting; they have found many hours of pleasure and relaxation in arranging their finds systematically and in adding new and striking specimens. It is by no means difficult to build up a fine shell collection, for along the coasts of North America alone there are over a thousand different kinds.

Shells are produced by a wide variety of the soft-bodied animals that are called mollusks. (See the article The Mollusks, in Volume 2.) The two groups of mollusks whose shells are most often collected are the gastropods and the lamellibranchs. The gastropods, of which the garden snail is an example, can generally be recognized by the spirally coiled shells. They are also known as the univalves, because they have only one valve or shell.

There is an amazingly wide variety of gastropod shells, which include some of the finest and rarest specimens. Cone shells and cowries have always been popular with collectors because of their lovely shapes and colors and their smooth texture, suggesting that of porcelain. Unfortunately they are not too often seen along the coasts of North America. Other gastropods with beautiful shells are found only in certain areas of this continent. Among these are the abalones, which occur along the west coast, and the beautiful conchs, which are often washed up on the beaches of Florida. Certain species of snails and limpets have a far more widespread distribution, and their shells offer considerable interest to the collector.

The lamellibranchs, also known as the bivalves, of which the oysters and clams are examples, have two shells or valves. They are found in considerable variety along the coasts of North America, particularly in the southern areas. The pectens, or scallops, are undoubtedly the most varied and colorful bivalves to be found along the southern and eastern coasts. Because of the bright colors and varied forms of their shells, they are much sought after by shell collectors. A number of pecten species are found only in deep water;

GASTROPODS

European garden snail.

Periwinkle.

Turret shell.

Cowrie.

Cowrie.

Spindle shell.

Abalone.

Volute.

Volute.

they are most often brought in by shrimp fishermen from the deep waters of the Gulf of Mexico. Collectors also treasure such bivalve shells as the delicate rising-sun shells, or tellinas, and the large, spectacular pen shells, or pinnids.

Another group of mollusks, the chitons, are sometimes collected for their interesting shells. The shell of a typical chiton consists of eight overlapping plates; it is sometimes called a coat-of-mail shell, because it suggests a type of armor worn by medieval knights. Though a few kinds of chitons are found along various rocky coasts in North America, they are most abundant and varied on the shores of California. The shells of some chitons are remarkably colored; but because of the retiring nature of these animals, they are often overlooked by collectors.

The shells of two other mollusk groups, the cephalopods and the scaphopods, are occasionally collected, but because of their relative rarity they are not common in collections. The squid is a cephalopod with a small, weakly developed internal shell. The common squid of Europe — the cuttlefish — secretes an internal, calcified shell commonly known to bird fanciers as cuttlebone; it is fed to canaries as a source of lime. The shells of two other cephalopods — the chambered nautilus and the paper nautilus — are large and beautiful. They are only occasionally found washed up onto the ocean shores.

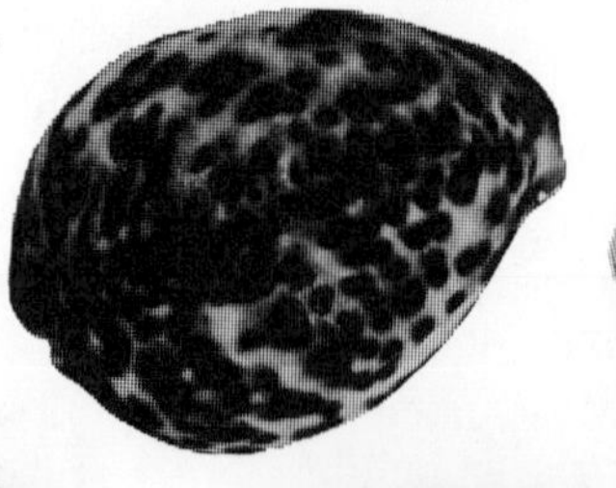

The scaphopods, also called the tusk shells, are small mollusks that live buried in sand and mud. They are rarely found in shallow water; they are most often discovered when they are washed up on shore after storms. The shells of scaphopods have a striking resemblance to the tusks of elephants. The shells were once used as wampum (money) by the Indians of the Northwest Pacific coastal areas.

Where and how
to collect shells

Shells are commonly found along all sandy beaches; some beaches, however, are better collecting areas than others. The shell collector finds a greater variety and number of shells after storms, because the heavy wave action sweeps up many mollusks living on the sea bottom in deeper water. There are certain disadvantages, to be sure, in collecting on the beach. Most shells that have been washed up there are generally somewhat beach-worn because of the grinding action of the sand. Besides, as the shells are tumbled about by the waves, some of the more delicate ones chip and break. However, by careful searching, you will be able to find nearly perfect specimens.

At low tide sheltered beaches and mud flats are fine places to hunt for various clams and snails. If you look carefully about on the surface of the beach or mud

BIVALVES

Scallop.

Cockle.

Pen shell.

Clam.

Pearl oyster.

Paper nautilus
(a cephalopod).

All photos,
Amer. Mus. of Nat. Hist.

Tusk shells
(scaphopods).

flat exposed by the receding tide, you will see numerous small, paired holes, from which a jet of water will occasionally squirt. These are the tips of the siphons of clams that live buried in the sand or mud. The siphons are tubelike organs through which the clams feed and breathe. Once the siphons of a clam have been located, the animal must be dug out. It is quite a simple matter to dig up some of the smaller clams with a shovel. In the case of the larger and more active clams, a good deal of experience and some pretty hard work are required.

You need only a rock hammer, knife and plastic bag to collect mollusks.

A very good way to hunt small clams and snails that live in mud or fine sand is to use a sieve with a rather coarse mesh. Put a shovelful of mud or sand in it; after the finer silts and sands have passed through the sieve, a fair number of clams or snails may be revealed.

On open beaches where there is a strong surf, clams can usually be found in the area where the waves are breaking. If you watch the bottom closely you can often catch glimpses of clams plowing through the sand, as the waves sweep in and out. By quickly digging with the hands or using a clam rake, you will be able to obtain good specimens from this wave-washed zone.

You will find many shells if you visit the sheltered sand beach of a bay at night. If you wade through the shallow water and follow the trails on the bottom with the aid of a flashlight, you will be able to find many curious snails. Olive snails and moon snails are frequently found on such beaches. It is much better to collect in this way at night than during the day, since so many more mollusks are active at night.

Mollusks are abundant on rocky shores. These areas are best visited at low tide, since it is possible to collect in places that normally are covered with water. All you need in the way of collecting equipment are a couple of plastic bags or other plastic containers, a knife and a rock hammer (mason's hammer). Do not use glass jars to hold your collection, since these are too easily broken.

On the exposed surfaces of rocks, along cracks and in depressions or holes you will find periwinkles, limpets, turban shells (turbinids), chitons, mussels, dog whelks and many others. You can remove limpets and chitons from the rocks with a knife; slip the blade quickly under the mollusk and lift. Without a knife it is very hard to collect these animals, since they can hang on to rock with amazing power. You will find other interesting shelled mollusks by searching through the seaweed in tide pools and looking along the bottoms of the pools.

When you turn over large rocks, you will come upon a variety of mollusks. Some kinds of limpets and other mollusks live only on the underside of rocks. Put the rocks back in place after you have collected your specimens; otherwise you may spoil the area for those who may want to gather shells there in the future. You will often encounter several interesting types of rock-boring clams if you break a rock open with a hammer. These clams are found in comparatively soft rocks that are exposed only at low tide. The clams work their way into rock either by grinding it away with their shells or else by secreting acids that dissolve the rock.

To collect shells most effectively in deeper water, it is best to work with a face mask, snorkel and swim fins. Use either plastic bags or canvas bags to hold your specimens. By diving down eight or ten feet at low tide you will open up a whole new collecting area. You will come upon many kinds of mollusks that are rarely found along the shore. Not all these animals will be plainly in sight; it may be necessary to turn over rocks and to examine sea fans and sea whips. Some small scallops and other bivalves hide in sponges. The large seaweeds found along the Californian coasts harbor some interesting mollusks.

Not all mollusks are to be found in the ocean; a considerable number live in lakes, rivers and ponds. There are several families of fresh-water clams, of which the family called the Unionidae is an example. Water snails are usually found in any permanent body of water; they are particularly common on aquatic plants and on rocks covered with algae. Most of the water snails are rather dull in color, but quite varied in size and shape.

The land snails are an interesting group; the shells of these animals are often very beautiful. A great variety can be collected in Florida and several other states in the southern part of the United States. It is best to hunt land snails at night with a flashlight, especially after there has been a heavy rain. At that time the snails are particularly abundant; they feed busily on vegetation or crawl through the leaf litter on the ground. During the day the best place to look for these snails is under stones and logs, if the soil is moist. As a matter of fact, you will usually find them in any damp place where there is a variety of flourishing plants.

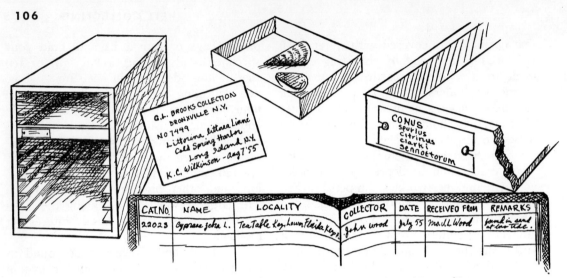

A study collection of shells should be properly labeled, catalogued and housed in a cabinet.

How to prepare
a shell collection

Some of the shells found along the beach will require no preparation whatsoever. A great number, however, will still be inhabited by their mollusk owners. The vast majority of these shells can be cleaned of their soft parts by boiling them in water for several minutes and then removing the animal with a pin or other pointed object. This method does not always work, since in some cases the meat sticks firmly to the shell. It then becomes necessary to soak the shells a few days in warm water; this generally causes the meat to rot away. Some collectors use ants and beetle larvae to clean the shells of all traces of fleshy material.

Shells such as cone shells and cowries, which have a glossy, porcelainlike finish, should never be thrown into boiling water. A sudden change in temperature will cause the surface to crack and will destroy its beauty. It is best to place such shells in warm water, heat them gradually and then allow them to cool in the same water. Some shells are covered with growths of coral and algae. These growths can usually be scrubbed off with a good stiff brush and soapy water.

Shells can be collected for a small display or for other decorative purposes. If you are a serious collector, however, it is much better to group the shells scientifically, according to family. In this way, particularly if you collect steadily and read up on your hobby, you will learn a great deal about these interesting animals.

It is advisable to keep shells in a cabinet that has many shallow drawers, about two inches deep. Shells of the same kind are placed in a flat open cardboard box with the appropriate label; they should be kept in the same drawer with other closely related species. Specimens must be labeled if the collection is to have any scientific value. Three important details should be included on every label; the place where the shell was collected, the date of collection and the kind of shell. By following these simple rules you will soon have an interesting collection.

The beginner will find the following handbooks and field guides on shell collecting particularly useful, since by using them he will be able to identify many of the specimens he may find:

ROBERT TUCKER ABBOTT, *Introducing Seashells;* Van Nostrand, New York, 1955.

PERCY A. MORRIS, *Field Guide to the Shells of Our Atlantic and Gulf Coasts;* Houghton Mifflin, Boston, 1951 (No. 3 in The Peterson Field Guide Series).

—— *Field Guide to Shells of the Pacific Coast and Hawaii;* Houghton Mifflin, Boston, 1952 (No. 6 in The Peterson Field Guide Series).

THE FOREST INDUSTRIES

How Man Uses One of His Most Precious Resources

WOOD has been supplanted by other materials for so many purposes nowadays that it might seem at first glance as though we were becoming independent of the forests in which our ancestors lived. Coal and gas and oil have largely replaced wood as fuel, except in rural areas; the use of wood in the fireplaces of modern homes generally represents a luxury and not a serious effort to supplement other fuels. The great sailing ships, for which vast forests were once cut down, have been replaced almost entirely by ships of steel. Wood is still widely used in some countries, including the United States and Canada, for the construction of private homes, but other materials are coming to the fore increasingly for this purpose. For example, the outer walls of many private dwellings are now made by pouring concrete into molds; laths made of metal are used quite often to replace wooden laths for the interior of houses. Of course, large buildings are not constructed of wood but of steel, stone, brick, concrete and other fire-resistant materials. Wood is still used on a large scale for furniture; but other materials, particularly metals and plastics, have become exceedingly popular.

All this might lead one to think that wood is becoming less and less important in modern life. Exactly the contrary is true; never has the demand for this natural resource been so widespread. It serves a great variety of purposes in addition to those that we have listed above. Vast quantities of trees are felled annually in order to meet the insatiable demands of the paper industry. There is a vast market for plywoods and veneers, bonded together by synthetic resins. Timber is also in great demand for railroad ties and telegraph and telephone poles; for false work used in underground and steel construction; for molds for concrete; for packing cases. Mining companies, in particular, use great quantities of timber. Wherever mining is carried on underground, it is necessary to shore up the walls and ceilings of tunnels and galleries with timber to keep them from caving in.

As a result of the incessant demands upon the timber industry, vast areas in North America and elsewhere have been entirely denuded of their forest resources. Fortunately, timber, unlike coal or oil, is a renewable resource: that is, new crops of trees can be grown to replace those that have been used up.

In the United States, the Government and many farsighted individual owners of forest areas have already done much to replenish the denuded timber lands. Private forests and tree farms are now being cultivated to provide new crops of timber. Many millions of acres in the United States are devoted to the production of this commodity. The problem of conserving timber supplies is not nearly so acute in Canada as in the United States, but the Government has taken steps to assure the conservation of Canada's vast forests. Forest resources as a whole are owned and administered by the provinces; the Federal Government is responsible for the administration of forest areas included in the national parks, the forest experimental stations and Yukon and the Northwest territories. Under the system adopted by both the federal and provincial governments, the state generally retains ownership of the land and control of all cutting operations.

Chemical science has found many uses for timber and other products of the tree.

This grove of giant redwood trees is located in Humboldt County, California. More than 70,000 acres of such stands are set aside for public use.

California Redwood Association

As a matter of fact, products other than lumber make up about one half of the total volume of wood annually harvested from American forests.

When the trunks of several species of pine are tapped, they yield pitch, from which turpentine and rosin are distilled. This process is not necessarily fatal to the tree. Various other processes, however, require its complete destruction.

From cellulose, derived from raw timber, comes a vast variety of products—surgical dressings, ammunition, wallboard for building, celluloids, plastics, and solid alcohol. Cellulose also yields rayon yarns, which closely resemble such natural fibers as linen and silk when they are made into fabrics. Cellulose fermentation gives butyl and various other alcohols, acetic, lactic, propionic and butyric acids, and acetone. From lignin waste, a product related to cellulose, we get tanning materials, fertilizers, dyestuffs and oxalic acid.

When wood is decomposed chemically, it gives sugar, food for livestock and ethyl alcohol. Charcoal, methyl alcohol, acetic acid, wood creosote, acetone and wood pitch are obtained by the dry distillation of wood. Steam distillation and extraction produces the so-called naval stores — turpentine, pine oils and rosin. Turpentine is used in paint, varnish, synthetic camphor and solvents; pine oils, in cleaning compounds, disinfectants, ore flotation and the textile industry; rosin, in varnish, soap, linoleum, adhesives, greases and matches.

Volatile oils and tannins are other important industrial products made from wood. Wood flour, which is finely powdered wood, or sawdust, is used in making plastics, linoleum and explosives, and also in tinplate polishing and cleaning.

There seems to be no limit to the useful possibilities of the products of the forest. At the present time, however, not just waste wood, stumps and small limbs are being used up in various industrial processes, but much valuable timber, too. This is a very serious matter when we remember that wood is indispensable to modern industry.

Apart from its use as lumber and as fuel, wood is important today chiefly because it is employed in papermaking. Ninety per

mands are being made on the Canadian forests to supply the deficiency. So far, no adequate substitute for wood for papermaking processes has been discovered.

Present demand is far in excess of any natural processes of growth, for even small trees take years to grow. The United States government is replanting vast tracts of treeless land with seedlings, and seedlings are free for the asking to landowners who will set them in their cut-over prop-

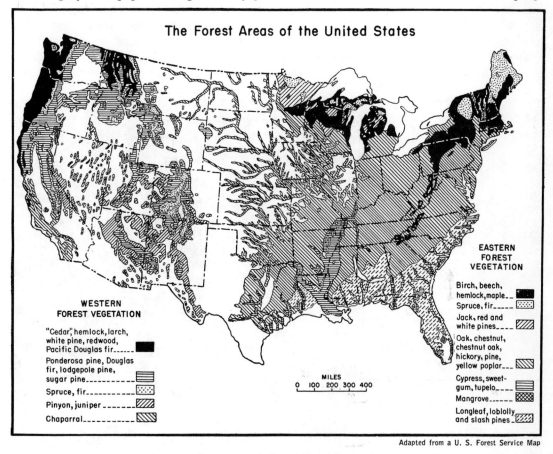

The Forest Areas of the United States

WESTERN FOREST VEGETATION

"Cedar", hemlock, larch, white pine, redwood, Pacific Douglas fir_____
Ponderosa pine, Douglas fir, lodgepole pine, sugar pine_____
Spruce, fir_____
Pinyon, juniper _____
Chaparral_____

MILES
0 100 200 300 400

EASTERN FOREST VEGETATION

Birch, beech, hemlock, maple___
Spruce, fir_____
Jack, red and white pines_____
Oak, chestnut, chestnut oak, hickory, pine, yellow poplar___
Cypress, sweet-gum, tupelo_____
Mangrove_____
Longleaf, loblolly and slash pines_____

Adapted from a U. S. Forest Service Map

This map will give a good idea of the great extent and variety of America's forest areas.

cent of all paper used in the United States is made entirely or in part from wood pulp. Vast forests are being leveled to satisfy the ever-increasing demand for pulp for paper. The worst feature of this particular use of wood is that so much goes to waste. Paper is used extravagantly, and little effort is made to collect and rework the old material. The forests of the United States that are available for pulpwood are rapidly becoming exhausted, and great de-

erty. However, more and more Americans must become aware of the necessity of protecting their forest heritage if it is to continue to be a national asset.

At the beginning of the colonial period in what is now the United States, the forests were unequalled in extent and value by those possessed by any other civilized country. (Canada was almost as fortunate in the size of her forested area, but not so fortunate in the variety of her trees.)

From the Atlantic to the Mississippi and from Georgia almost up to Hudson Bay stretched an enormous forest of white pine, spruce, hemlock, cedar, balsam fir, birch, cherry, maple and other kinds of trees. Toward the south there was another immense forest stretching along the eastern coast from New Jersey to Mexico and covering large parts of Delaware and Maryland, as well as Virginia, the Carolinas and other states of the South. This forest was largely coniferous, yellow pine predominating; but it also included cypress, magnolia, poplar, oak and other hardwoods.

Between the northern and southern forests and merging into them on either side

As a matter of fact, there are still immense timber tracts extending from Alaska to San Francisco and covering much of the country from the sea to the snow line of the coastal mountains. In British Columbia, Washington and Oregon, they consist mostly of Douglas fir, with cedar, spruce and some hardwood trees, all of them of great size compared to those of the same kind elsewhere. The Douglas fir frequently grows to a height of 300 feet or more, and a diameter of 10 to 12 feet is not uncommon. The great trunks rise from the ground as straight as arrows, and the lowest limb is usually 90 to 100 feet from the ground. North of Monterey, Cali-

American Forest Products Industries, Inc.

Sixty-year-old fir, marked with a white tag to show that it has been selected for harvest.

was a great hardwood forest containing vast growths of walnut, elm, oak, maple, cottonwood, hickory, basswood, chestnut, ash and sycamore. The slopes of the Rocky Mountains were covered with magnificent conifers, including fir, yellow pine, red cedar and other valuable woods.

On the Pacific slopes nature elected to plant forests the like of which, perhaps, was not to be found elsewhere in the world.

fornia, along the coast to southern Oregon are forests of tall, straight redwoods (*Sequoia sempervirens*). In these forests there is a profusion of smaller growths, such as shrubs and ferns, giving these areas an almost tropical appearance.

Stands of large and valuable pine trees are to be found on the upper slopes of the Sierra Nevada range in California. This big western state also boasts of the larg-

Massive equipment is necessary to handle the logs cut from giant redwood trees. Lumber cut from these trees is noted for its durability.

est trees in the world: *Sequoia gigantea,* allied to the redwoods, but much larger. They occur in groves, none of which number more than a few hundred trees. Practically all are preserved by the government for national parks. Here are trees over 300 feet high and 110 feet in circumference. These patriarchs of the forest are the oldest things living, some of them being at least 5,000 years old. They were husky saplings when Khufu went forth to build the Great Pyramid; they had bark a foot thick when Christ was born. Many other great events have taken place during their existence.

Such then are the forest resources of the United States. The original forests covered not less than 850,000,000 acres; they contained not less than 5,000,000,000,-000 feet of merchantable timber.

To the north of the United States lie the great evergreen forests of Canada, covering an area of something like 1,209,-000 square miles. Actually a third of this is useless timber. The unproductive areas are located on the northernmost fringe of the heavily forested area. In this region, the size of the trees, combined with their slow growth, gives them little economic value. The remaining two-thirds of the total forest area is productive. It extends over 800,000 square miles of territory. This is an area equivalent to that of Saudi Arabia. But only one-half of the productive forests are accessible to trucks or other transportation devices. The provinces of Quebec, British Columbia and Ontario contain the main body of the productive, accessible forests. Most of the trees in these forests — some 70 per cent — are evergreens. They furnish practically all the wood used in Canada. Today they support a lumber industry that is valued at something like $2,800,000,000.

The job of removing the trees from the forest has always required skill and courage. Modern engineering advances have produced better and safer methods. But in spite of all the newest machines, the ax is the logger's most important tool. He uses it for clearing the underbrush, for making the undercut and for removing the limbs of the tree. The professional woodsman of the north uses a double-edged ax. One edge is thin and sharp, for fast cutting. The other is thick and dull for harder cutting and for work around stones and soil. The art of chopping is easily mastered by most Canadians and Americans, who swing a club in many of their games. The lumberjack stands with his legs apart, his weight on the right leg. The right hand grips the ax just under its head. The left hand holds the base of the handle. The ax is held at shoulder level and is swung through a semicircular path to the point of impact. As the swing is in progress, the right hand slides down the handle to meet the left hand which is still at the base. The weight is also shifted to the left leg. It is not necessary to use much force in the blow, for accuracy is more important than strength.

Another important tool of the lumberman is the saw. The crosscut saw and the Swedish bow saw are the most common types of hand saws. Two men may operate the crosscut saw; one sawyer pulls his end while the other lets his hand ride back easily on the saw handle. Several kinds of power saws are also in use. Among these are the circular saws, drag saws and chain saws. Certain two-man chain saws can cut timber twelve feet in diameter. However, this type is used only in large-scale logging operations. In general, the circular saws and drag saws are used to cut the felled trees into shorter logs. This process is known as bucking.

The wedge is indispensable for the woodsman's work. It is a five-sided triangular block about seven inches long. The logger saws the wedge out of any nearby tree. Dogwood, ironwood and hard maple are preferred for this purpose. The wedge is used to tip the tree in the proper direction during felling, to split wood and to insert into the cut that has been produced by the saw.

To roll large hardwood logs about, the lumberman uses a peavy. This is a heavy wooden pole about four feet long. At the lower end there is a steel spike set in a steel collar. A large hook called a dog is hinged to the collar. A so-called pulp hook lifts shorter logs (called bolts) onto a pile. It is often useful in breaking ice-covered bolts loose from one another. The hook itself resembles one half of a pair of ice tongs.

There are six main processes involved in bringing the wood from the forest to the mill. These are felling, limbing, bucking, skidding, loading and hauling. All of these require strong men with a keen eye and a daring temperament.

These logs have been brought to the water's edge from the forest where they were cut; they will float downstream to the sawmill.

Weyerhaeuser Timber Co.

After selecting the tree to be cut the woodsman must decide in which direction to fell the tree. This depends on a number of factors. The tree must not fall on other trees with many dead branches. Such limbs may loosen and catapult back toward the cutters. They are rightfully called widow-makers. Nor must the tree become lodged in the branches of nearby trees during its fall. Among lumberjacks, this position of the fallen tree is called sky-hung. Half a day may be wasted getting the caught tree down. In addition, the felled tree should do as little damage as possible to young saplings surrounding it. It should not fall on any boulders or other obstacles. The tree may damage itself or it may thrash about unpredictably. Finally the tree must be dropped at a suitable angle to the slope of the hill. Trees that fall too far up the incline will kick back when they hit the ground. Those that fall too far down the slope are apt to break. Indeed, to fell a tree in the correct direction requires a great deal of judgment.

In order to bring a tree down in the desired place, an undercut is made in the side which is in the direction of the fall. The undercut is a wedge-shaped space at the base of the tree. It extends one quarter of the way into the tree trunk. To make the undercut the logger first saws horizontally into the tree. Then, with the ax, he chops diagonally into this cut until the desired pie-shaped space is obtained. When the undercut has been made, the backcut is started. The backcut is a horizontal slit, two inches above the base of the undercut. This second cut is placed on the side of the tree opposite to the direction of the expected fall. As the logger saws, he places wooden wedges in the part of the cut that lies behind the saw. This tips the tree and prevents pinching. (Unless a wedge is present, the extreme weight of the tree will press down and pinch the saw. This force would stop the sawing motion.) The logger does not saw all the way to the undercut. About two inches of wood are left uncut so that they may act as a hinge. The hinge helps to guide the tree in the proper direction. When the cutting is finished, the

saw is removed from the tree. All the lumbermen step back and the familiar cry — "timber-r-r" — rings through the woods.

After the tree has reached the ground, its limbs must be removed. This procedure is known as limbing. A power saw is used for the larger branches. The smaller ones are hewn off with an ax. All the limbs are cut off close to the tree trunk.

The process of cutting trees into logs or bolts is known as bucking. Standard sawlog lengths may vary with the area in which the trees grow. In the northeast log lengths are about sixteen feet. Much longer logs are handled in the northwest. Here, twenty-four to forty feet are the usual length, though forty-nine to sixty-five foot lengths are favored.

How the logs are transported

When the logs have been sawed, they are gathered together and sent down to a concentration point known as a landing. Transporting the logs down the mountainside is known as skidding. There are several ways to skid a log. In large logging operations, tractors are used to pull chained bundles of logs along the skid trail. Another method is high-lead skidding. The logs are carried aloft via a steel cable which may be strung across canyons or valleys. Dragging the log along the ground by means of an aerial cable is known as ground-line skidding.

Loading is simply piling the logs onto a truck or other means of transportation. Small wood may be loaded by hand. Generally, the logger uses the pulp hook as an extension of his right arm. He jams the hook into one end of the log. Picking the other end up with his left hand, he shoves the log onto the pile. Various mechanical devices may also be used.

The bottom of the pole is attached by a swivel to the base of a tree. The top of the pole, tied loosely to the tree by a cable, makes a thirty degree angle with the tree. Other cables, managed by pulleys, hoist the log onto the truck. The truck or railroad car hauls the log to the mill which is not too far away. It has always been the common practice to build the mill near the forest, or even within it. Logs are hauled to it on cars drawn by steam locomotives; the lumber is transported to the market in the same way. These mills generally operate all the year round; in a busy season they often run day and night.

In mountainous regions a timber slide or chute is built; down this the logs coast, sometimes into rivers or ponds. The finished products of inaccessible mills are sometimes brought out in a similar manner. A long flume is constructed at such an angle that the lumber is transported down the flume quite rapidly. The rate at which the lumber is fed to the flume must be carefully calculated in order to reduce the chances of serious jams.

Some of the most interesting methods of logging are now to be found in the great forests of the Pacific slope, where the trees that have been marked out for felling are unusually large. In the mild climate of this area, operations are carried on throughout the year.

At first the loggers adopted methods that were in common use elsewhere. They often used twelve or fourteen oxen, paired in six or seven yokes, to haul the logs out of the woods to the mills or to the water. For this purpose they frequently prepared so-called skid roads: they set partly sunken logs, called skids, across roads at intervals of about five feet. The name "skid road" came to be applied to the part of a town frequented by loggers.

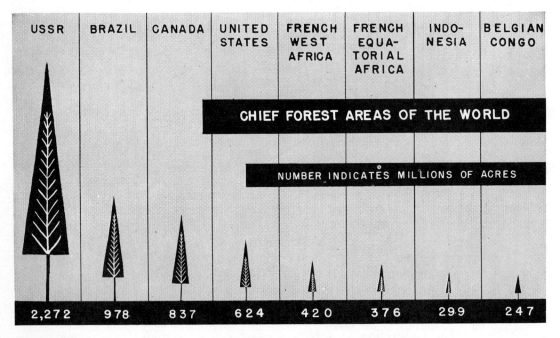

USSR	BRAZIL	CANADA	UNITED STATES	FRENCH WEST AFRICA	FRENCH EQUATORIAL AFRICA	INDONESIA	BELGIAN CONGO
2,272	978	837	624	420	376	299	247

CHIEF FOREST AREAS OF THE WORLD

NUMBER INDICATES MILLIONS OF ACRES

Acreages in the diagram are from the 1951 Yearbook of Forest Products Statistics published by the authority of the United Nations Food and Agriculture Organization.

The logs are often transported to the mills by barges; in the Great Lakes region, on the Pacific Coast, in Norway and in other areas, logs are often chained together and towed as great rafts. Such rafts have been successfully transported from the Columbia River to Californian ports. In some of the early attempts, the logs broke loose from the chains when struck by heavy seas and became a menace to shipping.

The bull punchers, as the drivers of ox teams were called, were decidedly picturesque characters. They were big of limb, muscular and wiry, and much addicted to colorful profanity. They were wont to encourage their straining teams to even greater efforts with sharp-pointed goads and with endless volleys of oaths.

But, like many other picturesque things, the bull puncher and his team have given way to machines. For a long time, in the western forests, the work of rolling the logs out of the woods and onto the skid roads or to the railway or water's edge was done by the picturesque steam engine called the "bull donkey," which wound a steel cable around a drum. Instead of handling single logs, the cable often dragged a train of them, held together, end to end, by heavy chains. The engine was permanently located at the objective point. A small return rope, passing over a sheave (a grooved wheel) at the extreme outer end of the skid road, was used to draw the large cable out to the scene of cutting operations. In some camps not even a skid road was used; only enough guidance was given the cable to insure that the logs would not be blocked in passing through the forest. The powerful "bull donkey" would drag out the logs, pulling them by main force past all obstacles. Of course this required powerful engines and strong cables.

Nowadays most of the work of log-hauling in the forest of the Northwest is done by powerful tractors and trucks.

Enormous advances have been made in lumbering, in methods of felling and logging. Other advances that are no less important have taken place in the methods of sawing the logs into marketable lumber. The settler had to shape the logs for his cabin with his ax, a process that resulted in back-breaking labor. Then he learned to elevate the log in such a way that a long whipsaw, operated by a man at each end of the saw, could be used to cut the log into planks. The first sawmills were driven by water. The single saw, called a sash saw, was set in a sash or frame that moved up and down. The log was guided and pressed against it by hand. Then came the gang saw, made like the sash saw, except that the frame held a number of saws set parallel to each other. This saw cut an entire log into planks by one passage through the sash. Hand-feed gave way to power-feed. Obviously, when the saws were once set in the sash, they could not be changed without considerable trouble. Every log passed through had to be cut into planks of the same thickness, without regard to

The large band saw in this sawmill cuts the whole log into large pieces. These pieces are cut into different shapes by gang saws and circular saws.

Standard Oil Co. (N. J.)

Trim saw in a Vancouver sawmill. The operator, pulling little levers, lowers different circular saws and cuts the moving lumber into any length that is needed.

economy. This difficulty led to the introduction of the circular saw, which is still widely used, particularly in small mills. The circular saw rotates about a horizontal axis. When a log is to be cut with this type of saw, it is fastened to a carriage which brings it up to the rapidly whirling blade. Any thickness of board or plank can be cut with this saw.

A circular saw, however, is comparatively wasteful in its operation. It must be thick enough to be perfectly rigid as it rotates. A circular saw seven feet in diameter has to be about half an inch thick; there is considerable waste, in the form of sawdust, from its wide cut. For that reason the so-called band saw is now widely used, especially in large mills. This saw is an endless ribbon or band of steel running over two extremely wide pulley wheels, one placed above the other. The upper wheel can be moved vertically so as to tighten the band; this prevents slipping as the lower wheel — the driving wheel — rapidly moves the band. Usually only one edge of the band is provided with teeth. The logs are brought against the cutting toothed edge by a traveling carriage. In some cases the band saw is toothed on both edges. The log is held stationary; the saw moves forward and backward along the long dimension of the log, sawing on both the forward and return movements. Some mills employ both circular and band saws.

Sawmills vary greatly in size and in the completeness of their equipment. In a large modern plant the building itself may be 100 feet wide and three or four times as long. From one end of the upper floor, a long incline, or slip, extends to the ground or to the water, as the case may be. Logs are drawn up this incline by an endless chain, the links of which may be as much as an inch and a half in diameter. The logs are thoroughly washed as they are drawn upward. When a log arrives at the upper floor, it is rolled by machinery onto a carriage and is made fast. The carriage brings the log up to the saw, which cuts a slice from its side with a deafening grating sound, suggesting a particularly horrible shriek. The carriage flies back, the log is set over the required distance and is sent on its way again for another cut. The operation is repeated until the log has been sawed up into a considerable number of long slices.

A long line of power-driven rollers conveys these slices to other parts of the mill, where smaller saws cut them up into boards and planks of different sizes. These are finally trimmed to the correct length by crosscut saws. A good deal of the refuse that results from the sawing operations is used to make such articles as shingles and laths. It also serves other purposes, as we shall see.

At one time all the power required for the various sawmill operations was derived from steam engines, which generally used sawdust and wood scraps as fuel. Power was transmitted from the engines to the machines by a complicated system of belts and pulleys. In modern mills, electricity is now usually employed, its flexibility being particularly adapted to some of the operations involved. Formerly the refuse and sawdust not used in firing the boilers was usually disposed of in a burner — a boiler-plate shell, lined inside with brick and fitted with draft doors at the bottom. Nowadays most sawmills salvage the refuse and sawdust that was formerly disposed of in the burner. The bark of certain trees, particularly oak and hemlock, is treated with hot

ing the moisture in the lumber before it is finished in the planing machines. It is generally considered preferable to let wood dry in the open air instead of in kilns. But drying in the open air is a long process, while the dry kiln removes the moisture in a matter of hours. Natural seasoning also requires large yard space if big quantities are handled.

Large sawmills are generally to be found in places to which logs can easily be

Douglas Fir Plywood Assoc.

Processing exterior-type panels, consisting of layers of wood bonded together by phenolic-resin adhesives. The adhesives are impervious to water and weather. Large hot presses, like that shown above, make the adhesives set under both pressure and heat.

water and yields an extract that is employed in the tanning of leather. Waste wood can be converted into wood flour and pressed board. Sawdust can be used for many purposes. It makes good packing and insulation material; it can be pressed into briquettes (brick-shaped blocks), which make fine fuel for fireplaces. Sawdust is sometimes mixed with glue, linseed oil and other substances and molded into all kinds of ornamental columns and a great variety of carvings.

Attached to most of the large sawmills are planing mills and dry kilns for remov-

brought by rail, truck or water. Since logs take up a good deal of space, the mills are usually located on a river or beside a pond or lake, so that logs may be kept in "floating storage" until they are needed. When the mill is situated in an isolated place, a whole town will often grow up around it, wholly supported by the industry and sometimes owned by the proprietors. Sometimes small sawmills are built in the forest itself. After all the trees in the vicinity have been cut down, the mill, or at least its machinery, is moved to a new location.

See also Vol. 10, p. 283: "Lumber."

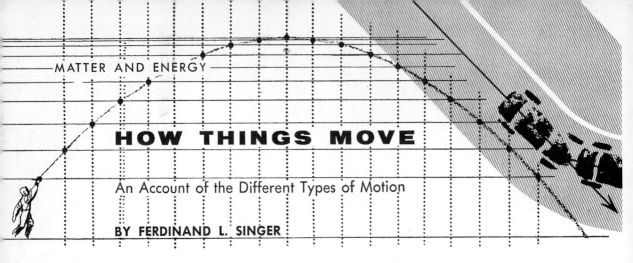

HOW THINGS MOVE

An Account of the Different Types of Motion

BY FERDINAND L. SINGER

FROM one point of view, nothing is ever at rest. It is true that the chair on which you sit, the table on which you write and the bookcase by the wall are not moving toward you or away from you. But the earth on which they rest revolves around the sun. The sun itself moves constantly in space.

It would be very confusing if we were to take into account all these different kinds of motion in discussing, say, the movement of an automobile in a city street. For most purposes it suffices to consider motion only with respect to the earth. We can define motion as change of position in relation to certain fixed points. For example, an automobile moves past a road sign; a hit in baseball moves out from home plate. The road sign and home plate would be the fixed points of reference.

If the size of a moving body is negligibly small compared to the size of its path, we need not consider the motions of the individual parts that compose the body. When we discuss the motion of an automobile as it rounds a curve, we need not take into account the movements of the valves, or pistons or other parts of the car. A body such as an automobile, considered only as a self-contained unit, is called a particle. We can think of the earth as a particle when we trace its orbit around the sun; we can disregard the motions of the automobiles that are traveling along its surface as it whirls through space.

The different kinds of motion

There are various kinds of motion. To begin with, there is *rectilinear* motion, or motion in a straight line, as when an automobile travels along a straight road. When we go around a curve in a car, our motion becomes *curvilinear*. We may travel at *constant speed* by traveling over equal distances in equal intervals of time, or we may let our speed vary. If our speed increases, we say that we are *accelerating;* if we slow down, we are *decelerating*.

The simplest type of motion is rectilinear motion at constant speed. Suppose that an automobile covers a mile in two minutes. If its speed has been constant, it will have traveled at the rate of 30 miles an hour. Actually, try as he may, no driver would be able to keep the speedometer needle exactly at the 30-miles-per-hour mark. The needle will sometimes go above and sometimes below this mark. When we say, therefore, that an automobile travels over a certain stretch of road at 30 miles per hour, we really mean that its average speed is 30 miles per hour. (See Figure 1.) The average speed is equivalent to the distance divided by the elapsed time.

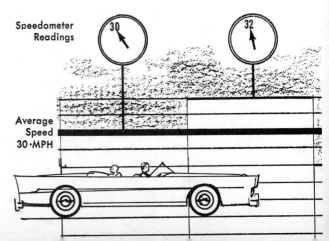

Speedometer Readings

Average Speed 30·MPH

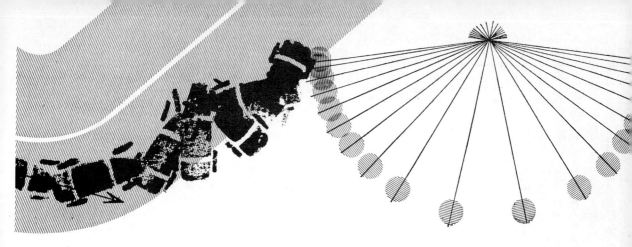

What we mean
by acceleration

Changes in speed involve acceleration — the rate at which we change our speed. If an automobile increases its speed by 2 miles per hour for every second of time, we say that it has an acceleration of 2 miles per hour per second. Starting from rest, the car will be traveling at 2 miles per hour at the end of 1 second, at 4 miles per hour at the end of 2 seconds, at 6 miles per hour at the end of 3 seconds and so on. This car is increasing its speed at a constant rate; for this reason it is said to have motion together with a constant rate of acceleration.

The average speed in a uniformly accelerated motion is the sum of the initial speed and the final speed divided by 2. This relationship also applies to objects which come to rest while losing speed at a constant rate. The rate at which speed is reduced is called the deceleration, or negative acceleration. (We sometimes give the name positive acceleration to acceleration involving an increase in velocity.)

Freely falling bodies move with constant acceleration. The force bringing this about is the gravitational attraction of the earth. We discuss this type of attraction in the article The Force of Gravitation, in this volume. As we point out in the article, the force of gravitation differs at various locations; it is stronger, for example, at the poles than at the equator.

The gravitational attraction of the earth causes all objects to fall with an acceleration of about 32 feet per second per second, or 980 centimeters per second per second. The exact rate will depend on the gravitational force at a given part of the earth's surface. Suppose we drop a baseball from the top of a skyscraper (Figure 2). At the end of 1 second, the ball will have attained a velocity of 32 feet per second.* At the end of 2 seconds, the velocity will be 64 feet per second; at

* We assume that the rate of acceleration is exactly 32 feet per second per second at this particular place.

1. Variations in speed of an automobile traveling at an average speed of 30 miles per hour.

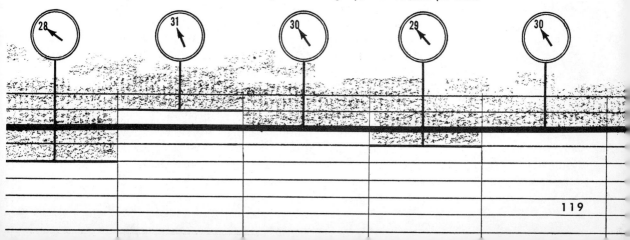

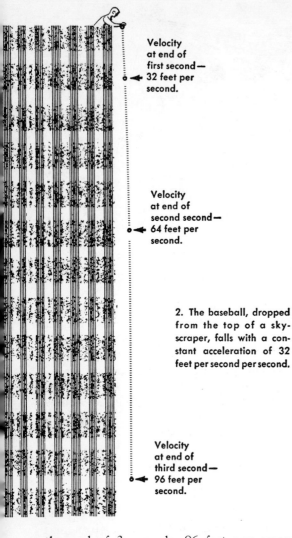

Velocity at end of first second— 32 feet per second.

Velocity at end of second second— 64 feet per second.

2. The baseball, dropped from the top of a sky-scraper, falls with a constant acceleration of 32 feet per second per second.

Velocity at end of third second— 96 feet per second.

the end of 3 seconds, 96 feet per second and so on. In this case, of course, we have positive acceleration. Actually, the velocity in each case would not be quite so great as we have indicated, because the air resistance would hold the baseball back by a slight amount.

If an object is cast straight up in the air, the force of gravity will decelerate it (decrease its velocity) at the rate of 32 feet per second per second. Suppose a boy throws a baseball straight up in the air at a velocity of 96 feet per second. At the end of the first second, the ball will be traveling at the velocity of 64 (96−32) feet per second. At the end of the second second, the velocity will be reduced to 32 (64−32) feet per second, while at the end of the third second the velocity will be zero. This is a good example of deceleration, or negative acceleration. Of course the ball will not remain

motionless in the air after its velocity has been reduced to zero. The force of gravity will pull it down so that it will fall with an acceleration of 32 feet per second per second.

At one time it was thought that the speed of fall depended on the weight of an object. The great Italian scientist and mathematician Galileo Galilei (1564-1642) is said to have proved, in a famous experiment, that this was not the case. He caused several objects of different sizes and materials to be dropped from the Leaning Tower of Pisa at the same instant of time. According to the traditional account, observers saw these objects hit the ground at the same time. Some modern authorities are rather skeptical about the story. They point out that the resistance of the air would affect the objects as they fell, and that the lighter objects would be held back most by this resistance.

However, we can prove, by a familiar experiment, that the weight of an object has nothing to do with the rate at which it falls. We put a feather and a coin in a long glass tube, which is made airtight (Figure 3). When the air is pumped out of the tube and the tube is suddenly inverted, the feather and the coin will be seen to fall at the same rate. When air is admitted to the tube, the coin will fall more rapidly, because the resistance of the air will affect the feather much more than the heavier coin.

The difference between speed and velocity

We often use "speed" and "velocity" interchangeably, and sometimes we are justified in doing so. However, speed is not always the same thing as velocity. Strictly speaking, speed measures the rate at which we travel, while velocity involves not only speed but also direction. In rectilinear motion (motion in a straight line), velocity and speed are practically synonymous, since only one direction is involved. In motion along a curve, however, the direction of the velocity is always different from the actual path along which the moving object travels.

To show what we mean, let us assume that a car (Figure 4) is traveling along a straight road in the direction *A* at the rate of 40 miles an hour. Suddenly it comes to a curve. The car will now be headed toward a new direction, *B*. It will really cover a greater distance in going from *a* to *b,* on the curved path, than the arc *ab*.* To maintain the speed of 40 miles per hour, it will have to travel faster; i.t other words, there will be an acceleration. The same thing will happen when the car changes its direction from *B* to *C*.** Each time the car changes its direction, there will be an acceleration. The direction of the car at any one time will be at a tangent to the curved path that the car will follow — that is, the direction will *touch* the curve at one point and then will diverge from it. (*Tangere* means "to touch" in Latin.)

The velocity, then, is always changing as a vehicle moves in a curved path. If the vehicle covers equal distances along the path in equal intervals of time, it has a constant speed; but its velocity cannot be constant since its direction constantly changes.

A familiar example of curvilinear motion is that of the bob, or weight, suspended at the end of a pendulum (Figure 5). In this case, neither the velocity nor the acceleration remain constant. The acceleration varies directly with the distance from the central position of the bob. This produces what is called simple harmonic motion, found in most vibrating objects. This concept is too complex to discuss further here.

Galileo seems to have been the first to observe that a pendulum takes the same time to complete each swing; the time is independent of the extent of the swing, provided the swing is not too large. The time required for a pendulum to make one complete vibration (that is, to swing back and forth once) is called the period. The extent of the swing is known as the amplitude of the pendulum.

* An arc is part of a circle.
** We have greatly exaggerated the changes of direction involved, in order to make our point.

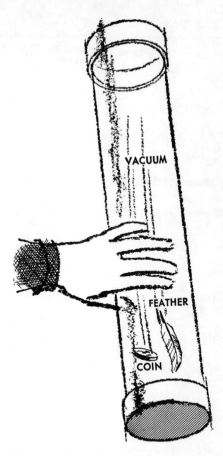

3. When air is pumped out of the tube, creating a vacuum, the coin and feather will fall at the same rate.

4. When the car starts to go around the curve, it will change direction from A to B. It will have to travel a greater distance than arc ab. To maintain a given speed, there will have to be an acceleration. Actually, the car changes direction much more often than shown here.

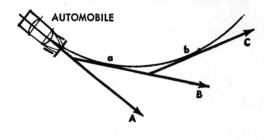

5. A simple pendulum. The time that is required for it to swing back and forth once is known as the period; the extent of the pendulum's swing is called the amplitude.

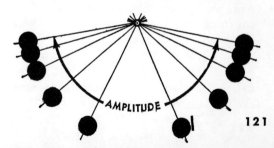

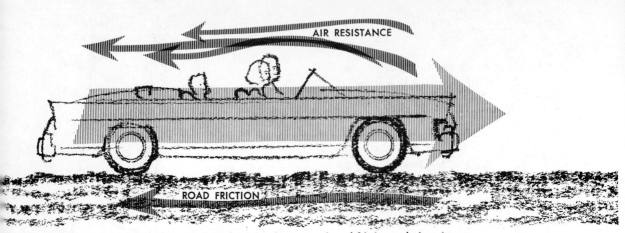

AIR RESISTANCE

ROAD FRICTION

6. As an automobile moves, it is held back by the forces of road friction and air resistance.

The motion of the pendulum is expressed by the following laws:

1. *The period of vibration does not depend upon the weight of the bob.*
2. *The period of vibration does not depend upon the amplitude.*
3. *The period of vibration is proportional to the square root of the length of the pendulum.*
4. *The period of vibration is inversely proportional to the square root of the acceleration due to the force of gravity.*

The last law explains why a pendulum clock has to be adjusted when it is moved, say from Cambridge, Massachusetts, to Rio de Janeiro, in Brazil. The pull of gravity is weaker in Rio de Janeiro and it will affect the rate at which the pendulum swings.

Newton's three laws of motion

So far we have discussed motion without considering the forces that cause it. We analyze these forces by applying three laws known as Newton's laws of motion because they were advanced by the great English scientist Sir Isaac Newton (1642-1727). They are usually stated as follows:

1. *A body at rest stays at rest and a body in motion continues in motion at a constant speed in a straight line unless acted upon by an external force.*
2. *The rate of change of motion of a body is proportional to the applied force and takes place in the direction in which the force acts.*

3. *To every action, there is always an equal and opposite reaction.*

As we apply these rules, their meaning will become clearer.

The first law of motion

A body at rest stays at rest and a body in motion continues in motion at a constant rate in a straight line unless acted on by an external force.

To understand the second part of this first law of motion, let us point out that when a body is in motion, two factors cause it to resist change. One is its velocity; the other is its mass. We know that it is hard to stop the motion of a bullet, because of its velocity. It is also hard for us to stop the motion of a slowly moving automobile, because of its mass. The two factors of mass and velocity of a body, when multiplied together, give us what is called the body's momentum.

The mass of a body is always constant. Hence, to change the momentum, it is necessary to change the velocity. To change the velocity (either the rate of speed or the direction or both) and thus cause an acceleration requires a force. That is what Newton meant by saying that a body in motion will move in a straight line at constant speed unless acted on by an external force.

"But," you may say, "an automobile can travel at constant speed along a straight line only because we apply a force to it — the power supplied by the motor. Why

122

shouldn't the automobile be able to travel at constant speed in a straight line without any force being applied to it, if Newton's first law is valid?"

The answer is that when an automobile moves along a road, it is continually held back by the resisting forces of road friction and air resistance (Figure 6). To counteract these resisting forces and to enable the automobile to maintain a constant speed in a straight line, there must be an external force, originating in the motor and applied at the wheels. We should, therefore, interpret the first law of motion to mean that when the forces acting upon a body are balanced, there is no acceleration. This condition would apply equally to bodies at rest and to those moving with constant velocity. For example, the automobile mentioned before, traveling at constant speed in a straight line, does so because balance exists between the driving forces developed at the wheels and the resistance of the air and the road. To change the velocity, we must upset this balance.

The second
law of motion

The rate of change of motion of a body is proportional to the applied force and takes place in the direction in which the force acts.

This second law of motion will apply when we upset the balance of forces by increasing the driving force. There will be a net accelerating force as long as the driving force is greater than the resisting force. However, air resistance increases with gain in speed. Hence the unbalance (lack of balance) between driving force and resisting force is gradually reduced, thereby decreasing the rate at which we gain speed. To continue accelerating, we must feed more power to the engine. Again the air resistance will increase, and again the unbalance between driving and resisting forces will be gradually reduced. It will become zero at the limit of engine power. When we have reached this condition, we shall then be traveling at our maximum possible speed.

Another way to upset the balance between driving and resisting forces is to apply the brakes. The large decelerating force created in this way brings the car rapidly to a stop. In a collision, a car is stopped almost instantaneously. The large deceleration that is developed corresponds to a large stopping force. It is this force

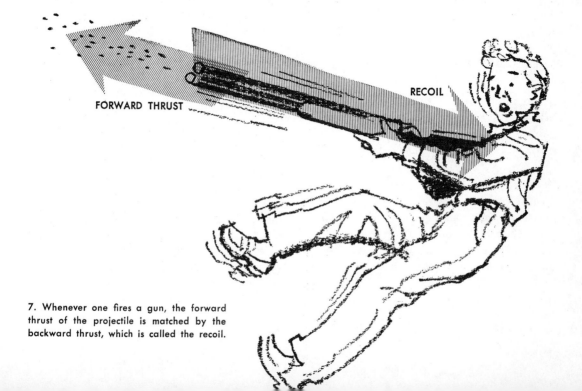

FORWARD THRUST

RECOIL

7. Whenever one fires a gun, the forward thrust of the projectile is matched by the backward thrust, which is called the recoil.

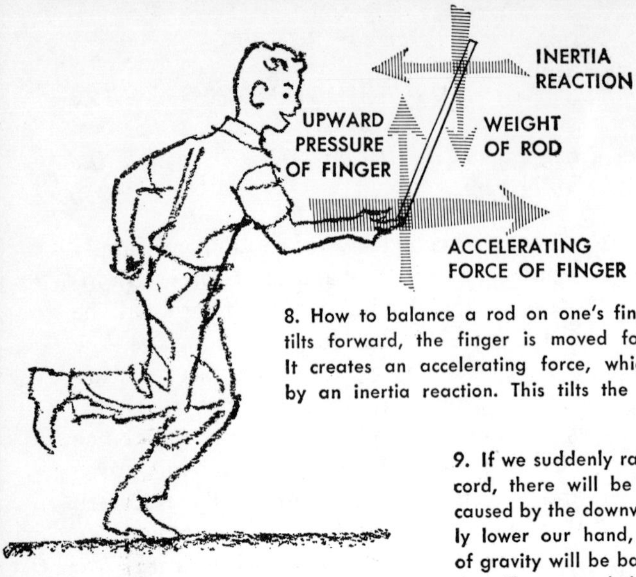

INERTIA REACTION

UPWARD PRESSURE OF FINGER

WEIGHT OF ROD

ACCELERATING FORCE OF FINGER

PULL OF HAND

PULL OF GRAVITY

TENSION IN CORD

8. How to balance a rod on one's finger. If the rod tilts forward, the finger is moved forward rapidly. It creates an accelerating force, which is balanced by an inertia reaction. This tilts the rod backward.

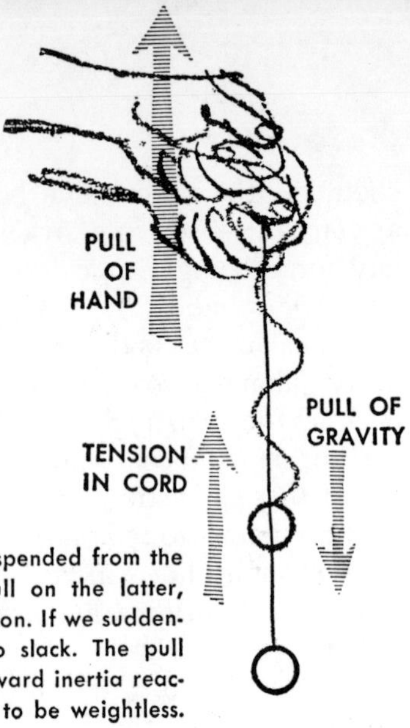

9. If we suddenly raise the weight suspended from the cord, there will be an increased pull on the latter, caused by the downward inertia reaction. If we suddenly lower our hand, the cord will go slack. The pull of gravity will be balanced by an upward inertia reaction. The suspended object will seem to be weightless.

that damages cars in collisions. The faster a car is moving at the instant of impact, the greater the decelerating force and the more damaging the effect upon the car will be.

Here is another example which shows the relation between force, acceleration and stopping distance. If a milk bottle is dropped into a pile of sand, the bottle will not be damaged; it will be shattered if it is dropped the same distance upon a concrete floor. This is because the sand is yielding and permits a lower deceleration than when the bottle drops against concrete. Since concrete is harder than sand, it will stop the bottle more quickly and will therefore exercise a larger force.

The third law of motion

To every action, there is always an equal and opposite reaction.

The third law tells us that even when bodies are being accelerated, the forces that affect them remain in balance. The forces that bring about action and reaction always occur in pairs. We may not be aware of the reacting force, but it is always there. When we stand upon a floor, we exert a force; this is opposed by the force that the floor exerts upon us. If we kick a football, it reacts with equal force upon our foot. In the case of jet-propelled planes, the backward thrust of the gases issuing from the jet engine reacts against

the engine and causes a forward thrust.* Sometimes, we can feel the reacting force. If we fire a rifle, the forward thrust of the projectile is matched by the backward thrust, which we call the recoil or "kick" of the rifle (Figure 7).

The opposite and equal reaction that balances an accelerating force is called inertia. It is equal to the product of the acceleration and the mass of the body being accelerated. When we ride in a train, the starting forces that accelerate it and us forward create an inertia reaction which causes us to lurch backward. A sudden stop throws us forward because the deceleration is opposite to the forward motion of the car. The decelerating forces are balanced by the forward reaction effect of inertia.

We can demonstrate this effect very simply. Suppose that while we balance a rod on a finger, the rod tilts forward, as shown in Figure 8. The balance can be restored by a rapid forward movement of the finger. The movement of the finger creates an accelerating force which is balanced by an inertia reaction, acting at the center of gravity of the rod. If our forward motion is too rapid, the inertia reaction will tilt the rod backward. Then a quick backward movement of the finger will again restore balance by creating a forward inertia reaction. We can keep

* It is not true that the gases escaping from the rear of the jet plane bounce from the air at the rear of the plane and thus cause the plane to move forward. See the Index, under Jet propulsion.

the rod in balance by alternate forward and backward movements.

The effect of inertia can be demonstrated by another simple experiment. Let us suspend a weight from a cord (Figure 9). If we hold the weight stationary, the tension in the cord just equals the pull of the weight. Suppose we raise the weight suddenly; that is, accelerate it upwards. We will notice an increased pull of the cord, brought about by the inertia reaction to the accelerating force. If we lower the weight, not at a uniform velocity, but faster and faster, the pull becomes less when the weight is held still. This is because the weight acquires a downward acceleration, causing an upward inertia reaction. Since the inertia reaction counteracts the weight, the net pull on the cord is decreased. If we lower our hand suddenly, the cord will go entirely slack. The pull of gravity on the weight will cause it to fall with an acceleration of 32 feet per second; this gravity pull will be balanced by an upward inertia reaction, which will make the suspended object seem to be weightless.

The third law of Newton always applies to curvilinear motion. When we whirl a stone around by a string, our hand exerts an inner pull — a centripetal force — upon the stone to keep it moving around in a curve. We also become aware of an outer pull, which is called centrifugal force.

If we release the stone, so that there is no longer an inward pull, the outward pull, or centrifugal force, will cause the stone to fly off in a straight line. The centrifugal force is the inertia reaction to the inward pull our hand exerts on the stone. A centrifugal inertia force always acts on a body moving in a curve because such bodies are always being accelerated.

Centrifugal force, representing an inertia reaction, makes itself felt when a car begins to skid (Figure 10). Suppose we make a left turn too sharply or too quickly. The centrifugal inertia force of the turn becomes greater than the friction of the tires against the road, and the car will start to skid to the right. The only way to overcome the momentum of the skid is to create a force to overcome it. This we can do by immediately turning the front wheels to the right — that is, in the direction of the skid. The car will then tend to turn in a rightward curve; in this way it sets up a leftward centrifugal inertia force which stops the skid. The car may overbalance and tend to skid leftward again; the driver, therefore, must be prepared to turn the front wheels to the left if this should happen. This maneuver is done expertly by racing car drivers, who deliberately skid their cars around turns in order to avoid losing speed.

One is particularly likely to skid on an icy road, because on such a road the

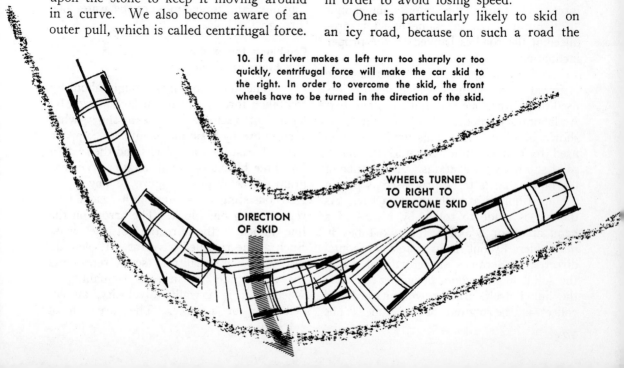

10. If a driver makes a left turn too sharply or too quickly, centrifugal force will make the car skid to the right. In order to overcome the skid, the front wheels have to be turned in the direction of the skid.

DIRECTION OF SKID

WHEELS TURNED TO RIGHT TO OVERCOME SKID

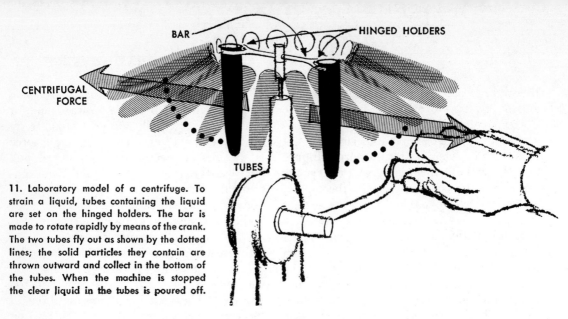

BAR — HINGED HOLDERS

CENTRIFUGAL FORCE

TUBES

11. Laboratory model of a centrifuge. To strain a liquid, tubes containing the liquid are set on the hinged holders. The bar is made to rotate rapidly by means of the crank. The two tubes fly out as shown by the dotted lines; the solid particles they contain are thrown outward and collect in the bottom of the tubes. When the machine is stopped the clear liquid in the tubes is poured off.

road friction is reduced to a minimum. The turning of the front wheels will not bring us into an opposite turn as quickly as on a dry road, because the car will have traveled further in the direction of the skid. That is why we should always travel at reduced speed when a road is slippery.

A method commonly used to prevent skidding when rounding a curve is to construct the curved roadway so that the outer part of the road is higher than the inner. This construction is called banking the curve. It brings about the same effect as leaning inward when rounding a flat curve on a bicycle. The bicyclist leans inward to balance the effect of centrifugal inertia force. Of course the automobile cannot "lean inward" but the same effect is produced if the road is banked at the proper inclination.

A familiar application of inertia force is found in centrifuges, which are devices used to separate one material from another. A laboratory model of a centrifuge is shown in Figure 11. This device is often used to remove from a liquid the small solid substances it contains. A test tube of the liquid that is to be processed is put in a hinged holder at each end of a bar. As the bar is made to rotate by means of a hand crank or a motor, the two tubes in the holders fly out in an almost horizontal direction. Because of centrifugal force, the solids in the liquid, being heavier than the liquid itself, are thrown outward and collect in the bottom of the tube. The

machine is then stopped and the clear liquid is poured off.

The same principle is used to separate cream from milk in the device known as the separator. In the separator, the milk is passed into a spinning bowl. The milk, being heavier than cream, is forced to the outward part of the spinning bowl and is drawn off. The cream, which is lighter, stays near the center and is drawn off from that point.

The washing machine spinner also applies centrifugal inertia force. The wet clothes are damp-dried by whirling them rapidly in a container perforated with numerous small holes. Centrifugal force presses the clothes strongly against the container and forces most of the water out through the holes.

Combined forces that bring about motion

Sometimes motion is brought about by combined forces, which can be analyzed by means of vectors. We can show what vectors are by a simple example. Suppose we walk east for four blocks and then north for three blocks of equal length. We diagram our walk east (Figure 12) by a line *AB* consisting of 4 equal units, each unit representing one block. The arrow on the line indicates the direction of the walk. Such a line is called a vector. Its length, drawn to some arbitrary scale, represents the magnitude, or size, of a quantity — whether it is a walk, a velocity, an acceleration or a force. The direction of

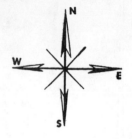

the quantity is denoted by the arrowhead drawn on the line or, as we can now call it, the vector.

The three-block walk north is represented by the vector *BC*. We now draw a line connecting *A* and *C,* and also provide it with an arrowhead. It constitutes another vector, *AC;* it represents the net change in our position and is called the resultant. It shows that we would have walked the equivalent of five blocks if we had walked straight from *A* to *C,* instead of using the roundabout route from *A* to *B* and from *B* to *C.* In either case, we would be the equivalent of five blocks from our starting point, *A,* at the end of our walk.

The numbers 4 and 3 in this example are known as vector quantities. They answer the question "In what direction?" as well as the question "How much?" As a physicist would say, they possess direction as well as magnitude. They differ from what we call scalar quantities, which have only magnitude. We are all familiar with scalar quantities. When we speak of 4 apples or 3 apples, we are referring to scalar quantities. We can add 4 apples and 3 apples by the ordinary processes of arithmetic, giving the result 7 apples. We cannot add vector quantities arithmetically. We must add them by drawing vectors in a diagram such as the one shown in ·Figure 12.

When we add scalar quantities together, the results are always the same. The sum of 4 apples and 3 apples is always 7 apples; the sum of 4 bananas and 3 bananas is always 7 bananas. But the addition of vector quantities does not always give the same result, if their directions differ. To illustrate our point, suppose we had walked northeast for three blocks from *B* instead of north. We would now diagram our walk as in Figure 13. The resultant effect, *AC,* would be about 6½ blocks. If we had walked from *B* in a northwesterly direction (Figure 14), the net effect *AC* would be a little less than 3 blocks. A more extended walk along the path *A-B-C-D-E-F-G,* diagrammed in Figure 15, would produce an effect *AG* of 2.83 blocks. In fact, if after following the

12. Suppose we walk east for four blocks and north for three blocks, and diagram our walk as indicated below. AC is the resultant, and is equivalent to five blocks.

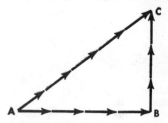

13. If, now, we were to walk four blocks east and three blocks northeast, the resultant effect, AC, would be equivalent to something like six and one-half blocks.

14. We change our route again, walking four blocks east and three blocks northwest, as shown below. In this case, the resultant, AC, is a little less than three blocks.

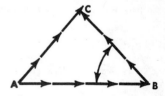

15. If we adopted the roundabout route shown below, in walking from A to G, the resultant, AG, would be equal to a little less than three blocks. If we continued our route from G to A, the resultant would be zero.

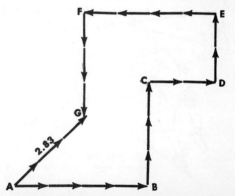

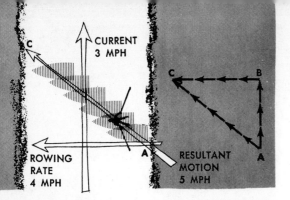

16. Here we see the effect produced by rowing at 4 miles per hour across a stream which is flowing at 3 miles per hour. *AB*, in the right-hand diagram, indicates the rate of flow and direction of the stream; *BC*, the rate of travel and direction of the boat; *AC*, the resultant effect.

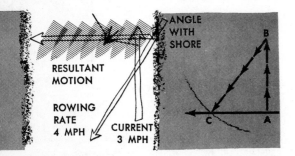

17. As in the preceding illustration, a boat is traveling at 4 miles per hour across a stream flowing at 3 miles per hour. If the boat heads upstream in the direction *BC* (right-hand drawing), it will reach the opposite shore at a point that is directly opposite the point of departure.

18. Player A, skating toward point *a*, wishes to pass the puck to player B, traveling in the direction *c*, so that the puck will arrive at *c* at the same time as player B. If we know the velocity and direction of travel of players A and B, we can calculate how fast and in what direction the puck will have to travel to reach *c* in time.

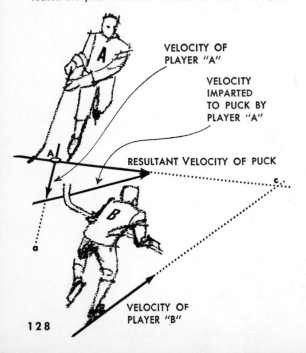

path *A-B-C-D-E-F-G*, we returned to *A*, there would be no net change in our position at all; the resultant would be zero.

Here, then, are the rules for this new type of addition — the addition of vector quantities. We draw the vector quantities correctly to scale and indicate the direction. We carefully place the "tail" of each vector at the "tip" of the vector to which it is added. The resultant vector will be represented to scale and in direction by the vector drawn from the tail of the first vector to the tip of the last one.

Let us consider a few applications of vector addition. Suppose we row at 4 miles per hour straight across a river flowing at 3 miles per hour. Our net motion will be the vector combination of both movements; the resultant would be 5 miles per hour, as shown in Figure 16. The river would carry us downstream as we rowed across so that we would arrive at *C*.

To travel straight across the river, we would have to row in such a direction that the resultant movement would be at right angles to the flow. Figure 17 shows what to do. We draw the vector *AB* to represent the rate of flow of the river — 3 miles per hour. Then setting a compass to represent a value of 4 miles per hour, we draw an arc with *B* as a center to intersect *AC*, the direction we wish to travel, at point *C*. In order to reach the opposite shore, at a point directly opposite the point of departure, the boat would have to be pointed upstream in the direction *BC*. Once we know the angle *ABC*, we could set our course. To find the angle, we would use a protractor — an angle-measuring device.

Another example concerns a situation that often occurs in hockey. A player, *A* (Figure 18), moving in one direction, wishes to pass the puck to another player *B*, who is moving in another direction. Experience tells player *A* how to pass the puck so that it may reach *c* at approximately the same time as player *B*. If *A* could analyze the vectors involved at the time that he is making the shot, there would be no guesswork in the maneuver. Figure 18 analyzes the problem.

See also Vol. 10, p. 280: "General Works."

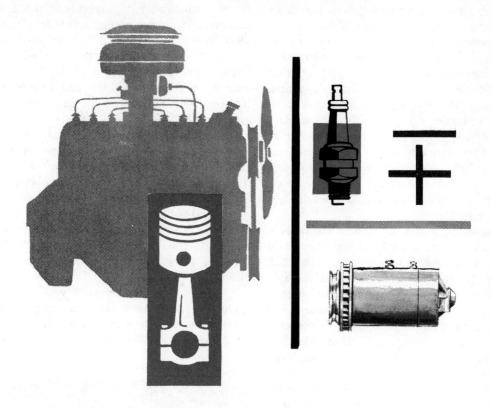

THE AUTOMOBILE

The Universal Vehicle of Modern Times

BY JOSEPH HEITNER

LESS than a century ago the automobile was regarded as a curious sort of contraption, in which only eccentric people were interested. In some places, a man had to walk in front of each car with a red flag in order to warn travelers on the road; in other communities an automobile was required to stop when a horse-drawn buggy or wagon approached. Today the automobile practically monopolizes our highways. It is perhaps the nearest approach to a universal vehicle that man has ever devised.

For centuries before the development of the modern car, men had been working on the idea of a self-propelled carriage that could travel on roads. Early vehicles of this type took the form of wagons provided with sails or propelled by hand or by spring motors. It was not until the invention of the steam engine in the eighteenth century that appreciable progress was made. Nicolas-Joseph Cugnot, a French military engineer, is generally credited with having built the first self-propelled vehicle driven by a steam engine about 1770. It was a three-wheeled affair; the engine was set in front of the vehicle and operated the single front wheel.

As time went on, much progress was made in developing steam-driven carriages or coaches. By the 1830's a number of such vehicles were traveling in and around the city of London. Various companies had been formed to build and operate steam-driven coaches on English roads. Naturally the stagecoach companies protested violently. At their instigation Parliament passed a Road Locomotive Act in 1836, imposing excessively high taxes on road vehicles operated by steam power plants. The Act slowed down the development of these early automobiles but did not stop it entirely.

Americans also interested themselves in steam-driven vehicles from the early years of the nineteenth century. In 1805 Oliver Evans displayed a steam-driven amphibious monster — a combination wagon and flatboat. By the time of the Civil War a certain number of steam-driven carriages were in operation. From that time on, progress was fairly steady, if not spectacular. As a matter of fact, steam-driven road vehicles competed with automobiles powered by gasoline engines until the early 1920's. Among the notable makes of American "steamers" were the Stanley, the Mobile and the White. These vehicles were very powerful.

Of course "steamers" have been entirely supplanted now by automobiles with internal-combustion engines using gasoline as fuel. In 1678 the Dutch scientist Christian Huygens had described an engine in which a piston was driven in a cylinder by the explosion of gunpowder. Not much progress was made in developing an internal-combustion engine until the nineteenth century. In 1851 W. M. Storm patented an engine that compressed illuminating gas in the cylinder and ignited it. Nine years later, Etienne Lenoir, a Frenchman, built an internal-combustion engine that ran on illuminating gas, ignited by an electric spark. In 1862 he mounted one of his engines on a vehicle.

About the middle of the century the Frenchman Beau de Rochas first worked out on paper the principles of the four-stroke type of internal-combustion engine

now in common use. In 1876, the Germans N. H. Otto and E. Langer built the first successful four-cycle engine. It first used illuminating gas; later it ran on gasoline.

Gottlieb Daimler, who worked for Otto, improved the design of the Otto engine by making it lighter and increasing its speed. He patented his improved engine in 1885–86. About the same time, Karl Benz patented a three-wheeled motor car driven by gasoline. His three-wheeled cars proved to be an outstanding success; they spurred interest in automobiles in France, England and the United States.

The brothers Charles E. and J. Frank Duryea built the first gasoline-driven vehicle in the United States in 1891. By the year 1894 they had constructed several "horseless buggies."

At the turn of the century the manufacture of automobiles was growing in the United States. It was based chiefly on a patent issued in 1895 to George B. Selden

STEAM HORSELESS CARRIAGE

of Rochester, New York, on an automobile with an internal-combustion engine. An Association of Licensed Automobile Manufacturers was formed to manufacture cars under the Selden patent. At one time 90 per cent of all American cars were manufactured by members of the Association.

Certain manufacturers, including Henry Ford and Alexander Winton, refused to join the group. Suit was brought against these independents. In 1911, the courts decided that Ford, Winton and the other independent manufacturers were not infringing the Selden patent. The Association was then disbanded and the automobile field in the United States was left wide open.

Cars were first produced on a mass basis by Ransom E. Olds; he manufactured 1,500 of his Oldsmobile cars in 1901 and sold them at a moderate price. A few years later he turned to a more expensive car, intended for a quality market. Automobile mass production did not get under way again until 1907, when Henry Ford developed his famous Model T Ford. He stripped cars of all nonessentials, painted them all one color (black), manufactured them in great quantities and sold them at a low price. The Model T was a resounding success. In the years that followed, mass production was carried on more and more widely.

The history of the automobile in the present century has been one of constant

ground. A host of refinements — heaters, radios, windshield wipers, cigarette lighters and so on — have been introduced. In the early days manufacturers were primarily concerned with turning out cars that would run. Nowadays the comfort and convenience of the driver and his passengers are considered to be just as important.

The modern car is a complicated mechanism with many hundreds of working parts; a book would be required to explain every detail of its operation. Yet the basic principles on which it works are comparatively simple.

The automobile receives its motive power from an engine that is generally placed in front of the vehicle. (It is set in back in some cars, such as the American Corvair, the French Renault and the German Volkswagen.) The engine derives its energy from a fuel — generally gasoline — that is burned *in* the engine. That is why this type of power plant is called an in-

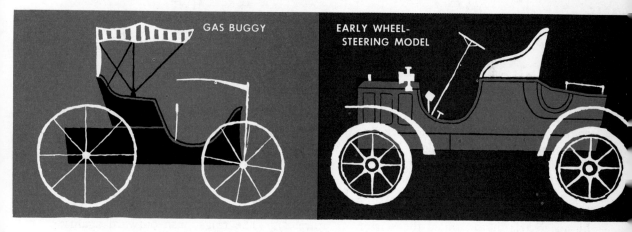

GAS BUGGY

EARLY WHEEL-STEERING MODEL

improvements and innovations. The list is very long. It includes battery ignition, replacing ignition by magneto; the electric self-starter; balloon tires; lacquer finish; four-wheel brakes; safety glass; independent front suspension; automatic transmission; and power steering. Body construction and design have also undergone many changes. All-steel bodies have replaced the all-wood or wood-and-steel construction of earlier cars. Bodies are more streamlined, and set closer to the

ternal-combustion engine. In an external-combustion engine, such as the reciprocating steam engine, fuel is burned *outside* of the power plant.

The reciprocating steam engine and the gasoline engine have much in common. Both are heat engines, in which pistons are made to move in smooth cylinders by the action of hot gases that develop great pressures. In a steam engine the motive force is steam, produced when water is heated in a boiler; in a gasoline engine tremendous pressure is supplied when a mixture of gasoline vapor and air is ignited in the cylinder.

A gasoline engine is not self-starting. The pistons in the cylinders have to be moved by some outer force in order to create a vacuum or suction in the cylinder. This suction draws the combustible mix-

for the liquid used in the cooling system. We describe this system below.

The cylinder head, a casting of gray iron or aluminum alloy (Figure 1), is bolted to the top of the cylinder block. It contains part of the combustion chamber as well as water passages for the cooling system. A gasket is set between the cyl-

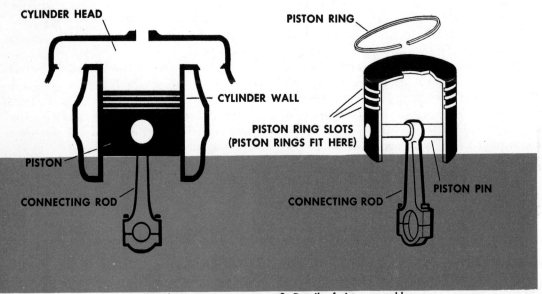

1. Cylinder head, cylinder wall and piston.

2. Details of piston assembly.

ture of air and gasoline vapor into the engine; the mixture is ignited as a spark is produced by the spark plug. The application of external force to move the pistons up and down in the cylinder is called cranking. Formerly all cranking was done by hand; in modern cars the engine is cranked by an electric motor, called the starter.

The cylinders of an engine are round and smooth openings in a cylinder block — a single casting of iron alloyed with another metal, such as nickel or molybdenum. These openings are machined and honed so that their walls take on a mirror-like appearance. (In some cars the cylinder walls consist of removable linings.) Most engines nowadays have six or eight cylinders in a block. The eight-cylinder types are generally in the **V**-form, with four cylinders on each bank of the **V**. The block contains water jackets, or passages

inder head and cylinder block to prevent the escape of gases.

In each cylinder a piston, generally made of an aluminum alloy, is fitted so that it can move up and down easily. Slots are cut in the upper part of each piston; piston rings are fitted in these slots (Figure 2). The rings push outward against the cylinder walls. They prevent gases from making their way between the piston and the cylinder walls. They also control the passage of the lubricating oil that is forced onto the cylinder walls along which the piston slides.

Each piston is joined to a rigid steel rod, called a connecting rod, by means of a pin through the center of the piston (Figure 2). The piston moves up and down in the cylinder in a straight line; the lower end of the connecting rod moves in a circle. The circular motion is transmitted to a crankshaft, to which the lower end of the connecting rod is fastened. The action of the crankshaft is like that of a carpenter's brace. A heavy metal wheel called the flywheel is attached to one end of the revolving crankshaft in order to make it turn more smoothly and also to keep it turning during the intervals between explosions.

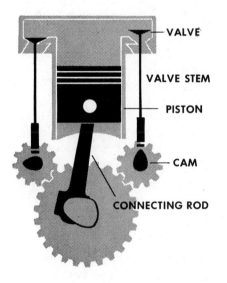

3. Valve-operating mechanism of T-head engine.

When a gasoline engine is in operation, the engine is constantly sucking in the gasoline-and-air mixture. It is also continually expelling waste gases resulting from the ignition of combustible gases in the cylinder. The entrance and exit of gases to and from the cylinder is controlled by "doors" called valves. These are opened and closed automatically at the correct time by a special mechanism that operates the appropriate valves.

In the engine known as the L-head engine, the valves are placed in the cylinder block alongside the cylinder. They are opened by the action of a shaft, called the camshaft, which runs parallel to the crankshaft. The camshaft is driven by the crankshaft; it is connected to it by meshed gears or by a pair of sprockets (wheels with teeth along their rims), connected by a chain. In Figure 3, we show a T-head engine, which works on much the same principle as the L-head.

A number of projections, called cams, are set at intervals on the camshaft; there is one cam for each valve. As the camshaft rotates, the cam pushes up a tappet, set beneath the valve stem, against the pressure of a spring; the valve opens. As the camshaft continues to rotate, the cam no longer presses against the tappet. The valve is closed by the action of the spring.

In the overhead valve engine (Figure 4), intake and exhaust valves are located in the head of the engine above the cylinder. A vertical pushrod is connected to one end of a rocker arm — a lever that can pivot about a shaft. The other end of the rocker arm maintains contact with the valve stem. When the cam pushes up the tappet, it lifts the pushrod. This raises one end of the rocker arm and depresses the other end, thus pushing down on the valve stem and causing the valve to open. When the cam no longer pushes up the tappet, the end of the rocker arm to which the pushrod is attached is depressed; the action of a spring closes the valve.

The engines used in all modern automobiles are of the four-stroke cycle type. As the crankshaft is made to rotate by the action of the starting motor, it pulls the piston down and thus creates a partial vacuum in the engine. The intake valve of the cylinder is open at this time to allow the combustible mixture to be forced into the cylinder. This is the intake stroke (Figure 5A).

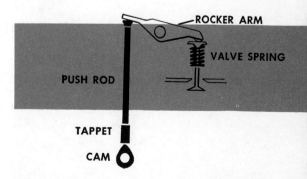

4. How the rocker arm of a typical overhead valve engine operates. Note that the valve is open in this drawing.

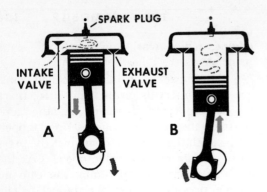
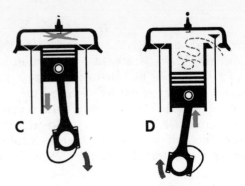

SPARK PLUG

INTAKE VALVE

EXHAUST VALVE

A B C D

5. Simplified diagram of four-cycle automobile engine at work. A represents the intake stroke; B, the compression stroke; C, the power stroke; D, the exhaust stroke. Arrows indicate the direction in which the piston moves.

As the crankshaft continues to revolve, the piston pushes the fuel and air into the combustion chamber — the space between the top of the piston and the cylinder head. This is the compression stroke (Figure 5B). Both valves remain closed during most of this stroke.

When the piston approaches the top of the compression stroke, the ignition system (which will be described later) furnishes a hot electrical spark to the spark plug, which protrudes into the combustion chamber. This causes the mixture to be ignited; the resulting gases expand so rapidly that they develop great pressure and force the piston down. This is the power stroke (Figure 5C).

At the end of the power stroke, the camshaft starts to force open the exhaust valve so that when the piston is again thrust upward, it pushes the exhaust gases out of the cylinder and thus prepares for the entrance of a new charge of mixture. The intake valve remains closed during this time. This is the exhaust stroke (Figure 5D).

During this cycle of events, the piston has moved through two upward and two downward strokes, forcing the crankshaft to make two complete revolutions. Since the valves opened and closed only once during the two revolutions of the crankshaft, the camshaft has moved at only half the speed of the crankshaft. This result is brought about by using gears of different sizes to connect the two shafts.

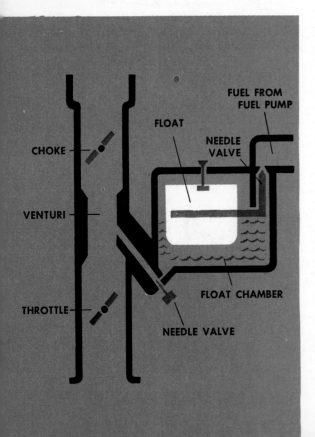

FUEL FROM FUEL PUMP

FLOAT

NEEDLE VALVE

CHOKE

VENTURI

THROTTLE

FLOAT CHAMBER

NEEDLE VALVE

6. How the carburetor works. Gasoline is fed to the float chamber by means of the fuel pump. A float pushes up a needle valve when the gasoline reaches the proper level in the chamber, thus shutting off the flow of gasoline. When the gasoline level falls, the needle valve drops and gasoline enters the float chamber again. Air is pulled into the carburetor proper from above by the suction of the engine cylinders. The carburetor tube narrows as it approaches the opening leading from the float chamber; as a result it forms the shape known as a venturi. (See Index, under Bernoulli's principle.) Gasoline is sprayed into the venturi from the float chamber and it is mixed with air. The throttle controls the amount of the air-and-gas mixture that is admitted to the cylinders, and it regulates the speed of the engine. The choke, which is near the other end of the carburetor, serves to control the proportion of air in the mixture.

The fuel system of a modern automobile consists of a gasoline storage tank, which is generally located in the rear of the car, a fuel pump, metal connecting pipes and a carburetor.

The fuel pump is a force pump, whose action is much like that of a toy water pistol; it is driven by the camshaft of the engine. It sucks fuel from the gas tank and pumps it in squirts into the reservoir bowl of the device called the carburetor. (See Figure 6 and the accompanying description.) The fuel pump sends enough fuel into the carburetor to keep it at the desired level, regardless of the speed of the engine.

The reservoir bowl of the carburetor contains a float mechanism that helps to keep the level of the gasoline constant. From the bowl, the fuel is fed to discharge jets. Here it is mixed with the stream of air from above. A valve, called a choke, is placed at the air entrance. Its function is to cut down the supply of air when a cold engine is started so as to furnish a mixture that is rich in gasoline. Formerly all chokes were operated manually. Nowadays most cars are supplied with an automatic choke; in this, the extent to which the choke is closed will depend upon the temperature of the engine.

The modern carburetor contains various refinements, such as accelerating pumps, power jets and idling systems. With devices such as these the carburetor can supply a more powerful or less powerful mixture than the one needed for ordinary driving. It is able, therefore, to meet the demands of special conditions — rapid acceleration, or heavy loads or a freely running engine, which is not supplying power to the rear wheels.

A valve called the throttle (see Figure 6) controls the amount of combustible mixture reaching the engine. This valve is located between the mixing chamber and the exit that leads to the engine cylinders. When the driver steps on the accelerator pedal of his car, he brings into play a series of levers that force the throttle to open. The wider open it is — that is, the greater the amount of mixture that enters the cyl-

inders — the faster the engine will run. An intake manifold — a pipe with several branches — serves to lead the combustible mixture to the different cylinders.

The exhaust system of an automobile consists of the exhaust manifold, the muffler and the tail pipe (Figure 7). The exhaust manifold serves to collect the gases from the exhaust ports of the different cylinders. The muffler (Figure 8) deadens the sound of the gases as they pass through it from the manifold. The tail pipe leads the gases to an exit in the rear of the car. Great care must be taken to prevent the exhaust gases from penetrating into the inside of the car, as they contain a large percentage of deadly carbon monoxide gas.

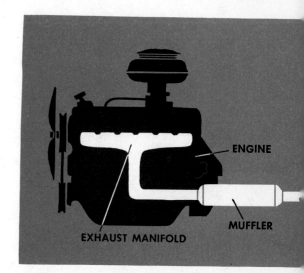

7. Above: exhaust manifold and muffler.

8. Below: two types of mufflers. In A, as waste gases are conducted through a series of baffle plates, the pressure and velocity of the gases are reduced. In B, a pipe leading from the exhaust manifold is set within a larger concentric chamber. Some of the gases escape to the chamber through a number of perforations in the pipe. The insulation filling in the chamber serves to absorb sound waves.

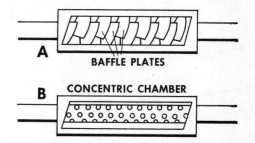

An automobile converts into mechanical energy only about a quarter, at most, of the heat it generates. Some of the remainder has to be carried away by the cooling system, as well as by the exhaust and lubrication systems. If an engine becomes too hot, the oil lubricant is burned up; as a result, cylinder walls are scored, valves are warped and bearings are burned out. That is why it is exceedingly important to keep the temperature of the engine from rising too high.

The cooling systems of almost all automobiles are based on the circulation of a liquid — either water or a mixture of water and antifreeze (see Index, under Antifreezes). In the typical cooling system (Figure 9) water circulates through passages (water jackets) in the cylinder block and cylinder head. Here the water absorbs the excess heat that has been created by the combustion of gases within the cylinders. The hot water is made to flow, by way of an inlet hose, to the radiator, whose function it is to release heat to the outer air. From the radiator the cooled liquid returns to the engine through an outlet hose. A water pump helps to keep the water moving rapidly through the circulating system, so that it will not get hot enough to boil.

There are various types of radiators. In the tubular radiator (Figure 10A), the water descends in vertical tubes. Set at right angles to the tubes are large flat metal surfaces. As water passes down the tubes, it loses much of its heat to these metal surfaces, which in turn pass the heat on to the surrounding air. The cellular, or honeycomb, type of radiator, consists of a great many air cells, or passages, surrounded by water (Figure 10B).

A fan, operated by a belt connected to the crankshaft, helps to draw air through the radiator. It adds greatly to the amount of air that would pass through the radiator in any event because of the forward motion of the car.

The lubricating system of an engine is extremely important; failure of this system to operate is a very serious matter. The oil that is used not only lubricates the many moving parts of an engine, thus reducing friction and wear; as we have seen, it also serves as an additional cooling system to carry away some of the engine heat. The oil is kept in a reservoir called the oil pan — a steel container attached to the bottom of the crankcase.

The engine lubricating system (Figures 11 and 12) is automatic. A gear-type or rotor-type pump, driven by the engine, forces the oil to all the surfaces where it is needed. The rotating crankshaft also helps to distribute the oil by causing it to splash on the inner surfaces of the engine. An oil filter removes many injurious materials that find their way into the oil during the operation of the engine.

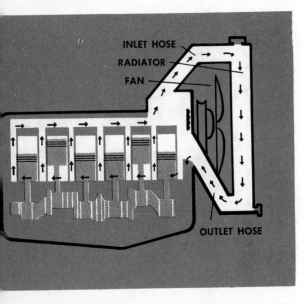

INLET HOSE
RADIATOR
FAN
OUTLET HOSE

9. The cooling system of the automobile engine. The arrows indicate the direction in which the water flows.

10. Two varieties of radiators used in the cooling systems of automobile engines. A represents the tubular type of radiator; B, the cellular, or honeycomb, type.

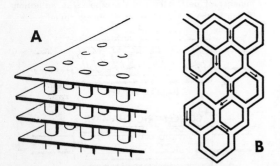

A

B

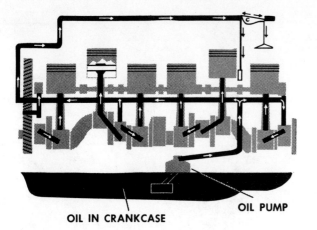

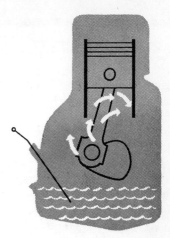

OIL IN CRANKCASE

OIL PUMP

11. This diagram and the one at the right show the lubricating system of an automobile engine. Above: a pump forces the oil to various surfaces where it is required.

12. In addition to the pump, the rotating action of the engine crankshaft, moved by the pistons, causes oil to be splashed vigorously onto different engine surfaces.

The electrical system of a modern automobile is very complicated. For the sake of simplicity it can be divided into two parts — the ignition system of the engine and the system that supplies current to operate various devices mounted on the body and chassis. Both systems receive their electrical energy from a lead storage battery and an engine-driven generator. The battery supplies the electricity for operating the starting motor that cranks the engine; it also supplies various other electrical devices while the engine is not running. When the engine is running, the electrical energy for ignition and other purposes is supplied by the generator, which also recharges the battery. All cars have a six-volt or twelve-volt system.

The ignition system (Figure 13) supplies the electric spark that is used to ignite the combustible mixture of gasoline and air. The spark is produced between the two electrodes of the spark plug (Figure 14). The plug is screwed into the cylinder head. The end that protrudes into the combustion chamber has two electrodes, separated by a gap that varies from 25 thousandths of an inch to 40 thousandths of an inch. In order to have a spark jump across this gap, an electrical pressure, or voltage, of at least 10,000 volts is required. The voltage supplied by the generator is at most about eight or fifteen volts; that of the battery is about six or twelve volts. To raise the voltage to the required amount, an induction coil — the ignition coil — is used.

13. Ignition system. Its operation is described on this page.

14. Close-up of spark plug.

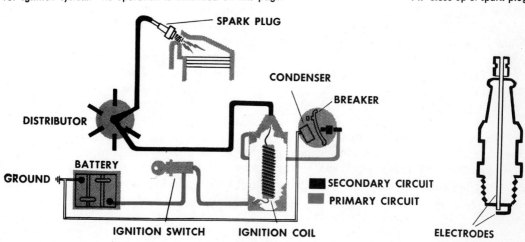

SPARK PLUG

CONDENSER

BREAKER

DISTRIBUTOR

BATTERY

GROUND

■ **SECONDARY CIRCUIT**

■ **PRIMARY CIRCUIT**

IGNITION SWITCH

IGNITION COIL

ELECTRODES

It consists of an iron core around which are wound two coils of insulated wire, not connected to each other; they are called the primary and secondary windings. The primary coil consists of several hundred turns of heavy wire; the secondary, of about 20,000 turns of fine wire. A cam, rotated by a camshaft-driven device, repeatedly opens the six-eight volt or twelve-fifteen volt circuit, which is connected to the primary coil. Every time this low-voltage current is interrupted or broken, a high-voltage current is produced in the secondary coil.

An important part of the ignition system is the rotor, a sort of revolving switch, which is turned by the same shaft that moves the ignition cam. The rotor distributes the high-voltage current to the wires leading to each spark plug. The rotor is placed on the shaft in such a way that it will connect the secondary of the coil to the correct spark plug in order to ignite the mixture at the beginning of each power stroke. A condenser, connected across the point where the primary current is broken, helps to produce a better spark.

The other electrical circuits of the car are designed to operate on the six-eight volt or twelve-fifteen volt range; they are connected to the battery and generator in a parallel hookup (see Index, under Parallel electrical circuits). In order to save wire, each device is connected to one end of the battery-generator combination by means of insulated wire and to the other end through the metal frame in order to complete the circuit.

The rear wheels of all present-day motor cars receive their power from the engine through a power transmission system, consisting of the clutch, transmission, universal joint (or joints), propeller shaft, rear axle gears, differential, rear axles and rear wheels.

The clutch is used to connect the engine to the power transmission system or to disconnect it at the will of the driver. It consists of a disk that can be held against the flywheel. When it makes contact with the flywheel, it turns through the force of friction. To have some idea of how it

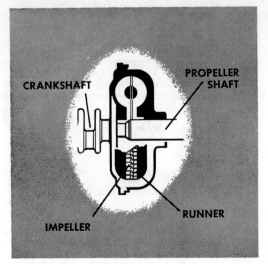

15. Fluid drive transmits power smoothly.

works, hold two books pressed tightly together and start turning one of the books around. The other book will also turn. The clutch disk is connected by means of a shaft to the transmission or gear box that is located directly behind it.

To connect the engine to the transmission, a heavy spring, or a series of springs, forces the disk against the flywheel. If the driver wishes to disconnect the engine from the transmission, he pushes down the clutch pedal, located on the floor of the car. This pedal operates a system of levers that removes the pressures from the disk and thus prevents the flywheel from turning it.

In a vehicle equipped with fluid drive (Figure 15), a fluid flywheel is placed between the clutch and the transmission. This type of drive consists of two units — the impeller and the runner — enclosed in a single housing. Both units have interior fins radiating from the hub; the two sets of fins face each other without touching. The housing in which the impeller and the runner are enclosed is kept about four-fifths full of oil. When the impeller turns, it churns up the oil and gives it a great deal of centrifugal force. The impact of the flying oil against the runner forces it to turn. The entire unit can be used to transmit power and take up loads slowly without jerking.

The function of the transmission or gear box is to provide the engine with a system of gears that will furnish various mechanical advantages or leverages. In this way the force that the engine produces can be multiplied in accordance with the demands of the driver.

Following is a description of the standard transmission. In the so-called neutral position, the engine is not connected to the propeller shaft even when the clutch pedal is not pressed down. In low gear, the engine turns about three times as fast as the propeller shaft, which is connected to the rear of the transmission. This is brought about through a double pair of gears in which small gears are made to drive large ones. The engine can supply maximum power to the rear wheels while it is in low gear. This proves very helpful in starting the car from rest and in climbing very steep grades.

In intermediate speed, or second gear, the gear ratio is less than in low gear. This arrangement is used when the car is already in motion or when the grade to be overcome is not too steep. In high gear the drive is direct and no leverage or

16. The conventional gear-shift system.

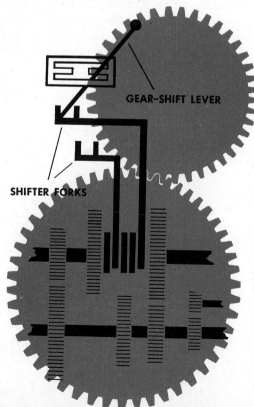

GEAR-SHIFT LEVER

SHIFTER FORKS

mechanical advantage is provided by the transmission. Maximum speed is provided by this gear. Much less power is supplied than in first or second gear; but the momentum of the car as it rolls along the road at a good rate of speed added to the power supplied by the engine keeps the car running smoothly. However, if the speed of the car falls below a certain point, third gear will not supply enough power and the car will stall. To prevent this from happening, the driver shifts to second gear; thus he obtains more power.

Another system of gears in the transmission causes the direction of rotation of the propeller shaft and of the rear wheels to be reversed. The operator can cause the car to move backward by simply operating a lever that changes the gear arrangement in the transmission.

The shifting of gears, which provides three speeds forward and one reverse, is accomplished by a system of levers attached to forks inside the gear box (see Figure 16). As the driver moves the hand of the gear-shift lever, he causes the gears that are attached to these forks to move and thus engage other gears. In this way different gear combinations and ratios are produced. In early-model cars this gear-shift lever was located above the transmission. In most present-day models that use the conventional gear shift, the lever is mounted on the steering wheel column under the steering wheel.

Some modern cars use a fourth forward speed, called overdrive. With this device, which is used above a minimum speed, the crankshaft turns only about 70 per cent as rapidly as the propeller shaft. This saves gasoline and reduces vibrations. The overdrive is located between the transmission and the propeller shaft.

Since 1936 the use of semiautomatic and fully automatic transmissions has made driving much simpler.

The semiautomatic transmission is used in conjunction with a fluid drive and a clutch. It resembles the standard transmission except that the shift control lever has only three positions: high, low and reverse. When the gears are shifted to either

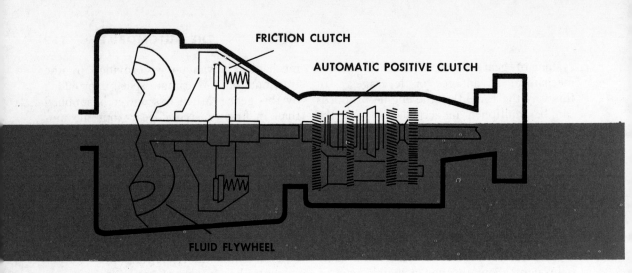

FRICTION CLUTCH

AUTOMATIC POSITIVE CLUTCH

FLUID FLYWHEEL

17. All-gear type automatic transmission.

of the forward positions and the car reaches a set speed, the transmission can be shifted automatically to a higher speed by momentarily releasing the accelerator pedal. The shifting to a higher gear is done by a hydraulic piston controlled by an electric circuit. The clutch is used only for shifting in and out of the speed ranges.

There are three types of fully automatic transmissions currently in use. In one (the Hydra-matic), all gear ratios are obtained by the use of planetary gears, in which one cogged wheel is made to move around the circumference of another. This all-gear type automatic transmission (Figure 17) has four forward speeds and a reverse. The shifting is done by hydraulic mechanisms controlled by valves linked to the accelerator pedal and a car speed governor. The timing of the shifts depends

on throttle position and vehicle speed. One valve is connected to the driver control lever. Its position determines whether the car will be reversed, allowed to shift in all ranges or limited to two or three speeds.

Another type of automatic transmission is the straight torque converter. In this design no gears are used for most operations (the so-called drive range). In structure and operation it resembles a fluid drive. Oil is thrown off from a pump driven by the engine onto the vanes of a turbine that is linked to the output shaft. At the start the oil does not strike the turbine with enough force to move it. Only when it is redirected back to the pump by a stationary set of vanes called the stator does the pump supply enough oil pressure to the turbine to turn it and so move the vehicle. In some designs the angle of the

18. A common form of universal joint.

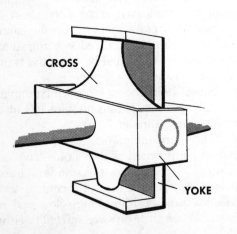

CROSS

YOKE

19. Rear-axle and differential gears.

PROPELLER SHAFT

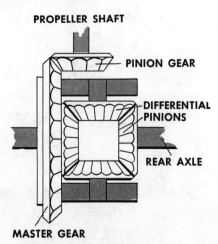

PINION GEAR

DIFFERENTIAL PINIONS

REAR AXLE

MASTER GEAR

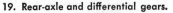

vanes is linked to the car's accelerator pedal so that a variable pitch is obtained. This causes the volume of redirected oil to be altered. The effect of the redirected oil is to produce the same results as a series of gears. As the vehicle gains speed, the torque multiplication gradually decreases and the unit becomes in effect a fluid drive. To provide extra leverage for unusual conditions and for a reverse gear the converter transmissions are combined with a planetary gear set.

In the third type of automatic transmission a torque converter is used in conjunction with a planetary gear transmission for all types of driving as well as for low and reverse gear. Some designs have only one forward speed. Others have two or three speeds combined with the converter.

The propeller shaft is the connecting link between the transmission and the gears that drive the rear wheel axles. As the rear axles of an automobile are suspended by springs, there will be an up-and-down movement in the rear end of the propeller shaft, and a slight change in the distance from the transmission to the rear axles. In order to provide for this, one or more universal joints are used. A common form of universal joint consists of two **U**-shaped members placed at right angles to each other and connected by a joint in the form of a cross (see Figure 18). With a universal joint at one or both ends of the propeller shaft, both this shaft and the rear axles can move up and down, and there are no bad effects as the car passes over a rough road.

The rear axle gears consist of a small gear, called a pinion, which is in line with the propeller shaft, and a large master gear, mounted in such a way as to turn at right angles to the pinion (Figure 19). The rear axle gears serve two purposes. One is to transmit the power at right angles; the other, to produce a mechanical advantage by having a small gear drive a large one. All modern cars use hypoid gears in their rear axle gear assembly. In this arrangement the pinion is set below the center of the large master gear. This arrangement permits the drive shaft to be placed below the center line of the rear axles, and makes it possible to provide the car with a low chassis and body.

When an automobile turns a corner or goes around a curve, the outside wheels have to travel farther than the inside ones and therefore must turn faster. To make this possible, a set of gears known as the differential is employed (Figure 19). Small bevel gears are attached to the inner ends of the two rear axle shafts so that they face each other. Meshed between these are two or four smaller bevel gears, called the differential pinions. If the two rear wheels revolve at equal speeds, the differential pinions will not turn. If one wheel turns faster than the other, in rounding a corner, say, the differential pinions

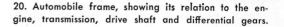

20. Automobile frame, showing its relation to the engine, transmission, drive shaft and differential gears.

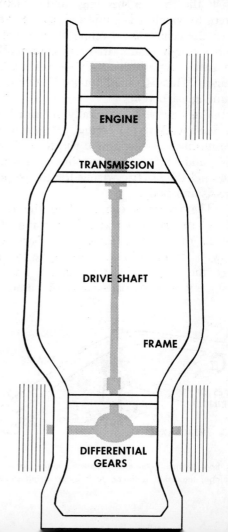

will move about their axes. This will cause one axle shaft to revolve faster than the other.

The rear wheels are fastened to two independent axles, which are turned by the differential. The rear axle assembly is enclosed in a case or housing, which holds lubricating oil and supports the rear of the vehicle through a pair of springs.

The automobile chassis contains the power plant — that is, the engine — and the driving mechanisms — that is, all the parts concerned in the actual forward (or rearward) motion of the vehicle. It is made up of the engine, power transmission system, frame, springs, axles, wheels, tires, brakes and steering system.

The frame (Figure 20) is the backbone of the automobile. It is generally made of cold-rolled open-hearth or heat-treated steel. This is strong and stiff enough to resist the severe bending and twisting forces to which it is subjected, particularly when the vehicle is traveling at high speed over a rough road. In some automobiles the underpart of the body serves as the frame. This is called integral body-and-frame construction.

The engine is generally mounted on the front end of the frame. Between the side members of the frame run the exhaust pipes and muffler, the gasoline and brake lines and the electric wiring for the engine, chassis and body.

The frame is connected to the front wheel supports and rear axle housing by a system of springs, shock absorbers and sway or stabilizer bars, which serve to support the weight of the vehicle and to cushion it against road shocks or bumps.

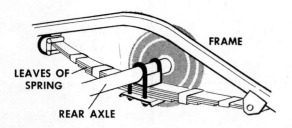

FRAME

LEAVES OF SPRING

REAR AXLE

21. Rear springs. One end is fastened to the frame with a hinge; the other is linked to it by a spring shackle.

Most vehicles use longitudinal leaf springs between their rear axle housings and frame. These springs consist of about half a dozen flat steel plates or leaves, of different lengths, assembled as shown in Figure 21. The longest leaf is curled at either end, forming an eye that can easily be bolted to a frame or axle housing. One end of the spring is generally fastened to the frame with a pivotlike hinge. The other end is linked to the frame through a device called a spring shackle. This end of the spring can move back and forth as the bumps on the road cause it to flex and change in length. A certain number of older cars have transverse (crosswise) leaf springs for the rear suspensions; others have coil springs.

The front wheels of all modern cars are mounted so that they can act independently of each other in absorbing road shocks. In other words, they are independently suspended from the frame. Instead of a rigid front axle, they employ a system of flexible arms in conjunction with a coil spring (or torsion bar) to support the front of the vehicle and to hold the steering system in place.

Shock absorbers are connected between the wheel supports and the frame in order to control the up-and-down movements of the springs and so prevent the automobile from bouncing violently on rough roads. Most modern shock absorbers operate like hydraulic door checks. A special liquid is forced through their openings when the car passes over a bump in the road. This creates a resistance that controls the rebounding action of the springs. Some shock absorbers are of the two-way type: that is, they cushion the upward bounce and downward rebound.

The mounting of the front wheels is entirely different from that of the rear wheels since they do not have to transmit power but are used for steering purposes (Figure 22). Each wheel is mounted, by means of bearings, on a spindle-shaped axle. This spindle is part of a steering knuckle that can turn about a nearly vertical axis called a king pin. (Some cars use ball joints in place of the king pin.) A series

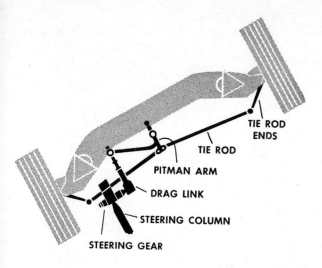

22. The steering assembly of a modern car.

tached to the axle, while the part holding the tire is being removed. This makes it easy to change tires; it also helps to keep the brake mechanism entirely enclosed.

The tire is generally made up of an inner rubber tube, which holds the air, and an outer casing, or shoe. (In a tubeless tire the air is held between the wheel rim and the casing.) A rubber valve stem is attached to the inner tube; it holds the valve that controls the entrance and exit of air. The body of the outer casing consists of rubberized cotton cord, rayon or nylon fabric. The tread, bonded to the body by other fabric layers, is composed of a mixture of rubber and synthetic rubber. Layers of rubber compound make up the sidewalls — the sides of the tire.

The braking system of all cars is divided into two parts: the foot-operated service brake system, used almost exclusively while the car is actually being driven, and the hand-controlled parking, or emergency, brake system.

All modern cars have a hydraulic brake system for service use (Figure 23). In this system, a brake pedal, operated by the driver's foot, is linked to a large cylinder, called the master cylinder. Pipes, called brake lines, lead from the master cylinder to cylinders in the wheel assemblies. The master cylinder, wheel cylinder and the brake lines contain a special liquid, called brake fluid.

Each of the wheel cylinders is set within a drum, a wide-rimmed, hollow wheel attached to the automobile wheel and

of levers connect the movable knuckle to a single lever called the Pitman arm, which is controlled by the steering gear.

When the driver moves the steering wheel in front of him, he causes a strong steel tube that is attached to it to turn in a case called a steering column. The lower end of the steering tube is machined in the form of a worm, or screw. The worm meshes with a gear or other part and causes the Pitman arm to move, thus controlling the movement of the steering knuckles. In some cars hydraulic pressure, obtained from a belt-driven pump, is used to help the driver turn the steering mechanism. This is called power steering.

Most modern cars are equipped with steel disk wheels and balloon tires. The wheels are so designed as to allow the hub and brake drum combination to remain at-

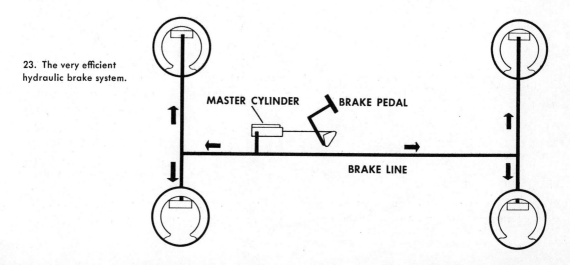

23. The very efficient hydraulic brake system.

revolving with it (Figure 24). Within the drum there are also two curved steel pieces, called brake shoes; they are set close to the inner surface of the drum. The outer surface of each shoe is covered with an asbestos composition fabric, called brake lining. One end of each shoe is pivoted; the other end is linked to a wheel cylinder piston, as shown in Figure 24.

When the operator presses down on the brake pedal, a piston within the master cylinder forces brake fluid to move along the brake lines and transmits pressure to each of the pistons in the wheel cylinders. These pistons move outward and force the brake shoes against the inner walls of the drum. The friction that is produced as a

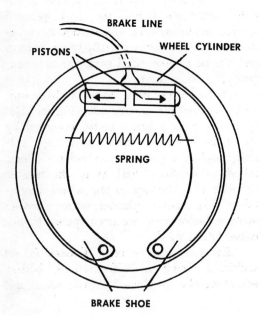

BRAKE LINE

PISTONS

WHEEL CYLINDER

SPRING

BRAKE SHOE

24. The brake-drum assembly.

result is enough to slow down or stop the rotating drum and the wheel that is fastened to it. When the brake pedal is released, the action of a spring set between the shoes forces them to break off contact with the walls of the drum.

All emergency brakes are of the mechanical type. In one design the rear shoes only are forced against the inner surface of the drum by the action of a wedge, cam

or lever, linked by a system of cables to a hand brake. In some cars the mechanical brake system is located in back of the transmission. When the hand brake is applied, in this case, the propeller shaft is prevented from turning and so locks the rear wheels. In power brakes the driver's pedal pressure is increased by a piston operated by engine vacuum.

The lighting system of the modern car includes the headlights, taillights, dashboard lights, stop lights, directional signals and dome lights. All automobiles in the United States and Canada have sealed beam headlights; in these the lens is sealed to the reflectors to give more light and longer life. Two filaments are used. When current passes through one of these filaments, the beam is projected straight ahead. When the other filament is used, the beam is projected downward and to the right. This filament is employed in city driving or when a car approaches from the opposite direction on a highway.

Automobile bodies are made up of a number of sections, pressed into shape by giant hydraulic presses, assembled and then welded together. Some type of insulating material is cemented to the body panels. This material reduces the conduction of heat through the steel and absorbs any sound that may be produced by the vibration of the panel.

The body is bolted to the chassis. Rubber, cork or fabric shims or gaskets are placed between body and chassis to prevent squeaking and to keep engine vibrations from being transmitted to the body. Hoods and some fenders are attached to the body. Many fenders form an integral part of the body or are welded to it.

The instrument panel is the control center of the car. A gasoline gauge records the amount of gasoline in the tank. Speed is indicated by a speedometer; the distance that has been traveled, by an odometer. A temperature gauge shows how hot the cooling-system water is. An oil pressure gauge indicates how much pressure is being applied to the lubricating oil that is being forced through the engine's oil-circulating system. By looking at the ammeter, the driver can tell whether his generator is charging adequately. (Some cars use lights in place of some of these gauges.) Other devices control the lights, radio, heaters and so on.

A good deal of the equipment for automobiles comes under the heading of accessories; they are not necessary for the operation of the car but add to the comfort and pleasure of driving. Among them are radios, heaters, air-conditioning apparatus, windshield defrosters, fog lights, spotlights, clocks, cigarette lighters, bumper guards, directional turn indicators, seat covers and windshield washers. In some cases, articles formerly thought of as accessories have become standard equipment on practically all cars. Among these are wheel disks and dual windshield wipers.

The automobile is an outstanding example of a fine product built by mass production methods. Automobile manufacturers generally purchase many parts of their cars from other companies. These units usually include the generators, the storage battery, the self-starter, the lighting system, the carburetor, the ammeter and the speedometer.

There are several stages in the mass production of a given automobile model. First, the style of the new model is created; specifications are drawn up. Experimental cars are built and are put through an exhaustive series of tests in the laboratory and on the road. Any "bugs," or defects, that show up in these tests must be corrected before the model is put into production. Finally special patterns, dies and machine tools are prepared and the manufacture of the new model begins.

The second stage is machining: the different parts of the car are cast, forged, stamped, or welded. Cylinder blocks and various other parts are cast by means of molds into which molten metal is poured. Some castings are hardened by being baked in ovens; others are shaped by machines; still others are polished. Crankshafts, connecting rods, camshafts and valves are forged from steel. Many parts, including fenders, gasoline tanks and crankcases, are stamped in huge presses, operated by

hydraulic pressure. Lathes are used for certain units; grinding tools, for others. Drilling tools sometimes bore twenty holes at a time in steel parts, each at exactly the right distance from the rest.

The final assembly of the car is perhaps the most spectacular part of the manufacturing process. After all the parts made in the manufacturing plant have been completed and have been supplemented by parts made by other manufacturers, they are ready for the assembly lines. First, they are conveyed to the subassemblies, where certain basic units, such as the engine and the frame, are put together. After leaving the subassemblies, the basic units go to the final assembly lines.

The frame is placed on one of these lines and the different parts of the car are added to it. The springs, axle assemblies, shock absorbers and brake drums are installed. The engine has been assembled and tested on another assembly line; it is conveyed to the frame by an overhead hoist, and is lowered onto the chassis. The body, in the meantime, has been put together on still another line. The dash has been set in place; wiring has been installed; fenders have been added.

The completely assembled body is raised by an overhead hoist to the frame and is put into position. The steering wheel and hood are now added; all bolts are carefully tightened. Gasoline and oil and grease are supplied. By the time the car has reached the end of the assembly lines, it is ready to start off under its own power. The new car is thoroughly inspected; it is put through a test on the road before it is shipped to a waiting automobile dealer.

Sometimes the finished parts that will go into an automobile are shipped to outlying assembly plants and are put together there. These plants may be hundreds or thousands of miles away from the main plant; they may even be in a foreign country. The cars that roll off the assembly lines in these far-off places are comparable in every respect to those that have been assembled in the main plant.

See also Vol. 10, p. 285: "Automobiles."

SPONGES, JELLYFISH AND SEA STARS

Familiar Marine Animals without Backbones

BY FRANCIS J. RYAN AND ELIZABETH J. RYAN

A TRIP to the seashore becomes a rewarding experience when you recognize and know about the animals living in the low-tide zone. In shallow waters or in tide pools you will find sponges, hydroids, corals and sea anemones — all attached to stones or pilings, rockweed or shells. Jellyfish swim feebly at the surface. Sea stars, sea urchins, sand dollars and sea cucumbers rest or move slowly on the sandy or gravelly bottom. These marine invertebrates, or animals without backbones, make up three main groups, or phyla. Inland representatives of these animals include freshwater sponges and the hydra.

Sponges (phylum Porifera) — simple multicelled animals

At first glance sponges resemble odd gelatinous plants. They are fan-shaped or dome-shaped, formed like vases, bowls, goblets or trumpets, branched like trees or flattened out in lichen fashion. They are animals, however, although very unusual ones. Basically, the sponge is a hollow tube, attached at one end to a support and open at the upper end. Some sponges exist in colonies of many individuals united to each other at their bases.

Sponges are many-celled animals lacking specialized organs and incapable of movement. A layer of flattened, protective cells covering the body's surface is perforated by tiny pores (the phylum name "Porifera" means "hole-bearing"). The pores open to canals that run through the jellylike substance, or mesenchyme, of the body. The canals, in turn, open into a large central cavity. In the more complex sponges, these canals lead to spherical chambers and pass from them into the cavity.

Lining the chambers or central cavity are collar cells, or choanocytes; each has a collar of protoplasm, which encircles the base of a whiplike structure known as a flagellum. As the flagellum undulates, it creates a current of water. The waving of many flagella causes water to enter through the sponge's pores, circulate in the canals and chambers and flow into the central cavity. Microscopic plants and animals and organic debris are brought in with the water. The food particles are drawn to the collar cells, where they are engulfed. They are then digested or passed on to cells that creep about like amebas in the mesenchyme. Incoming water currents also bring oxygen to the cells.

After water circulates in the central cavity, it passes out through a large open-

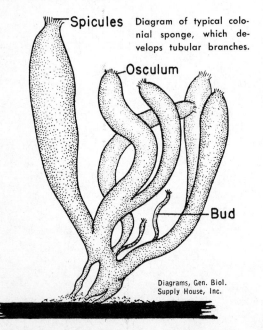

Spicules

Osculum

Bud

Diagram of typical colonial sponge, which develops tubular branches.

Diagrams, Gen. Biol. Supply House, Inc.

ing, the osculum. Carbon dioxide and other wastes, discharged by the cells, are eliminated in the escaping water.

A skeletal framework supports the soft mass of the sponge. This prevents the canals from collapsing and allows considerable growth. (Some sponges may be as much as six feet high.) Special mesenchyme cells secrete this skeleton, which is made up of needles, called spicules, or of protein fibers, known as spongin. Spicules may be either straight or curved and are often pronged; they may be sharply pointed, knobbed or frayed at the ends. Often they project beyond the body, making the sponge appear bristly. These spicules, together with the unpleasant secretions and odors produced by the sponge, protect it from enemies.

Sponges are classified by the type of skeleton they possess. One class (Calcispongiae) secrete spicules of calcium carbonate. Another class (Hyalospongiae), called glass sponges, have siliceous spicules — that is, spicules made of silica, which is familiar to us as quartz or sand. Deep-sea glass sponges form a skeletal network suggesting spun glass. The third class (Demospongiae) have siliceous spicules, or a skeleton of spongin, or else a framework made up of both spicules and spongin. Some have no skeleton at all. The Demospongiae are the most common; they include the fresh-water sponges and the boring sponge, which protects itself by etching its way into rock and mollusk shells. The sponge that we use in our homes — the bath sponge — is not the whole animal but only its framework of spongin, which is elastic, chemically inert and similar to silk and horn.

Sponges may reproduce by. sexual means. Special mesenchyme cells increase in size as food is stored within them and become egg cells; others divide into sperm cells, which are discharged into the water. The egg remains in the mesenchyme, where it is fertilized by sperm from another sponge. The fertilized egg becomes a flagellated larva (a larva with flagella), which escapes through the osculum and swims away. Soon the tiny larva attaches to a

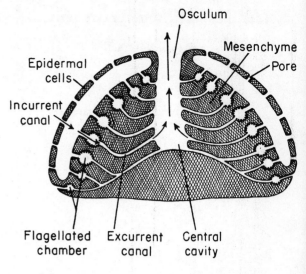

A cross section of a fresh-water sponge.

support and begins growth as a young sponge.

Reproduction may be by budding. Cells grow out from the body and develop into miniature sponges; depending on the species, these either remain attached as members of a branching colony or drop off from the parent to lead an independent life. Some sponges form internal buds called gemmules; these are small masses of food-enriched mesenchyme cells, protected by a resistant coat and often strengthened with spicules. Gemmules are commonly produced by fresh-water sponges — those dull-colored or greenish irregular blobs that grow on submerged leaves and water-soaked logs in the clean water of lakes, ponds and streams. When the parent sponge dies, the gemmules withstand freezing and drying. They grow into adults when conditions for sponge life again become favorable.

One type of sponge (*Suberites*) grows on empty snail shells that house hermit crabs. The sponge absorbs the shell; thereafter it serves as a covering for the crab as the crustacean moves about. This arrangement is mutually beneficial. The crab gains protection; the sponge is transported from one place to another by the crab and thus comes in contact with new sources of food. Most sponges are veritable "apartment houses" for a host of animals. Marine worms, pistol crabs, shrimps and slender fishes find a haven in the canals and chambers ; barnacles attach themselves to the surface.   They all get food from the water passing through the sponge's body.

Sponges probably evolved from an aggregate of individual protozoans, perhaps the choanoflagellates, which are much like the sponge's collar cells.   The sponge has no sense receptors, no nervous system.   However, it can close its pores and osculum and contract its body cells when harmful substances are in the water.   A unique animal indeed, the sponge is set apart from all other many-celled creatures by its simple structure and the somewhat specialized but un-co-ordinated cells of its body.

N. Y. Zool. Soc.

The mouth of this sea anemone is surrounded by tentacles.

The sea anemone's gastrovascular cavity, or gut, is divided by partitions, as shown.

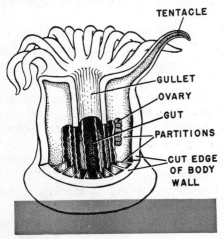

TENTACLE

GULLET
OVARY
GUT
PARTITIONS

CUT EDGE
OF BODY
WALL

Hydroids, jellyfish and sea anemones (phylum Coelenterata)

Like sponges, coelenterates are essentially tubular animals with a central cavity.   Here food is digested (Coelenterata means "hollow intestine") as well as circulated ; therefore, it is called the gastrovascular (digestive and circulating) cavity.   Food enters by the mouth at the upper end of the body and is broken down by enzymes secreted by gland cells   The nutrients then diffuse into the body.   (Often food is only reduced to particles, which are engulfed and fully digested, as with the sponges, by certain cells lining the cavity.)   The beating of flagella gives rise to water currents, which bring in food particles and oxygen.   Countercurrents carry wastes out through the mouth.

The outer surface of the body consists of a layer of tightly packed protective cells.   Interspersed in this layer are sensory cells, sensitive to touch and chemical substances, and specialized cells called thread capsules, or nematocysts.   Each nematocyst contains a fluid under pressure and a spirally coiled, hollow thread.   When the capsule is stimulated by touch, and possibly by chemicals as well, the thread is forcibly ejected.

Some of these threads pierce the coelenterate's prey and then inject a benumbing poison into it. Other threads either stick to the prey or wrap around its appendages. Nematocysts are very abundant on the coelenterate's tentacles, which grow as a crown around the mouth. Once prey is paralyzed and held fast by the threads, the tentacles enfold it and draw it into the mouth.

Between the surface cells and those lining the gastrovascular cavity is a layer of supporting jellylike substance. Mesenchyme cells are found in this layer; these are unspecialized cells that form nematocysts and sex cells. Numerous nerve cells lie below the outer covering and join together to form an extensive nerve net.

The animal we have just described — a sort of living tube crowned with tentacles — is known as a polyp. The different types of coelenterates are merely variants of this polyp form. They are grouped into three classes: Hydrozoa, the hydroids and fresh-water hydras; Scyphozoa, the jellyfishes; and Anthozoa, the sea anemones and corals.

Hydroids are made up of hundreds of tiny polyps united by a stalk to form a branching colony. The gastrovascular cavity of each polyp joins with that of the stalk so that there is a cavity common to the entire colony. Often the stalk and polyps are held erect and protected by a horny sheath. Hydroids feed on minute worms and various small crustaceans.

A hydroid colony resembles a fern or other "feathery" plant; such colonies are commonly found attached to wharf pilings, rocks and kelp. The colony reproduces by giving off buds. Some buds form a mouth and a circlet of tentacles at the tip to become what are known as feeding polyps. Others develop into reproductive polyps; they have neither mouth nor tentacles but produce tiny saucerlike appendages. When mature, these saucers break off and swim away. They are called medusas; they look like miniature jellyfish with tentacles hanging from the rim of the saucer.

Below: sea whip in foreground; brain coral in background. Right: branch of tropical stony coral, showing expanded polyps and a contracted polyp.

Kitchen-Kinne,
Nat. Audubon Soc.

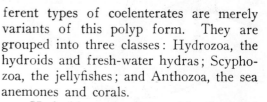

Gen. Biol. Supply House, Inc.

The polyps of this branching hydroid colony are united by a common stem.

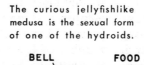

The curious jellyfishlike medusa is the sexual form of one of the hydroids.

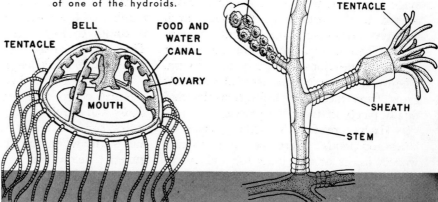

TENTACLE   BELL   FOOD AND WATER CANAL   OVARY   MOUTH

MOUTH   REPRODUCTIVE POLYP   FEEDING POLYP   TENTACLE   SHEATH   STEM

These two kinds of sea stars
are found in shallow waters.

The function of the medusas is to reproduce sexually. Sex cells, on the underside of the saucer, produce eggs or sperm, which are shed into the water where fertilization takes place. Each fertilized egg becomes a ciliated larva — one provided with hairlike processes called cilia. The larva swims about for a time before attaching itself and forming a polyp; the polyp then buds and a new hydroid colony is produced. The process whereby the colony forms asexual buds that give rise to sexually reproducing organisms is called alternation of generations. This behavior, which is also found in plants (see Index), serves to spread the species into new localities.

Some species of Hydrozoa have insignificant polyps; the medusa is the conspicuous stage in their lives. Others flourish as hydroid colonies producing only attached, degenerate medusalike structures that shed eggs and sperm into the water.

The fresh-water hydra, a minute individual polyp, does not go through a medusa stage. Instead, the fertilized egg remains affixed to the outside of the body until a heavy membrane forms around the embryo. Then it separates from the parent and later develops into a young hydra. The hydra also produces asexual buds that grow from the body, form tentacles and finally pinch off from the parent.

Hydras prefer the clean waters of lakes and ponds, where they feed on tiny worms, insect larvae, young fish and microscopic crustaceans. They glide along the bottom and on submerged plant stems by creeping movements of the cells at the base of the body. They also move by somersaulting. First, they bend over and attach their tentacles to a support while releasing the base; then they swing the base over and attach it, freeing the tentacles, and so on.

The coelenterate known as the Portuguese man-of-war is related to the hydroids and hydras. It is a complex colonial animal supplied with a crested, gas-filled float, from which hang feeding polyps, clusters of attached medusas and long, trailing tentacles armed with stinging thread capsules.

The typical jellyfish has a bell-shaped, gelatinous body. Under the central part of the bell is a short process bearing the mouth. The corners of the mouth are pulled out into grooved oral arms; these carry nematocysts that paralyze and entangle small aquatic animals. The prey is swept along the ciliated grooves of the arms, through the mouth and into the spacious gastrovascular cavity, which has branched radial canals going to the margin of the bell. Numerous tentacles fringe the edge of the bell; sense organs that are sensitive to light, chemicals and the directions of movement are also located on the bell's margin. The jellyfish weakly swims by rhythmically contracting its bell.

Ovaries or testes (as the case may be) lie on the floor of the gastrovascular cavity. Sperms are released in the water and fertilize the eggs in the cavity of another jellyfish. Each fertilized egg then lodges in a fold of an oral arm, where it develops into a ciliated larva. This escapes and grows into an inconspicuous polyp. Eventually the polyp develops a number of horizontal constrictions, so that it comes to look like a pile of saucers. The saucers break away as medusas and develop into adult jellyfish.

The stout-bodied sea anemone is a noncolonial polyp that attaches to rocks or shells and rarely changes its place. Tentacles rim the upper part of the animal and surround the mouth, which leads to a gullet. Below this is the gastrovascular cavity, which is divided by partitions. These increase the digestive capacity of the animal so that large prey, such as crabs and fish, can be consumed. The sea anemone can reproduce itself by dividing its body in half longitudinally. Sometimes, too, as the animal slides along on its slimy basal disk, or foot, fragments of its body are left behind. Small anemones are regenerated from these pieces. Eggs and sperms are produced on the partitions of the gastrovascular cavity and are released through the mouth. Ciliated larvae develop from the fertilized eggs and form single anemones. There are no medusas in the anemone's life cycle.

The stony corals are colonial animals similar to anemones; they remain attached to one spot and secrete cups of calcium carbonate into which they can retract. Stony corals are found in deep, cold water, but it is only in the tropical and subtropical seas that they contribute to the building of reefs. We describe the reef builders in the article The Islands of the Main, in Volume 4.

The anemones and stony corals have various kin. These include the organ-pipe corals, which live in calcareous tubes joined together by platforms, and the precious, or red, corals, which are stiffened by calcareous spicules and are used in making jewelry. The related sea whips, sea fans and sea plumes are branching colonies of polyps supported by a flexible horny material.

The coelenterates display a somewhat higher organization than the sponges, particularly in the development of a true digestive cavity and in the elaboration of special sensory cells, a nerve net and muscle fibers. External stimuli affect the sensory cells, and impulses are conducted by way of the nerve net to the muscle fibers. Longitudinal muscles cause the polyp to shorten; circular muscles cause it to lengthen. Muscle fibers circling the mouth can close it off when harmful substances are in the water or when a falling tide leaves the animal high and dry. The various muscle fibers, co-ordinated by the nerve net, also allow polyps to bend in one direction or another and move their tentacles. The muscles of the medusa provide contractions of the bell for swimming.

It has been commonly held that the coelenterates developed from colonial protozoans much as did the sponges. But a revolutionary theory, which has gained considerable support, assumes that the coelenterates evolved from a primitive flatworm. If this theory is true, the sea anemones are the most primitive of coelenterates, and the jellyfish and hydroids, with their life cycles of alternating polyps and medusas, are a secondary development.

Sea stars, sea urchins and sea cucumbers (phylum Echinodermata)

Echinoderms are much more highly evolved than sponges and coelenterates; yet they are almost sedentary in habit and show a minimum of responses. The skin of a typical echinoderm covers an internal

The numerous spines of the sea urchin are stiff and movable. Sea-urchin spines, usually short and stubby, may grow to be several inches long.

Above: the shell-like skeleton of the sea urchin after the removal of the skin and spines.

skeleton of calcareous ossicles, or small bones, which give a more or less rigid structure. Projecting outward from the ossicles are numerous calcareous spines. (Echinodermata means "hedgehog," or "spiny," "skinned.") Inside the skeleton is the large body cavity, or coelom, in which lie the internal organs. The coelom contains a lymphlike fluid that bathes the organs; amebalike cells creep about in it removing wastes and carrying nutrients to all parts of the animal's body.

There is a complete digestive system, leading from the mouth, on the underside of the body, to the anus. Digestive glands pour their secretions into the stomach. A unique arrangement called the water vascular system allows water to enter a sieve plate on the body's surface and then circulate by way of another canal to a ring canal, which branches into radial canals. Each radial canal gives off many pairs of tube feet; when these are distended with water, they are used in locomotion and serve as respiratory surfaces. Encircling the mouth is a nerve ring from which branches radiate. Tiny nerves go to the internal organs, the skin and the tube feet.

The sex glands shed their products into the water, where fertilization occurs. Fertilized eggs give rise eventually to larvae that swim freely by means of ciliated bands. The larvae go through many stages of development before they begin to look like miniatures of their parents.

Starfishes, or sea stars (class Asteroidea), are perhaps the best known of the echinoderms. The body is a central disk from which radiate five or more arms. Between the blunt spines on the upper surface project skin gills, which are finger-like extensions of the coelom; they are excretory and respiratory organs. Small pincers interspersed among the spines protect the skin gills and clear the surface of foreign matter. On the underside of each arm is a groove from which protrude the slender tube feet. A light-sensitive eyespot and a short tentacle, which may be sensitive to chemicals, are located at the tip of each arm. Sea stars prey on tube worms, crustaceans and mollusks.

The brittle stars and serpent stars (class Ophiuroidea) have a small, flattened body disk with five many-jointed arms; in some cases (as in the basket star) the arms repeatedly branch. The stomach is saclike; there is no anus. These animals use their flexible arms to move jerkily about and to swim; the arms also catch worms, mollusks and other animals and bring the prey to the mouth.

Sea urchins and sand dollars (class Echinoidea) are globular-shaped, oval-shaped or flattened into thin disks. The skeleton forms a hard shell of flattened immovable ossicles; the spines are numerous, stiff and movable. Rows of tube feet radiate over the surface, converging at the upper and lower centers of the body. Some sea urchins feed on algae; others consume small marine animals.

Sea cucumbers (class Holothurioidea) are elongated animals with a mouth, surrounded by tentacles, at one end and the anus at the other. The skin is either leathery and muscular or delicate and transparent and possesses only microscopic calcareous ossicles. Sea cucumbers move by muscular contractions or by using the tube feet, which extend in five rows the length of the body. They eat organic material taken from mud or small animals entangled by the tentacles.

The sea lilies and feather stars (class Crinoidea) are flowerlike animals having flexible branching arms. Many are attached, mouth upward, to the sea bottom by means of a horny stalk; others have no stalk and swim freely by using the arms. Microscopic plants and animals, which are caught by the arms and swept to the mouth, form the food. The depth of the sea inhabited by these brilliantly colored echinoderms ranges from 12,000 feet to just below the low-tide line.

The echinoderms have no near kinship with any of the other invertebrates. They are highly interesting to biologists, nonetheless, because of their larval forms. These show close affinities with the larvae of the protochordates, the animals whose ancestors gave rise to backboned animals.

See also Vol. 10, p. 275: "Invertebrates."

THE WORMS

Dreaded Enemies and

Humble Benefactors of Man

BY F. L. FITZPATRICK

THE word "worms" is popularly applied to a great variety of long, slender and limbless animals — earthworms, tapeworms, hookworms, shipworms (which are mollusks), blindworms (which are lizards) and the larvae of various insects. A worm is commonly held to be a rather repulsive creature. There are various traces of this belief in our language. If we call a man a "worm," we imply that he is a cringing sort of a person; if, on rare occasions, he decides to assert himself, we say that "the worm has turned." A flatterer is said to be trying to "worm his way" into favor.

To a zoologist the word "worms" has a much more restricted meaning. It is applied particularly to three groups of animals; these are the flatworms, or platy-helminths, the roundworms, or nemathelminths, and the segmented worms, or annelids. The animals belonging to these groups are found in almost all parts of the world. Some of them burrow in the earth; others crawl along the ground; still others swim in the water. A considerable number are parasites upon other animals. Some worms, such as the earthworms, are considered to be benefactors of mankind; others, including the tapeworms and the liver flukes, rank high among the dangerous pests of man and his domestic animals.

Flatworms (platyhelminths)

The flatworms, or platyhelminths ("flat worms," in Greek), are placed lower in the animal classification than either

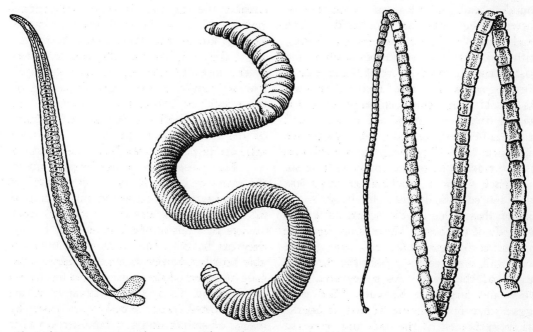

The trichina worm — a roundworm.   The earthworm — a segmented worm.   The tapeworm—a flatworm.

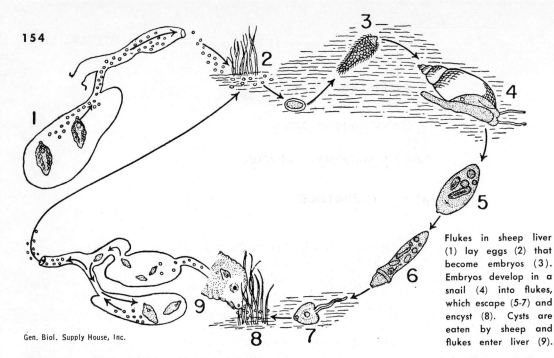

Flukes in sheep liver (1) lay eggs (2) that become embryos (3). Embryos develop in a snail (4) into flukes, which escape (5-7) and encyst (8). Cysts are eaten by sheep and flukes enter liver (9).

Gen. Biol. Supply House, Inc.

the roundworms or the annelids. There are about 10,000 known species of flatworms. In some of them, the outer layer of the body is provided with vibrating, hairlike structures called cilia; in others, the outer layer is smooth or spiny.

Perhaps the best-known of all the flatworms are the tapeworms, or cestodes; many species are important parasites of man and his domestic animals. The body of a tapeworm generally consists of a rounded head, or scolex, and a number of flattened segments, or proglottids. The head bears hooks or suckers (or both), with which the worm attaches itself to the host — usually to the lining of the intestine. New segments are formed next to the head. As the older segments keep on growing, the largest of all, naturally, are to be found at the tail end of the body. A fully grown tapeworm looks like a long, narrow ribbon; it may reach a length of thirty feet or so.

Each segment functions more or less as a self-contained unit; the head is the anchor that keeps all the segments within the body of the host. There is no digestive system; each segment absorbs, through the body wall, digested food from the digestive cavity of the host. As a segment gets older and larger, it becomes filled with eggs; when it is mature at last, it breaks off from the rest of the body and passes to the exterior with the wastes of the host.

A common tapeworm that attacks man is the so-called beef tapeworm (*Taenia saginata*). This animal must live in the bodies of two different hosts to complete its life cycle. The adult beef tapeworm is found in the human intestine, where it sometimes reaches a length of thirty feet. When the tail-end segments, filled with eggs, break off, they pass to the exterior with the wastes of the human host. If the wastes are not disposed of in a sanitary manner, the eggs may be deposited on grass and are likely to be swallowed by cattle. Boring larvae are then freed from the eggs; they migrate into the muscle tissues of the host and form cysts. If a man eats raw or partly cooked meat from one of these infected cattle, the cyst around the young worm will dissolve in the stomach of the human host; the worm will then take up its place of abode in the intestine.

The presence of a beef tapeworm in the intestine is not likely to prove fatal or even dangerous, because the animal cannot fill human tissues with cysts; its eggs must always pass out of the human body before they can hatch. The worm is an undesirable boarder, however, since it deprives the host of a part of the nourishment he should obtain from his food. Fortunately it can be eliminated from the body quite easily by means of simple drugs, administered under a doctor's direction.

The pork tapeworm (*Taenia solium*) is far more dangerous as far as man is concerned. Normally the adult worm lives in the human intestine. Here it develops the usual mature, egg-filled segments, which break off and pass to the exterior from time to time. If any of the eggs are swallowed by pigs, the larvae that hatch from them will form cysts in pig muscle. When infected pork that is only partly cooked is eaten by a human being, the cysts dissolve and the adult worms become established in the human intestine. The pests can be disposed of, as in the case of beef tapeworms, by drugs prescribed by a physician.

Unfortunately, now and then some of the pork-tapeworm eggs develop into young in the human body before they can pass out to the exterior with the body wastes. When

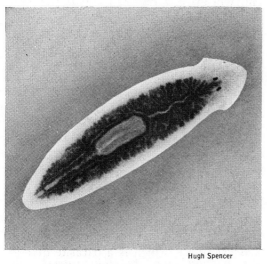

Hugh Spencer

In this stained preparation of the turbellarian *Planaria,* anterior eyespots are seen.

this happens, the young ultimately penetrate into muscle tissues, causing inflammation. The consequences are particularly serious when the encysted larvae lodge in vital areas of the body, such as the eye and brain.

Dogs and rabbits act as hosts for a good many kinds of tapeworms. Most of the parasites form their cysts in fish, mice, rats, rabbits, sheep, cows and pigs. One tapeworm (*Echinococcus granulosus*) that occurs as an adult in dogs forms cysts in human muscle, liver, lung, brain and bone

tissue. We become infected when we eat unwashed vegetables that have been contaminated by dogs, or drink contaminated water or kiss dogs to whose fur the eggs are clinging. All of our domestic birds are also subject to the attacks of tapeworms. Adult worms are developed in the bodies of these birds after they devour infected earthworms, houseflies, ants, beetles and the like.

Another important flatworm group is made up of the flukes, or trematodes. The best-known member of the group is the liver fluke (*Fasciola hepatica*), which lives as a parasite in the liver of sheep, cattle, pigs and sometimes man. This fluke is widely distributed throughout the world. It has a short and flattened body, about an inch long, with a sucker, containing the mouth, at one end. There is also a ventral sucker on the lower surface of the body; this is used for gripping. Unlike tapeworms, flukes possess a digestive tract; this has only one opening to the exterior — the mouth, which also serves as an anus.

The common liver fluke of sheep has a most amazing life cycle. About 200 adult flukes may be housed in a sheep's liver. These commonly produce eggs; as many as 100,000,000 eggs may be formed within the body of a single sheep host. After the eggs have begun to develop, they pass through the bile duct of the liver into the intestine and then to the exterior with the wastes.

The egg of a sheep liver fluke must get into water of the right temperature if it is to continue its development. If this happens, the egg gives rise to a tiny ciliated embryo. The little creature will die unless it finds a certain type of snail to serve as its host. If this host is forthcoming, the embryo burrows into it. Within the snail great numbers of young flukes are produced by a complicated budding process. The young escape from the snail and swim about freely for a time; then they climb upon blades of grass at the water's edge and form cysts about themselves. If a sheep swallows the cysts, the young flukes will work their way in time into the liver.

Naturally very few sheep liver flukes are likely to meet all the conditions set by

USDA

These are sugar-beet roots that have been infested by the tiny white female nematodes.

The flatworms known as turbellarians, or true flatworms, are generally free-swimming animals which do not lead parasitic lives. They have short, flattened bodies and a digestive system with but a single opening — on the underside of the body. Their bodies are covered with cilia, which can be used to produce swimming movements. These worms are found in the sea, in fresh water and in some moist places on the land. Some feed on worms, insects and tiny mollusks; others on microscopic organisms.

The turbellarians belonging to the genus *Planaria* are particularly interesting because they can regenerate (grow again) lost parts of the body. If the head or tail end is removed, a new head or tail will develop. If the body is cut in two, the head end will grow a new tail and the tail end will develop a new head. *Planaria* is often studied in biology courses.

Roundworms (nemathelminths)

The roundworms, or threadworms (the name "nemathelminth" is equivalent to "thread worm" in Greek) number about 12,000 species. A number of these are parasitic upon man and animals; some attack plants. The roundworms are slender creatures; they do not have cilia, like some of the flatworms, nor are they segmented.

The most notorious of the roundworms, or nematodes, from the human standpoint, is the trichina worm (*Trichinella spiralis*), which is a parasite of man, the pig, the house rat and probably other animals. It is a tiny creature; adult males are only a millimeter and a half in length while female adults are three to four millimeters long. The presence of the trichina worm in the human body causes the disease known as trichinosis. People are infected when they eat raw or rare pork from pigs that had adult trichina worms in their intestines.

The female worms in the pig host bear tiny young, which penetrate the walls of the intestine, enter the blood vessels and work their way into muscle tissues. Here each tiny worm embryo forms a cyst about itself. Life in the muscle tissues of the

such an exacting life cycle. If these worms continue to thrive and flourish, it is because of the enormous number of eggs they produce. Sheep may be seriously injured, and sometimes killed, by liver flukes. If the victims are not too far gone, it is possible to cure them by means of drugs that kill the worms.

There are many other species of parasitic flukes; they live in such organs or structures as the intestines, the lungs and the blood vessels. Various kinds of flukes attack man; there are several human liver flukes in Africa and the Orient.

host represents a dead end for the trichina unless a man or some other carnivore eats the tissue in which it is located. If the host is not devoured, the cyst wall will begin to harden after about six months and the embryo within the cyst will eventually die.

If the infected pig is butchered and used as human food, the story may be very different. The meat looks perfectly wholesome, because the cysts are too small to be seen by the naked eye. Thorough cooking will kill the trichina embryo within the cyst; but if the meat is eaten raw or only partly cooked or smoked, there is acute danger of human infection.

By the time the meat containing the parasites has reached the intestine the cyst walls have dissolved. The young worms soon grow to adult size. The human victim may suffer from digestive disturbances, including nausea, diarrhea and abdominal pain, if enough of the worms are present. If the disease is recognized at this stage, the parasites may be driven out of the intestines through the use of drugs under a doctor's direction, and no lasting harm will be done.

If the worms are not molested, the females bear a new generation of young. These bore into blood vessels of the intestinal wall, are carried to all parts of the body and form cysts in the muscle tissues. Muscle soreness and fever are typical symptoms of the disease at this stage. Breathing, swallowing and chewing movements are likely to be painful for a period of three or four weeks. The consequences are particularly serious when the trichina larvae damage vital areas of the body, such as the heart and diaphragm.

Once the young trichina parasites have gotten into the muscle tissues, they cannot be disposed of by means of drugs. It is possible to kill adults remaining in the intestines, so that no more young will be produced; otherwise little can be done. In the course of time calcareous matter is laid down in and around the cyst, which is ultimately transformed into a granule of lime in the muscle.

It has been estimated that there may be as many as 100,000,000 trichina cysts in some human hosts. In other cases, the number of cysts is comparatively small. A number of people have had trichinosis without being aware of the fact; there have not been enough worms in their bodies to cause serious damage.

Hookworms are parasitic roundworms that also infest man

The detested hookworms are also members of the roundworm group; they are a pest in tropical and subtropical regions. The species known as the American hookworm (*Necator americanus*) is considerably larger than the trichina worm; it is about a centimeter long (roughly, two fifths of an inch).

Adult American hookworms suck blood from the wall of the host's small intestine. The female produces large numbers of eggs, which pass to the exterior with the wastes. If these eggs are deposited upon warm and loose, moist soil, they develop into tiny larvae.

The larvae generally get into a human body through the soles of the feet. They bore through the skin, producing a sensation known variously as "ground itch," "dew itch" or "skin itch." Entering the blood vessels, the larvae now start on an amazing journey through the body. First they are transported by the blood stream through the heart to the tiny blood vessels of the lung tissue. They bore their way out into the air spaces of the lungs and then move upward through the bronchial tubes and windpipe to the back of the mouth cavity. They now pass down the esophagus and through the stomach and finally reach the small intestine. After completing this remarkable journey, the hookworms settle down to perhaps six or seven years of life.

The hookworm victim usually suffers from loss of blood and becomes thin and anemic; the skin takes on a waxy appearance. Often he suffers from heartburn and constipation; he is an easy prey to various diseases. Child victims are often retarded in their development.

The first line of defense against hookworms is to adopt the practice of wearing

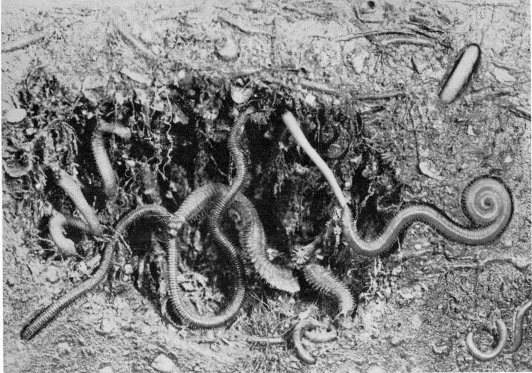

These marine annelids (segmented worms) may be found burrowing among the roots of eelgrass in the muddy bottom of coastal waters.

shoes. This will prevent most of the parasites from entering the body, even in localities where they are abundant. Another effective measure is to arrange for the sanitary disposal of human wastes containing hookworm eggs. Adult worms may be driven out of the human intestine by certain drugs used under the guidance of a doctor. Of course, hookworms in the human body will die of old age in time, but after all six or seven years is a long time to wait.

Another parasitic nematode of tropical and subtropical regions is the filarial worm *Wuchereria bancrofti,* which is transmitted from one human to another by various species of mosquitoes. The adult female worms measure between three and four inches, while the males are half the size. They usually occur in the lymphatic vessels and lymph nodes. The females produce eggs that develop into embryos known as microfilariae, some of which reach the blood circulating near the host's skin.

Here the embryos are taken up by a mosquito as it feeds on its human victim. Within the tissues of the mosquito vector, the young filarial worms develop into infective larvae; they enter a human host the next time the mosquito feeds and eventually reach the lymphatic system where they mature. The condition known as filariasis results from inflammation and from the obstruction of lymphatic channels by both the bodies of the mature worms and by scar tissue caused by the worms' presence. A further complication in which the limbs and other regions of the body swell to enormous size is known as elephantiasis.

The Guinea worm (*Dracunculus medinensis*), another parasitic roundworm of man, is found in Africa, Arabia and India. Humans are infected by drinking water containing water fleas (branchiopods) that carry the infective stage of the worm. After the infected copepods are swallowed, the worms mate and the female migrates through the tissues of its human host. About ten months later the fertile female, which may now reach a length of several feet, comes to lie just under the skin through which it frees its young. To extract the worm, one end of the animal is rolled up on a stick; each day the stick is given a few turns until the entire worm is drawn out.

Dogs, cats, poultry, cattle, sheep, horses, pigs and goats are also attacked by parasitic roundworms. The parasite called the heart worm (*Dirofilaria immitis*) lives as an adult in one chamber of a dog's heart or in the arteries that lead from the heart to the lungs. The tiny young of the heart worm are transmitted to dogs through the bites of mosquitoes.

Another parasitic roundworm is the stomach worm (*Haemonchus contortus*), which attacks both sheep and cattle. A fully grown female stomach worm is about an inch and a quarter in length; a male is somewhat smaller. Eggs produced by the female pass to the exterior with the wastes and hatch within a very short time. The young pass through several stages of development. As larvae they crawl up on blades of grass where they are likely to be swallowed by grazing sheep or cattle.

Various species of roundworms attack plants. The sugar-beet nematode (*Heterodera schachtii*) is a good example. It is never more than one twentieth of an inch in length; its small size together with the fact that it lives in the roots of the sugar beet make control a difficult problem. This worm has been present in European beet fields for many years; it appears to have been brought into the United States accidentally some time after 1900. The most effective control measure is to change to another crop when sugar-beet nematodes appear in a beet field.

Segmented worms (annelids)

There are about 7,000 known species of segmented worms, or annelids, which are sometimes called the true worms. These animals are slender, segmented creatures; they have a complete digestive tract, with a mouth at one end and an anus at the other. Most species have setae; that is, short, bristlelike hairs extending from the body wall and used in locomotion. The hairs also serve another purpose. It

is because earthworms cling so tenaciously with their setae to the walls of their burrows that birds find it so hard to pull them out of the soil.

The earthworms are among the most common members of the annelid group. They show a rather striking variety of colors: brown, purple, blue, green and a nondescript pallid color. The common earthworm, belonging to the genus *Lumbricus,* has long served as the classical example of the phylum. The body of this worm has more than a hundred segments, which are very noticeable because of the grooves extending around the body. Each segment, except the first and the last, bears setae, which are moved by muscles within the body wall. An earthworm's body is covered by a thin, transparent membrane,

The giant earthworm of Australia may reach a length of 6 to 12 feet. Its native habitat is the wet river slopes in Victoria.

Australian News and Information Bureau

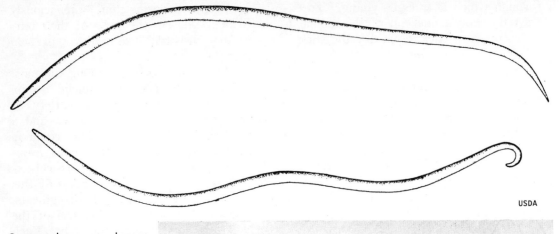

Common large roundworms (*Parascaris equorum*) are found in the stomachs of young horses.

The clamworm (*Nereis*) is a marine annelid that lives near the low-tide mark of ocean beaches.

called the cuticle, which is secreted by the skin layer just beneath it. The cuticle is always kept moist by glandular secretions; it is through this membrane that an earthworm breathes. There are hundreds of different species distributed all over the earth except in localities that are very cold or very dry.

The earthworms are exceedingly valuable to man because of the way in which they turn up the soil. Charles Darwin called attention to the "plowing" activities of the worms in his FORMATION OF VEGETABLE MOULD THROUGH THE ACTION OF WORMS, published in 1881. "The plough," he observed, "is one of the most ancient and most valuable of man's inventions, but long before he existed the land was, in fact, regularly plowed and still continues to be thus plowed by earthworms." He pointed out that a certain field had once been covered with stones. These had entirely disappeared after some thirty years had passed; they had been completely covered by the castings, or wastes, of earthworms.

The worms literally eat their way through the soil, obtaining nourishment from organic matter contained in it. They bring their wastes to the surface; it is in this way that they turn over the soil. It has been estimated that over 50,000 worms may be found in a single acre. The earthworm population in black loam will bring a one-inch layer to the surface, on the average, in five years. The burrows of the worms make the soil porous, and cause rain water to penetrate within the earth.

During and following heavy rains, large numbers of earthworms are often seen crawling about on the surface of the ground; the reason is that the water has flooded them out of their burrows. Fishermen looking for bait go out on rainy nights in order to collect some of the larger worms, which are called night crawlers.

Certain earthworms are very small, not exceeding an inch in length. Others, found in Australia and South America, are imposing animals six or seven feet long; they are sometimes mistaken for snakes. There are many variations in length between these two extremes.

Earthworms serve as food for other animals, such as birds and mammals (including men). Some authorities think that they may do a certain amount of harm by spreading disease. If they have previously burrowed through the decaying bodies of diseased animals, the worms may transmit diseases to domestic animals that feed upon them. It is known that some earthworms contain the young of parasitic nematodes that live as adults in domestic poultry.

Certain popular beliefs about earthworms are either entirely erroneous or only partly true. For example, some people maintain that the worms turn into fireflies — an absurd notion, based perhaps on the fact that the firefly is a beetle, which passes through a larval stage. Another belief, which is only partly true, is that if an earthworm is cut in two, both parts will continue to live and finally will develop new segments to replace those that have been lost. It is true that the head part of an earthworm that has been cut in two often continues to live and may add, or

regenerate, tail segments as time goes on. If the cut has been made too near the tail, however, the tail part never succeeds in redeveloping the important internal organs, in the forward part of the body; it dies after a comparatively short time.

Leeches are also well-known members of the annelid group. They are usually somewhat flattened in form; the body is divided into segments, as in the case of all the annelids, but, except in one species, no setae are developed. Leeches have a sucker at the rear end of the body; many species, too, have a sucker, which surrounds the mouth, at the head end. Some species are found in the sea, some in fresh water and some on land.

The leech attaches itself to the host by means of its suckers. Once this is done, the animal makes an incision in the host's skin and gorges itself with blood; then it drops off. Not all leeches suck blood; some of them capture and devour small forms of life that live in the water. Leeches use their suckers to help them move, by looping movements like a measuring worm, over solid surfaces. They swim through the water with undulating movements of the body.

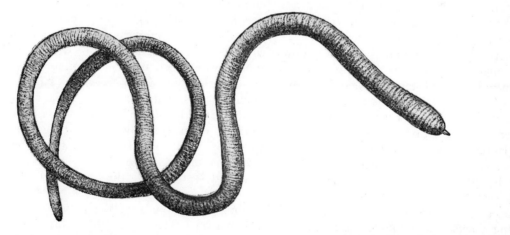

Canadian Dept. of Agriculture

Shown above is the giant thorn-headed worm (phylum Acanthocephala) which infests swine.

This clamworm, unlike the familiar earthworm, has a head bearing sensory appendages.

Gen. Biol. Supply House, Inc.

Insect larvae, snails and vertebrate blood
are the usual fare of these pond leeches.

During medieval times and for several centuries thereafter, bloodsucking leeches were used by physicians to draw blood from patients. After it was discovered that bleeding had little or no curative value, the practice of using leeches to draw blood was largely (although not entirely) abandoned, at least among the more civilized races of mankind. Leeches now serve mankind chiefly as the source of an anticoagulating substance, called Hirudin, derived from certain glands of the worms. Hirudin is used in surgical operations to prevent the formation of clots.

In the temperate regions of the world, leeches annoy bathers but are not particularly harmful to man. Sometimes, however, they get into the throat and nasal passages of certain forms of wildlife, including ducks, and strangle their victims. Certain species, such as *Limnatis nilotica* in the Near East and *Dinobdella ferox* in India, live in springs or wells. They enter the mouth or nasal passages of the men or beasts who drink from these springs or wells. Attaching themselves to the walls of the nasal passages, they obstruct respiration and cause hemorrhages.

Bloodsucking land leeches, found in great numbers in tropical rain forests, also enter the nostrils, which they block until they have had their fill of blood. It is a very serious matter if they enter the sinuses, because once they have become swollen with blood they cannot make their way out again.

Among the most interesting of the annelids are those living in the sea. Some of them, such as the clamworms, belonging to the genus *Nereis,* are free-swimming animals that prey on other marine creatures. Certain marine forms have beautifully colored gills — large, plumelike projections on the head or sides of the body. The odd sea mouse (*Aphrodite*) has an oval body covered on top with a thick mat of long, silky and iridescent hairlike setae. Several of the marine annelid families are well-known tube builders. Some line the burrows in which they live with a thin, limelike secretion; others build tubes in the sand. The parchment worm (*Chaetopterus*) constructs a parchmentlike U-shaped tube that is buried with only the openings jutting above the sandy mud. The appendages of the middle segments of this worm are united to form three pairs of circular fans that draw water in through one opening of the tube and force it out through the other. The numerous tiny organisms carried into the tube by this water current serve as food for the worm.

The palolo worm (*Eunice viridis*), found in the South Pacific, is famous for its breeding habits. During most of the year the worm lies coiled up in its burrow, generally in a coral reef. As time goes on, eggs or spermatozoa develop in the hind-end segments of the animal. In the last quarter of the October-November moon the hind ends of the palolo worms are cast off. They make their way to the surface of the sea in vast swarms and the eggs and spermatozoa are then discharged into the water. The natives collect the worms by means of nets and use them as food. A related species, *Eunice fucata,* of the West Indies, breeds similarly in the third quarter of the June-July moon.

See also Vol. 10, p. 275: "Invertebrates."

THE FERTILITY
OF THE SOIL

The Scientific Cultivation of the Land

IN OTHER chapters, we consider the soil from several different viewpoints. We observe it in the making. We see barren rock gradually decay and become fertile soil; we examine the forces that have effected this change and we note the different kinds of soil that have resulted. We view the soil particles under the microscope and we discuss their different properties. We also turn our attention to the water contained in the soil and to the infinitely varied forms of life, many of them extremely small, that are found in the earth. In the pages that follow, we shall discuss the problem of soil fertility.

In the article called The Soil (Volume 2), we have given a list of the food elements that a plant must have in order to grow. If even one of these elements is lacking, the growth of the plant is limited; until the deficiency is made good, the soil does not reach its full productivity. Other factors, too, have an important bearing on the fertility of the soil. The physical condition of the soil should be good; certain organic materials should be available; the soils should contain the proper amount of water — neither too much nor too little; temperature conditions should be right; certain bacteria should be present in the soil and should be functioning normally. The raising of cattle, sheep, swine and poultry may also help to maintain the fertility of the soil. The manure of these animals is the best and cheapest means of restoring needed food elements to plants. As a matter of fact, the animal is the complement of the crop. If the animal's manure helps restore the fertility of the soil, the crop grown on the land creates food in the form of carbohydrates, fats and proteins for the animal.

If soil fertility is to be maintained, we must take all of these factors into consideration. If we neglect any one of them, the crop-producing power of the soil will be lowered, as is evidenced today in some of the world's poorer agricultural countries. It is important, therefore, to have some idea of the methods used by the farmer to keep up the store of food in the soil and to make available those elements that are already present there.

Green manures

Green manuring is decidedly valuable in helping to restore the productivity and humus content of the soil. This is best accomplished by plowing under various deep-rooted nitrogen-fixing crops. The deeply penetrating roots of such plants bring up mineral elements from the subsoil and in this manner help to restore the deficiencies of the surface soil.

History has shown us that the turning under of green crops has long been an approved agricultural practice. The use of beans, vetches and lupines for this purpose was well understood by the farmers of ancient Rome and probably also by the agriculturists of certain nations that came before them. At the present time, the use of green manures, in some form or other, is accepted as an integral and important part of soil and farm management.

The green material that is to be used for manuring should be plowed under when it is most succulent, or moist. When it is in this condition, a considerable amount of water is added to the soil and, as a consequence, decay goes on more rapidly. When the soil is turned over, the furrow slice should not be thrown completely over, for if this is done the green crops will be deposited as a layer between the upper and lower soil and act as a barrier to water movement. The green-manure crop absorbs plant food that would otherwise be washed or drained away. When the crop is plowed in, the plant food is present in the soil, ready to be released to the next crop. Green-manure crops are grown before, after or between the regularly grown crops. In some poor land areas, they are grown in place of the main crop. Legumes are preferred to nonlegumes as green manure because, in addition to raising the store of organic matter, they also can fix nitrogen. The legumes commonly used for green manures are field peas, cowpeas, soybeans, vetch and ordinary sweet clover. Such nonlegumes as rye, oats and buckwheat also contribute organic substances to the soil.

If a green-manure crop follows a crop that has been heavily fertilized, new fertilizer need not be added. It must be used, however, if the preceding crop has been lightly fertilized. Green-manure crops are generally planted in the spring before the hot-weather crops are started and in the late summer and fall after the midseason crops have been harvested. The fall is considered a particularly favorable time for green-manure crop planting, because the crop protects the soil, during the winter months, from erosion by wind and water. As a result, both the soil and the crops benefit.

It is not considered advisable to plant green-manure crops during the regular growing season — for one thing, because such special-purpose plants may use up water that is needed by the regular crop. The best results can be obtained by planting green manures regularly and frequently. Although green-manuring is helpful in all farming regions in the United States, it can be practiced much more easily and to much better advantage in the southern part of the country than in the northern areas, because the growing season is considerably longer in the South.

There are substantially larger crops when green manures are added to the soil. The carbon, hydrogen, oxygen and, in the case of leguminous plants, nitrogen content of the soil is greatly increased. Green-manure crops with long roots bring up the plant food to the surface of the soil, where the food can easily be absorbed by shallow-rooted plants.

To derive full benefit from their use, green-manuring crops should be plowed

A manure spreader in operation on a dairy farm in Bristol County, Massachusetts. The spreader, which has a working capacity of 450 bushels, shreds the manure and spreads it evenly. This helps to maintain soil fertility.

USDA

under and mixed with the soil before they are matured. Rye or other grain that has begun to turn yellow is coarse and stiff and holds the soil loosely, aiding its erosion by water. Fully-grown nonleguminous plants are low in nitrogen. They must take an additional quantity from the soil, depriving the main crop of some of its supply. If this happens, the yield may be reduced rather than increased.

Farm manures

Farm manure is an important by-product of general and livestock farms. It maintains crop yields and increases the long-term productivity of the soil. The amount of plant-food elements it supplies is quite low, however, when compared with that of prepared fertilizer. One ton of average mixed manure contains 10 pounds of nitrogen, 10 of potash and 5 of phosphoric acid. Good mixed fertilizer has 100 pounds of nitrogen, 100 of potash and 400 of phosphoric acid. A ton of concentrated fertilizer, then, carries a much greater quantity of plant food than does a ton of ordinary manure. But the availability of large amounts of farm manure clearly offsets the disadvantage of low plant-food content.

The quantity of manure depends on the age, kind and number of animals and the kind and amount of feed. The grain part of corn is largely digested. Only one tenth of the dry matter is recovered in manure as contrasted with one half in timothy hay. About one third dry matter is recovered from grasses and green legumes, and two fifths from clover and alfalfa hay.

Some animals retain more of certain food elements. The manure of young, growing animals and of dairy cows holds more phosphorus and nitrogen than that of mature, fattening animals, work horses and mules. A considerable quantity of phosphorus is contained in the liquid part of pig and sheep manures; very little is found in horse and cow manures.

Pig manure is about 78 per cent water and cow manure, 80 per cent. These are called cold, or wet, manures, because they decay slowly and remain cool. Sheep ma-

Cornell University

Chemist analyzing soils for content and fertility in the Soil Testing Laboratory of Cornell University.

nure contains only 55 per cent water, and horse manure, 70 per cent. These are called hot, or dry, manures; they decay readily at any temperature. The steaming snow-covered piles of manure that can be seen in cold climates are an example of rapid decay at low temperature.

On the smaller farms manure is spread by hand; the manure spreader used on larger farms saves time. As with green manure, moderate quantities of farm manure added frequently give the best long-term results. At times it may be necessary for a farmer to use dried manures. Some are dried at ordinary room temperature and others with artificial heat. If applied too liberally, dried manures are sufficiently concentrated to burn plants.

About one half of the plant food contained in manure is at once available for plant use. The billions of tiny decay organisms eventually break down the complex compounds of the remaining half. As the manure rots, the amount of available plant food continually increases.

Manures do not give up all their plant food in one season; some of it is carried over to crops of the next season. Decay is nearly complete in one season where the soil is loose, open, sandy or gravelly; it is less rapid in nonporous soils, such as silt loams and clayey soils. On well-drained silt loams, crops get about one half of the plant food the first year, one fourth the second year and the rest in the following year or two.

How to avoid wasting manure

It is necessary to take certain precautions in the rotting of manure. For one thing, it should be kept moist and well compacted. However, it should not be subjected to too much moisture. It is obvious that if the materials of the manure are becoming more and more soluble, excessive amounts of water will wash away the valuable constituents of the fertilizer. It is an extremely wasteful practice, for example, to place a manure pile under the eaves of a barn; the pile will be soaked every time there is a heavy rain.

The best place to store manure is a covered shed with a tight bottom; the fertilizer should be kept carefully spread out and moistened in the shed. Manure can also be stored effectively in a covered concrete pit. Here both solid and liquid animal wastes are kept until it is convenient to haul them out to the fields.

Farmers should try to conserve the constituents of manure as much as possible in the barn. Plenty of litter should be used. It is true that the materials used as litter — generally straw, shavings or sawdust — are usually poorer in fertilizing elements than the manure with which they are mixed; however, they serve to absorb the valuable liquid and soluble portions of the manure. Litter will also keep the animals in the barn clean — a very important feature, especially in the case of dairy cattle.

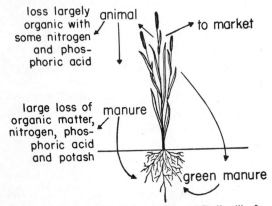

From Lyon's "Soils and Fertilizers," The Macmillan Co.

Diagram showing how plant foods are added to the soil either as green or farm manure. It will be noted that losses must occur if the crop is fed to farm animals.

The floor of the barn should be kept as tight as possible in order to prevent the liquid manure from running off before it can be absorbed by the litter. Various experiments have shown that farmers can bring about considerable savings by taking all these precautions.

Application of manure

After the manure has been produced in the barn, the farmer must decide how it is to be applied. In general, it is most economical to haul the manure directly to the field where it is to be used. The soil is an excellent absorbing agent; therefore, once the manure has been spread on the fields, there is little chance for loss. It is not always possible, however, to place manure upon the land without delay. The soil may be too wet, or it may be carrying a crop. If it is winter, the ground may be frozen, or else the snow may be too deep. Under such conditions it is often necessary to store manure, perhaps for a considerable period of time, until it is convenient to use it. As we have pointed out, it is best to store the manure in sheds or pits that are suitably protected from the elements.

There are two principal methods of applying fertilizers of all types. The first of these methods is to broadcast the fertilizer — that is, to scatter it far and wide. The second is to apply it row by row to the area that has been prepared for cultivation. In the case of barnyard manure, it is considered best to spread it by broadcasting with a suitable spreader.

The functions of manure

What happens to the manure once it is in the soil? What functions does it perform? In the first place, this fertilizer adds greatly to the organic matter of the soil and improves its physical condition. It ensures better granulation of the soil particles; it brings about improved drainage and air movement. The use of manure intensifies chemical action in the soil. Manure serves as a food for bacteria, which work over the plant food elements that are present in the soil and make these ele-

Soil Conservation Service

When saturated, a soil poor in humus becomes sticky and tightly compacted. This is unhealthy soil for seedlings.

This type of soil, rich in humus, is porous even when saturated; roots of growing plants can easily absorb food.

ments available for plants. The manure also serves as a fresh source of bacteria.

Besides these more or less indirect effects of manure, it supplies considerable amounts of plant food elements, including nitrogen, phosphorus, potassium, magnesium, calcium and sulfur. The manure releases these mineral nutrients slowly, and therefore gives the growing plant a better chance to assimilate them.

We have already referred to the fact that only a part of the plant food contained in manure is used up in a single year. Generally there is a considerable residue for the use of the crops of the next few years. Ordinarily manure placed on the soil will continue to supply food elements to plants only for a period of four years or thereabouts; but in extreme cases its beneficial action may last for as long as forty years. The long-lasting effects of manure, as compared with other types of fertilizers, make it possible to store up in the soil considerable quantities of organic matter as well as plant food.

Manure is a fine fertilizer, therefore, and in certain respects it is superior to any other. Unfortunately the supply is quite limited, particularly in countries, such as the United States, where machines have replaced animals to a large extent in the work of the fields.

In view of its superior qualities as a fertilizer, a careful farmer will try to utilize manure as effectively as possible. He will see to it that the floors in his barn are tight; he will use plenty of litter for his stock.

Once the manure is produced, he will use as much of it in the fields as possible without delay. He will apply it to the soils where the greatest possible benefit will result. He will handle the manure that must be stored with great care, in order to cut down the losses due to leaching and fermentation. It is true that a certain amount of wastage in the collection and use of manure is inevitable; but with care, millions of dollars worth of plant food would be saved every year in the United States alone.

The use of lime

A number of substances are added to the soil with the idea of increasing its productivity indirectly by bringing about certain changes in its physical, chemical or biological conditions. Such materials are called amendments; they amend, or alter, conditions within the soil. Some of them may also contain certain food constituents that plants can use. Where this is the case, however, the presence of these constituents is not the important factor.

Lime is one of the most widely used of all the amendments. As we shall see, what we call lime is not a single substance but a group of substances, each consisting of a calcium compound. Lime has various beneficial effects upon the soil. It corrects soil acidity, caused by the deficiency of certain essential elements; it brings about a decided improvement in soil texture; it favors the fixation of nitrogen, which is one of the most essential of plant foods. (See Index, under Nitrogen fixation.)

The compounds of calcium that are principally used as amendments of the soil are ground limestone, also known as calcium carbonate ($CaCO_3$), water-slaked lime (calcium hydroxide: $Ca(OH)_2$) and burned lime (calcium oxide: CaO). These compounds are referred to collectively as "lime"; the term may refer to all or to any one of the three substances. Since calcium is the active constituent of all three, their relative effectiveness will vary to a considerable extent upon the percentage they contain of this particular element. On this basis, burned lime is the most effective of all, since 56 pounds of this compound contains as much calcium as 74 pounds of hydroxide of lime and 100 pounds of lime-

Caterpillar diesel tractor pulling two 10-foot disks together with a spike-tooth harrow, preparing a seed bed for barley. The tractor shown below runs for about 10 hours a day on just 2½ gallons per hour of fuel.

Caterpillar Tractor Co.

Benefits of lime

One of the greatest benefits of lime is the correction of soil acidity. When the soil is acid, such basic elements as calcium, magnesium, and potassium are either quite lacking or else are unavailable. Under such conditions, a good many plants, including many of the common crops, do not do well at all. The food elements that are necessary for these plants do not go into solution, the granulation of the soil particles is seriously interfered with and bacteria cannot thrive. If there is an unusually high degree of acidity, certain kinds cannot function at all.

The acidity of the soil severely affects the nodule organisms that are so important in nitrogen fixation — that is, the conversion of free nitrogen into combined form. Nitrogen is an essential food element for plants; it is only available to plants, how-

stone. Because of the caustic properties of the first two forms of lime and also because of their far greater solubility, they are considerably more active than the ground limestone. Consequently, when quick results are desired, they are generally preferred by farmers. Over a long period of time, however, the results that are obtained from limestone are about the same as from the other two kinds of lime.

ever, when it is in the form of a compound. Hence any condition that affects nitrogen fixation is bound to have a serious effect upon the growing crops; the farmer will find his harvest rapidly dwindling and for no apparent reason.

The obvious way to correct acidity of the soil is by the addition of some material containing necessary basic elements. Of all compounds lime seems to be the best,

USDA

Drill-type lime spreader attached to a tractor. Lime can be effectively spread on the soil with this device.

as it is plentiful, cheap and effective. Applied in any of the three forms that we have mentioned, the calcium seems to perform the necessary function of supplying active bases.

As calcium is removed by plant growth from the soil, its place is taken by hydrogen ions (see Index, under Ions) until the soil becomes too acidic for use. (A soil's acidity is determined by finding its hydrogen ion concentration.) The liming material neutralizes the hydrogen ions by combining with them to form relatively inactive compounds. At the same time the material releases calcium.

The calcium content of lime is an essential nutrient to plants. When calcium is taken into the plant's cells, it is used to form calcium pectate, a kind of cementing material which is laid down between the cells to help hold them together. A calcium deficiency first becomes evident when the cells in the growing points of the plant's shoots and roots die or else become badly distorted.

Nitrogen fixation is carried on with great effectiveness if the soil has been adequately supplied with lime. Lime also seems to release potassium and to cause it to become

useful to crops. This is brought about because calcium changes places with the potassium in the complex chemical reactions that occur in the soil. Lime, therefore, is one of the keys for unlocking some of the otherwise unavailable stores of plant food in the ground.

Other compounds, such as gypsum and common salt, have also been added to the soil to increase its fertility. None of these substances, however, have the favorable and lasting effects of lime; none of them intensify and increase the effectiveness of other added materials as lime does. Farm manure, for example, gives much better results if the soil is well limed; its decomposition is more thorough and its decay products are more valuable to the crops. Green manure is affected in the same way. Some farmers mix manure with lime before it is distributed, thus insuring the desired reaction and saving an extra operation.

The lime need of a particular soil is usually estimated from the acidity of the soil. Different types of soils having the same degree of acidity require different amounts of lime. The fineness of the limestone, which determines its reactivity, is an important factor.

Lime is best applied with a distributor so that definite amounts may be added uniformly over the land's surface. The farmer's main aim is to mix it with the surface layer of soil. Tillage is necessary after the application in order to make the calcium in the lime more rapidly available to the plants. When lime is applied to the surface, the calcium it contains moves downward through the soil rather slowly.

Commercial fertilizers

Some "health authorities" have stated that chemical fertilizers damage the nutritive value of crops, or are in other ways inferior to natural manure used as a fertilizer. This is definitely not true. Nutrients released to plants by decaying organic matter cannot be told from nutrients applied in commercial fertilizers. Nor are chemical fertilizers detrimental to earthworms and to soil microorganisms, as is sometimes stated. In fact, they are beneficial to earthworms in that they increase plant growth and therefore the amount of plant residues that will be returned to the soil. The earthworm's diet is composed of these residues.

Commercial fertilizers usually carry readily available plant food which can be utilized by the crop immediately. Very little beneficial action is carried over to crops of succeeding seasons. This is in contrast to farm manure, whose influence is felt over a longer period of time. Commercial fertilizers are bought and sold on a definite money basis, expressed in dollars per ton. The value, of course, depends on the content of nitrogen, phosphorus and potassium.

These three chemical elements exert a powerful influence on plant growth. Nitrogen is especially important. Plants need large amounts since all their life processes depend on it. Unfortunately, this element is easily lost from the soil and is fairly expensive to supply. Nitrogen is necessary for a good rate of growth. Even the green leaf pigment, chlorophyll, is a nitrogenous compound.

Phosphorus is necessary for cell division, for the production of fats and for the manufacture of sugar by photosynthesis in the plant.

Potassium is required for the formation and successful functioning of the chlorophyll of leaves, and it also serves other purposes, of which we know less. It is known that the plant takes tremendous amounts of this element from the soil.

Various plants are particularly sensitive to the absence of one or another of these three elements. Phosphorus and potassium may be added in large amounts to a soil and no harmful effects will result. An excess of nitrogen, however, will cause undesirable changes in the plants. It will increase the above-ground parts of the plant at the expense of the roots, and it will delay ripening.

Food elements in commercial fertilizers should be properly balanced. If one element is present in too small amounts, it becomes the limiting factor in the growth of the crop. No matter how much of the other constituents are present, the crop cannot develop, because of the deficiency in this one element. The other elements, therefore, are wasted. A fertilizer should have the proper proportions of nitrogen, phosphorus and potassium so that, when it is added to the soil, the crop will get a balanced ration.

Research programs in the use of fertilizers have shown that it is not enough to base fertilizer procedures on the old rule of putting in what the crop takes out, for the soil may have been deficient in plant food to begin with. It is necessary for the farmer to develop and maintain a balanced supply of plant nutrients at the most efficient level. The line between applying too much fertilizer per acre and too little is very fine indeed. If too much is added, the crop will be overfed and valuable plant food wasted. The profit from the crop yield may not pay for the fertilizer. On the other hand, if the application is too small, the potential from the crop will not be realized.

The lime level of the soil is shown by means of a color test.

Fertilizer mixtures

The basic elements of plant food — nitrogen, phosphorus and potassium — are applied to the soil with various other elements, forming compounds, which are commonly known as carriers. The carriers of nitrogen are called ammoniates. The so-called organic ammoniates are composed of material from animal and plant sources. Among the animal ammoniates are guano, consisting of the bodies and manure of seals, bats and sea birds that have accumulated on the arid islands off the coast of Peru; animal tankage, composed of slaughterhouse refuse and waste; dried blood; sewage sludge, which is a mixture of animal and vegetable materials. The plant ammoniates include cottonseed meal, pomace, cocoa cake, linseed meal and tobacco stems.

There are also inorganic nitrogen compounds, derived from minerals. The two most commonly used are nitrate of soda and sulfate of ammonia. Nitrate of soda (16 per cent nitrogen) corrects soil acidity; it makes alkaline soils more alkaline. Ammonium sulfate (21 per cent nitrogen) increases soil acidity. Ammoniated liquid solutions may also be sprayed onto soil.

The carriers of phosphorus are usually known as phosphates. Rock phosphate and bones are natural phosphates. There are also treated phosphates, such as superphosphate, made by mixing 1,000 pounds of Florida pebble phosphate with 900 pounds of sulfuric acid. A certain number of phosphates are by-products; such is basic slag, derived from certain iron ores.

The carriers of potassium are potassium salts. Muriate of potassium (52 per cent potassium) is soluble in water and available to crops as soon as it is dissolved in the soil moisture. There are also by-product potassium carriers, such as hardwood ashes and low grades of molasses.

The carriers of nitrogen, phosphorus and potassium can be bought and applied separately or mixed on the farm; usually the American farmer prefers to buy them already combined. A mixed fertilizer is called complete if it contains nitrogen, phosphorus and potassium. If it combines only two of these, it is termed incomplete.

Special terms are used by the fertilizer industry to measure the plant-food content of a given fertilizer. The nitrogen content is given in terms of the total percentage of nitrogen in the fertilizer; the phosphorus content, in terms of the percentage of available phosphoric acid; the potassium content, in terms of the percentage of water-soluble potassium. The ratio of the percentages of nitrogen, phosphoric acid and potassium is called the analysis of the fertilizer. For example, a fertilizer with an analysis of 8–16–8 contains 8 per cent each of nitrogen and potassium and 16 per cent of phosphoric acid.

The so-called ordinary-analysis fertilizers have less than 20 per cent of plant food. High-analysis fertilizers have between 20 and 30 per cent; concentrated fertilizers, more than 30 per cent.

Determining fertilizer needs

By utilizing the results of the constant research that is being done today, the farmer can efficiently use many soils that gave low yields a generation ago. Soils are dynamic and can be changed. Through necessity we are learning to use the land wisely. The pioneers of former days were able to move to virgin land when the lands under cultivation were worn out. The modern farmer can no longer do so.

Many processes, going on in the soil at all times, affect the supply of nutrients. Research on the clay portions of soil, for instance, has shown that the clay is very important in the maintenance of soil fertility. Apparently, it is the clay fraction of the soil that has the capacity to hold nutrient elements such as calcium and potassium.

By following research results closely, a farmer can readily make use of new discoveries in soil fertility. As a consequence, he will be in a position to improve his economic standing by producing greater yields more efficiently.

Farmers of the United States spend more than a billion dollars a year to improve the fertility of their soil. Many of these fertilizer dollars are used unwisely or ineffectively. In some cases, however, it would be to the farmer's advantage to improve plant growth by using higher levels of fertilizing.

Too much or too little fertilizer can adversely affect the yield and quality of a crop and the profit realized, as we have mentioned. It is no longer necessary for the farmer to fertilize in haphazard fashion, for the soil can be tested in order to determine his needs. However, soil tests are subject to error unless samples are properly taken and unless proved tests are made and interpreted by soil technicians. Soil testing laboratories are operated in every state in the United States by agricultural experiment stations and extension services. The county agent or local extension representative can tell you how to obtain tests. The backyard gardener is entitled to this service, too.

Of course, the farmer can do much to determine whether his soil needs fertilizer and the type needed if he carefully observes the health and productiveness of the plants growing in it. Plants show signs of sickness just as animals do. However, it pays to have the soil tested to get precise information about its state. This is especially important before trying new crops, in order to compare the proposed crop's needs

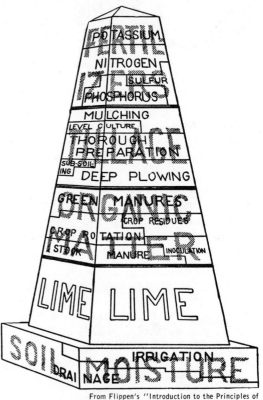

From Flippen's "Introduction to the Principles of Soil Fertility," N. Y. State College of Agriculture

A diagram showing the various substances and practices that will help ensure the constant fertility of the soil.

with the elements supplied by the soil in question.

The adjustment between the fertilizer, the soil and the crop makes a very intricate study. The soil's organic matter, type, lime content, drainage and water relations all play a part in determining soil fertility. The crop, climate, season and possible plant diseases must also be considered. In order to get the best results from fertilizers, every other soil condition must be at its best.

See also Vol. 10, p. 273: "Soil."

THE COVERING OF THE BODY

Fact and Fancy about the Skin, Hair and Nails

BY MAC V. EDDS, JR.

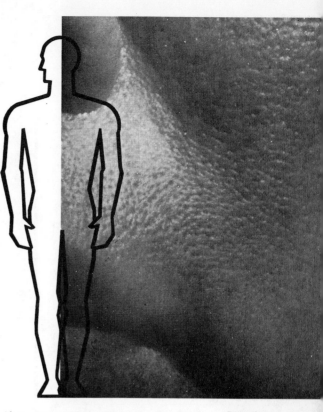

Photo: pores of the skin near the lips and nostrils of a Japanese man.

F. Hamilton— Frederic Lewis

THE outward appearance of a normal human body, sleek and seemingly uncomplicated, can give us no idea of the immense networks of tissues, nerves, bones, blood vessels, muscles and what not that extend from head to toe. The reason is that the body is covered with a more or less smooth envelope, the skin, and with certain outgrowths of the skin that we call the hair and the nails.

The Skin

The skin is the largest organ in the body, outweighing even the liver. Its surface area, in the case of the normal adult, averages over three thousand square inches. Every square inch of skin in most areas of the body contains hundreds of oil glands, sweat glands and nerve endings, several feet of small blood vessels and many thousands of cells.

The thickness of the skin ranges from approximately $\frac{1}{250}$ of an inch to $\frac{1}{6}$ of an inch. It is particularly heavy in regions that are constantly exposed to friction, like the palms of the hands and the soles of the feet. Friction is not wholly responsible, however, for the thickness of such areas; the skin is well developed here at birth.

The skin is composed of two main layers, the epidermis on the surface and the dermis lying just beneath.

The outer portion of the epidermis is the layer that peels off in thin sheets after a sunburn. When examined under the microscope, the epidermis is seen to consist of row upon row of flattened cells piled up on one another like the bricks in a wall. The exposed outer cells of the epidermis are continually dying and being worn away; just as continually, they are replaced by new cells pushed out from below.

From the deepest layer of the epidermis to the outermost one, the appearance of the cell constantly changes. The cells of the lowest levels look like somewhat squashed cubes with rounded edges; many of them are dividing to produce new cells. Farther out, the cells become even more flattened, their nuclei become faint and cell

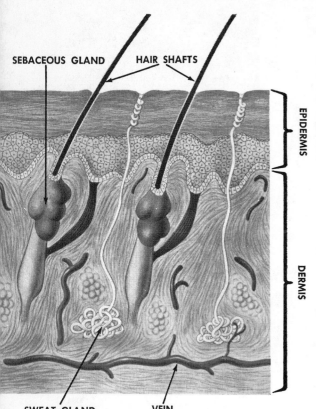

SEBACEOUS GLAND   HAIR SHAFTS

EPIDERMIS

DERMIS

SWEAT GLAND   VEIN

This diagram shows the two principal layers of the skin—the epidermis, lying on the surface, and the dermis, just below the surface. The diagram also shows sebaceous, or oil, glands, sweat glands, hair shafts and a vein.

At the bottom of these two pages are a number of fingerprint patterns, which are formed by the folds along the junction between the epidermis and the dermis. The many whorls in such patterns furnish the basis for the fingerprint classification system.

Federal Bureau of Investigation

boundaries are difficult to distinguish. As the cells die, they become hard and horny. Near the surface, they are clumped in flakes.

As a result of the constant replacement of worn-out or damaged cells, the skin remains youthful over a period of many years. Stains of ink, grease, iodine, tar and paint do not mar it permanently as they do, say, a tablecloth. The cuts and bruises, the burns and scratches to which the skin is always exposed are generally soon healed.

In the optical microscope, the deeper-lying epidermal cells appear to be connected with one another by minute "bridges" of cytoplasm. (See Index, under Cytoplasm.) When observed with the electron microscope, however, each such bridge is seen to consist rather of two processes (from two adjacent cells) that make close contact but do not actually fuse. Farther out in the epidermis, where the cells are dead or dying, the bridges cannot be made out.

Beneath the epidermis is the second and deeper layer of the skin, the dermis. It consists of a dense network of connective tissue lying under and nourishing the epidermis. Besides being made up of many irregular connective-tissue cells, the dermis contains innumerable microscopic fibers.

There are two kinds of fibers in the dermis. The so-called collagenous fibers are strong and hard to stretch; it is because of their presence that leather can be successfully fashioned from human skin, as it can be fashioned from the skin of animals, by treatment with certain chemicals. Leather made from human dermis is fine and soft, somewhat like kid leather. It is understandable, therefore, that some barbaric peoples once made battle cloaks from the skins of fallen enemies.

The dermal fibers of the second type are elastic and enable the skin to adapt itself readily to the changing contours of the body

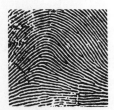

PLAIN ARCH

LOOP

LOOP

PLAIN WHORL

during movement. In old age, these elastic fibers largely disappear and this is one reason why the skin becomes wrinkled. The pattern of wrinkles in the face depends in part on the manner in which the skin has been pulled and stretched by various facial muscles. Expressions that become habitual are truly engraved into the face as the skin loses its elasticity. There is some justification, therefore, for the saying that if you would be attractive in old age, you should think noble thoughts as a youth.

Unlike the epidermis, the dermis is richly supplied with blood vessels. These provide nourishment, not only for the connective tissue, but also for a bewildering variety of glands, nerve endings, muscle cells and other structures. The boundary between the dermis and the epidermis is not regular and even; it consists of small, interlocking folds. Nourishment-bearing fluids pass from the dermis to the epidermis through these folds.

The folds along the junction between the two layers of the skin are best developed in areas where it is thick. Over the palm of the hand and the sole of the foot these folds produce a series of ridges and grooves on the surface of the skin. The patterns formed on the fingertips by the arching and looping of the ridges produce the familiar fingerprints. There are so many possible variations of the ridge patterns that no two individuals have ever been found with identical fingerprints. The pattern on each finger tip remains unchanged from infancy to old age; it is so constant that it redevelops in all its detail after the skin is scraped or burned.

There are a number of creases, called flexure lines, on the palms; the skin is folded along these creases during hand movements. There are many superstitious beliefs concerning the significance of these

Santa Fe Railway

Interesting pattern of wrinkles in the face of a ninety-year old Navaho Indian. Habitual expressions were engraved in this fine face as the skin lost its elasticity.

lines. Some persons think that their extent and depth reveal the past and future as well as the character of an individual. These beliefs, which form the basis of the "science" of palmistry, are without foundation. We might point out that there are flexure lines, closely similar to those found in man, on the palms of apes and monkeys. Yet who would attempt to "read the palms" of these animals in order to find out if they are going to be successful in business and in love?

The varying colors in the skins of different races of men depend partly on the amount of blood circulating through the dermis. They depend also to a certain extent on the texture of the dermis; since this

TENTED ARCH

CENTRAL POCKET LOOP

DOUBLE LOOP

ACCIDENTAL

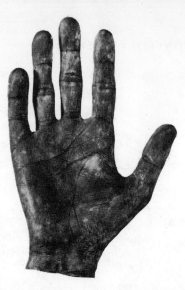

Hands of man (left) and gorilla (right), showing the flexures, or creases, on the palms. The "science" of palmistry maintains that the extent and depth of these creases, in the palm of a human being, reveal his past, future and character.

texture varies considerably in different people, the light that falls on the skin is not always reflected in the same way.

But differences in skin tints are due even more to the presence of variable amounts of a pigment, or coloring matter, known as melanin. Small granules of this blackish brown substance are found in the deep epidermis even in white people and, of course, they are found in greater quantity in the epidermis of dark skins.

Skin pigment is present at birth but it is very lightly deposited, even in newborn Negro infants. In the latter, however, the skin darkens rapidly and soon attains its characteristic color. The tan that one acquires on exposure to the sun is due in part to an increase of melanin in the epidermis. There are other pigments that contribute to skin color; but these are much less important than melanin.

One of the most vital functions of the skin is the protection of underlying structures. Since under normal conditions the skin is waterproof, it helps to conserve the water content of the body. Again, since the skin is a poor conductor of light, it shields the rest of the body, within certain limits, from the harmful effects of excessive light. Skin pigments contribute greatly to the effectiveness of the screening process. Natives of tropical countries, where the sunlight is intense, have an unusual abundance of skin pigment for this screening purpose.

The continuous outer layer of the epidermis forms an ideal barrier against bacterial invasions. Being both tough and pliable, it protects the body from minor mechanical injuries. The strength and elasticity of the dermis make it an effective cushion which protects the delicate nerve endings, blood vessels and other structures lying within it.

The skin is also vitally important in the regulation of body temperature. Even though a man is exposed to great changes of external temperature, the temperature of his body remains nearly constant in health. When the body becomes overheated, the small blood vessels of the dermis enlarge and carry more blood close to the surface. The blood is then cooled by heat radiation. The evaporation of sweat from the skin aids materially in cooling the body. When, on the other hand, it becomes necessary to conserve heat within the body, blood channels are reduced in size and sweating ceases.

The sweat glands of the skin aid in getting rid of certain waste products. The openings of the canals through which the secretions of these glands reach the surface can be seen by examining the fingertips with a magnifying glass. Down the center of each of the ridges a row of tiny depressions will be found. The canals that open into each depression spiral downward through the epidermis and into the dermis where each connects with a sweat gland.

The gland itself consists of a twisted tube of specialized cells that are able to extract water and other materials from their surroundings. The sweat produced by these glands is largely water; it contains at most 1 per cent of dissolved solids, consisting chiefly of ordinary table salt, or sodium chloride. Since salt is excreted when perspiration takes place, it is important to replenish the body's supply of salt by including this food in the diet during hot weather.

Ordinarily the kidneys rid the body of 99 per cent of the urea resulting from cell metabolism. But as much as 10 per cent of urea may be carried out through the sweat glands when we perspire profusely.

The quantity of sweat produced naturally depends on such things as external temperature, activity, diet, emotion and state of health. Under average cool conditions, the normal healthy adult secretes about one-half pint every day; but this quantity may be increased many times by hard labor in the hot sun. There are about two million sweat glands scattered through the dermis in man; their activity is most pronounced in areas like the hands and feet, face, neck and armpits. Many animals are not so well provided for. In the dog, for example, only the footpads sweat, and nearly all cooling by evaporation takes place from the lungs and tongue as the animal pants.

A second type of gland, also lodged in the dermis, is the sebaceous, or oil, gland. The sebaceous glands produce the oil that lubricates and waterproofs the skin and lends a gloss to the hair. Of the various regions of the skin, only the soles and palms are free of oil glands. The appearance of these areas after the body has been in water for a long period of time illustrates the importance of skin oil as a waterproofing agent. In the ear canal, sebaceouslike glands secrete a heavy wax material; under the eyelids the secretion has the consistency of soft cheese.

In addition to its other functions, the skin serves as a large sensory organ. Nerve fibers extending out into the skin, for the most part, conduct sensory messages from the surface of the body to the spinal cord and brain. At the terminal point in the skin, each fiber may branch freely into a treelike structure or it may coil up as a fine spiral of varying form. It is well established that different types of sensory messages are carried by different nerve fibers. Thus nerve fibers that are excited by painful stimuli, for example, are different from those stimulated by touch or cold.

When something warm is pressed against the skin, a specific group of nerve fibers is stimulated by the increased temperature. This sets up a series of impulses which pass back over the specific fibers to the central nervous system. When the stimulus is due to touching the skin, or pressing it, the story is the same except that different nerve fibers are involved.

As a sensory organ, the skin is exceedingly important. Countless stimuli are con-

Diagram of the sweat glands, showing the gland bodies, their excretory ducts, leading to the surface of the skin, and their pores, through which water and dissolved solids are excreted. The sweat glands of the skin help regulate the temperature of the body; they also aid in getting rid of wastes, such as urea and salts.

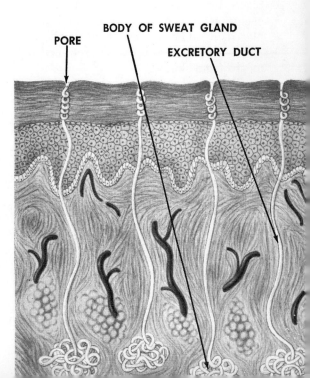

PORE   BODY OF SWEAT GLAND   EXCRETORY DUCT

tinually falling on its surface, exciting its nerve endings and sending volleys of impulses on their way to the brain. The awareness that comes to us from these impulses supplements the information gained through our other senses. If the nerves to the skin are destroyed, this awareness is lost. An individual so afflicted feels the loss as keenly as though he had been deprived of his ability to taste or smell; in fact, he may feel the loss even more keenly.

The Hair

We come now to the modified kind of skin that we call the hair. One of the things that seems to set man off from other mammals is the small amount of hair over the surface of his body. As a matter of fact, however, the "naked" human skin is really covered with a great many fine hairs. Only a few regions, such as the lips and parts of the hands and feet, are completely hairless. If the human skin appears naked, it is only because the hair is generally inconspicuous.

A baby has hair before it is born; it usually has more hair, in fact, while it is still within the mother than at birth. At birth, the scalp is often covered with hair, which soon falls out. During the first few months of life a short, downy fuzz appears all over the body. This hair is soon replaced by a coarser type over the scalp and eyebrows; much later, it is similarly replaced in other regions, such as the armpits. But the downy hair is retained over most of the skin.

When most people use the word "hair," they have in mind scalp hair. This differs considerably among the various peoples of the world in both texture and quantity. The hair of Oriental peoples is generally quite straight; in Negroid types it is so short and tightly curled that it is almost woolly. There are many gradations between these two extremes. The degree of curliness depends in part on the shape imparted to each shaft of hair as it grows. Despite considerable research, however, we still cannot explain precisely how a curly hair differs from a straight one.

The first sign of hair in a developing human being is a little knot of specialized

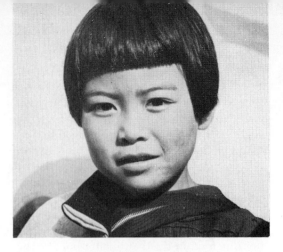

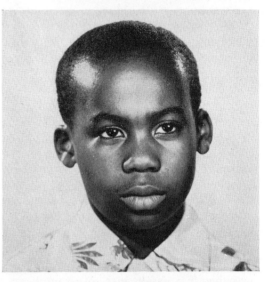

(top) Palmer Pictures
(middle) Ewing Galloway, N. Y.
(bottom) Ewing Galloway, N. Y.

The hair of different peoples varies in texture. The hair of Japanese people (top) is generally straight; in Negroid types (middle), it is tightly curled. In Caucasians (bottom), there are variations. The hair may be straight, slightly curled (as here), curly and so on.

cells lying deep in the epidermis. These cells multiply rapidly and push down into the dermis to form a slender rod of tissue. Thus begins the formation of the follicle, the depression in the skin from which the hair grows. At the inner end of the rod of tissue, a cup-shaped bulb is fashioned.

The cells lining the interior of this bulb now begin to form the hair shaft. They continue to multiply actively; some of them become flattened and tightly packed together. As more and more cells accumulate, they form a bud which pushes upward. This bud is the hair shaft; it is made up of hundreds of flat, horny cells so closely packed that the individual elements can hardly be recognized. The cells of the hair, like those of the other epidermis, are gradually dying as they move farther from their source of nourishment.

Finally the shaft pushes through and beyond the surface of the skin. The growth center at the base of the follicle remains active; as new cells are packed into the base of the hair shaft, its outer end continues to extend farther and farther from the surface of the skin. Clearly, the growth of a hair depends entirely on its follicle. If the latter is destroyed, the hair that arose from it is gone for good.

A varying amount of brownish black pigment is loaded into the hair shaft as it grows; this is the same melanin that is found in the epidermis. The amount of pigment that is present naturally determines the actual color of the hair. In old age, the center of the hair shaft is not very well formed and it tends to become filled with minute air bubbles, which make the hair appear gray or white. Air enters the hair only in the region where it is actually growing, at the base of the follicle, and it takes time for the air-filled part of the hair shaft to reach the surface of the skin. That is why it is difficult to believe accounts of the hair turning gray overnight as a result of some emotional strain.

At the right is shown a typical hair shaft. It grows from the follicle, which is a depression in the skin. At the base of the follicle is the growth center. As long as this center remains active, new cells are packed into the base of the hair shaft, and it continues to grow.

The hair shaft consists of two layers built up around a central core. The outermost layer is the cuticle; its flat, four-sided cells overlie one another like shingles on a roof. The second layer makes up the bulk of the hair shaft. Its cells are so arranged that they give the hair maximum strength and flexibility. The cells of the central core are shrunken and separated by numerous spaces. This core is not always present in the hair shaft, particularly in the case of hairs far thinner than the average.

The life of human hairs is limited. Most of them probably drop out after two or three years, though some may last as long as six years. In many animals the hair is shed every year during the approach of warm weather and it grows again in preparation for winter. Certain hairs, for example those in the tail of a horse, appear to last as long as the animal lives.

When a hair drops out or is rubbed off, its follicle does not always die as a consequence; on the contrary, it generally persists and begins to fashion a new hair shaft. Each individual hair goes through a life cycle of its own. There is a period of youth when it grows rapidly; there is an interval during which its growth is not so marked; finally the hair stops growing and is shed. Over any particular area of the scalp, about 90 per cent of the hairs will be actively elongating at a given time.

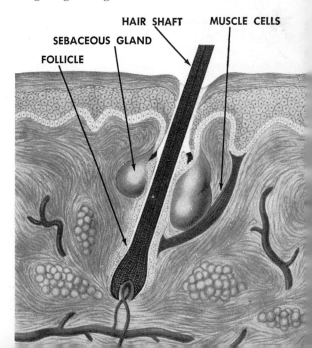

HAIR SHAFT   MUSCLE CELLS
SEBACEOUS GLAND
FOLLICLE

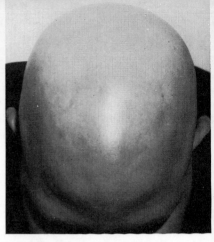

Three cases of loss of hair, or baldness. The hair of the man at the left is receding at the crown of his head; the hair of the man in the middle photo has been reduced to a fringe around the temples and the back of the head. These two instances of baldness are not due to any particular disease. The total baldness (alopecia totalis, in technical language) of the person at the right is an aftermath of scarlet fever. This type of baldness is usually temporary; the hair starts to grow again in a few weeks or a few months after shedding.

Contrary to popular belief, the rate at which hairs elongate is not increased by shaving them. It is true, however, that hair grows more quickly in the summer than in winter and more slowly at night than during the day. The normal rate of hair growth may be maintained even though various other tissues of the body have been severely affected by a condition of prolonged malnutrition.

There is a curious superstition that the hair keeps on growing even after death. This belief is a mistaken one. As we have seen, the extension of a hair from its follicle is a vital process depending on the activities of the living cells at its base. When a hair follicle is deprived of its blood supply at death, its cells die and no further growth can possibly occur. It is true, however, that the hair present at death may become somewhat more conspicuous as the skin of the corpse shrinks.

Many hairs can be moved slightly. A small pimple arises at the place where the hair emerges from the surface of the skin; the shaft itself no longer lies flat but stands upright. This condition, known as "goose flesh" or "goose pimples," is caused by cold (sometimes by fear). The movement of the hair shaft is produced by smooth muscle cells, a few of which are attached to the side of each hair follicle. In the vertical position, the hairs serve to keep a thicker layer of stagnant air about the body, and this provides added protection against cold since air is a good insulator. Since man has lost most of his body hair, the added protection does not amount to much.

The hair is lubricated and made glossy by secretions that frequently pour out from the oil glands through the hair follicles. If it were not for this homemade lubricant, the hair would be brittle.

Some people suffer a partial or total loss of hair — the familiar condition known as baldness. There are several kinds of baldness. In some cases, it does not seem to be due to any disease; the victim simply finds that his hair is growing thinner at the crown of his head or at the temples. At last, the follicles will not produce any more hairs and the skin is left bare.

In other cases, loss of hair is due to a diseased condition. The most striking symptom is generally a scaly dandruff; this may be caused by any one of a number of ailments, including tuberculosis. Dandruff continues to appear while the hair is falling out; it disappears when the hair is all gone.

There is no sure cure for baldness, in spite of the extravagant claims of certain hair-tonic manufacturers; however, it may be checked by skillful professional treatment. Simple precautions, like frequent dry-brushing of the hair, are also helpful.

The Nails

Like the hair, the nails are nothing more than modified skin. The tips of the fingers and toes of a young human embryo are covered only with skin; at the end of the third month of embryonic life, this skin starts to change and it is gradually converted into nails. When the nail first begins to form, it lies beneath the horny outer layer of the epidermis. This outer layer usually disappears before birth, but part of it remains as the cuticle at the base of each nail.

Two areas are easily visible in a well developed nail. The larger part is pink, due to the rich blood supply of the underlying dermis. Behind the pink region is a pale whitish area known as the half-moon, or lunula. All the growth that constantly pushes the nail forward takes place beneath the lunula. The remainder of the nail merely slides along passively.

The tissue under the nail is called the nail bed; it is actually a direct continuation of the deep, actively growing layer of the epidermis. As we just noted, the tissue under the pink area of the nail contributes nothing to it and serves merely as a smooth surface on which the nail glides forward. However, the portion of the nail bed beneath the lunula presents quite a different picture. Here, the tissue-forming cells are more numerous and are dividing continually; as they increase in number, those closest to the nail root become flattened and they are gradually pressed tightly together.

Each cell is gradually transformed into a thin, horny plate. The tiny plates are then piled in lamellae, or layers, which make up the substance of the nail. Nuclei are still visible in the horny cells near the root of the nail; but as the cells are pushed forward, all signs of structure seem to disap-

pear. However, if even the fully formed nail is soaked in caustic soda, it can be broken up into small scales, each representing an original cell containing a nucleus.

The ridges and bumps often seen on a nail result from uneven growth of the nail at its root. Occasionally white, irregular flecks appear in the nail substance. According to popular belief, these are "good-luck spots," indicating that the person on whose nails they appear is going to be very fortunate in the near future. Actually, the alleged good-luck spots are simply bubbles of air trapped between the cell layers.

Nails grow at very different rates. Those on the fingers advance about three or four times as rapidly as those on the toes. The fingernails on the longest fingers (the middle fingers) grow most quickly; those on the shortest or little fingers, most slowly. There appears to be no significant difference, with respect to growth, between the nails of the right and left hands. In summer, the nails, like the hair, advance faster than in winter; the thumbnail, for instance, grows an average of one-ninth of an inch per month in the winter and one-seventh of an inch in the summer.

Beyond providing a livelihood for manicurists and nail-polish manufacturers, the function of human nails is not clear. Fingernails can be used for scratching; they also provide a mechanical support for the tips of the fingers and they help us to manipulate certain thin objects, such as needles. But human toenails, as far as we can see, serve no useful purpose, though they may have been useful at one time.
See also Vol. 10, p. 276: "Anatomy"; "Physiology."

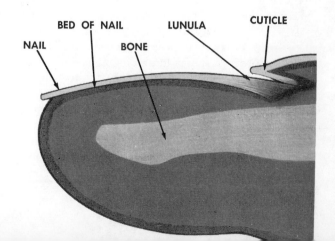

Cross section of fingertip, showing the structure of the nail. The nail moves along the nail bed; the growth that pushes the nail forward takes place under the lunula, or half moon.

NAIL   BED OF NAIL   LUNULA   CUTICLE

BONE

Left: the luminous fungus *Polyporus Hanedai* in daylight. Below: how the same fungus looks, illuminated by its own light in the nighttime.

LIVING LIGHT

The Amazing Phenomenon
of Bioluminescence

BY E. NEWTON HARVEY

IF YOU have ever taken a walk through deep damp woods you may have been startled when you came upon a shining stump or tree. This natural glow, sometimes called fox fire, is caused by the mycelia, or threadlike processes, of a luminous plant — a fungus that grows on wood. The fungus threads finally form a fruiting body — a mushroom, which also glows. Quite often one finds clumps of such mushrooms on stumps of trees, emitting their eery light. These plants have given rise to many a hair-raising tale of ghosts and hobgoblins and other supernatural beings.

The emission of light from a living thing, such as a luminous fungus, is called bioluminescence ("living glow"). There are a great many instances of it in nature. For thousands of years seafarers have known that the sea sometimes glitters with light when a boat passes through it or when an oar strikes it. The Greeks thought that this glow was of the same nature as lightning, which was supposed to be due to a violent explosion in the clouds. Later, some observers compared sea light to the sparks that appear when a piece of flint is struck. Others held that the sea soaked in sunlight by day and gave it off at night. After the discovery of the element phosphorus, many believed that sea light was due to the phosphorus contained in the ocean. Certain people maintained that the light was caused by putrefaction, or rotting; they pointed out that dead fish or rotting wood sometimes become luminous. Others thought that an electrical phenomenon was involved.

Benjamin Franklin was inclined at one time to accept the theory that sea light represented an electrical display. He quickly changed his mind, however, when he visited the seashore and was able to experiment. He found that a bottle of luminous sea water glowed brightly when it was shaken, but that after a while it did not glow at all. He knew that certain well-known marine animals could produce light; he came to the conclusion that the glow of sea water was due to much smaller living things. Their presence, he thought, could be detected only by their wake as they passed through the water. Franklin was quite right. We know now that sea light is due mostly to tiny luminous protozoa, called flagellates. They float on the surface of the water and they give off light when they are disturbed.

Those who live near the seashore may have seen dead fish shining at night. In this case the glow is due to the myriads of luminous bacteria that grow on the fish.

Legs of mutton or other cuts of meat hung in a cold room may become luminous for the same reason. Bacteria also account for the glow sometimes emitted by bodies that have been left on battlefields.

We are all familiar with the flickering light emitted by fireflies and by glowworms, which are the larvae of fireflies. These insects have been celebrated in song and story since the earliest times. Many a country child has collected dozens of fireflies in a glass jar, hoping to light his room by their glow.

These are but a few examples of bioluminescence; there are many others. Some of the organisms that produce light are easily visible to the naked eye; others must be viewed with a magnifying glass; still others can be seen only with the highest powers of the microscope. Only the simplest forms of plants — bacteria and fungi — have luminous species. Many groups of animals — forty that we know of — emit light. Probably there are others that have not yet been identified by zoologists who specialize in this field.

A number of land-animal groups are luminous. Among insects there are beetles (fireflies and glowworms), springtails, flies (fungus gnats and New Zealand glowworms*) and the lantern fly (*Fulgora*),

---

* New Zealand glowworms are the larvae of the fly called *Bolitophila luminosa*. These larvae hang in vast numbers from cavern roofs; the myriads of lights they emit produce the effect of a star-studded sky.

Below: this dead fish, lying on a sandy beach, had been infected by luminous bacteria. At night they cause the fish to glow.

Noctiluca miliaris, shown below, is a luminous flagellate, found in vast numbers on the surface of the sea. It gives rise to the spectacular marine displays in which the sea seems to be aflame.

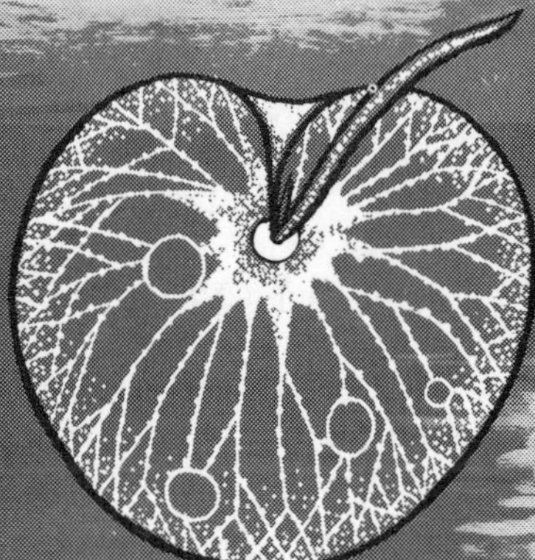

Above: a colony of nonluminous mutants of luminous bacteria has been grown in this flask. The mutants in the colony cannot luminesce because they lack aldehyde, one of the substances necessary to produce light. If one blows the vapor from an open bottle containing aldehyde over the flask colony at night, it will glow.

The cone-shaped *Beroë rufescens,* a luminous ctenophore, is shown below. Ctenophores are very soft jellyfishes.

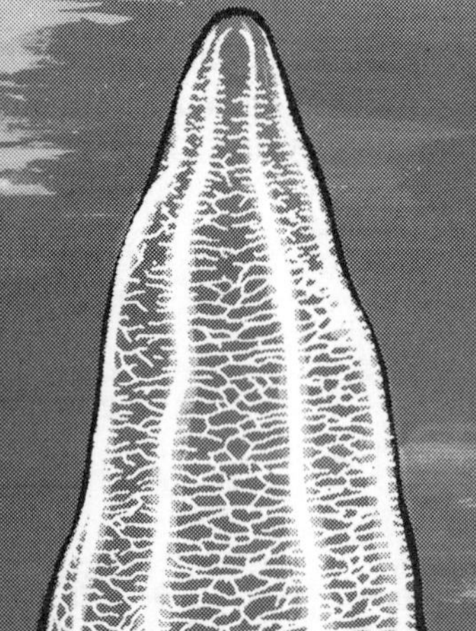

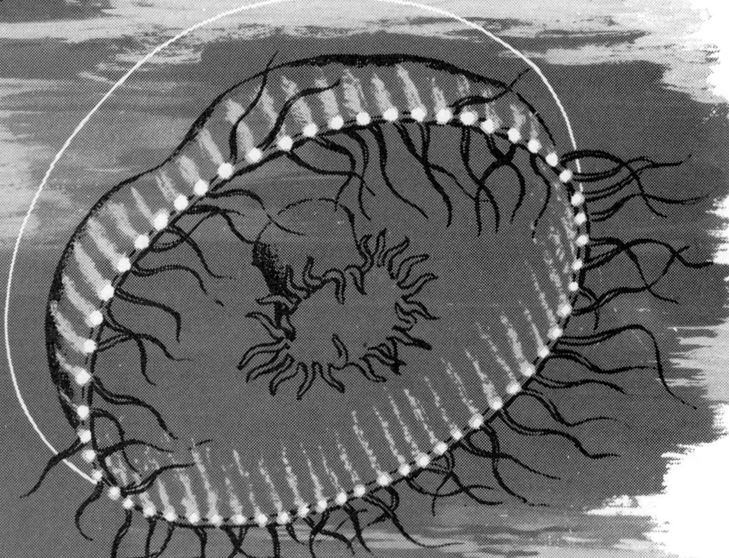

Above: the luminous jellyfish known as *Aequorea aequorea.* When disturbed, the animal displays luminescence from the base of its very numerous tentacles.

Right: luminous hydroid colony. It consists of a number of tiny hydralike animals, living together and forming structures that look like branches.

belonging to the order Homoptera. There are also luminous centipedes, millipedes, earthworms and land snails. It is interesting to note that no parasitic land animals produce light.

The only luminous animal that lives in fresh water is a limpet (*Latia*), found in New Zealand; it clings to rocks in fresh-water streams. It is true that the luminous larvae of certain fireflies also live in fresh water. However, the adult forms of these animals are land-dwelling.

It is rather surprising that no luminous animals have ever been found in large bodies of fresh water, such as the Great Lakes of the United States or Central Africa or Lake Baikal in Russia. The depths of these lakes are fully as dark as those of salt-water seas, which are renowned for their luminous deep-sea forms.

By far the greatest variety of light-producing species are found in the oceans. Among the microscopic protozoans, there are luminous radiolarians and flagellates. The flagellates, especially the species called *Noctiluca miliaris,* give rise to the spectacular displays of sea light in which a ship seems to move through liquid fire.

Certain sponges, a number of jellyfish and siphonophores and many comb jellies (ctenophores) emit light. There are luminous hydrozoans and sea pens; they are attached to rocks or grow in the sand. Various marine worms, nemertines, brittle stars, nudibranchs and marine snails produce light as they crawl over solid surfaces.

The bivalve mollusk, *Pholas dactylus,* bores in the sea floor and secretes a luminous slime. This is squirted out into the sea water through a tubular organ, called a siphon, whenever the animal is disturbed. The Romans considered this mollusk a delicacy and served it at their feasts. "The pholades," wrote Pliny the Elder in his NATURAL HISTORY, "shine in one's mouth as one chews them; they shine in one's hands. If any drops of their fatty liquid fall on one's garments or on the floor, these drops also shine."

Of the free-swimming marine animals, many squid, deep-sea shrimps and prawns produce light. A considerable proportion of deep-sea fishes are also luminous. In some cases a luminous organ is located at the end of a long process extending in front of the fish. In other fish, there are rows of lanternlike lights along the sides of the body. Sometimes only a few of these "lanterns" are lit; sometimes all of them are aglow. They provide an amazing display of luminescence.

Usually, luminous marine organisms are found at considerable depths. However, certain marine animals living on the surface also produce light. Among them are the plankton, tiny forms of life that drift about or swim very slowly; they include protozoans, jellyfish and comb jellies, which we have already mentioned. A few additional surface forms, such as the transparent snail *Phyllirrhoë* and the tunicate *Pyrosoma,* are also luminous. They account for the prominent individual flashes of light that one can observe on the sea at night.

Certain fish produce light not because they themselves manufacture a luminous material, but because they harbor luminous bacteria in certain structures of the body. The bacteria are always present in these structures. They receive food substances

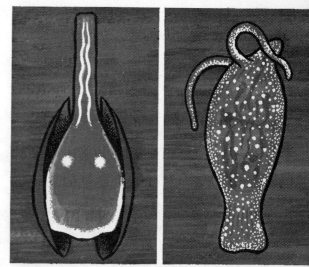

At the left is shown the luminous bivalve mollusk *Pholas dactylus*. It was considered a delicacy by the ancient Romans. Right: the transparent luminous snail *Phyllirrhoë*, a marine animal found on the surface of the sea. The flashes of light it emits can be seen at night.

from the fish, and in return supply the fish with light. They do not harm the host at all. This is a remarkable example of symbiosis — a condition in which two dissimilar organisms live together to the mutual benefit of both.

In the East Indian fishes *Photoblepharon* and *Anomalops,* luminous bacteria are always present in a special light organ that has developed under the eye. The bacteria live among long cylindrical cells that are richly supplied with blood; they emit light continuously. The fish, however, can shut off the light by a screening mechanism. In *Photoblepharon,* a fold of black membrane, suggesting an eyelid, can be drawn up over the light organ. The screening mechanism of *Anomalops* is quite different. The light organ can be turned over and downward, by means of a hinge, into a black-pigmented groove or pocket. While the organ is in this position, none of the luminous surface is visible. As the fish swims through the water, alternately masking and exposing the light organ, it emits light in a series of flashes.

In other species of fish, such as *Physiculus,* there is a glandlike reservoir, which has an opening to the outside of the body. The luminous bacteria grow in the gland; they can be forced outside by muscular contraction. As they are ejected, they form a sort of animated secretion.

Luminous organs vary in structure. The light may come from within a single cell, as in a bacterium or flagellate, or a group of cells, as in the lighting region of the firefly. In some cases the light is directed by reflectors or lenses. This type of structure, called a photophore, is like a highly complicated lantern. It is found in squid, shrimp and fishes.

Light may also be produced outside of a cell or cells. In this case it is a glandular secretion that makes its way to the outside of the body. Secretions of this kind are found in the mollusk *Pholas* and in certain crustaceans, earthworms and centipedes.

Occasionally a living animal will emit light when it is infected by luminous bacteria. These spread through the body and cause a disease that is usually fatal. An infection of this sort is common among sand fleas, those lively little creatures that hop about on piles of seaweed washed up on a sandy beach. Infected sand fleas are very active and very luminous at first. In a few days, however, as the infection spreads, the little insects become sluggish. Finally they die and their little bodies no longer emit light. Luminous bacteria also infect fresh-water shrimp, mole crickets, May flies, caterpillars, midges and sow bugs.

Generally speaking, we can be reasonably sure that a living animal that produces

In the fish called *Physiculus japonicus,* there is a glandular reservoir in which luminous bacteria grow. This reservoir is shown in longitudinal section at the left. The fish ejects the bacteria from the gland by muscular contractions; the bacteria form a luminous cloud in the water.

light has been infected by luminous bacteria if the light is continuous. Luminous plants (bacteria and fungi) emit light at all times; luminous animals, only when they are stimulated. The firefly flashes when an impulse passes along its nerves and acts upon its light organ. The mechanical disturbance caused by the tossing of the waves or the passage of a boat causes various marine forms to luminesce. Certain sea animals produce light if they are stimulated chemically. This can be done by adding ammonia to sea water. Electrical stimulation may also be effective; a flash of light will always be produced when an electric current is passed through a light-producing animal.

The glow one sees in the eyes of a cat in the dark certainly looks like bioluminescence. As a matter of fact, it was classified for many years among "spontaneous lights," such as those produced by luminous fungi. However, the so-called "glow" in the cat's eyes is simply the reflection of weak external light. If the animal's eyes shine in the dark, you may be sure that there is at least some illumination, however feeble it may be. Put the cat in a completely dark room, and the glow will vanish.

The nature of
living light

Light has generally been associated with heat in human experience. Until fairly recently the artificial light used for working or reading was always a hot light. Heat was applied to a pine knot, or a candle, or whale oil, or kerosene or illuminating gas and light was produced. In the development of the incandescent lamp, men sought to raise a solid material to the highest possible temperature without its burning or evaporating. Edison heated a carbon filament in a vacuum by passing an electric current through it. Later, a tungsten filament was substituted, because tungsten can be heated to a considerably higher temperature without burning out.

The incandescent lamp is based on the general law that all substances give off light when they are heated to a certain degree. The higher the temperature, the more total

radiation there is and the more visible light. Accompanying the visible light, a great deal of invisible radiation, or radiant heat, is emitted. Obviously, since this radiation is invisible, it is of no use to us for illumination purposes. That is why incandescence is such a wasteful way of producing light.

Incandescence could not possibly account for the production of light by living things. The heat that would accompany the light would soon prove fatal to any organism. Obviously bioluminescence must be due to so-called cold light, in which little heat is produced. This fact has been known for a long time. Referring to the glowworm in his play THE ELDER BROTHER, the Elizabethan dramatist John Fletcher writes:

"You gaudy glowworm, carrying seeming fire,
  Yet have no heat within ye."

There are various kinds of cold light. Researchers have found that in a certain type of chemical reaction practically no heat is produced. The energy released by the reaction is largely converted into visible light. This is called chemiluminescence. It accounts for the glow of phosphorus, an element discovered nearly three centuries ago. The organic substance luminol, called aminophthalic hydrazide by chemists, provides a brilliant light by chemiluminescence.

When light, especially ultraviolet light, strikes certain compounds, they will continue to glow in a dark place, without noticeable emission of heat. Such sensitive solid materials are called phosphors; the process involved is known as phosphorescence. If the sensitive material — the phosphor — emits light only while it is being illuminated, or for a short time afterward, the light that is emitted is called a fluorescence. Fluorescence (and also phosphorescence) can be excited by X rays as well as by light. Hence a fluorescent screen will make the X ray shadow of the bones of the body visible. Electrons will cause certain solid materials to fluoresce — a principle that has been applied to the television screen. The scanning beam of electrons literally paints the picture on a fluorescent substance in the short space of a fraction of a second.

A modern fluorescent lamp for illumination is simply a tube filled with gas at low pressure — a tube whose walls are coated with a very thin but uniform layer of fluorescent material. When an electric current is passed through the lamp, the gas emits radiation that is mostly in the ultraviolet invisible region of the spectrum. These ultraviolet rays strike the fluorescent material, which then gives off bright visible light. Very little heat is produced; such lamps are highly efficient.

We can produce cold light by still other means. An electric current sent through a gas at low pressure gives rise to an electroluminescence. We find this sort of light in neon signs, so widely used for advertising. When certain crystals are rubbed or broken, they give rise to the light called piezoluminescence, from the Greek *piezein,* to press. Light is also emitted when certain solutions crystallize — a process called crystalloluminescence.

There are, therefore, various kinds of cold light. Which kind accounts for the light production of animals? We have already mentioned the fact that cold light may be brought about by a chemical reaction at a low temperature. An infinite number of low-temperature chemical reactions are continually taking place in living cells. They supply the energy for movement, for secretion, for cell division, in fact for all vital processes. It is not surprising, therefore, that for the production of light in living things a chemical reaction of the chemiluminescence type should have been selected during the course of evolution.

Raphael Dubois, a French physiologist, was the first to point out the chemical nature of bioluminescence. In 1887, he suggested that the light of the boring mollusk *Pholas dactylus* was due to a reaction involving a substance he called luciferin. He maintained that luciferin combined with oxygen (was oxidized, a chemist would say) in the presence of an enzyme that he called luciferase, and that the reaction produced light. The enzyme was not used up in the light-emitting process. It was a catalyst — a substance that serves to further a chemical reaction and that is not affected by the reaction.

Dubois's hypothesis was not confirmed until years later. It was found that luciferin is not a single compound. Actually many kinds of luciferins occur in luminous animals or plants; these luciferins are not necessarily closely related in the chemical sense.

In recent years, researchers have made very careful studies of the light-producing processes of three different organisms — luminous bacteria, fireflies and the crustaceans belonging to the genus *Cypridina.* It was found that the luciferins in these three groups have little in common. In two of the groups, certain accessary structures play a part in the light-producing process.

The luciferin found in luminous bacteria is a complex (combination) of organic compounds; it is made up of reduced flavin mononucleotide plus an aldehyde. When these compounds and bacterial luciferase are brought together in solution in the presence of dissolved oxygen, they produce a bright light. This lasts until the luciferin is used up. The end product of this oxidation process is acted on by another compound — reduced diphosphopyridin nucleotide — and luciferin is reformed.

Black Star

Luciferin, luciferase and adenosinetriphosphate (ATP) are ingredients of firefly light. When ATP is added to the other two substances in increasing quantity, it brings about increasing luminosity, as is shown below.

It is oxidized, reformed again and so on. All this results in a continuous light emission, which, as we have seen, is characteristic of bacteria.

The firefly has a particularly complex system for producing light. In addition to firefly luciferin, oxygen and luciferase, a biological compound, called ATP for short (the full name is adenosinetriphosphate), and magnesium ions are necessary. When all these substances are mixed together in a test tube, light will be produced; no light will appear if any one of them is missing. The empirical formula * for firefly luciferin is known; it is $C_{13}H_{12}N_2S_2O_3$. This means that the luciferin molecule contains thirteen atoms of carbon, twelve atoms of hydrogen, two of nitrogen, two of sulfur and three of oxygen. However, scientists have not yet worked out the way in which the atoms are arranged in the molecule. Both firefly luciferin and firefly luciferase have been crystallized.

Cypridina is responsible for much of the sea light observed in the Far East. The luciferin and luciferase are manufactured in separate gland cells and poured into the sea water from openings near the mouth of the animal. The luminescence appears in the water as a puff of light. As far as is known, only luciferin, luciferase and oxygen are necessary for the production of light in *Cypridina*. The luciferin of this crustacean has been crystallized, but its composition is not yet known; apparently it is related to the proteins. *Cypridina* luciferase has not been crystallized.

Usually a luminous animal or plant emits light of only one color; the colors most frequently produced are blue, green and yellow. One remarkable insect — the "railroad worm" of South America, emits light of two colors — yellowish-green and red. This worm is a grublike luminous female beetle, belonging to the genus *Phryxothrix*; the male is winged and nonluminous. The railroad worm is about two inches long. It shows a bright red luminescent spot in the head region and a yellowish-green light on each side of eight segments

The fireflies shown here are beetles, belonging to the family Lampyridae. The larva is known as a glowworm. Light flashes produced by adult fireflies serve as signals to attract the sexes to one another. Each species has a special kind of signal.

The fantastic "railroad worm" of South America is a grublike, luminous female beetle belonging to the genus *Phryxothrix*; the male is winged and nonluminous. Right: railroad worms in daylight; below: the worms at night. Lights on the abdomen suggest lighted train windows.

* An empirical formula indicates the number and kind of atoms in a molecule.

of the abdomen. At night it offers a truly startling spectacle. The lights on the abdomen look like lighted windows; the red on the luminous spot of the head suggests the rear light of a train. As the worm crawls along on the ground, it looks for all the world like a tiny, fully illuminated train backing up slowly.

The evolution of bioluminescence

Bioluminescence is scattered in haphazard fashion throughout the animal kingdom. There is no indication that light production arose at a particular time or in a particular group and that it then followed definite evolutionary pathways. The first appearance of luminescence in a living organism was probably a chemical mutation,* resulting in a luminous spot. Once such a spot appeared on an animal or plant, the light may have been of value and may have persisted by natural selection.

The reverse process also occurs. A luminous organism such as a bacterium may suddenly produce nonluminous mutants. This type of mutation is due to the loss of one or another of the substances necessary for light production; the cell suddenly loses its ability to manufacture the substances in question. In the luminous bacteria, three kinds of dark mutants are known. One type lacks luciferase; another, the flavin mononucleotide; the third, the aldehyde. If the missing substance is added, light will appear. Suppose, for example, that a colony of nonluminous mutants lacks aldehyde. If one blows the

* A mutation represents a sudden variation in a plant or animal. The offspring will differ from its parents in some character or other because of changes in the genes, the units of heredity. The changed animal or plant is called a mutant. See Index, under Mutations.

vapor from an open bottle containing aldehyde over the colony, it will suddenly begin to glow.

The uses of bioluminescence

It is doubtful whether the ability to emit light benefits the simple species of animals or plants. Of what use would light be to a luminous bacterium or fungus? How would it help a marine flagellate, with no nervous system and little power of locomotion, blown hither and thither by the winds? Such light probably represents a chance mutation, which persists for no apparent reason.

In the case of animals with a nervous system and definite behavior reactions, we can suggest various possible uses for bioluminescence. It is definitely known that the light flashes produced by the firefly serve as a signal to attract the sexes to one another. Each species has a special kind of signal. An expert can go into the field and identify the different firefly species by the length of the flashes and the intervals between them.

In deep-sea forms, living in perpetual darkness, the light organs probably serve to provide illumination and also for recognition. Many luminous marine forms live in regions of the sea where light penetrates. In such cases the animals may luminesce at night in order to lure prey or to elude natural enemies.

The deep-sea squid *Heteroteuthis* has often been cited as an example of a marine animal that uses luminescence in order to escape from its foes. This squid is found in the Strait of Messina and is sometimes brought to the surface by the strong cur-

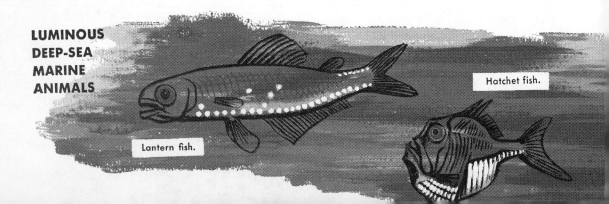

LUMINOUS DEEP-SEA MARINE ANIMALS

Hatchet fish.

Lantern fish.

rents in that area. It is readily caught and can be observed in an aquarium. *Hetero-teuthis* squirts a large amount of luminous fluid into the water whenever it is disturbed. The ordinary squid ejects black ink to divert the attention of a pursuing foe. It is believed that *Heteroteuthis* uses its luminous secretion for the same purpose. A pursuer would be confused by the glittering "liquid fire" and the squid would make good its escape.

The characteristic rows of lights on the sides and belly of deep-sea fish may serve to keep a school of fish together. We have already mentioned the fact that the lights are turned on and off as the fish swims through the water. Perhaps significant light patterns are produced in this way; perhaps the fish has a complex signaling system, like that of the firefly. However, we can only guess about such uses of luminescence at the present time.

Within comparatively recent years investigators have begun to penetrate the depths of the sea in bathyspheres, benthoscopes and bathyscaphes * and have used the television camera to pry into the secrets of the deep. With such devices they will be able to make detailed studies of deep-sea animals in their natural environment. Some day they may be able to solve the fascinating mysteries of bioluminescence occurring in the depths of the sea.

* The bathysphere, developed by C. W. Beebe about 1930, consists of a hollow steel globe, which is lowered from a surface vessel by means of a cable. One or more observers, stationed within the bathysphere, can observe and study the sea life outside the globe by peering through fused quartz windows. The benthoscope is a somewhat similar device, developed in the 1940's by O. Barton. The bathyscaphe, invented by A. Piccard in the 1940's, is a steel sphere suspended from a cigar-shaped, gasoline-filled steel tank; the device can be driven through the water by two electrically driven propellers. The bathyscaphe *Trieste* has reached a depth of over 37,000 feet.

See also Vol. 10, p. 271: "General Works."

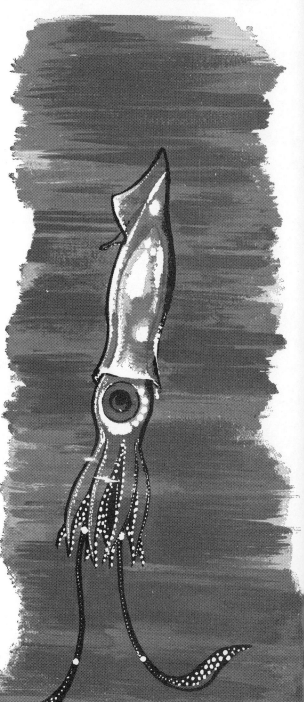

Deep-sea squid, *Lycoteuthis.*

Angler.

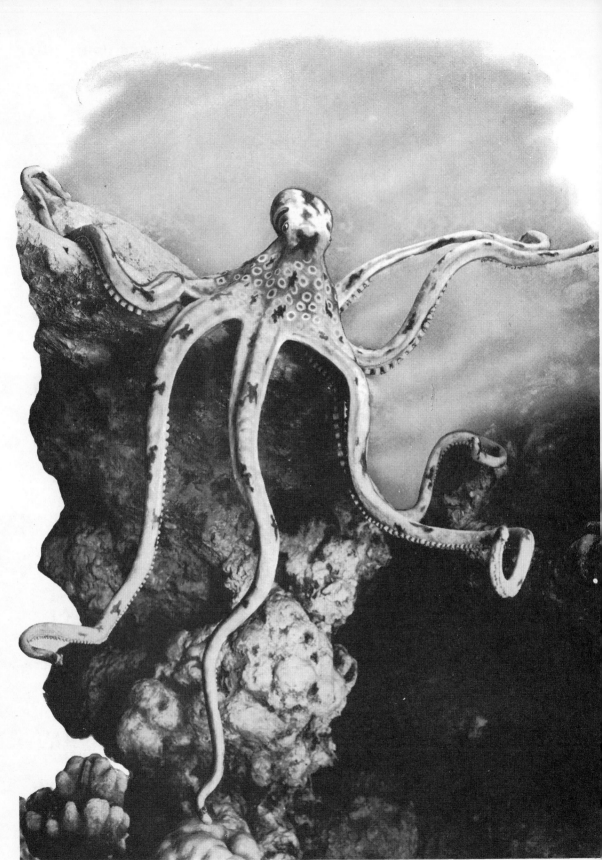

The bizarre octopus, contrary to many tales of its ferocity, is a shy, timid creature.

THE MOLLUSKS

Soft-bodied Creatures of Land and Sea

BY F. L. FITZPATRICK

IT WOULD seem to be a far cry from the tiny snail in a home aquarium to a fifty-foot giant squid; from the edible oyster, firmly attached throughout life to the same rock or shell, to the freely swimming scallop; from that gentle vegetarian, the slug, to the sinister-looking octopus, which is a greedy carnivore. Yet all these animals, varying so greatly in size, appearance and habits, belong to the phylum of the Mollusca, or mollusks. This is one of the largest groups in the animal kingdom; more than seventy thousand species have already been described. Many mollusks live in the sea; others are found in fresh-water lakes, ponds and streams; some dwell upon the land.

The word "mollusk" comes from the Latin *molluscus,* meaning "soft." The name is apt enough, for all mollusks have soft bodies. In most cases the body is protected by a shell, made up largely of calcium carbonate. This shell is secreted by the body covering known as the mantle. Most mollusks also have an unusual structure called the foot, which takes quite different forms in various species. In clams, for example, the foot is a muscular extension of the body and is used in plowing through mud and sand; in snails, it is flat and is used for creeping. In squids and octopuses, it is divided into arms, which serve to seize the animals' prey. Certain oysters have no foot.

Among the best-known of the mollusks are the striking creatures known as squids and octopuses. They belong to the class of the Cephalopoda, or cephalopods ("head-feet," in Greek; so called because the foot, which is separated into a number of "arms," encircles the head). The cephalopods differ from most other mollusks in one important respect: they generally do not develop shells, the mantle forming the outer part of the naked body. In some species, however, there is an inner skeleton, lying under the surface of the body.

The cephalopods all dwell in the sea. They are provided with arms (also called tentacles), which have suckers or hooks, or both. Almost all cephalopods secrete

Cornelia Clarke

N. Y. Zool. Soc.

A clam's wedge-shaped foot extends from the shell to the left; its siphons, to the right.

The land snail glides smoothly over a trail of mucus from a slime gland at the head end.

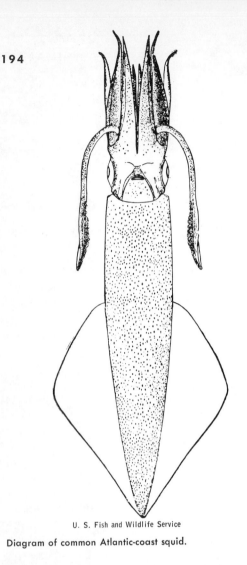

Diagram of common Atlantic-coast squid.

eyes have no lids; otherwise they look startlingly like human eyes.

The squid draws water through a central cavity of the body — the mantle cavity — and forces it out through a flexible tube, the siphon, when the mantle is contracted. The siphon is located just back of the arms; the jet of water that spurts through it serves to propel the animal swiftly backward. (Ink is also discharged through this siphon.) The fins, which are two flaplike extensions of the mantle, are used chiefly for steering; they also serve to propel the squid slowly forward or backward.

One of the most familiar species is the common squid, or *Loligo pealei,* which is found along the eastern coast of North America and in Mediterranean and Oriental waters. It is used by some fishermen as bait; it also serves as human food, particularly in the Mediterranean area and the Orient. The squid known as the flying squid (*Ommastrephes bartrami*) has been compared to the flying fish; it often shoots out of the water, particularly when the weather is rough, and sometimes lands on the decks of ships.

The giant squid is the largest of invertebrates

The most formidable of all the squids is the giant squid (*Architeuthis princeps*), the largest of all the invertebrates, or animals without backbones. The total length of the animal, including the body and the arms, may be fifty feet or more. This monster lives in the open sea, making its way far beneath the surface. Live giant squids have but infrequently been encountered at sea; however, they are sometimes cast up on beaches, especially along the shores of Newfoundland. According to some authorities, the giant squid may have given rise to the numerous legends of mighty serpents frequenting the depths of the sea and occasionally engulfing ships.

Few dwellers of the deep have stirred the imagination of mankind more than the octopuses (genus *Octopus*). Many tales have been told of these creatures lurking in crevices and amid rocks and suddenly

an inklike fluid, which is stored in a special sac. When they wish to escape a pursuer, the animals squirt the ink into the water, making it turbid and thus confusing the foe. Most cephalopods are capable of chameleonlike color changes. The skin contains cells, called chromatophores ("color-bearers"), which contain different pigments. When these cells become larger or smaller, the color of the skin changes rapidly. Because of such color changes, the animals generally blend effectively with the background.

The expert cephalopod swimmer called the squid is a streamlined, spindle-shaped creature; it is sometimes called the sea arrow because of the way in which it darts through the water. The foot is divided into ten arms, of which two are longer than the rest; these arms, which bear suckers, are used to seize and hold prey. The darting out to attack some hapless wader or diver. Such bloodcurdling tales are manufactured out of whole cloth, or else are grossly exaggerated. It is true that a large octopus with eight long, powerful arms, two large staring eyes and a vicious-looking beak, would be a rather unpleasant customer to meet under water; yet there is little evidence to show that even the larger octopuses attack man.

The foot of the octopus is divided into eight arms; it is this feature that gives rise to the name, which means "eight feet" in Greek. The animal has a parrotlike beak with which it rends its prey. Octopuses range in arm-and-body length from several inches to almost thirty feet; the larger species, sometimes called devilfish, may attain a weight of seventy-five pounds. The octopus can crawl along the sea bottom on its arms; sometimes it swims about by sucking water into the body and then squirting it out.

Most octopuses are shy, retiring creatures. During the day they are generally hidden in crevices; at nightfall they steal out in search of prey. Stealthily an octopus creeps up on some unsuspecting fish

or crab. Once the powerful arms are entwined about the victim, there is no escape; the beaklike jaws quickly end the captive's struggles, and the octopus feeds upon the prey. With the coming of dawn, the animal retreats to its lair. The octopus is itself the prey of certain animals, including conger eels, whales and sharks.

Octopuses are eaten in some of the larger seaboard cities of Europe and North America; they are eagerly sought after in various parts of the Orient and in the islands of the South Pacific. The islanders wrap the arms of these animals in taro leaves and bake them on hot stones.

A well-known relative of the squids and octopuses is the common sepia, or cuttlefish (*Sepia officinalis*). This small creature, ranging from six to ten inches in length, secretes a calcareous inner shell, which is known as cuttlebone. This substance is used to supply lime to canaries and other caged birds; it also serves as a polishing agent. The pigment called sepia is prepared from the deep brown fluid that the cuttlefish ejects in order to conceal its retreat.

The pearly, or chambered, nautilus (*Nautilus pompilius*) found in the South Pacific and the Indian Ocean, is a member of an ancient group of animals and is related to squids and octopuses; only a few

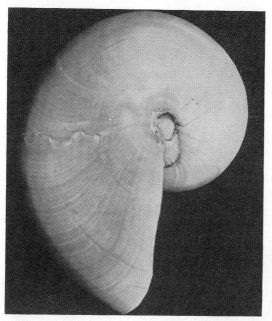

Photos, N. Y. Zool. Soc.

Intact and cutaway shells of the pearly nautilus. The nautilus occupied each chamber in turn as it grew up.

species survive today. The pearly-nautilus shell is spirally coiled; it is divided into compartments, each of which represents a chamber in which the nautilus lived at some stage of its growth. Naturally the animal is found in the outermost chamber. About ninety tentacles are set around the mouth; though these tentacles have no suckers, they can cling tenaciously to solid objects. The head can be withdrawn into the shell; a hood at the back of the head partly closes the opening.

The female of the paper nautilus, or argonaut (*Argonauta argo*), secretes a spirally coiled and symmetrical white shell. This shell serves as an egg case; the argonaut can drop it at will. The female may reach a length of eight inches. The male, however, is a puny little creature, only about an inch long; it never secretes a shell.

The clams, oysters, mussels and teredos belong to the class of the Pelecypoda, or Lamellibranchia; they are also known as bivalves, because their shells are divided into two parts, known as valves. The inner surface of the shell is coated with a layer known as nacre, or mother-of-pearl. This layer is fine-grained; it may be white, or it may show all the colors of the rainbow.

The two valves are joined by one or two strong muscles, which can hold the

Scallop bed on the sandy ocean bottom in shallow water. The animals swim by flapping the two parts of the shell.

shell tightly closed; it is these muscles that are cut when a mussel or clam is opened. Some bivalves, such as clams, have a well-developed foot, which can be extended beyond the shell to move the animal from place to place. True oysters, however, cannot move about as adults, because they are firmly attached to solid objects on the bottom of the sea. Bivalves have no specially differentiated head.

Some bivalves have two tubes, or siphons, through which water is drawn in and forced out. The water that is sucked in contains the tiny organisms that serve as food: protozoans, eggs, larvae, the spores of algae and the minute plants called diatoms. Food is taken into the digestive canal by way of a mouth opening; oxygen enters the blood through the two gills. Wastes are carried away as water is forced out of the excurrent siphon.

The true oyster, or edible oyster (genus *Ostrea*), leads a sedentary life, as we have seen. The shell is quite asymmetrical. The valve that is fastened to a submerged object is large and quite thick; the other one is smaller and thinner. The two parts of the shell are closed by a single muscle, popularly called the "heart," which extends from about the center of one valve through the animal's body to the other. True oysters occur in many parts of the world, particularly along the coasts of Europe, North America and Japan.

L. W. Brownell

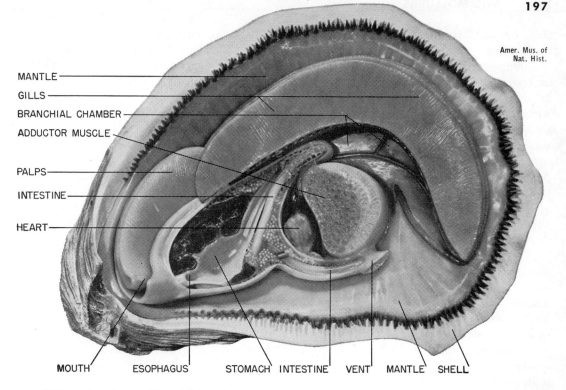

MANTLE

GILLS

BRANCHIAL CHAMBER

ADDUCTOR MUSCLE

PALPS

INTESTINE

HEART

MOUTH   ESOPHAGUS   STOMACH INTESTINE   VENT   MANTLE   SHELL

Anatomical model of common American oyster (*Ostrea virginica*). The important internal organs are shown.

When the first white settlers came to North America, they found that Indian tribes along the coast depended upon oysters for a considerable part of their food. Evidently they had been eating these mollusks for generations, because large piles of oyster shells had collected around Indian towns and encampments. The first settlers and those who followed them picked and dredged oysters from the shallow bays; for a long time it was thought that the supply would never be exhausted.

Increasing demand, however, led to overfishing in the latter part of the nineteenth century. It then became necessary to supplement the natural supply by planting barren bottoms with young oysters, thus starting new beds. Today a considerable portion of the oyster supply in North America comes from privately owned beds. Oysters are also raised in Japan and in various European countries, particularly France and Holland.

To raise oysters successfully, the oysterman must be familiar with the life cycle of these shellfish. The female of a typical species, such as *Ostrea virginica,* which is found along the eastern coast of North America, produces millions of eggs a year. They are discharged into the water, where many are fertilized by sperm cells ejected by male oysters. If the egg is fertilized, it develops into a tiny larva, which swims about freely at first. After a couple of days it begins to develop a shell and in a week it is entirely enclosed. Dropping to the bottom it becomes attached to a solid object, such as a rock or shell. The spat, as the young oyster is now called, grows rapidly, and in time becomes a mature oyster.

In spite of the vast numbers of eggs produced by female oysters, the oyster population is not constantly on the increase. For one thing, many of the eggs are not fertilized. Again, vast numbers of the little larvae are eaten by fishes during the period when they are swimming about in the water. Even after they have dropped to the bottom and have become securely attached, they are by no means safe. They may be smothered by shifting sand and mud, or devoured by starfish or drumfish or other natural foes. Of course, once oysters have reached the adult stage, they are sacrificed by the millions to meet the demands of the market.

During the breeding season American oystermen locate places where the surface of the sea is covered with oyster larvae. They pave the bottom in such places with various hard materials, such as old bricks, tile, empty bivalve shells, brush and discarded metal parts. After a time the spat drop to the bottom and become attached to the paving materials. These materials are then dredged up and planted in favorable spots that have been selected for the development of beds.

Oysters are often planted in moderately shallow water, where the bottom is of hard mud. In such a place one is likely to find marine plants, and these will provide food for the microscopic organisms upon which oysters feed. Oystermen avoid places where there is shifting mud and sand, or where starfish or other natural enemies of oysters abound or where the waters may be contaminated with sewage.

Oysters that are ready for the market are collected in shallow waters by means of oyster tongs; these are like two long-tined rakes, hinged so as to open and close like shears. In deeper waters the oysters are taken by means of a dredge.

In France young oysters are removed

to partially enclosed growing ponds, admitting the tides through sluices and floodgates. When fully grown, the oysters are fattened in small enclosed ponds, called *claires*. Japanese oyster farms are generally in shallow, brackish water; each farm is enclosed by a bamboo fence or hedge. The spat are collected and held on bamboo stakes thrust into the bed; the stakes are pulled out when the oysters are fully grown.

Clams are also very important as food for man. One of the most sought after of these bivalves is the soft-shelled clam (*Mya arenaria*), so called because of its rather thin and fragile shell. It is found along the Atlantic and Pacific coasts of North America and also in Europe. The soft-shelled clam is also called the long-necked clam, because of the unusual length of its "neck." This consists of two siphons, which are tubular structures; they are joined together and covered with tough skin.

Soft-shelled clams bury themselves in mud or sand

This clam burrows into mud or sand with its tongue-shaped foot to a depth of several inches. The "neck" extends just out of the sand at high tide, as the animal feeds. At low tide, holes in the mud or sand show where the clam is buried. It is then a simple matter for a clammer to walk along the beach and dig out quantities of the bivalves.

The hard-shelled clam (*Venus mercenaria*) differs in various respects from the soft-shelled variety. Its thick, solid shell is a rather dirty white in color and is marked with concentric rings. The inner part of the shell is whitish, turning to purple at the outer edges. This purple section was used by coastal Indians for the money known as wampum. The hard-shelled clam is also known as the quahog and as the littleneck clam, since its siphons are much shorter than those of the soft-shelled variety.

The hard-shelled clam is found in great numbers along the southern portions of North America's Atlantic coast. It dwells on sandy or muddy bottoms at depths ranging up to fifty feet; it makes its

The land slug inhabits damp vegetation.

Hugh Spencer

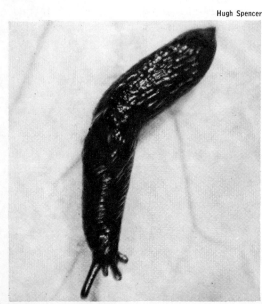

Piece of timber attacked by teredos.

food. Only a small portion of the body is eaten: this is the single large muscle that in life serves to hold the two valves of the shell together.

The marine mussel, another bivalve, has a wedge-shaped black or bluish shell. A bunch of threads, called a byssus, is secreted by a gland located immediately behind the foot; these threads harden when they come in contact with sea water and cause the animal to be firmly attached to solid objects, such as rocks. The byssus can be discarded and a new one secreted; in this way the animal can move to new surroundings if unfavorable conditions arise. The edible variety of mussel known as *Mytilus edulis* is popular in various parts of Europe; occasionally it is served in restaurants of American cities along the eastern coast. It abounds in Atlantic coastal waters and also in the Mediterranean. The fresh-water mussel is found mostly in rivers and lakes, where it burrows in mud. In the United States the pearly shells of fresh-water mussels, or clams, are used in the manufacture of "pearl" buttons.

way through sand or mud with its large foot. Clammers usually go out in boats to fish for hard-shelled clams; they gather them with a rake or dredge. The clams are served raw on the half shell or are used for clam fries and chowders.

Perhaps the most remarkable member of the clam group is the giant clam (*Tridacna gigas*), found in the coral reefs of the Pacific. This is the largest of the bivalves. Its shell may be as much as three feet long and may weigh up to five hundred pounds; the edible portion may come to twenty pounds or more. Giant clam shells have been used for baptismal fonts and babies' bathtubs.

The bivalves known as scallops are found in many parts of the world; their range extends from shallow water to fairly deep water. The shell is fan-shaped; the valves are arched and rounded. There are two winglike projections at either end of the hinge of the shell; about twenty ridges radiate from the hinge, increasing in width as they extend outward. Scallops are good swimmers, especially when young; the jets of water they spout as they alternately open and close their shells propel them through the water in a series of jumps.

Several species of scallops, found along the Atlantic and Pacific coasts of North America, are highly esteemed as

Teredos, or shipworms, burrow into submerged wood

The teredo, or shipworm, is a boring bivalve; it excavates burrows in wood that is under salt water. The two valves of the teredo are provided with fine ridges, suggesting the teeth of a file. Soon after it hatches from the egg, the teredo begins rasping with its double file at the wood of a pile, breakwater or ship bottom. As the burrow that is formed is deepened, it is lined with a pearly coating. In time the teredo becomes a long, wormlike creature; the tapering body dwarfs the tiny valves, which are at the innermost part of the burrow. Siphons protrude from the opening of the burrow to draw in water and food and force out wastes; when the siphons are drawn in, the hole is closed by means of two plates attached to the rear end of the body.

Outwardly, a piece of timber attacked by teredos shows only a number of small holes; inwardly it may be honeycombed with teredo burrows, sometimes so close together that the wood between them is as thin as paper. In time the most solid timbers are so riddled that they collapse. Metal or concrete sheathing is used to protect timber from the attacks of teredos; heavy impregnation with creosote has also proved effective.

Snails, slugs, limpets, abalones and conchs are included in the large class of mollusks known as gastropods. These animals have a foot and mantle cavity, like other mollusks; they have a well-developed head region and generally possess a spirally coiled shell that is all in one piece.

Snails live in the sea, in fresh water and on land

Snails are particularly widespread. Some dwell in the ocean; others in the fresh water of rivers, ponds and lakes. There are numberless land snails, too; they abound in tropical jungles and are also found in damp places in the temperate zones.

The snail's head bears the mouth opening and the tentacles (one or two pair); the eyes are set upon or at the base of the tentacles. The animal creeps upon its flat foot from place to place. Certain gland cells of the foot secrete mucus, which lubricates the path over which the snail crawls. This accounts for the slick trail that the animal leaves as it passes over a more or less flat surface. Both the head and foot of a snail can be withdrawn into the shell.

Fresh-water snails and land snails were probably eaten by primitive man before the dawn of history. Today, they are regarded as delicacies in various parts of southern and western Europe and in some of the larger cities of the New World. The market supply comes largely from snails that are raised in captivity. The snail farms of southern France, Italy and Spain are well known. About ten thousand snails can be kept in a pen twenty-five to thirty feet square; the animals are fed upon meal, vegetables and bran.

In many areas snails are a pest, because they feed voraciously upon garden crops. The giant African snail (*Achatina fulica*) has become a particularly serious menace. This creature, a native of east Africa, is sometimes more than six inches long and it is as big around as a tennis ball. Its diet is varied, including garden plants, flower petals, decaying tissues and manure. It is long-lived and fertile and can thrive under the most unfavorable conditions. It has already invaded India, Ceylon, China, Borneo, Java, Sumatra, Formosa and many of the islands of the South Pacific; every effort is being made to keep it out of North America.

Whelks and periwinkles are marine snails that are commonly used as food by Europeans. The whelk is widely distributed in the North Atlantic; besides serving as food, it is used as bait in cod fishing. Periwinkles are found in temperate and cold seas in many areas; they abound on rocks and in seaweed and feed on seaweed. The long tongue, or radula, of the periwinkle is a remarkable structure; it is provided with many rows of sharp, curved teeth.

The rasping radula of the snail, which is known as the oyster drill, is particularly well developed. This tiny creature, less than an inch long, drills a hole through the shell of an oyster near the hinge, and then sucks out the soft body of the victim through the hole. The oyster drill is one of the chief foes of the oysterman.

Among the kin of the snails are the curious animals called slugs. These mollusks, which range in length from one inch to several inches, have no external shell. Land slugs live in moist places; they are often found under stones and in holes in the ground. At night they emerge from their retreats to feed on vegetation; they sometimes invade vegetable gardens. Sea slugs crawl on rocks or seaweed in shallow water along the coasts of North America, Europe and Asia.

The gastropod known as the limpet has a rounded or oval shell, looking for all the world like a diminutive volcanic cone; some of these animals even have a small opening at the top of the shell, suggesting a crater. Limpets adhere so firmly to rocks near low-water mark by means of their suckerlike foot that they withstand the beating of the surf. At high tide they move about in search of the algae on which they feed; after their forays they again attach themselves to the rocks. Limpets are found in many parts of the world.

The shell of the abalone has a rather startling resemblance to a human ear; for that reason this gastropod is sometimes called an ear shell. The large shell is very ornamental, particularly after the rough outer surface has been polished. Abalones are found in the Orient and also on the Atlantic and Pacific coasts of the New World. They live on rocks near the shore, feeding on seaweed; when disturbed, they cling with surprising strength to rocky surfaces. The flesh is often used in stews and chowders; sometimes it is prepared in the form of a steak. It is generally dried or smoked in the Orient.

The conch is a large gastropod that is especially common along the coasts of the southern United States and the West Indies. The shell is sometimes a foot long and may weigh as much as five pounds; it has a small spire with a large lower whorl. The foot of the conch is provided with a clawlike appendage. The animal moves in a series of leaps, sometimes turning quickly to avoid capture. Conch shells are sometimes made into horns; they are also used for cameos and buttons. The flesh serves as food in certain areas, including the Bahamas and the Florida Keys.

The mollusk class of the scaphopods, or tooth shells, is a small one, numbering only about 200 species. In most species the long, curved, tapering, ivory-colored shell looks something like a boar's tusk. In some varieties, known as elephant-tusk shells, the shell is not curved. The tooth shell is generally found in fairly deep waters off the coasts in many regions. Occasionally the empty shell is found on our beaches, particularly after a severe storm.

The chitons and their kin make up the class of the Amphineura; they are found all over the world, except in the far north and south. The chitons have a shell consisting of overlapping plates; they may be seen at low tide crawling about or clinging to seaweed or rocks. The larger chitons are edible; the flesh is generally called sea beef. Some of the Amphineura have no shells and look like grubs.

The mollusks are exceedingly useful to mankind in many ways. We have already considered their importance as a source of food, and we have mentioned some of the other ways in which they serve mankind. Mollusk shells are particularly valuable. The beautiful shells of abalones, conchs and other varieties are commonly sold as souvenirs and used as ornaments. The mother-of-pearl inner layer of various mollusk shells is used for pearl inlays and knife handles and in hundreds of other ways. Tons of bivalve and other mollusk shells are ground up every year and used as material for surfacing roads. Because of their lime content, the ground-up shells

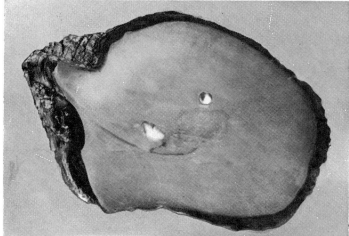

Oyster shell with a blister, which has been formed, in the same way as in a pearl, by successive layers of nacre secreted around an irritant that had lodged between the shell and mantle.

are used as fertilizer and are also fed to domesticated birds, such as chickens.

Undoubtedly pearls are the most glamorous products yielded by mollusks. Like mollusk shells, these precious gems represent the secretions of the mantle that envelops the body; they are made up of the same lustrous substance — mother-of-pearl, or nacre — of which the inner layer of the shell consists. Suppose that a foreign body, such as a grain of sand or a parasite, finds a lodging place between the mantle and the shell. It will serve as an irritant and will greatly stimulate secretion at that point. As the grain or parasite is slowly encased in a nacreous coating, it may be rolled about by slight contractions of the mantle, thus remaining free from the shell. In time it will be enclosed in many layers of nacre and will be a full-fledged pearl. By far the greatest number of pearls used in commerce come from the so-called pearl oysters, belonging to the genera *Avicula* and *Pinctada*. However, various other mollusks, including edible oysters and fresh-water mussels, have also yielded pearls.

More or less perfectly formed spherical pearls are few and far between. In many cases such pearls originate when parasitic worms form cysts in the mantle layer; as the cysts are more or less rounded in form, they make ideal development centers. A great many pearls, called baroque, are more or less irregular in form: they may be pear-shaped, or dome-shaped or rather flat. Baroque pearls are often made into pendants, brooches and rings; they are not nearly so valuable as spherical pearls.

Pearls are of many different colors, including white, cream, rose, brown, blue, yellow and green; the color depends on the oyster's diet, the temperature of the water and various other factors. The favorite colors for gems are white, cream, rose, steel-blue and black.

The matching of pearls has much to do with their commercial value. When large pearls of the same size and shape are matched to form a necklace, they bring a far higher price than if they are sold separately. Necklaces made up of pearls matched in a perfectly graded series are also costly. A perfectly matched pearl necklace may sell for several hundred thousand dollars.

Pearl fisheries are found in various parts of the world. The most valuable pearls come from the pearl oysters that grow in the warm waters of the Persian Gulf and the Red Sea and off the coasts of India, northern Australia, certain South Pacific islands and Central America. Pearl collecting is an uncertain business at best. In one instance a week's catch of thirty-five thousand pearl oysters yielded only twenty-one pearls, of which only three were suitable for commercial use. In a number of cases the collecting of pearls is carried on in connection with the more dependable business of collecting and marketing shells.

Men have succeeded in "growing" pearls by deliberately inserting a foreign substance within the shell of an oyster or mussel. A pearl produced in this way is called a culture pearl; it is very different in origin from the artificial pearl created by the chemist. The Chinese Buddhists were pioneers in the production of culture pearls. They inserted small plates bearing the image of Buddha between the shell and mantle of marine clams. These plates became coated in time with nacre; they were then sold as souvenirs and also as objects of religious veneration. This practice has continued to the present day.

The Japanese have succeeded in producing spherical culture pearls on a commercial scale, and they have almost a monopoly of the culture-pearl industry. A mother-of-pearl bead is carefully inserted in the mantle of a pearl oyster, which proceeds to cover the bead with a thin coating of nacre. The original bead makes up most of the finished product; the nacre coating is generally only about a millimeter thick. Of course, the longer the pearl is permitted to develop, the thicker the coating; the thicker the coating, the more valuable the pearl. An attempt to produce culture pearls in the United States failed because of high labor costs.

See also Vol. 10, p. 275: "Invertebrates."

EARTH'S INVISIBLE ARMY

Small Organisms in the Soil

SCIENTISTS have long recognized the part played by physical and chemical agencies in conditioning the soil. The force of gravity, for example, draws water deep into the ground; the erosive action of wind, water and glaciers shifts the soil and adds new elements to it. The chemistry of the soil is also very important; scientists have learned what chemical elements and compounds are essential and how they affect plants. There is a third vital factor in soil conditioning — the host of plants and animals living in the earth. Modern investigations have revealed the curious habits of the creatures that have gone underground to live, and practical information has been acquired about their value or destructiveness in agriculture.

Mounting evidence shows that certain tiny organisms are important in maintaining the fertility of the soil and that others directly influence the plants that extend their roots into the ground. Some of the organisms found in the soil even contribute to the field of medicine. Valuable antibiotic drugs, such as chloromycetin, aureomycin and terramycin, are derived from moldlike plants that live in the earth.

The larger soil dwellers are represented by such mammals as moles, go-phers, ground squirrels, mice, ground hogs and prairie dogs. They are often very injurious to the crops. Some of them undermine growing plants with their digging; others eat vast quantities of vegetable matter, such as roots and young shoots. However, they contribute greatly to soil fertility by moving and mixing a great amount of dirt. They also promote water drainage and soil aeration because of the tunnels and channels they dig.

Millepedes, centipedes, slugs, spiders, mites and several burrowing snakes do their share in providing channels for drainage and aeration. The waste products from the bodies of these animals put essential organic matter in the soil; so does the decomposition of their dead bodies.

Various insects make similar contributions. Numberless beetles, bees and flies spend at least a part of their lives in the ground. All of them help to keep the earth loose and open by constantly moving the numberless particles of soil. The ants undoubtedly make exceedingly important contributions to the conditioning of the soil. Have you ever watched a colony of these industrious insects hard at work bringing out, one by one, minute particles of earth? Slow and laborious digging, I

Pocket gophers help to make the soil fertile by bringing to the surface and mixing immense quantities of dirt.

suppose you will say. You should remember, however, that this digging has gone on for millions of years.

The most important of the large soil organisms

Earthworms are the most important and valuable of all the soil organisms larger than the algae, and their activities are entirely beneficial to the soil and its crops. Their lives are spent burrowing through the soil, cultivating it and increasing its fertility. Members of this family are found throughout the world in almost every kind of soil; they prefer a moderately moist, organically rich soil, not too acid nor alkaline.

The common earthworms of America and Europe seldom reach a length greater than twelve inches; but an Australian relative is known to measure seven feet in length and one inch in diameter, a little too much bait for anybody's hook. The common earthworm is sometimes called a night crawler, as it appears only at night; while it forages for food on the surface its tail remains in the burrow, making a quick escape possible in an emergency. Earthworms feed on dead plants and other organic remains, and sometimes on algae and bacteria. The worms ordinarily stay within a foot of the surface, but under certain conditions they burrow to depths of six or eight feet.

An average acre of soil may contain from thirteen to two hundred thousand earthworms, though concentrations in the millions occur in unusual cases; the number depends on the soil condition and available food. In general, the more fertile the soil, the more earthworms it contains. Experiments prove that the earthworm itself is responsible for this fertility with which it is linked.

The earthworm is always on the move, and its travels make it the best soil conditioner known. In its excursions to and from the surface it incidentally drags bits of dead plant matter into its burrows; as it moves about, this rich humus is distributed in the surface soil within the reach of plant roots. Its burrowing action results in a constant mixing and refining of the soil and provides canals for root expansion and the entry of water and air.

Earthworms burrow by ingesting soil particles and passing them through their alimentary canals, where they are digested and their food value is absorbed; the remainder, excreted through the anus, is known as castings. In hard soils the earthworm acts like a hydraulic drill, softening and breaking up the mass ahead with a mouth secretion. In a year's time, the earthworms of an average acre pass more than twenty .tons of soil through their bodies, and in ten or twenty years they can bring up to four inches of new topsoil to the surface. What is more important, their deep burrowings bring to the topsoil great quantities of minerals buried in the subsoil; thus, they accomplish in a short time a process that takes months and years when achieved by the action of the weather, the soil solution and the soil microbes.

The use of earthworm castings in farming

It has been found that some parts of the Nile valley in the Anglo-Egyptian Sudan possess two million earthworms per acre, producing some two hundred tons of castings annually. These castings account for the abnormal fertility of the region; they constitute one of the most perfect fertilizers available. Chemical analysis has revealed the richness of the castings in nitrogen (from urea and ammonia), carbonates and soluble phosphates, all of which are vital to plant life. Earthworms also moderate the acidity of the soil, tending to keep it neutral, by the secretions of their calciferous glands. For the proper functioning of these glands calcium must be available in the worms' food.

Because of their virtues as cultivators, fertilizers and "soil doctors" (they are often used to rid sick soils of poisons and harmful bacteria), earthworms are now added to the land by many farmers, and great pains are taken to insure their multiplication. Special strains are commercially bred for use in the improvement of particular crops and soils.

Plant roots contribute to the earth's productiveness in several ways. They penetrate the upper and lower depths of the soil and, on their death, leave vast quantities of organic matter to decay in intimate contact with the soil grains. Moreover, this decay opens up the channels that were bored in the soil by the growing roots. The channels serve as air passages and especially as routes of water movement in the soil. We little realize how much tile drainage is aided by such apparently insignificant factors as these.

The small organisms of the soil

We have seen that the greater proportion of the larger organisms in the soil belong to the animal kingdom. However, in the case of the minute forms of life, plant life reigns supreme. These plant forms may be divided into four groups: molds, fungi, algae and bacteria. The last of these groups is far and away the most important of them all.

In this section — Plant Life — we study the soil from the standpoint of its relation to the plant. Considering the small organisms in the soil from this viewpoint, too, we find that these tiny creatures fall into two main classes — those that are injurious to plants and those that are beneficial to them.

Harmful microorganisms

The microorganisms that are detrimental to plants are largely parasitic in their habits. They usually attack the plant through its roots. They stay in the soil for a long time even if the plant that the particular parasite uses as its host is not grown. As a soil once infested will remain so for several years, steps must often be taken to rid it of the organism. This can be done in the greenhouse by heating the soil with steam. Some growers apply steam to their soil every year, whether the soil is infected or not. They want to be sure that every precaution is taken to prevent disease among their plants. The common diseases that are due to microorganisms are galls, root rot, wilts of such important crops as flax, watermelon and tomato, and the damp-

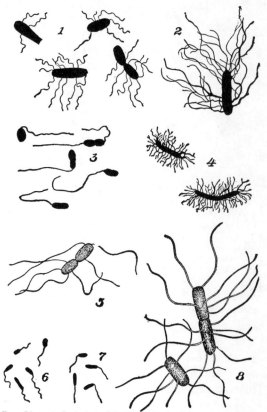

From Lipman's *Bacteria in Relation to Country Life*, Macmillan Co.

Different types of soil bacteria. These organisms are usually rod-shaped and may possess "arms" with which they swim about in soil water.

ing off of a very great number of plants. The latter is a common greenhouse disease that is much feared by gardeners and that they constantly seek to prevent.

Infection is easily carried from one soil or greenhouse to another and great care must be taken with rubbish when any disease is present. The germ may also be carried on implements such as shovels, rakes or hoes as well as large farm machinery. In all cases of diseased soil, a strict quarantine must be maintained until the germ has been destroyed and the soil has been disinfected. While disease may be wiped out of a greenhouse or hotbed, such control is not possible out in the field. Preventive measures must be adopted there to avoid the occurrence of disease. Care in bringing in the seed, use of manure that is free of disease and the introduction of disease-immune plants are common precautions. Plant breeders are now

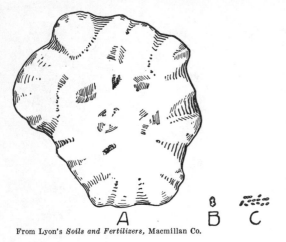

From Lyon's *Soils and Fertilizers*, Macmillan Co.

Diagram showing the extremely small size of soil bacteria. *A* represents a particle of sand; *B*, a clay particle; *C*, a number of soil bacteria.

doing a wonderful job in producing disease-resistant strains, just as stock breeders have succeeded in producing animals able to withstand various conditions. The rotation of crops — that is, the growing of a number of different crops in a regular succession — is also practiced.

This tends to discourage the disease organism as its host does not appear on the land every year. The addition of lime also is often beneficial, as it "sweetens" the soil. By "sweeten," we mean that it reduces the soil's acidity. Clubroot of cabbage is almost entirely prevented by the addition of lime.

In speaking of the organisms harmful to plants, we must remember that they make up only a small proportion of the total soil population. Most of the microorganisms in the soil are quite beneficial. When things are going smoothly, we tend to forget about them, but we would be in dire straits if they were not present and doing their job. They are almost exclusively responsible for the removal of dead plant and animal matter from the surface of the earth and its conversion into valuable plant food. They act as scavengers. They guard the sanitary condition of the soil and keep it wholesome for plant growth. Very often certain plant diseases are caused by poor sanitation in the soil. (Many human illnesses, of course, arise from lack of proper sanitation.)

The beneficial microorganisms do many other things. They take nitrogen from the air and make it a part of the soil. They aid in the production of carbon dioxide, the gas which acts as a helper to oxygen in chemical action and to water when in solution. They aid in tearing down complex compounds, both mineral and organic, and play an important part in the preparation of food materials for plants, especially those valuable in agriculture.

In all processes of simplification, the microorganisms are necessary. In fact, without them, plant and animal life could not survive. Plants and animals build up; microorganisms tear down. Were the latter process prevented, in a very short time all the necessary materials for life would be tied up in complex compounds which would be unusable for ordinary life processes. Under these circumstances, plants could not grow; domestic animals would starve and man would perish.

Bacteria and their division of labor

Of all the life forms in the soil, bacteria are the most numerous and most important. These organisms are the lowliest of all plants, being simple little cells, usually rod-shaped and filled with the active life-giving material called protoplasm. They are very, very small — a length of one thirty-thousandth of an inch is a common size, although many are much smaller. Many hundreds may be placed on the point of the finest needle. It is little wonder that so many billions of these organisms may live and function quite normally in a single pound of soil.

As bacteria are plants, they require the same conditions for growth as those needed by higher plants. However, there is one exception — that is, light. They need the mechanical presence of soil; they need air, water, heat and food but they avoid light. As a matter of fact too much light, especially sunshine, which contains ultraviolet rays, will kill bacteria. They therefore live in dark places and do their best work in the recesses of the soil. We do not find them responding to the sunshine, engaging in photosynthesis, as ordinary plants do. This is because they do not manufacture their food in the manner of most plants. Rather, they draw their food from the higher plants that use sunshine to manufacture the food. This difference is actually quite fortunate because the bacteria are able to live and work where ordinary plants would find it impossible to survive. They live mostly in the soil moisture, swimming about as chance may direct, or clustering in layers at various advantageous places. Their food comes from the soil, as does that of ordinary plants.

The best conditions for bacterial action (leaving out light) are exactly the same as for the higher plants. This is very helpful to the farmer. If he regulates the soil as to air, heat, moisture and food to best suit the needs of his crop, he does so equally for the bacterial hosts beneath his plow. He does not have to worry about his minute tenants, as they respond to the regulations beneficial to ordinary plants. The means of stimulating

bacterial action are common ones. Deep and thorough plowing, drainage, conservation of moisture so that an ideal amount may always be present and the maintenance of plenty of organic matter are well-known. Lime is sometimes beneficial as it sweetens the soil and removes some of the products that are harmful to bacteria. We must remember that the ordinary everyday practices are the means of stimulating and encouraging the teeming millions of this kingdom that lives beneath our feet.

With such a great number of different things to be done and such a great bacterial population, we should not be surprised to learn that some sort of a division of labor exists. We would hardly expect to find a single organism attacking a fragment of dead plant tissue, for instance, with the purpose of changing it through many complex stages to the simplified condition that it must attain before being used as a plant food. No particular individual is equipped to perform a task

Colonies of soil bacteria that have been grown on an artificial medium — agar. A clump or colony grows from a single individual; often it is large enough to be seen with the naked eye.

Lederle Laboratories Div., American Cyanamid Co.

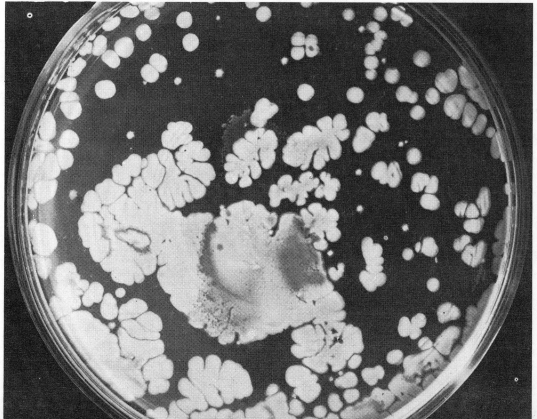

made up of so many difficult and complicated operations. Nor is it necessary. Millions of individuals exist in every fragment of soil. The work may be divided up, each individual or group of individuals performing one or two operations on the material and then passing the product on to the next and so on. It is a system much like that used in our modern factories where piecework is the common practice. Such a division of labor makes for efficiency in every sense. The work goes on faster and the quality of the product is better. Perhaps the wonders of the transformations that take place in the soil are partially due to this system.

The various divisions of labor

As such an organization exists among the bacteria let us consider first the divisions and then the departments or subdivisions of each. The divisions are based, as might be expected, upon the materials to be worked on. This is natural enough; it is just what we would expect in any factory or workshop.

The material to be broken down is either mineral or organic. Organic materials may be further divided into carbon compounds and nitrogen compounds. This gives us, then, three groups of bacterial workers: those that deal with mineral matter, those that transform carbon compounds and those that have to do with the very intricate changes of nitrogen. The three groups do not have separate areas of operation but labor side by side in what seems to be at first a terribly mixed up and haphazard fashion, but which in the light of present-day knowledge is perfectly reasonable and efficient. The bacteria are experts and in a normal soil the work goes on with a smoothness and a rapidity that excite wonder and admiration.

Mineral bacteria

The particles of the soil expose an immense amount of internal surface area, and upon this surface the bacteria are able to exert a tremendous effect. As they float about in the water which bathes the soil or as they lie in mats against some

of the larger particles, entrapping at the same time countless small fragments, they are in an advantageous position to carry on their work. Their influence is exerted in two ways — directly and indirectly. In the direct approach, the bacteria themselves attack the rocks and absorb the minerals directly from them. The bacteria obtain minerals from the rocks indirectly by producing substances that absorb the minerals or that break down the rock structure and make minerals available.

Exactly what the nature of the direct action of the bacteria on the rock fragments is, it is impossible to say at the present time. It is quite likely that the mineral materials are taken up by the organisms and are later excreted in a usable form, or they may be retained until the organisms' death, at which time they are released into the soil. Several different mineral organisms have been found and are named according to the elements on which they work, such as phosphorus, iron or sulfur. Just what proportion of the soluble mineral elements in the soil may be attributed to this source we cannot say, but we do know that the bacteria have much to do with making it available.

Mineral-releasing secretions

The indirect method involves the production of a material which will cause rock minerals to be released. The most common substance produced by the bacteria is the gas carbon dioxide. When it is released by the organism, a great deal of it combines with water to form carbonic acid, a weak acid that increases the solvent power of water. This combination enables the water to draw much more of the minerals from the rocks and to make them available to the plants as food. Some bacteria also produce certain organic acids, which have much the same effect as carbon dioxide upon water.

Of these two general modes of attacking the rocks and releasing the minerals they contain, the indirect method is more important because of the much greater quantity of minerals it causes to be released and to be made available to plants.

Carbon bacteria

Carbon is the main element associated with life on this planet. All living things contain this element in compound form. The cellulose of plants and the sugars, fats and proteins of animals are all compounds of carbon. The direct source of carbon for all forms of life is the carbon dioxide in the air. It is taken up by the plants through openings in their leaves called stomata. Once inside the plant, the gas is broken up into carbon and oxygen through the use of chlorophyll in the amazing process known as photosynthesis. The plant then converts it into the various complex compounds that make up living protoplasm. Animals get their carbon from plants. In the case of carnivorous animals, the carbon is obtained from the flesh of other animals who got their carbon from eating plants. There is, however, a missing link in this chain of events. The carbon used by the plants and animals must ultimately be returned to the air, for plants can obtain their carbon only from this gaseous form.

A great deal of carbon dioxide is returned to the atmosphere through the process of respiration, or breathing. When an animal or plant breathes, it releases carbon dioxide into the air. This gas has been produced in the cells as the organism has burned its body fuel to get energy for essential tasks. However, not all the carbon that an organism takes in is released in the act of respiration. A good deal of it remains tied up in the vital tissue of the plant or animal and eventually goes into the soil as a complex compound when the organism dies. The plant cannot use carbon in this form. If this process were continued for many years, eventually all the available carbon on the earth would end up in the soil, tied up in complex compounds that cannot be used by any living organism. The result would be that all the different kinds of living things would die out in a relatively short time.

Life on earth is redeemed from this fate by the tiniest organisms of all, the carbon bacteria. They are the sole life forms that can utilize the complex carbon compounds that are put into the soil as dead animal and plant matter. It is these organisms that break down the compounds, unlock the carbon and release it in the form of carbon dioxide so that it can be used again by the plants. In other words, without the work of the carbon bacteria, no life could survive.

Nitrogen bacteria

Like carbon, nitrogen is very closely identified with all life processes, and consequently the transformations that it undergoes are of vital importance. It exists in the air in an elementary form in vast quantities. All of the nitrogen in plants and in the soil have been drawn from this particular source.

We must first ask how this gas nitrogen can be taken from the air and made to become a part of the plant or soil. Nitrogen is a very inert gas. It does not readily combine with other elements at ordinary temperatures; even when it is so combined, the union is an unstable one. To capture nitrogen for use in plant life is truly a difficult feat.

The process is similar to the one in which carbon is taken from the air by the green leaves of ordinary plants. In the case of nitrogen, however, the work is done by certain forms of bacteria that live in the soil. They are able to appropriate free nitrogen from the air in the soil in the process known as nitrogen-fixation.

The "free fixers"

Nitrogen is appropriated by two distinct groups of bacteria. One of these lives in the soil. The bacteria in this group use the organic matter contained in the soil as their food. The nitrogen that they take in is either excreted into the soil or else is absorbed into their bodies and becomes a part of the soil when they die. Because they live free in the soil, these bacteria are known as "free fixers." Although the proportion of nitrogen that they add to the soil is not large, it is very important. A few pounds of nitrogen per acre is added yearly.

The bacteria belonging to the other nitrogen-fixing group lead an entirely different existence. They are parasites; but unlike most parasites they are a help and not an encumbrance. They live in the roots of certain kinds of plants called legumes, of which clover, alfalfa and peas are common representatives. Early in the life of the plant, the bacteria gain entrance into the rootlets; here they are segregated in small galls or nodules. The bacteria multiply in the nodules, deriving their food from the plant juices and working to fix nitrogen from the air. The relationship, therefore, is not strictly parasitic since the host also benefits. It is really an example of symbiosis, a process that we discuss elsewhere (see Index).

The nitrogen fixed by these organisms may be used in several ways. It may be taken up by the plant directly, giving that healthy green color possessed by legumes that are inoculated, or infected, by the bacteria. The nitrogen may also become a part of the soil, stimulating the growth of the plants growing near the legume as well as the host itself. The close association of clover and timothy is an illustration of the value of this relationship. The bacteria also make some of the nitrogen into part of their own tissues. When the crop is cut, the host plant dies and so do the parasites. The nitrogen their bodies contain is then added to the soil. The leguminous bacteria are far more important than the free forms in nitrogen-fixation. Forty or fifty pounds per acre of nitrogen may be added to the soil yearly by the parasites. Two complicating features enter into the practical control of this process of nitrogen-fixation.

Harvesting a crop of alfalfa. Bacteria living in nodules, or lumps, of alfalfa roots obtain free nitrogen from the soil air and fix it in complex forms, which can be used by the plant.

Philip D. Gendreau

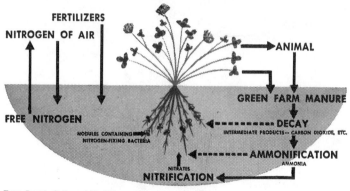

FERTILIZERS
NITROGEN OF AIR
→ANIMAL
GREEN FARM MANURE
FREE NITROGEN
NODULES CONTAINING
NITROGEN-FIXING BACTERIA
←------- DECAY
INTERMEDIATE PRODUCTS— CARBON DIOXIDE, ETC.
←------- AMMONIFICATION
AMMONIA
NITRATES
NITRIFICATION ←

The diagram shows the work of the two groups of nitrogen-fixing bacteria and the decay process, with the conversion of ammonia to the nitrates.

From Lyon's *Soils and Fertilizers*, The Macmillan Co.

The first of these is that different leguminous plants have different strains of nitrogen-fixing bacteria. Those that are associated with alfalfa cannot grow on clover and vice versa. Consequently, if the leguminous crop is changed from one year to another, the bacteria die.

The second complication is that the soil may not contain the nitrogen-fixing bacteria at all. If such is the case, the farmer must introduce them into his soil. This can be done in various ways. Leguminous plants that have nodules on their roots may be transplanted into a field that lacks nitrogen-fixing bacteria. Sometimes the bacteria are added directly to the seeds of the leguminous plants before they are put into the ground. A third method involves the transportation of soil from a field that is known to be amply supplied with the bacteria to the new field. At the present time, methods have been so perfected that failure seldom occurs. Generally the farmer does not have to seek expert aid; he has become his own bacteriologist.

Nitrogen transformations

The remains of dead animals and plants make up perhaps the most important source of nitrogen. The nitrogen is locked up in the complex compounds of which these bodies consist and is unusable until it is simplified. We saw that a special group of bacteria has the task of simplifying various compounds of carbon found in the soil. Another special group concentrates on the freeing of nitrogen contained in nitrogen

compounds. This important element is released by the process we call "decay." In this process, the bacteria pass the dead material through their systems, first forming complex nitrogen-protein compounds and finally breaking them down into simple constituents and the gas ammonia. Ammonia is a compound containing three hydrogen atoms attached to a single atom of nitrogen.

The ammonia is then treated by two other groups of specialized bacteria — the nitrite bacteria and the nitrate bacteria. The nitrite bacteria add seven molecules of oxygen to four molecules of ammonia to form four molecules of nitrogen dioxide and six molecules of water. The nitrate bacteria then combine the nitrogen dioxide molecules with metallic oxides (compounds of a metal and oxygen) to produce metallic nitrates. Nitrates such as potassium nitrate and calcium nitrate, for example, are formed from the combination of calcium and potassium oxide with nitrogen dioxide. Nitrates are the form of nitrogen that plants are able to absorb through their roots and assimilate in their tissues; they are, consequently, the chief source of nitrogen for plants.

The changes that complex compounds undergo in the soil are many and complicated. Without bacteria to help bring about these changes, plants would be deprived of necessary food and could not grow. The farmer must see to it, therefore, that these bacteria are in the soil.

See also Vol. 10, p. 273: "Soil."

Alto-cumulus clouds. These fleecy clouds, found at heights of 5,000 to 25,000 feet, do not give rain.

PROBLEMS OF CLOUDLAND

The Formation and Patterns of Clouds

THE clouds that hover serenely or scud rapidly in the atmosphere represent a gas — water vapor — that has condensed, or turned into a liquid or a crystalline solid. Some of this vapor comes from the evaporation of water in seas or streams; some of it is derived from the exhalations of animals and the transpiration of plants — that is, the evaporation that takes place in leaves and other aerial structures.

The atmosphere can hold only a certain quantity of water vapor. The amount will depend upon the temperature; the higher the temperature, the more vapor the atmosphere can hold. If the air is cooled at constant pressure without change in the vapor content, it will finally become saturated. The temperature at which this occurs is called the dew point. If further cooling takes place, a part of the vapor will condense on such air-borne particles as dust and ocean salts derived from sea spray. The condensed vapor, which is in the form of tiny droplets, becomes visible as fog, mist or haze at low levels. If it condenses at heights of half a mile and more above sea level, it forms clouds. When the temperature is below freezing, the water vapor passes directly into the solid state and is converted into ice crystals.

The chief difference, then, between fogs and clouds is their place in the atmosphere: that is, the height they reach. Fog may arise on sea or land. Its density depends upon the number and the size of the water droplets in it. A particularly dense formation may contain from 10,000 to 20,-000 droplets per cubic inch. Even the densest fog, however, has an astonishingly low water content. The water contained in a fog that blankets a harbor area would scarcely fill half a dozen fair-sized buckets.

Of course, the water content of a very light fog will be much lower. We call such a formation a haze. When the water particles in a fog are like tiny raindrops as they float or fall, the formation is known as a mist.

How do the invisible particles of evaporated moisture rise to the levels where clouds, rather than fogs, are formed? Some of the particles are carried upward by convection — the vertical movement of air that is revealed by the smoke from a bonfire on a quiet autumn evening. A mass of air will be forced up, much as a cork is forced up in water, if it is less dense than the air around it. Warm air is less dense than cold air; hence it will rise when it is surrounded by cold air.

Road and roof surfaces respond to the warming influence of the sun much more quickly than field, wood and water surfaces, and they warm the air above them. Consequently, on a hot summer's day, the air temperature over a town soon rises above the temperature of the surrounding countryside. The mass of air above the city is warmer and therefore lighter than the air around it; hence it floats upward. Its place is then taken by cooler air, which in turn warms up.

The rising mass of air keeps moving away from the warm town. It gradually gets cooler until it reaches the saturation point. When it goes beyond this stage, the water vapor begins to condense, and a cloud begins to form. As long as the temperature of the cloud is higher than that of the air around it, it will continue to ascend. When it has the same temperature as the air outside and is no lighter than that air, it will come to rest. The height the warm air will reach and the size of the cloud it will form will depend largely on how fast the temperature of the atmosphere changes as the air rises.

The rate of change in temperature above ground level is called the lapse rate of the air. While this lowering of the temperature is by no means steady, over thousands of feet it averages about 1°F. for every 300-foot rise. This means that even in summer the temperature six or seven miles above New York City, for instance, may be as much as 20 to 30°F. below zero. This cooling rate, however, applies to the condition of the atmosphere only when it is at rest, or where there are no up-and-down currents in it. Suppose such currents are set in motion, as happens when warm air starts to rise. Then, provided the rising air does not give heat to its surroundings or receive heat from them, it will diminish in temperature at a steady rate of something like 1.6°F. for every 300-foot rise. After the mass of air exhibits a visible cloud, the rate of cooling decreases to about one-half the former rate.

Convection is only one of the ways in which invisible moisture is turned into visible clouds. There are other equally effective ways. For example, when a stream of damp air flows as a wind over the tops of a range of hills, the temperature at the hilltops may be low enough to cool the air below its dew point. Air that was comparatively dry at sea level may form clouds at these high altitudes. This explains why mountains, on the side from which winds are blowing, are so much cloudier and wetter than the valleys around them.

Clouds may be formed in this way even where there are no mountains. Cold, heavy air, like that which flows out from the Arctic periodically, makes an excellent "mountain" for this purpose. Any warmer, lighter air mass that happens to meet this cold air over a broad front will ride over it; it will become cooler and in time it will condense. This is what usually happens in winter when the warm air that flows up into the northern United States or Canada from the Gulf of Mexico meets the cold air moving southward from the polar regions. The warm and cold air masses behave like oil and water; instead of mixing, the lighter mass flows over the heavier. Clouds originating in this way are called frontal.

Another common way in which clouds can form is by the passage of damp air over a colder surface, either land or water. This horizontal atmospheric movement is known as advection, to distinguish it from the vertical movement known as convection. If the air is moving slowly, this process will be more apt to produce fog than cloud.

A great many clouds in the atmosphere result from a combination of two or more of the processes we have described. Certain clouds, known as airplane condensation trails, are man-made; they are produced by moisture from the exhaust pipes of planes. Each gallon of gasoline that is burned as the airplane wings its way through the skies adds nearly a gallon and a half of vapor to the air. When the gases of explosion are hurled into a subzero atmosphere, the chances are that they will instantly condense and cause a persistent trail of thin cloud to be formed.

At one time, meteorologists believed that clouds "float" in the sky. Actually, they do not float at all. The droplets of water of which the cloud consists are generally falling, because of the gravitational pull of the earth. If the overall shape of the cloud is preserved, for a time at least, it is because, as the droplets fall, others are formed in the area of condensation to take their place. A striking example of this phenomenon is provided by the famous cloud formation, known as the "Tablecloth," which hangs over the edge of Table Mountain, south of Cape Town, in the Republic of South Africa. The lower fringed edge of the cloud is generally dripping rain, and yet the cloud will keep its shape and size for days at a time because a warm, wet wind is giving up its moisture to the mountain.

·As we point out elsewhere (see the chapter Transformations of Water Vapor, in Volume 2), rain, snow and other forms of precipitation are derived from the condensed water vapor of clouds. But what would happen if there were no particles in the air upon which the water vapor could condense?

Ragged-roll cumulus clouds. These clouds are thick and spreading, with horizontal bases which are seldom more than about 5,000 feet above the ground. Cumulus clouds may, however, develop to enormous heights above their low-lying bases. Usually they give no rain.

Photos on this page, Standard Oil Co. (N. J.)

LOW

CLOUDS

Upslope stratus cloud. It is often found near valleys and hillsides and resembles mist. Stratus clouds are low (under 6,000 feet) and may give rain.

Strato-cumulus clouds. This big, lumpy formation often covers the whole sky at heights of up to 6,000 feet or so. Such clouds may lead to rain.

The condensation of atmospheric water vapor on mountain tops and hill tops would cause a partial vacuum to be created there; hence moisture-laden winds would be drawn to these areas, forsaking the plains. The plains would be deprived even of dew and their vegetation would die; they would soon become desolate, barren deserts.

The presence of dust in the atmosphere, therefore, serves to render our planet habitable. Nor is dust ever wanting. Constant supplies of it are belched from volcanoes or torn by the winds from the deserts of the world, as well as from the topsoil of once fertile regions subjected to continuous drought. Smoke from countless chimneys contributes its quota.

Not all clouds condense into drops large enough to produce rain, nor does all the rain produced by clouds reach the earth. In the Karroo, an extensive plateau of the Union of South Africa, rain-bearing clouds accumulate day after day in the dry season. The sky is darkened with these heavy, lowering formations, which seem almost to touch the tops of the *kopjes,* or hillocks; but the great cloud army passes

Roll-cumulus cloud formations slowly breaking up as cirro-stratus and alto-stratus clouds begin to replace them in the skies.
Standard Oil Co. (N. J.)

over the area and not a drop of rain reaches the earth. And yet the clouds may have contained enough moisture to make the desolate Karroo fertile if this moisture had reached the earth in the form of rain.

No wonder that men have long sought to find a way to cause the water droplets in clouds to condense still more and drench the land with rain. Early attempts were based on tribal superstition and rituals. During the nineteenth century, several supposedly scientific suggestions for producing rain were advanced. Among other things, it was maintained that thunder brings rain and that thunderous salvos of artillery fire would produce the same effect. In the 1890's General Robert G. Dyrenforth carried out a number of experiments in Texas based on this idea; he set off explosives on the ground and detonated oxyhydrogen balloons in the air. Dyrenforth claimed that his experiments were successful; but most scientists maintained that any rain that had fallen in the vicinity of the experiments had been produced by natural causes and not as a result of the explosions.

As a matter of fact, the idea that thunder or any thunderous noise produces rain is thoroughly unsound. It is not the thunder that produces the rain so much as the

Below: dense-hooked cirrus clouds merging into cirro-stratus clouds. They are found at altitudes of 20,000 feet or more. Cirro-stratus clouds may fall and become stratus rain clouds.

Above: cirro-stratus clouds merging into cirro-cumulus clouds. They occur at altitudes greater than 20,000 feet and are composed of ice crystals. Of themselves they do not cause rainfall.

droplets of water within the clouds that produce the thunder. According to one theory, these droplets have either a positive or negative charge. The positively charged droplets tend to accumulate at the top of the cloud; the negatively charged ones, at the bottom. Unlike charges attract each other; therefore the negative charges at the bottom of the cloud attract positive charges on the ground. When the accumulation of negative charges in the cloud is great enough, electrons (negatively charged subatomic particles) stream across the gap between the cloud and the ground. A series of sparks — that is, a flash of lightning — is produced. The energy that is liberated heats the air through which the lightning passes. The air suddenly expands as it is heated; a pressure wave travels from the scene of the disturbance and a resounding clap of thunder is the result.

The electrical discharge of a stroke of lightning produces ions in the air, and these may serve as centers of condensation for water vapor in the atmosphere. It has been suggested that artificially produced flashes of lightning might produce great numbers of such centers of condensation and perhaps cause rainfall. This suggestion has never been seriously put to the test.

"Seeding" clouds
to produce rain

More or less successful attempts at rainmaking, based on a different principle, have been carried out in recent years. In 1946, an American scientist, Vincent J. Schaefer, carried out certain experiments with man-made clouds — supercooled clouds containing water vapor at below-freezing temperature. He found that by introducing material at $-40°C$. or lower into a supercooled cloud he could produce great numbers of condensation or sublimation nuclei — microscopic particles on which water vapor condenses to form water droplets or ice crystals. Solid carbon dioxide (dry ice) was found to be ideal for this purpose because of its low temperature.

By dropping large numbers of carbon-dioxide pellets into natural supercooled clouds, Schaefer and another American scientist, Irving Langmuir, produced miniature snowstorms in 1946. In the following years various attempts were made to "seed" clouds with dry ice in order to produce rain. In certain cases generators on the ground were used to discharge minute particles of silver iodide into clouds; these particles produced much the same effect as solid carbon-dioxide pellets. In a number of cases, "seeding" was followed by rainfall. Certain scientists are skeptical about such results, however, particularly because it is difficult to distinguish between natural rain and man-made rain.

Clouds serve other purposes besides storing up water vapor which may later be released to the earth in the form of snow, rain, hail and so on. Among other things, they help to conserve the heat that is radiated from the surface of the earth after it has been warmed by the sun.

How clouds help
conserve the earth's heat

The sun emits waves of varying length which penetrate substances to different degrees. Most have some heating effect; some are really "hot," more so than others. The radiant heat from the sun easily passes through the atmosphere and the clouds in the atmosphere and is absorbed by the soil or surface water. The warmed earth then emits radiant heat in its turn. The heat waves it radiates are too long to pass through the clouds and are therefore reflected back to earth. If the day is sunny, clouds in the sky act as a blanket; they reflect back the heat that otherwise would escape from the earth's surface.

The colors and shapes of clouds are striking. In an eloquent passage, the French geographer Jean-Jacques-Elisée Reclus declared: "Among all the images, whether fearful or graceful, that the fancy of man can dream of, there is not one which is not to be found in the vapors of space.

"By their fugitive outlines clouds resemble flights of birds, eagles with outstretched wings, groups of animals, reclining giants and monsters like those of fable. Other clouds are chains of mountains with snowy summits. . . . Superstitious people, pur-

The Lake of Lucerne in Switzerland. The Rigi peaks, over 5,000 feet high, jut through low-lying clouds.

sued by the terror of their own crimes, see in them bundles of weapons, war horses, armies in battle array and massacres. The light playing in this fantastic world of images increases still more their astonishing variety; all imaginable shades shine over these floating bodies, from snowy whiteness to fiery red; the sun colors them successively with all the graduated tints of dawn, daylight and sunset."

Many other observers have commented on the surpassing beauty of cloud formations. The distinguished English essayist and critic John Ruskin once asked: "What should we have thought, if we had lived in a country where there were no clouds but only low mist or fog, of any stranger who had told us that in his country these mists rose into the air and became purple, crimson, scarlet and gold?"

How does it happen that the clouds take on particularly beautiful colors in the early morning and evening sky? They would not be colored at all if it were not for the molecules of air and the particles of dust and other substances in the sky. The white light of the sun, like all white light, is made up of all the colors of the rainbow. The air molecules and the particles in the higher sky are of the right size to scatter the blue light, which is part of sunlight, more than the light of other wave lengths. That is why our daytime sky is blue. When the sun is close to the horizon, at dawn and dusk, the light passes through the lower atmosphere, which contains larger atmospheric particles. These are of the right size to scatter the longer waves of light — the various shades of orange and red. It is this scattered light of longer wave length that makes possible the brilliant colors of the clouds.

The formation of
dew and hoarfrost

Not all the atmospheric water vapor that condenses is found in fog or cloud. It is also present in dew and hoarfrost.

For centuries, scientists had no true conception of how dew was formed; as a matter of fact, it was generally believed that it "fell." We realize now that dew is simply water vapor that has condensed on cold surfaces. During the day, the ground is heated by the rays of the sun. At night, if the air is clear, a good deal of this heat escapes; the soil, therefore, is chilled, and it cools the air that is in contact with it. When the temperature of the air has been lowered below the dew point, water vapor begins to condense in the form of tiny droplets, not only upon the ground itself, but also upon the leaves and stems of plants.

When dew is formed at a temperature below the freezing point of water, the condensed moisture forms tiny ice crystals, and then we have the deposit known as hoarfrost, or rime or simply frost. Frost forms upon windowpanes in very cold weather; the moisture in the room crystallizes as it comes in contact with the thoroughly chilled glass. The frost designs found upon panes are astonishingly varied because of the multitude of tiny scratches and dust particles on the panes; also because of air currents that modify the shape of the frost patterns as they are being formed. These patterns are often very striking; they show an amazing variety of forms: stars, forests, ferns and fairy castles with lofty pinnacles and slender pillars.

The classification
of cloud formations

The first serious attempt to classify the different cloud formations was made by an Englishman, Luke Howard, in 1803. He recognized three basic types of clouds: (1) stratiform (layer-shaped); (2) cumuliform (heap-shaped); and (3) cirriform (fiber-shaped). In 1894, the International Meteorological Committee divided cloud shapes into ten classes, and with certain modifications this arrangement still prevails. According to the present internationally recognized classification, the ten cloud forms are as follows: cirrus, cirrocumulus, cirrostratus, altocumulus, altostratus, stratocumulus, stratus, nimbostratus, cumulus and cumulonimbus. In the following table, we give a brief description of each cloud type, together with the symbol used to identify it.

Standard Oil Co. (N. J.)

Cumulo-nimbus cloud or thunder-cloud, whose vertical dimension may be as much as 50,000 feet. It is charged with water, high winds and much electrical energy.

At the right is another cumulo-nimbus cloud, shown discharging its energy in the form of rain from its base. In the process, the atmosphere loses much heat.

U. S. Weather Bureau-U. S. Navy

CLOUD TYPES

cloud type and symbol	description	possible precipitation	comments
HIGH-CLOUD FAMILY—average height, 20,000 to 40,000 feet			
Cirrus (Ci)	Detached clouds of delicate, fibrous structure, often silky-looking, generally white in the daytime. Appear in isolated tufts, plumes or long strands.	None	Ci are often colored bright red or yellow before sunrise or after sunset.
Cirro-cumulus (Cc)	Layers or patches composed of thin ripples, small tufts or globular masses, white in color, without any darker parts.	None	Cc are relatively rare and are always associated with Ci or Cs.
Cirro-stratus (Cs)	A thin, whitish veil that does not blur the outlines of the sun or moon. Cs may give the sky a milky look or show a fibrous structure. When sun shines through Cs, it casts shadows on the ground.	None	Watch for a halo when Cs drift in front of the sun or moon. The halo is a large rainbowlike ring with red inside and blue outside
MIDDLE-CLOUD FAMILY—average height, 6,500 to 20,000			
Altocumulus (Ac)	One or more nonfibrous layers or patches composed of sheets, rounded masses or rolls, which may or may not be fused or shaded.	Wisps of rain or snow called virga	A corona forms when Ac pass before the sun or moon. The corona is a small, colored ring with blue inside and red outside.
Altostratus (As)	A sheet or layer of a fibrous, striated or uniform aspect, rather gray or bluish in color. If the sun or moon shines through As, it does not cast shadows and seems to be shining through ground glass.	Light rain or snow	As are differentiated from Cs by darker color and absence of halo or shadows on the ground.
LOW-CLOUD FAMILY—average height, 2,500 to 6,500 feet			
Strato-cumulus (Sc)	One or more nonfibrous layers or patches, composed of large, sometimes soft sheets, rounded masses or rolls, grayish with darker parts, with distinctly visible outlines.	None	Sc have a wavy appearance when they cover entire sky. Sc may be distinguished from Ac by absence of corona and by larger size of cloud elements.
Stratus (St)	Uniform clouds of indefinite shape, with some lighter parts but little or no relief, giving the sky a hazy appearance.	Drizzle	The outlines of the sun or moon can be seen through a thin layer of St. Stratus clouds become fog if they rest on the ground.
Nimbo-stratus (Ns)	A low, dark gray, shapeless and wet-looking cloud layer that appears to be feebly illuminated from within.	Steady rain or snow	Low, ragged clouds or bad weather are often present below a layer of Ns and may merge with it.
VERTICALLY DEVELOPED FAMILY—average height, 1,600 feet to cirrus levels			
Cumulus (Cu)	Dense, vertically developed clouds shaped like domes or towers, with rounded protuberances that are brilliantly white in color when lit by the sun. Their nearly horizontal bases are dark.	Infrequent light rain or snow	Over land, Cu generally appear in the morning and dissolve toward evening.
Cumulo-nimbus (Cb)	Massive, vertically developed clouds rising in the form of cauliflowerlike mountains, whose upper parts are fibrous and often spread out in the shape of an anvil.	Heavy rain, snow or hail	Thunderstorms are accompanied by gusty winds and heavy static on AM radios.

See also Vol. 10, p. 271: "Weather and Climate."

CHEMICAL
REACTIONS

How the Chemist
Transforms His Materials

BY HILTON A. SMITH

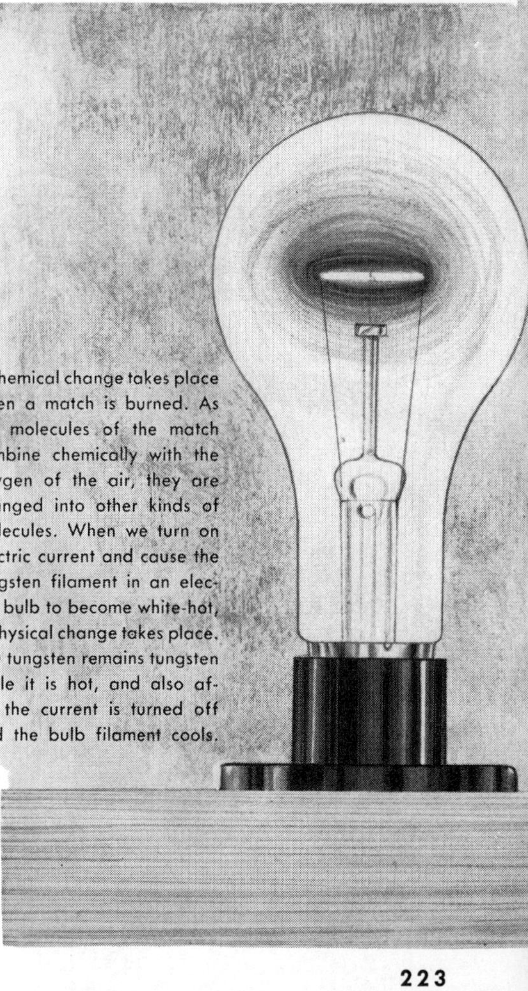

A chemical change takes place
when a match is burned. As
the molecules of the match
combine chemically with the
oxygen of the air, they are
changed into other kinds of
molecules. When we turn on
electric current and cause the
tungsten filament in an electric bulb to become white-hot,
a physical change takes place.
The tungsten remains tungsten
while it is hot, and also after the current is turned off
and the bulb filament cools.

CHANGE is the keynote of all things, both
living and nonliving, from the microscopic
ameba to man, from the particles of dust
dancing in a beam of sunlight to the proud
monument built for the ages. Certain
changes, with which we are all familiar,
are spectacular and rapid. A blazing fire
consumes many square miles of forest; a
mountain slide sends thousands of tons of
rocks crashing into the valley below. Other
changes are slow and obscure. The restless
waves of the ocean gradually carve away
the land in one place; in another, the winds
just as gradually deposit tons upon tons of
dust and create new soil. Nothing escapes
change; the so-called ageless hills are really
no more ageless than the fragile May fly
that lives only a few days.

All changes, great and small, swift and
slow, may be divided into two classes —
physical and chemical. A physical change
does not cause any basic alteration in the
molecules * of which a given substance is
composed. Consider, for instance, what happens when ice melts. The basic particle of
ice is a molecule in which two atoms of hydrogen and one of oxygen are held together
as a unit. If the ice is allowed to melt so

Editor's note: A molecule is the smallest possible
particle of a given substance. It is built up of atoms: it
may contain one or more atoms of the same element or it
may be made up of atoms of different elements. See the
articles How Molecules Behave and Inside the Atom, in
Volume 1.

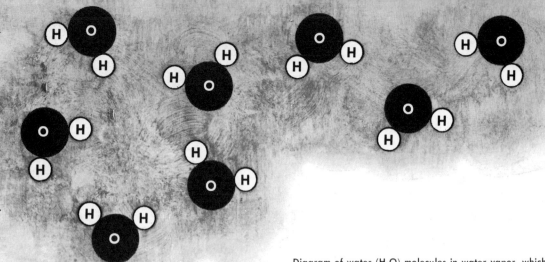

Diagram of water (H_2O) molecules in water vapor, which is a gas. In each molecule of water, two atoms of hydrogen are chemically combined with an oxygen atom.

that liquid water is formed, the water molecule remains unchanged: it still contains two atoms of hydrogen combined with one of oxygen. It remains unchanged, too, if the liquid water is heated so that it becomes steam. The liquefying of the solid ice and the vaporization of the liquid water are physical changes; they do not alter the composition of the water molecule.

Chemical change is something else again, for it involves the transformation of the molecules of a substance. We saw that only physical changes take place when ice melts or when water turns into steam. But we can bring about a chemical change if we pass a direct electric current through water between two electrodes. The water will gradually disappear, as hydrogen gas forms at one of the electrodes and oxygen gas at the other. In other words, the hydrogen and oxygen atoms that make up the water molecules will break apart and will become molecules of hydrogen and of oxygen.

Physical changes are discussed in other chapters of THE BOOK OF POPULAR SCIENCE. In this chapter, we shall turn the spotlight on chemical changes, or chemical reactions, as they are generally called.

The nature of chemical reactions

Some chemical reactions are produced under natural conditions. Molds and bacteria penetrate a decaying log in a forest and cause the elements of which it is composed to combine with the oxygen of the air so that in time the log is utterly consumed. Natural chemical reactions also take place when iron rusts, or when peat is formed or when food is digested in our bodies. Many chemical reactions, however, are deliberately brought about by man under conditions of his own choosing. It is as a result of such reactions that coal and petroleum yield synthetic rubber, that the sticky substance called coal tar produces gorgeous dyes, that the stems and stalks of plants give rayon.

Chemical symbols, formulas and equations

Of course we can describe chemical reactions in everyday language. We can say that mercuric oxide, a substance whose basic particle is a molecule made up of an atom of mercury and an atom of oxygen, is transformed when heated into two other substances — mercury, whose molecule is made up of a single mercury atom, and oxygen, whose molecule is made up of two oxygen atoms. A chemist would indicate all this much more simply and directly by the following combination of letters and figures:

$$2HgO \rightarrow 2Hg + O_2$$

We find here (1) chemical symbols, (2) chemical formulas and (3) a balanced equation. This may all seem like Greek to you; but we promise that you will find it perfectly clear long before you have reached the end of this chapter.

To begin with, what do we mean by symbols? The answer is simple enough: a chemical symbol consists of a letter or of two letters representing a given chemical element. The letter C, for example, stands for carbon, the letter H for hydrogen and the letter N for nitrogen. A symbol, in other words, is an abbreviation — as much so as the abbreviation UN, standing for the United Nations, or Dr., standing for doctor.

If there were twenty-six or fewer chemical elements and each began with a different letter of the alphabet, we could use single letters as symbols for all of them. But as there are more than a hundred elements, we use combinations of two letters for the symbols of most of them.

There are four elements, for example, that begin with H: hafnium, helium, holmium and hydrogen. We indicate hydrogen by H; hafnium by Hf; helium by He; holmium by Ho. Similarly, B is the symbol for boron; Ba for barium; Be for beryllium; Bi for bismuth; Bk for berkelium; Br for bromine.*

Some of the symbols may seem rather odd. Why does Hg, for instance, stand for mercury; Fe for iron; Sn for tin? The reason is that the symbol of an element is sometimes the abbreviation of its Greek or Latin name. Hg stands for *hydrargyrum* ("liquid silver"), a slightly Latinized form of the Greek word for mercury. Fe represents the first two letters of *ferrum*, the Latin word for iron. Sn comes from the Latin *stannum*, meaning tin.

The symbols of chemical elements stand for various things

The symbols of the elements represent a sort of international shorthand system, used by the chemists of all nations. Obviously, a laboratory worker saves a good deal of time by writing H for hydrogen, Pt for platinum and U for uranium. But this is a special kind of shorthand, quite different from the ordinary kind. In the Isaac Pitman stenographic system, for example, the symbols used for hydrogen stand only for that word. To the chemist H is

not merely a convenient way of abbreviating the word hydrogen; it also represents an atom of hydrogen. O stands for an atom of oxygen, Cr for an atom of chromium and so on. When a chemist adds a small figure after and near the bottom of a symbol he gives still another important detail; he indicates in this way the number of atoms. Thus O_2 stands for two atoms of oxygen; C_4 for four atoms of carbon. The "2" and the "4" are sometimes referred to as subscript ("written under"). A chemist reading "O_2" and "O_4" aloud would say "O-two" and O-four."

When two or more symbols are written together, it means that the atoms they represent are joined to form a molecule. H_2O means "a molecule consisting of two atoms of hydrogen plus one atom of oxygen" — a water molecule. CO_2 means "a molecule consisting of one atom of carbon plus two atoms of oxygen" — a carbon-dioxide molecule. Since molecules are always made up of a definite number of atoms, we can use symbols to indicate any kind of molecule, no matter how complicated. The molecule of cane sugar, for example, is made up of 45 atoms — 12 atoms of carbon, 22 of hydrogen and 11 of oxygen; in the chemist's shorthand it is simply $C_{12}H_{22}O_{11}$. Of course, if a molecule is made up of the atoms of a single element, it may be written with a single symbol. A hydrogen molecule consists of two atoms of hydrogen; we write it H_2. A helium molecule consists of a single atom of helium; we write it He.

The symbols that we use to indicate the molecule of a substance are called the formula for that substance. The formula for water is H_2O; for cane sugar, $C_{12}H_{22}O_{11}$; for boric acid, H_3BO_3; for lye (sodium hydroxide), NaOH.

Let us see now how we can use symbols and formulas to express chemical reactions. Here is how we would set down the reaction in which mercuric oxide yields mercury and oxygen:

$$HgO \rightarrow Hg + O_2$$

A chemist would interpret the symbols in

---

* *Editor's note*: The complete list of symbols is given in the Appendix in Volume 10.

this way : "The molecule HgO, made up of one atom of mercury (Hg) plus one atom of oxygen (O), yields (→) a molecule made up of a single atom of mercury (Hg) plus a molecule made up of two atoms of oxygen (O_2)."

We give the name "chemical equation" to the combination of symbols that indicates a chemical reaction. The substance that reacts — on the left-hand side of the arrow — is called the reactant; the result of the reaction is called the product. Thus HgO, above, is the reactant; Hg and O_2 are the products.

The chemist must balance his equations

A chemist would not be satisfied with the equation $HgO \rightarrow Hg + O_2$; he would say that it is not balanced. Just what does that mean?

The law of the conservation of matter tells us that in the usual chemical reactions matter is never destroyed, though it may be transformed. Hence none of the atoms of a substance that undergoes chemical change are destroyed in the process, nor are any new atoms added to the product. There must be just as many hydrogen, or oxygen or nitrogen atoms in the reactant as in the product, however much they may be shifted about in order to form new molecular patterns. If an equation fulfills this condition, we say that it is balanced.

What of the equation $HgO \rightarrow Hg + O_2$? One atom of mercury and one atom of oxygen are in the reactant; in the product we find one atom of mercury but two atoms of oxygen. Obviously when a single molecule of mercuric oxide decomposes into mercury and oxygen, only one atom of oxygen can be produced, for there is only one available.

To balance the equation, we put a 2 before HgO and another 2 before Hg. 2HgO, for example, stands for "2 molecules, each made up of one atom of mercury plus one atom of oxygen." The equation is now

$$2HgO \rightarrow 2Hg + O_2$$

In other words, "two molecules, each made up of an atom of mercury plus an atom of oxygen, yield two molecules of mercury, each made up of a single mercury atom, and one molecule of oxygen, made up of two oxygen atoms." We have now balanced the equation : there are two atoms of mercury and two of oxygen on the left-hand side, and the same number on the right-hand side.

You will note that in the product we wrote 2Hg; not Hg_2. The reason is that the mercury molecule, Hg, is made up of a single mercury atom. If we added a 2 subscript, we would really be saying that the molecule contains two atoms and that would be an error. Remember that we can-

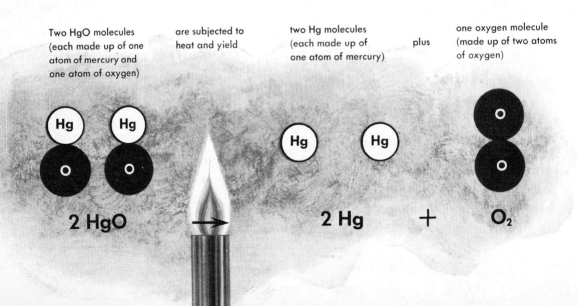

Two HgO molecules (each made up of one atom of mercury and one atom of oxygen) are subjected to heat and yield two Hg molecules (each made up of one atom of mercury) plus one oxygen molecule (made up of two atoms of oxygen)

2 HgO   →   2 Hg   + O_2

not change a molecule in balancing an equation; we can only change the *number* of molecules.

What balanced equations tell us

Our equation

$$2HgO \rightarrow 2Hg + O_2$$

Mercuric oxide yields mercury and oxygen

tells us that mercuric oxide decomposes in such a way that two molecules of mercury and one of oxygen are produced from the reaction of two mercuric-oxide molecules. Now each of these molecules is very small and weighs very little. When we heat a test tube of red mercuric oxide, we are heating billions and billions of tiny molecules of this material. Yet it does not matter how many molecules are involved in the reaction; the general relationship expressed by the equation $2HgO \rightarrow 2Hg + O_2$ still holds. Thus, if we heated exactly two billion molecules of mercuric oxide, the product would be two billion molecules of mercury plus a billion molecules of oxygen.

In the chapter Inside the Atom, in Volume 1, it is pointed out that the weights of elements are indicated by a system of relative weights called atomic weights. In this system, the weight of each element is given not in ounces or grams but in relation to the weights of the other elements. The list of atomic weights appears elsewhere. (Appendix, Volume X.) If we consult the list, we find that mercury has 200.6 atomic-weight units and oxygen 16 * (that is, an atom of mercury is about $12\frac{1}{2}$ times as heavy as an atom of oxygen). We can easily calculate the atomic-weight units in the reactant and in the product of the reaction, $2HgO \rightarrow 2Hg + O_2$.

This is how we go about it. We know that each mercuric-oxide molecule (HgO) is made up of one atom of mercury, weighing 200.6 atomic-weight units, plus one atom of oxygen, weighing 16 units — that is 216.6 units in all. Each mercury molecule will contain 200.6 units and each oxy-

* To be more specific, the atomic weight of mercury is 200.59; that of oxygen is 15.9994.

gen molecule 32 units (2×16). If now we substitute atomic-weight units for symbols throughout the equation, we have

$$
\begin{array}{ll}
2HgO & \rightarrow 2Hg \quad + O_2 \\
2 \times (200.6 + 16) & \rightarrow 2 \times 200.6 + 16 \times 2 \\
2 \times 216.6 & \rightarrow 2 \times 200.6 + 32 \\
433.2 & \rightarrow 401.2 \quad + 32
\end{array}
$$

Thus our equation tells us that 433.2 atomic-weight units of mercuric oxide will produce 401.2 atomic-weight units of mercury and 32 atomic-weight units of oxygen. The same ratios would hold if any weight of mercuric oxide were decomposed into mercury and oxygen. If, for example, we heated 2 grams of mercuric oxide until it was completely decomposed, we could find out by simple proportion the weight of mercury and oxygen that would be produced. The figures would be 1.85 grams of mercury and 0.15 grams of oxygen.

The equation $2HgO \rightarrow 2Hg + O_2$ gives us the atoms and molecules and the weight relationships involved in a particular reaction. However, it does not yield any information about the conditions under which the reaction will take place. If we stored mercuric oxide in a bottle under ordinary conditions, it would continue to be mercuric oxide indefinitely. We would have to apply heat to the substance to make it decompose into mercury and oxygen. We could indicate that fact by writing the word "heat" above the arrow, thus:

$$
\overset{\text{heat}}{2HgO \rightarrow 2Hg + O_2.}
$$

"Mercuric oxide when heated yields mercury plus oxygen."

The speed of chemical reactions

Chemical equations do not show how rapidly a given reaction takes place. Some chemical processes proceed very quickly. In the cylinders of an automobile engine, vaporized gasoline and air (that is, the oxygen in air) react almost instantaneously when fired by an electric spark. Other chemical reactions are very slow. Water, portland

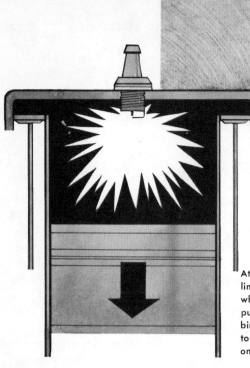

At the left, we see a rapid chemical reaction. Vaporized gasoline and air in an automobile cylinder react almost instantly when ignited by an electric spark; the explosion that is produced pushes the piston down in the cylinder. Above: spreading a combination of portland cement, sand and water, which will react to form concrete. In this case, the reaction will be completed only after several weeks or perhaps even months have elapsed.

cement and sand, blended together in suitable proportions, react to form concrete; but it takes weeks or months for the reaction to be completed.

The principal factors that influence the speed of a chemical reaction, apart from the very nature of the molecules involved, are (1) the temperature, (2) the degree of contact between the reacting materials, (3) the concentration of these materials and (4) the presence of substances called catalysts.

The effect of temperature is an obvious factor. Practically all chemical processes are speeded up by an increase in temperature. In the discussion of the kinetic theory of matter (see Index, under Kinetic theory), it is pointed out that all molecules are constantly in motion except at the extreme temperature called absolute zero, corresponding to −459.69° F.* As the temperature of a reaction mixture rises, the molecules of reacting substances move with greater speed than before; they collide more often and more vigorously. More and more molecules are jarred so effectively that their atoms are released to form new patterns.

Reactions that do not proceed at all under ordinary conditions may become very rapid when the temperature is raised. A giant firecracker may be left on a store shelf

*Editor's note: See Index, under Absolute zero.

for days and nothing will happen. But if anybody sets fire to its fuse with a lighted match, he does not linger near it; he knows that as soon as the fire comes in contact with the explosive contained in the firecracker, there will be a violent blast.

The chemist is generally able to control the temperature at which reactions take place in the laboratory. Sometimes, however, reactions are speeded up by temperature rises that are not due to any human agency. You may have heard of piles of greasy rags, or oily wastes or fermented straw catching fire of themselves through spontaneous combustion. This is what happens. All these materials undergo oxidation — that is, combination with the oxygen of the air — even under ordinary room temperatures. As a result heat is released. Since the substances in question are poor conductors, they retain a good deal of heat. This raises the temperature, and as the temperature rises oxidation goes on at a more rapid rate. At last combustible gases are expelled, and by this time the temperature is so high that the materials burst into flame.

The degree of contact between reacting molecules also influences greatly the speed of reaction. The grinding up of large solid particles into very fine ones speeds up a reaction because it causes contact over a vastly increased area. Let us take the fuel coal as an example. Coal burns because the carbon of the coal reacts vigorously with the oxygen of the air at a high temperature. It takes time to set fire to large chunks of coal, because the amount of surface which is exposed to oxygen is limited. But powdered coal offers an almost infinite number of points of contact. If such fuel is blown out of a nozzle, so that the particles will not pack together, it burns almost as rapidly as liquid fuel.

It is because particles of coal dust, sawdust and grain dust are so finely divided that dust is an ever-present danger in coal mines, sawmill factories and grain elevators. The total surface exposed to the oxygen of the air is so great that a mere spark may cause a terrible explosion. Even aluminum and bronze dust will be ignited under such conditions.

To increase the speed of a reaction, then, the chemist often grinds up his materials in order to increase the surface area that they offer. The stirring and mixing of batches of materials that are undergoing chemical union also increase contact in certain processes. If a gas is involved, increasing the pressure of the gas gives a greater concentration and thus speeds up the chemical reaction.

Even when the temperature is high and when reacting substances are in intimate contact, some reactions will take place slowly. In such cases outside materials, not involved in the reaction, will sometimes speed up the chemical change. These outside materials are called catalysts; they are generally solids, but they may be liquids or gases. They modify the rate of a reaction without themselves undergoing any permanent change. Different catalysts are used to modify the rate of different reactions. Living cells contain natural catalysts, called enzymes, which make possible many of the chemical changes occurring within the cells.

The chemist makes frequent use of catalysts. Sometimes he adds them in small quantities to reacting materials. Thus he combines finely divided nickel with cot-tonseed oil so that the oil will react with hydrogen gas to form the solid fats sold as shortening or used in the manufacture of soap. In other cases, the catalyst is present in a bed over which the reacting materials are passed. A mixture of air and sulfur dioxide, passed over a catalyst consisting of finely divided platinum, reacts rapidly to produce sulfur trioxide.

Reversible reactions and equilibrium

The chemical equation

$$2HgO \xrightarrow{\text{heat}} 2Hg + O_2$$

tells us that mercuric oxygen when heated yields mercury and oxygen, but it does not show how complete the reaction is. If the mercuric oxide is heated in a closed tube, a twofold reaction will take place at one and the same time. As the mercuric oxide decomposes into mercury and oxygen, the mercury and oxygen will react to form mercuric oxide:

$$2Hg + O_2 \rightarrow 2HgO$$

Naturally, if this continues, the mercuric oxide will never decompose completely. A chemist would call this a reversible reaction.

We indicate a reversible reaction by using two arrows in the equation. One of these shows the decomposition or forward process; the other shows the recombination of the products: that is, the reverse process. This is how we would show that mercuric oxide produces mercury and oxygen, while at the same time mercury and oxygen yield mercuric oxide:

$$2HgO \xrightleftharpoons{\text{heat}} 2Hg + O_2$$

Let us follow through with this reversible reaction. Let us suppose that we begin by heating mercuric oxide (HgO) in a closed tube that is evacuated (that is, from which the air has been removed). At first, there is neither mercury nor oxygen in the tube and therefore the reaction can only proceed in the forward direction. As mercury and oxygen are formed, however, the reverse reaction commences. It is very slow in the beginning since only a little mercury and oxygen are present. These substances accumulate, however, as decomposition continues. Since increased concentration increases the speed of a reaction, the rate at which the mercury and the oxygen recombine to form mercuric oxide slowly increases. It continues to increase until the rates of the two opposing reactions are the same; that is, the mercuric oxide is being reformed at precisely the same speed as it is being decomposed. A reversible reaction at this stage is said to be in equilibrium.

In some cases the reaction mixture at equilibrium will consist mainly of reactants, in other cases of products; the exact ratio depends on the nature of the chemicals involved. This ratio is also affected by certain variable factors. One of these is the temperature at which the reaction is carried out; another is the concentrations or the pressures of the reactants and the products. By controlling the variable factors, the chemist can modify to a great extent the ratio between reactants and products at equilibrium.

We can carry a given reversible reaction to completion by entirely removing one or more of the products from the reaction mixture. We have seen that the gas oxygen is one of the two products formed by the decomposition of mercuric oxide. If we allow this gas to escape from the reaction mixture into the atmosphere, it will be unable to unite with the mercury that is also formed as a product. Therefore, mercuric oxide will completely decompose into oxygen and mercury whenever the reaction is carried out in an open tube.

The chemist at work on a typical reaction — the Haber process

To show how the chemist analyzes chemical reactions and then modifies the factors that govern them, let us examine the Haber process, in which nitrogen and hydrogen are made to react in order to produce ammonia. This process, named after Fritz Haber, the German chemist who discovered

Right: a greatly simplified diagram of the Haber process for the production of ammonia. A mixture of nitrogen gas and hydrogen gas is compressed and then led into a synthesis chamber. Here, under high temperature and pressure and with the use of a catalyst, the nitrogen and hydrogen are converted into ammonia. A reverse reaction also takes place; some of the newly formed ammonia decomposes to form nitrogen and hydrogen. When the state of equilibrium is reached, only about one-fourth of the nitrogen and hydrogen has been converted into ammonia. The mixture of gases—ammonia and unconverted nitrogen and hydrogen — is led to a condenser, where it is cooled. The ammonia gas is converted here into a liquid and is led to a storage tank. The nitrogen and hydrogen gases pass to a compressor; after they have been compressed, they again make their way to the synthesis chamber.

it, is extremely important. The product, ammonia, is in great demand, particularly in the manufacture of fertilizers, explosives, refrigerants and certain types of rayon; the reacting materials, nitrogen and hydrogen, are cheap and readily available. Because of the Haber process, an important chemical can be manufactured cheaply and in great quantities.

We can represent the chemical reaction by the following equation:

$$N_2 \quad + \quad H_2 \quad \rightarrow \quad NH_3$$
Nitrogen plus hydrogen yields ammonia

The reaction is not balanced as it stands, for there are two atoms of nitrogen in the reactant, but only one in the product; and there are two atoms of hydrogen in the reactant, but three in the product. The fact that there are two atoms of nitrogen in the reactant means that there must be two ammonia molecules in the product:

$$N_2 + H_2 \rightarrow 2NH_3$$

Still the reaction remains unbalanced, for the six atoms of hydrogen in the two ammonia molecules will require six atoms of hydrogen; that is, three molecules of

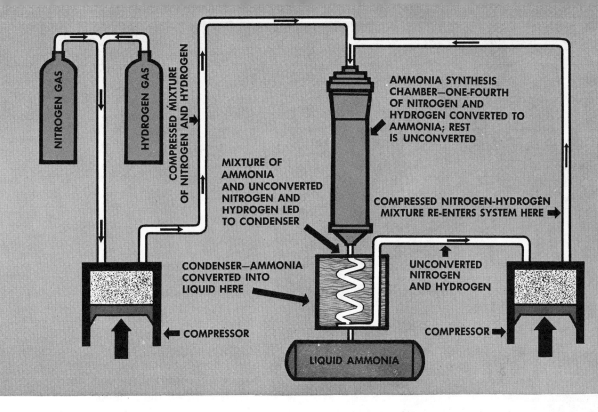

NITROGEN GAS

HYDROGEN GAS

COMPRESSED MIXTURE OF NITROGEN AND HYDROGEN

MIXTURE OF AMMONIA AND UNCONVERTED NITROGEN AND HYDROGEN LED TO CONDENSER

AMMONIA SYNTHESIS CHAMBER—ONE-FOURTH OF NITROGEN AND HYDROGEN CONVERTED TO AMMONIA; REST IS UNCONVERTED

COMPRESSED NITROGEN-HYDROGEN MIXTURE RE-ENTERS SYSTEM HERE ➡

CONDENSER—AMMONIA CONVERTED INTO LIQUID HERE

UNCONVERTED NITROGEN AND HYDROGEN

⬅ COMPRESSOR

COMPRESSOR ➡

LIQUID AMMONIA

hydrogen, on the left-hand side. By adding the figure 3 before the symbol for the hydrogen molecule in the reactant, the equation is completely balanced, thus:

$$N_2 + 3H_2 \rightarrow 2NH_3$$

"A molecule of nitrogen plus three molecules of hydrogen yields two molecules of ammonia."

The atomic weight of nitrogen is 14; of hydrogen, 1. Making the appropriate substitutions in the equation, we have:

$$N_2 \quad + 3H_2 \quad \rightarrow 2NH_3$$
$$2 \times 14 + 3 \times (2 \times 1) \rightarrow 2 \times (14 + [3 \times 1])$$
$$28 \quad + 6 \quad \rightarrow 34$$

That is, 28 atomic-weight units of nitrogen will combine with 6 atomic-weight units of hydrogen to form 34 atomic-weight units of ammonia. We have seen that the same proportion would hold, no matter what weight units we used. Hence, if we combined 28 pounds of nitrogen with 6 pounds of hydrogen, the yield would be 34 pounds of ammonia.

The reaction $N_2 + 3H_2 \rightarrow 2NH_3$, unfortunately, goes on too slowly at ordinary temperatures and pressures to be of any use. To speed up the reaction, the temperature is increased to about 500° centigrade and the pressure is raised to between 500 and 1,000 times that of the atmosphere. Furthermore, a catalyst, generally iron, is employed. Under such conditions the reaction is fairly rapid.

This reaction is reversible; that is, some of the ammonia that is produced decomposes to form nitrogen and hydrogen. The high pressures that are used cause an increase in the yield of ammonia. Higher temperatures increase the rates of both the direct and reverse reactions; but that of the reverse reaction is increased more. When the state of equilibrium is reached, only about one-fourth of the nitrogen and hydrogen has been converted into ammonia. In order to get further production, it is necessary to lead the mixture of gases — ammonia, nitrogen and hydrogen — from the heavy steel bomb in which the reaction is taking place. After the ammonia has been extracted from the mixture, the nitrogen and hydrogen are reheated and recompressed in order to form still more ammonia.

Thus man modifies the conditions under which reactions are produced. Thus he transforms a chemical reaction from a natural event, such as the rusting of a metal, into one of his mightiest tools.

See also Vol. 10, p. 279: "General Works."

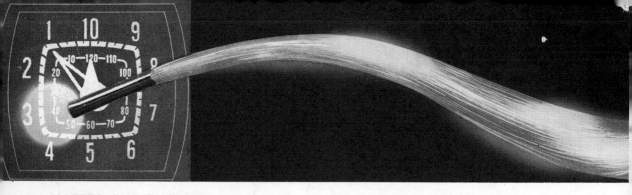

FIBER OPTICS*

A Recent Development in the Old Science of Optics

IT HAS been known for many years that light can be made to pass through a hollow pipe, even if the pipe is curved. Light entering one end of the device is reflected again and again from the inner walls. It makes its way down the pipe and at last emerges at the far end. A device of this sort can be made from highly polished silver or aluminum. It has no practical applications because it is not very efficient. There is some loss of light every time the light rays are reflected. In a pipe in which the length is many times the diameter, many reflections will take place, and there will be a substantial loss of light.

Fortunately, there is a way of bringing about an extended series of reflections virtually without light loss. This can be done by having total internal reflection take place at the interface, or boundary, between a dense medium, such as glass, and a rare medium, such as air. We describe this phenomenon in detail elsewhere (see Index,

* Article prepared with the assistance of the American Optical Company.

under Total internal reflection). To summarize briefly here, if a ray of light passing through the glass is refracted, or bent, by more than a certain angle, it will not leave the glass at all. It will be totally reflected again and again from the interface (see Figure 1). There will be a minimum loss of light as the rays make their way through the device. A light pipe of this sort is really not a pipe in the ordinary sense of the term, but a solid rod. All light pipes commonly used today are of this type. They have been made of glass and of transparent acrylic plastic. Glass is now the preferred material.

A light pipe consisting of a single glass or plastic rod will convey light energy but it will not transmit an image. Let us see why. When we look, say, at a postage stamp, we see it because the light reflected from it reaches our eyes. This light is reflected from different areas of the picture with different degrees of intensity. Thus there will be less light from a dark area, more light from a light area. This varying intensity makes up a definite pattern. If the

1. How light is totally reflected at the interface (that is to say, boundary) between glass and air in a light pipe.

2. Combining light pipes to form a fiberscope. A fiberscope has many more light pipes than are shown below.

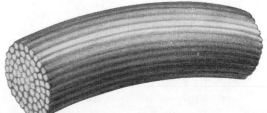

American Optical Co.

Seeing around a corner with a fiberscope. One end of the device is pointed at part of a laboratory timer dial. Each fiber in the fiberscope picks up a dot of light from the dial and this is transmitted along the fiber. At the other end of the fiberscope, an image of the dial appears.

light waves from a given area of the picture pass through a single light pipe with a diameter of, say, half an inch, they will follow a variety of paths as they make their way through the pipe. By the time these light waves and the light waves from the other areas of the picture reach the other end of the pipe, the image will be so mixed up as to be unrecognizable.

To convey an image, a great many light pipes must be used in combination (Figure 2). The image is divided into a number of small areas. The light from each of these small areas is carried through an individual light pipe to the corresponding point in the image at the other end of the bundle of pipes. The diameter of each of the glass or plastic rods combined in this way has been so greatly reduced that it is appropriate to call such rods "fibers." A device in which a number of fibers are combined in order to transmit an image is called a fiberscope. It forms the basis of the science of fiber optics.

Obviously, a flexible fiberscope would be able to transmit images around a corner and would make it possible for a person to look into his own ear. The idea of making such a device must have occurred to many students of optics in the last hundred years or so. However, there seemed to be insurmountable difficulties. For one thing, if simple fibers were in contact, light would leak from one fiber to another, causing a distortion of the image. Again, the surfaces of the fibers would become scratched as they came in contact. There would be loss of light at the scratched places.

Experimenters overcame these difficulties in the 1950's by creating a fiber consisting of two parts: an inner core and an outer coating, or jacket, both transparent. The inner core has a high index of refraction *; the coating that surrounds it, a low index of refraction. The total internal reflection takes place at the interface between the high-index and low-index material (Figure 3). Thus the reflecting surface is sealed in and kept away from other reflecting surfaces. There is practically no light leakage and no light loss due to surface scratches. Fibers of this type are found in virtually all fiber-optics devices in use today. Generally the fiber bundles in which they are combined are provided with flexible sheaths of metal or plastic.

If an image is to be formed, the relative position of the different fibers must be the same at one end of the fiberscope as at the other end. The fibers need not be so

* The index of refraction of a given medium (glass, mineral substance, plastic and so on) is the ratio of the velocity of light in a vacuum to the velocity of light in the medium. The higher the index of refraction, the less the velocity of light in the medium.

3. How light is transmitted by total internal reflection through a clad fiber. The latter consists of two parts: an inner core and an outer jacket. Both are transparent.

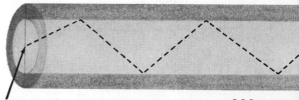

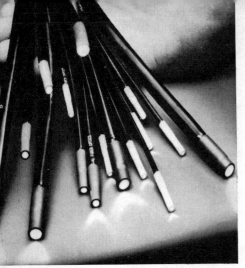

American Optical Co.

Left: a bunch of flexible light guides. These devices will transmit light but not images, since the relative position of the different fibers is not the same at one end of the device as it is at the other end.

The Camerascope™ combines the principles of fiber optics and camera miniaturization. It makes possible inspection and photographic recording in areas that were formerly inaccessible. A. The film magazine is inserted. B. The Camerascope™ is inserted in the tubing that is to be inspected. C. A photo taken with the device: a faulty internal weld.

Photos A and C, above, Iota Cam Corp.

precisely arranged elsewhere in the device; they can be left more or less loose and flexible. A great many fibers will have to be combined in one bundle in order to provide a satisfactory image. In a commonly used type of fiberscope, there are about 750,000 fibers, each being 10 microns in diameter. (A micron is a thousandth of a millimeter.) For certain applications, the diameter of the fiber may be as small as 5 microns — the minimum size.

In some cases, it is not necessary to transmit an image through a fiber bundle, but only to transmit light. A device of this sort is not called a fiberscope, but a flexible light guide. The fibers in such a bundle can be arranged at random. The bundle is called "incoherent," in order to distinguish it from "coherent" bundles, which transmit images. It is easy to make "incoherent" bundles and they are much cheaper than "coherent" bundles of the same dimensions.

Fiber-optics products have already found a host of applications. Flexible light guides — the fiber bundles that carry light energy but that do not transmit an image — are used to provide illumination for delicate surgery. They also serve to light up instrument panels and to detect fire in hard-to-get-at places.

Fiberscopes have a far wider range of applications. Physicians, for example, can see the inside of the stomach through a gastroscope ("stomach-viewer") based on the use of optical fibers. A miniature probe in the shape of a hypodermic needle has been developed for viewing muscle fiber, skin tissue and blood cells. It is expected that in time one should be able to look inside much of the circulatory system, including

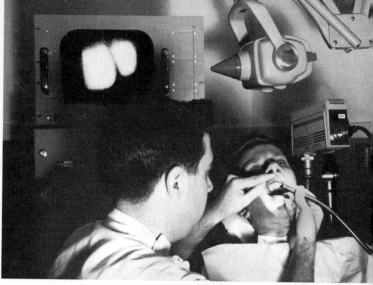

The TV probe we show here (it is called an optical dental probe) projects a magnified view of the teeth onto a television screen for either diagnosis or teaching.

This fused, tapered fiber bundle reduces the image in proportion to the reduction in diameter. Note how the image is transferred to the top surface of the bundle.

perhaps the heart. Truly, the fiberscope offers exciting possibilities in the field of medical diagnosis.

The device has also found wide use in industry. It serves for the inspection or control of operations in inaccessible areas. With the fiberscope, one can examine turbine blades, boiler tubes and various parts of nuclear reactors for flaws and cracks. The fiberscope has been used to check fuel-level indicators in gasoline tanks after these indicators have been installed. Tools left by careless workers in the wing sections of airplanes have been unerringly spotted by the device.

Bundles of fiberscopes, fused together in a solid plate, called a faceplate, have been used in television picture tubes and in other cathode-ray tube devices. The faceplate transfers images formed on the internal phosphor surface* inside the tube to the screen, or face, of the tube.

Pictures or documents can be coded or decoded by means of the fiberscope. This is accomplished by transmitting an image

* See Index, under Phosphors.

through a fiber bundle in which the arrangement of fibers at one end of the bundle is made to differ from the arrangement at the other end. The different parts of the image become scrambled (mixed up) and it becomes unrecognizable. However, when it is transmitted back through the same fiber bundle, it can be brought back to the original pattern. Thus the same device that produced the scrambling, or coding, also serves as a decoder. This principle has been put to use by banks in order to prevent forgery. The signature of a depositor is printed in coded (scrambled) form on his passbook. The bank teller is provided with a decoder. When the depositor presents the passbook in order to make a withdrawal from his savings account, the teller can immediately compare the decoded signature, seen in his decoder, with the signature on the withdrawal slip.

These are only a few of the ways in which devices based on fiber optics have been used. Because of the great versatility of these devices, we can expect a flood of new applications in the years to come.

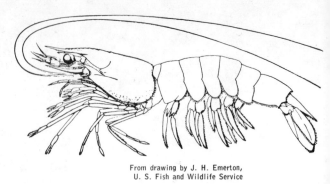

From drawing by J. H. Emerton,
U. S. Fish and Wildlife Service

The southern shrimp. It
swims backward by flip-
ping its tail beneath it.

A lordly crustacean—the
American lobster—may
reach a length of 2 feet.

Both photos, Amer. Mus. of Nat. Hist.

Fresh-water shrimp from
Panama. Its pincers are
modified walking legs.

The blue crab has bright
blue legs, the last pair of
which are paddle-shaped.

N. Y. Zool. Soc.

THE CRUSTACEANS

Lobsters, Crabs, Crayfish and Their Kin

BY F. L. FITZPATRICK

THE largest group in the animal kingdom is the phylum of the arthropods, or "animals with jointed feet." They include well over a million species; the number of the animals belonging to these species is so great as to defy calculation. In other chapters we discuss such arthropods as the spiders and their kin (including the scorpions, mites, millepedes and centipedes) and the insects (flies, mosquitoes, beetles, ants, bees and wasps, to mention only a few). We shall deal in the pages that follow with the arthropods known as the crustaceans. They include lobsters, crabs, crayfish, shrimps, barnacles, water fleas and a host of less well-known animals. Almost all live in the water.

The body of a typical crustacean is composed of distinct segments. It is usually divided into two chief areas: the cephalothorax, made up of the head and thorax, and the abdomen. There is an exoskeleton, or outer skeleton, consisting of a flexible substance called chitin. In most crustaceans the chitin becomes impregnated with calcium carbonate ($CaCO_3$), most familiar to us as the principal component of limestone. This results in a tough, crustlike shell, from which the crustaceans derive their name. (The Latin word *crusta* means "crust," or "shell" or "rind.")

The tough outer skeleton of crustaceans is shed at intervals so that the animals may contine to grow. The old exoskeleton splits along the back and the crustacean works its way out of its covering. It can then grow considerably before the new exoskeleton hardens. During this time the crustacean is in what is called the soft-shell stage; it generally retires to a secluded spot in order to avoid its enemies.

The crustaceans have two sets of antennae, which are provided with sense organs. In very small representatives of the group the antennae are also swimming structures; in *Daphnia,* for example, they serve as "oars." There is a pair of hard mandibles for chewing; two pairs of maxillae and the maxillipeds test food and pass it into the mouth. The eyes of many species are mounted on movable stalks. In some species the eyes are compound: that is, made up of a number of units. The crayfish, for example, has two compound eyes, borne on short stalks; each of these eyes consists of about 2,500 units.

The number of legs, or appendages, which occur in pairs, differs according to the species. The appendages located on the thorax serve as walking legs; the first pair, however, may be greatly enlarged to form grasping structures, or pincers. The rather small appendages borne on the abdomens of some crustaceans are called swimmerets; the eggs of female lobsters and crayfish are attached to these structures. In many cases appendages and even eyes may be regenerated (grown again), if they are damaged or lost. The walking legs of crayfish, for example, have a breaking point near the base. If one of these legs is injured, the animal may snap it off; in time a new growth will replace the old member.

The larger crustaceans have well-developed internal organs and systems for carrying on such processes as digestion, respiration, circulation, excretion, reproduction and nervous responses. The smaller representatives of the group lack a definite respiratory system; they breathe through the entire surface of the body.

The eggs of the marine crustaceans generally develop into free-swimming larvae, which are often decidedly odd-looking creatures. They usually pass through several larval stages before they attain the adult form. Fresh-water crustaceans commonly skip the larval stage; the young have the adult form when they hatch.

As we have seen, most crustaceans are water-dwellers, living either in the sea or in fresh water. Some have invaded the deeper regions of the ocean; they may dwell a mile or even more below the surface. A few species live on land. Many crustaceans, including the lobsters and crabs, eat both animals and vegetable matter, often decaying substances; to a certain extent, therefore, these animals act as scavengers. The so-called fish lice are crustaceans which live as parasites in or upon the bodies of fishes.

A large crustacean whose meat is especially prized is the true lobster, belonging to the family of the Homaridae. The larger members of the family may weigh thirty pounds, or even more; they may reach a body length of two feet, and the pincers may be fifteen inches long. However, such giants are not particularly common. In the United States most of the lobsters reaching the market are under two pounds in weight.

Some lobsters dwell on the sea bottom in shallow water throughout the year; others move into shallow water in the spring and migrate to greater depths as the water grows colder in the fall. Lobsters generally prefer rocky bottoms.

A female lobster produces thousands of eggs a season. The eggs are attached to the swimmerets on the lower side of the abdomen. When the larvae hatch, they make their way to the surface of the sea; there they swim or float about for a period of three or four weeks. During this period, the young lobsters are destroyed in vast numbers by surface-feeding fish. The survivors eventually drop down to the bottom, where they take on the appearance and habits of adults. In nature, the percentage of young that attain maturity is relatively small. In the United States, many young lobsters reach the larval stage in the comparative security of salt-water pools or tanks at hatcheries; they are kept in these waters until they are past the vulnerable stage in the early part of their life cycle.

For many years the preferred lobster-catching device has been the trap called the lobster pot. It is a cratelike affair, made of wooden slats; these are spaced far enough apart so that the smaller lobsters, which would not be acceptable for the market, can crawl out between the slats and escape. The trap is provided with a funnel-shaped entrance which makes it easy for the lobster to enter but practically impossible to get out. The lobster pot is carefully baited, generally with decaying fish; then it is weighted, so that it will sink to the bottom, and set out in shallow-water areas where lobsters are likely to be found. The position of the trap is marked by a buoy on the end of a rope attached to the trap. A lobster fisherman visits the pots at regular intervals to remove the catch through a hinged door and to replenish the bait.

The American lobster (*Homarus americanus*) is found northward from the Carolinas along the Atlantic coast of the United States and Canada. In the not too distant past American lobster fishermen sent 100,000,000 lobsters to the market each year, and lobster canneries worked overtime along the New England coast. In those days lobsters could sometimes be bought for ten cents a pound; they were not generally considered to be a luxury food. They are now much scarcer and the market price has soared accordingly. At present Canada's annual lobster catch surpasses that of the United States by a considerable margin.

Several varieties of lobsters thrive in European waters. The common lobster (*Homarus gammarus*) occurs off coastal areas from the Mediterranean to Norway, and is usually caught by means of lobster pots. A smaller species — the Norway

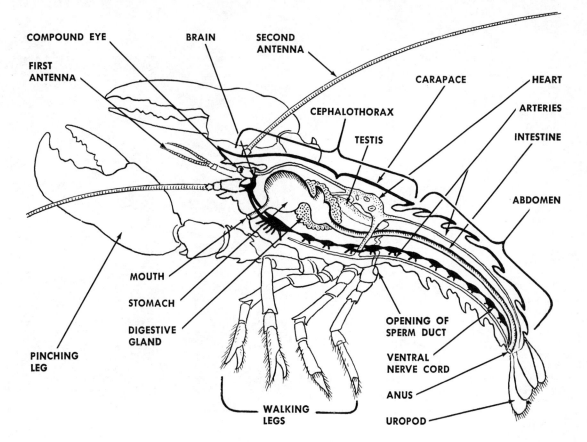

External and internal anatomy of male common lobster. Note the digestive, circulatory and nervous systems.

Labels: COMPOUND EYE, BRAIN, SECOND ANTENNA, FIRST ANTENNA, CARAPACE, HEART, ARTERIES, CEPHALOTHORAX, INTESTINE, TESTIS, ABDOMEN, MOUTH, STOMACH, DIGESTIVE GLAND, OPENING OF SPERM DUCT, VENTRAL NERVE CORD, ANUS, UROPOD, PINCHING LEG, WALKING LEGS

lobster (*Nephrops norvegicus*) — is an inhabitant of the same regions. It is found in deeper waters and is usually taken by trawling.

Lobsters without pincers occur in warm waters off various land areas, including Florida, the West Indies, South Africa, Australia and New Zealand. These animals, which belong to the family of the Palinuridae, are armed with spines, with which they can stun their prey or hold off pursuers. The meat of these lobsters is highly prized.

The fresh-water crustaceans called crayfish (family Astacidae) look much like diminutive lobsters. The comparatively small varieties belonging to the genus *Cambarus* are a familiar sight in and about fresh-water streams, lakes and ponds in the eastern part of North America. A larger variety, *Astacus,* is found west of the Rockies; it also occurs in England, Ireland, Europe and Asia.

Crayfish normally live in shallow water. Here they avoid their natural enemies by hiding in aquatic vegetation or under stones; they sometimes come out upon the banks under cover of darkness. Ordinarily they crawl forward, but if they are disturbed they can shoot backward with considerable speed. They feed upon a wide variety of plant and animal life, including other crayfish, tadpoles, small fish, snails, insects and aquatic plants; they also serve as scavengers. They are themselves the prey of raccoons, opossums, bears, alligators, ducks, fish and other animals.

In some relatively moist areas, crayfish may desert their ponds and streams and live on the land. Here they dig burrows down into the soil until they strike the water that will enable them to keep their gills moist. From time to time they sally forth from their retreats to feed upon young vegetation, including crop plants. They are an annoying pest in cotton and corn fields in certain areas of Mississippi and Alabama. In irrigated areas, their burrowing activities sometimes weaken earth dams and cause water to be lost from irrigation ditches.

Crayfish are considered edible in many areas where they are abundant. The larger varieties belonging to the genus *Astacus* are preferred because of their size. Crayfish also serve us by providing food for the fishes that form an essential part of our food supply. Fishermen often use these crustaceans for bait.

Like crayfish, shrimps look somewhat like small lobsters, with unusually long antennae and fragile shells. The larger shrimps are often called prawns. Various species of these small crustaceans are found in the deep sea; the varieties we eat, however, occur in shallow waters along coastal areas and in fresh-water streams. Vast numbers of shrimps are found along the Gulf and Pacific coasts of North America. They are caught in nets and are sold fresh, dried or in cans. Only the abdomens are eaten by humans.

The crabs are distinguished from such crustaceans as the lobsters and crayfish by

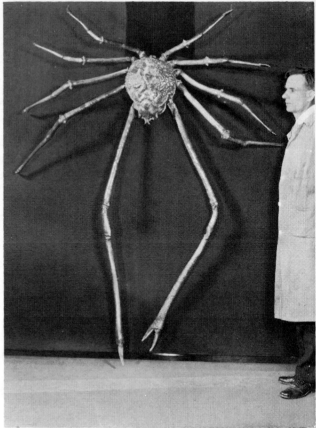

Photos, Amer. Mus. of Nat. Hist.

Above: Japanese spider crab, largest of crabs. Left: male fiddler crab. Females have claws of equal size.

the small abdomen, which is folded up under the body. They have five pairs of legs; the legs of the first pair end in pincers and are larger than the rest. The last pair of walking legs are often flattened and are used as swimming structures. Crabs usually walk or crawl with a curious, sideways gait. They generally have a varied diet, which includes dead animals and plants.

There are a great many species of crabs in various parts of the world. Most of them live in the sea; some are found in fresh water; a few species live on land. Water-dwelling crabs breathe by gills set in cavities at the sides of the body. These cavities are larger in the true land-dwelling species and serve as lungs.

One of the most important of food crabs is the blue crab (*Callinectes sapidus*), found along the Atlantic coast from New England to Brazil. The so-called hard-shelled crabs and soft-shelled crabs of commerce are really blue crabs at different stages of the molting process. The hard-shelled variety is a blue crab with a fully developed exoskeleton; a soft-shelled crab is the same animal after a molt has taken place and before the new covering has had time to harden. Hard-shelled crabs are caught in traps or nets of various kinds. Soft-shelled crabs commonly hide in the vegetation of shallow waters; they may be collected with dip nets.

Various other crabs are used as food. Among these are *Cancer pagurus,* found off the coasts of Great Britain and Europe, and the Dungeness crab (*Cancer magister*), occurring off the Pacific coast of North America. Certain swimming crabs, belonging to the genera *Scylla* and *Neptunus,* dwell off various islands of the southwest Pacific and in Indian waters.

Among the most interesting of the crustaceans are the small hermit crabs, belonging to the families Paguridae and Parapaguridae. The abdomen of these crabs is soft and quite unprotected. To shield this vulnerable part of its body, the animal seeks out an empty marine-snail shell and backs into it. The hermit crab's pincers and legs protrude from the front end when the animal crawls about in search of its food; it can withdraw entirely within its shelter if danger threatens. When a hermit crab outgrows one shell, it abandons it and seeks a larger one.

In some cases sea anemones establish themselves on the shells inhabited by hermit crabs. As the anemones are well armed with stinging cells, their presence undoubtedly brings added security to the crabs. The sea anemones also profit from the relationship since they are carried about from place to place. It has been reported that certain varieties of hermit crabs, upon changing from old snail shells to new ones, carefully transfer their sea anemone companions to the new shelters. The anemones do not appear to resist this action, though they generally sting other animals that try to uproot them.

A crustacean often found on beaches of temperate regions is the fiddler crab, belonging to the genus *Uca*. One claw of the male — generally, but not always, the right claw — is much larger than the other. The fiddler crab lives in a burrow that it tunnels in soft, moist soil above the high-water mark. Generally it sits at the mouth of its burrow moving its large claw slowly, somewhat after the fashion of a fiddler manipulating a bow. This is the animal's way of attracting the attention of the female of the species.

The largest of all crabs is the giant spider crab (*Macrocheira kaempferi*) of Japan, which measures ten feet or more from the tip of one of its fully extended pincers to the tip of the other. It is a rather inactive animal with a comparatively small, rounded body and long, ungainly legs. It commonly covers itself with seaweeds or sponges; thus camouflaged, it stalks its prey deliberately until the victim is within reach of the slender claws.

Not all spider crabs are as long as the giant Japanese variety. A common species found on the Atlantic and Pacific coasts of North America (*Libinia emarginata*) measures only a foot or so across the extended pincers. Crawling about the sea bottom it often makes its way into lobster pots and devours the bait.

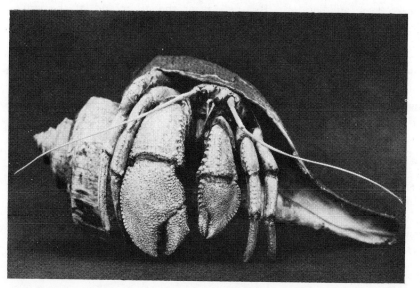

The hermit crab curls its soft, unprotected abdomen into the coils of an empty marine-snail shell.

One of the best-known land crabs is the robber crab (*Birgus latro*), found on the islands of the Indian and Pacific oceans. This large animal, often a foot or more in length, lives in a burrow at the foot of a coconut palm, lining its retreat with the fibers of coconut husks. Its pincers are very strong and heavy. It carefully strips the fiber from a coconut and then patiently hammers at the nut with its strong claws until the shell has been broken. It then extracts the meat of the nut.

The king, or horseshoe, crabs are a remnant of an ancient group, which is now almost extinct. They were at one time classified with the crustaceans but are now put in a separate class — that of the Merostomata. They are large arthropods measuring a foot or so across the shield, or carapace, which covers the top part of the body. When seen from above, the carapace has the outline of a horseshoe; this accounts for the name "horseshoe crab." The tail is long, pointed and hard. The king crab lives in shallow water; it plows through sand or mud seeking its prey — worms and mollusks.

The small land crustacean known as the pill bug (family Armadillididae) is often found far from ponds and streams. This little animal, which is about three fifths of an inch long when fully grown, rolls itself up in 'a ball when disturbed. It commonly lives in cellars and under stones, boards, dead leaves and other debris, in comparatively moist surroundings. Pill bugs feed upon plant materials, both living and decayed; they rarely become so numerous as to be a menace.

Some crustaceans, such as the gribbles and the barnacles, do not look much like their crustacean kin. The gribble (*Limnoria lignorum*), a small animal belonging to the isopod group, is a destructive creature. It looks like a small worm, not more than a sixth of an inch in length; it has two pairs of antennae and six pairs of legs. Swarms of gribbles burrow their way into submerged timbers of all kinds, including the piling of wharves and the bottoms of ships. The boring activities of the gribbles

N. Y. Zool. Soc.

Barnacles affix themselves to a support and kick food into their mouths.

are not entirely undesirable from the viewpoint of man, since they help to break up floating wreckage, which might otherwise be a menace to shipping.

The barnacles, belonging to the subclass of the cirripeds, look like crustaceans only in the larval stage. The larva is a free-swimming creature; after swimming about for a time, the larva attaches itself to some solid object in the water and secretes a calcareous outer shell.

The adult of the variety known as the goose barnacle (family Lepadidae) is attached to the supporting object by a fleshy stalk; the body of the animal, enclosed in its shell, is at the other end of the stalk. The shell is made up of several plates and is roughly conical in shape. Six pairs of long appendages, fringed with hairs, can be thrust out from a slit in the shell; they strain minute organisms from the water and sweep them toward the animal's mouth, inside the shell. Certain barnacles, called acorn shells, or acorn barnacles (family Balanidae), lack a stalk; the shell is attached directly to the support. An opening at the top of the shell can be closed by four movable plates, or valves.

When barnacles are firmly anchored in place, they look much more like mollusks, such as clams or oysters, than crustaceans; as a matter of fact, they were classified as mollusks by zoologists until

1830. In that year J. V. Thompson showed that barnacles developed from free-swimming larvae that were typically crustacean; since that time the animals have been grouped with the crustaceans.

Barnacles are very common in shallow sea waters, especially in the tropics and subtropics. The adults may often be seen attached to rock surfaces, seaweed, various marine animals, the piling of wharves and the hulls of ships and boats. In most cases they affect us neither for good nor for evil. However, when they become attached in great numbers to the hulls of ships, they become exceedingly annoying. An accumulation of barnacles, seaweed and other marine organisms may be gradually built up on the underwater surface of the vessel; the ship's speed may be so reduced as a consequence that it will have to be drydocked, scraped and repainted. Quick-drying, antifouling paints are often applied to ship bottoms to prevent the accumulation of barnacles and other growths. These paints consist of iron oxides to which poisonous materials, such as white arsenic, have been added. The poisonous substances gradually dissolve, and they discourage the growth of barnacles and other fouling organisms.

Among the close kin of the barnacles is the cirriped called *Sacculina,* which is a parasite of crabs. Its saclike body, from which it derives its name, is attached under the abdomen of the crab by means of a short stalk; rootlike processes extend from the stalk to all parts of the body, avoiding the vital organs. *Sacculina* causes sterility in both male and female victims. It has a particularly remarkable effect upon male crabs, causing them to take on female characteristics.

The crustacean group of the copepods is composed of small animals that are often microscopic in size. They make up a considerable part of the plankton — the vast floating population of the sea, consisting of tiny crustaceans, protozoa, the eggs and young of various marine animals (including fish, worms, jellyfish and mollusks) and also microscopic plants, such as the diatoms and other various small algae.

Since plankton forms an important part of the food supply of the fishes, including many varieties eaten by man, the copepods are even more important to us than are the lobsters, crabs and other comparatively large crustaceans that find their way to our tables.

The typical free-swimming copepods have a streamlined body, ending in a forked tail. There are two pairs of antennae, of which one is much larger than the other; both pairs are used in swimming. The four or five pairs of feet are also used for swimming purposes. A number of species of copepods are parasitic, either in the larval or adult stage, on a number of marine and fresh-water animals, including worms, fishes and whales.

The name water fleas is sometimes applied to certain copepods. The name is also used for a different group of minute crustaceans, belonging to the subclass of the branchiopods. Among the best-known of the branchiopod water fleas is *Daphnia*, which is found in vast numbers in ponds and ditches. Less than a tenth of an inch in length, *Daphnia* is a true crustacean, with a fairly complicated system of internal organs. The feathered antennae are the principal swimming organs; they propel the animal through the water in a series of jerking movements. *Daphnia* feeds upon microscopic organisms in the water; it is the prey of tadpoles, fish fry and other small aquatic creatures.

See also Vol. 10, p. 275: "Invertebrates."

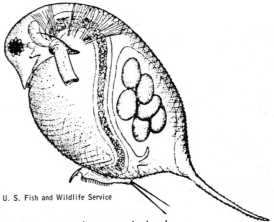

U. S. Fish and Wildlife Service

Daphnia—notice the eye at the head end and the egg sac containing eggs.

HEATING AND
VENTILATION

IF WE lived in hermetically sealed houses it would hardly be logical to discuss both heating and ventilation in the same article. Heating is the raising of temperature. Ventilation is the movement of air in such a way that fresh air replaces used air in an enclosed space such as a room or an auditorium. We could heat hermetically sealed houses but we would not be able to ventilate them, since no air could enter from the outside. Actually, however, even when we keep doors and windows tightly closed, there are enough tiny openings in walls, around windows and door jambs and along cracks in the floor to permit air to leave or enter a room. As a result, heating and ventilation are closely linked.

It is true that under certain conditions people can live in sealed spaces for long periods of time, provided certain precau-

tions are taken. In our newest submarines men can remain submerged for weeks on end with no access to the outer air. But this is possible only because of the complicated systems set up to provide adequate oxygen, to dispose of the waste products of exhalation (carbon dioxide and water vapor) and to circulate the air. No such elaborate arrangements are provided in our homes.

The simplest form of ventilation system would be a process of alternate heating and cooling. If the air in a room, with doors and windows closed, were heated the air would expand and exert pressure on the enclosing walls. Air would then be forced out of the room through even the smallest openings where leakage could occur. The volume of air within the room would remain unchanged, though it would

Closely Linked Systems
That Affect Our Comfort

BY WILLIAM T. INGRAM

be less dense than before. If the source of heat were removed the air in the room would become cooler and the air pressure would be reduced. Air from the outside would be forced through openings where leakage could occur, thus equalizing the pressure within the room and without.

Even if heating is maintained continually, as in our homes, there will be an exchange of air from inside and outside the room. As more and more hot air makes its way out of the room because of the added pressure caused by heating, cool air will be drawn in to replace it. The heating of air, therefore, brings about ventilation in any room that is not sealed. By the same token, the ventilation of a room will affect its temperature. If cold air is drawn into a room in winter the temperature will drop. The drawing-in of warm air in sum-

mer will, of course, make the temperature rise.

There can be no question, then, that heating and ventilation are closely linked. In the following pages, when we discuss heating, we shall have to consider the effects of the movement of air due to heating. When we deal with ventilation we shall have to consider its effect upon the temperature of a room.

Heating

Our bodies must function at a more or less even temperature to maintain life activities. We could not long survive if our body temperature fell to 80° F. or if it rose to 110° F. Fortunately, the living body is in itself a source of heat. It has, furthermore, certain mechanisms, such as the blood vessels of the skin and the sweat glands, to regulate body temperature. Hence, man can withstand rather extreme variations in temperature for limited periods of time.

We can endure low temperatures outdoors by putting on various extra articles of clothing, thus trapping the body heat and holding it as an insulating layer around the body. To maintain a comfortable temperature within a building space when the weather is cold, we employ a heating system. It raises the temperature to a level high enough to compensate for the heat losses of the building and its contents, including, of course, the air within it.

The simplest way to heat a room is by a stove. The heat from burning fuel is transferred to the iron or special brick of which the stove is made. The air in the room comes in contact with the hot surface of the stove; as the air becomes warm, it expands. It then pushes upward because the hot air is lighter than the surrounding colder air. This movement of air, caused by a difference in density between hot and cold air, is known as a convection current. (Convection currents also occur in liquids.) In this process hot and cold air come together and are mixed; heat is gradually transferred to more and more of the cooler air and the room becomes warmer.

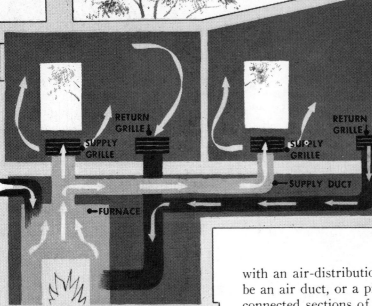

A simple hot-air heating system. Air is heated in a furnace. The hot air rises and flows by way of a supply duct and supply grilles, or registers, into the rooms that are to be heated. After the air cools, it flows back to the furnace by way of the return grilles and the return duct. It then enters the air space around the heating chamber of the furnace and is heated again.

Heating is also brought about by radiation — the direct transfer of heat from the surface of one object to the surface of another. If you sit close to a stove you will feel warm on the side next to the stove, but your body will be cooler on the side that is turned away from it.

Although a stove may provide quite adequate heat for a single room, it cannot heat several rooms efficiently. Heated air or a source of heat must be brought into each of the rooms. To bring this about, several different types of heating systems have been developed.

Hot-air
heating systems

In hot-air systems a furnace combustion chamber or some other source of heat warms the air passing around it. The hot air is held within a shell or bonnet surrounding the heat source and connected with an air-distribution system. This may be an air duct, or a pipe called a leader, or connected sections of piping called a stack. In the simplest form of hot-air furnace the hot air flowing through ducts escapes from them into the rooms to be heated. When the air cools, it flows through the return grilles and return duct to the furnace.

In many homes there is only one duct outlet, a central heating register, or grille, in the room located above the basement furnace. Very hot air escapes from the register into the room and then heats, by convection currents, the air in the other rooms into which it flows. Some homes have a series of pipes rising from the heated-air shell around the furnace. The pipes lead through spaces in the partition walls to registers in different rooms.

This general type of heating is called a gravity-circulation hot-air system. The hot air constantly rises and the displaced cooler air sinks, by gravity, to be warmed in the air space around the furnace. A system of this kind is adequate only when no pipe outlet in a room is so far from the furnace that the air cools off within the pipe before it reaches the room.

The gravity system may be varied in several ways. It may have a large insulated chamber mounted in the basement, with stacks leading from it to the room above. Or small units known as floor furnaces, usually gas-fired, may be used in each room. Cooler air at floor level flows downward through a space on the outer edge of this type of unit. Then it flows upward around metal fins that form part of the heater walls, and back into the room. The fire chamber has vents leading to the outside air.

In forced-circulation hot-air heating a blower is placed in the cold-air duct through which cold air passes to the furnace. The blower forces cool air over the heating space of the furnace. The heated air is then pushed on through the pipes or ductwork to registers located in the rooms to be heated. Cool air may be drawn from inside the house or from the outside. Dampers permit a small amount of fresh air from the outside to be mixed with the warmer air in the building. Thus the air is not only heated but freshened. This system is very flexible, since both the volume and the temperature of the heated air can be controlled easily.

Floor furnaces may be so mounted that a blower forces air over the heater fins and out into the room or building space. These units are sometimes used to heat large areas in factory buildings. The heater unit in this case may be a gas fire or it may be steam or high-pressure hot-water coils.

Gravity hot-air systems require larger registers than forced-air systems, since the velocity of air flow is less. The velocity of the air flowing from the duct must not be so great that it makes the occupants of the room uncomfortable. Many people find that velocities greater than one hundred feet per minute are objectionable. When such velocities are necessary, deflectors are put into openings to turn the air flow aside.

The cool-air return, for gravity hot-air systems, is usually taken from an opening on the first floor or in the basement. The location of return registers for forced-air systems depends on the inlet locations. If the warm air enters at the floor or the baseboard, the return will probably be located on the opposite wall near the ceiling. The registers are usually installed so that the cold wall surfaces will be blanketed with warm air. In large rooms, several outlets may be distributed around the outside walls. This is known as perimeter heating.

Steam-heating systems

In larger buildings and masonry structures it is advisable to carry the heat source to the space that is to be heated rather than to heat air at a central point. Steam or hot water may serve as the source of heat.

In steam-heating systems water is heated in a furnace, usually in the basement, and is converted into the vapor called steam. The steam is then conveyed to radiators in the different rooms of the house or building. The hot radiators warm the air, in much the same way as a stove does, by the contact of the cool air in the room with the hot surfaces of the radiator, by the radiation of heat to solid surfaces and by setting up convection currents in the room. Radiators are so called because most of the heat transfer is by radiation. The projecting ribs of a radiator are known as fins.

Radiators are usually constructed of cast iron. The heat of the iron surface passes in all directions to walls, floors, ceilings and objects within the room. A radiator located close to a wall beneath a window always acts as a convector as well. Cool air flowing into the space between the radiator and the heated wall is warmed and rises to mix with air flowing in around the windows.

A unit known as a convector type of radiator does the same thing on a planned basis. A radiator with more fins than the ordinary radiator is placed in an enclosure permitting the entrance of cooler air underneath. The air flows upward around the heater surfaces and warm air passes out through vents above. Combination radiator-convector units are used in both home and industrial heating.

In a steam-heating system the steam cools in the radiator and condenses, becoming water. The water is then returned by gravity to the heating unit. Relatively small pipes are used and very little steam volume is required to heat rooms adequately. Low-pressure steam, from almost nothing to five pounds per square inch, has been used for home heating for many years.

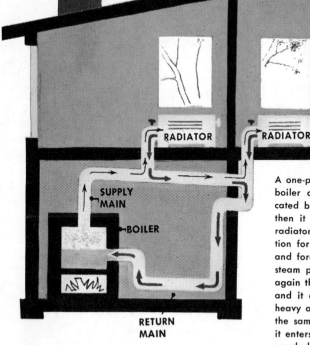

A one-pipe steam-heating system. Water is heated in a boiler and is converted into steam. The steam (indicated by light arrows) rises and enters a supply main; then it makes its way through pipes into the different radiators in the system. There is a single pipe connection for each radiator. Steam passes into the radiator and forces air out through an air vent at one end. As steam pressure is reduced, air moves into the radiator again through the vent. The steam, therefore, is cooled and it condenses into water. The water (indicated by heavy arrows) flows, through the force of gravity, down the same pipe through which the steam had risen, and it enters the supply main. The main has a slight downward slope away from the boiler; as a consequence it flows in the direction that is indicated in the diagram. Finally the water makes its way into the boiler again.

There are several kinds of steam-heating systems. In the one-pipe system, the steam flows to the radiator and forces air out of an air vent on the side. When the steam pressure is removed, air moves into the vent and the condensed steam flows as water back down the pipe from the radiator to the boiler. The one-pipe system is commonly used in homes and small buildings.

In the two-pipe system, steam flows to the radiators when the radiator steam valves are opened. As the steam enters the radiator, the cold air inside escapes from an air vent. The steam cools and gradually condenses while passing through the system; the water that has formed and the remaining vapor flow out of another pipe on the opposite end of the radiator and return to the boiler. Any radiator can be shut off completely without interfering with the system as a whole. This flexibility is essential in hotels and apartment houses where heat requirements are varied. The so-called vapor system operates much like a two-pipe system. It operates at lower pressures or in a partial vacuum.

Hot-water heating systems

In a hot-water system, water that is heated in a boiler flows in the liquid state to the radiators. Cooler water, displaced by the hot water, flows from the radiators back into the pipe system and returns to the boiler. An expansion tank prevents any strain on the piping from the expansion of the water as it is heated. The hot-water system may be a one-pipe loop — that is, it may have a single pipe leading from the boiler and returning to it. In this case each radiator has one connection from the loop and another leading back to it. Sometimes a pump is installed on the return line to speed up circulation. In the two-pipe loop system, the inlet side of the radiator is connected to one pipe and the outlet side to a returning line.

Sometimes high-pressure hot-water systems give better results than steam, especially in large industrial plants and big buildings. The high-pressure water system has both a feeding and a returning line; it is held at a pressure high enough to keep the water from changing to steam. At temperatures of from 300° F. to 400° F. the water can transport heat on long runs of pipe without any serious heat loss. Water under high pressure is used as a source of heat for convector-type radiators. It may also heat the water for the hot-water supply of a building and for special industrial processes.

Variations are possible with both high-pressure steam or high-pressure hot water as a heat source. The main boiler, for example, may be located in the basement or at some other point in a large building or industrial plant. The steam or hot water may then be routed to another location, as to the upper floors of a skyscraper. There it gives up its heat as it is passed through a so-called heat exchanger. The heat exchanger at that point heats water for use

in an ordinary hot-water heating system for that particular part of the building. In an industrial plant each of the buildings may be heated by a local hot-water system, for which a central-heating plant furnishes the primary source of heat. This primary source may be high-pressure hot water or it may be steam.

Individual heating units

Individual heating units for rooms may operate as either convection heaters or radiant heaters, or as a combination of the two. They are, in effect, miniature furnaces built to fit into a room instead of into a basement.

A radiant-heater unit may be set into a wall. It may be portable, with electric coils to provide the heat, which radiates to a reflecting surface in the unit. From the reflector the heat is transferred out to the surfaces of objects in the room. A fireplace is a radiant heater, since it radiates

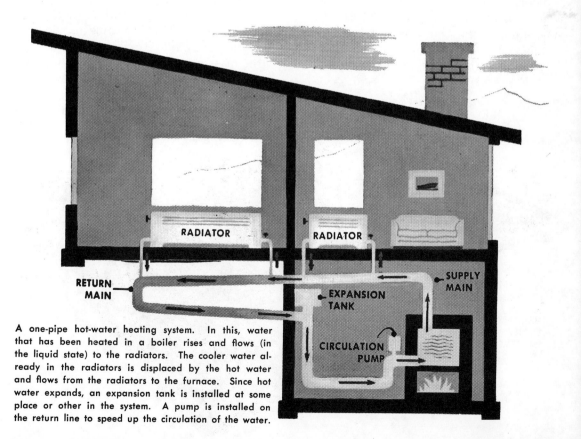

A one-pipe hot-water heating system. In this, water that has been heated in a boiler rises and flows (in the liquid state) to the radiators. The cooler water already in the radiators is displaced by the hot water and flows from the radiators to the furnace. Since hot water expands, an expansion tank is installed at some place or other in the system. A pump is installed on the return line to speed up the circulation of the water.

heat from its bricks as well as from burning logs of coal and embers, although it also heats by convection.

A gas-fired radiant heater should never be used without a vent to carry off the fumes. The products of combustion from the gas flame include carbon monoxide, a highly dangerous gas in an enclosed space. Such a heater also very quickly uses up the oxygen in a closed room and this lack of oxygen may cause asphyxiation.

The radiant heater heats more efficiently if it also heats by convection. An air space can be constructed around the metal backing of the heater so that cool air flows into the air space at the bottom and comes out of the top as hot air. Fans may be attached to electric heaters to draw cool air across the heater coils and metal fins and to blow hot air out into the room — a form of forced warm-air heating.

Panel
heaters

Panels for heating may be sections of floor, walls or ceiling. The source of heat may be hot air, warm water or electricity; steam is used in some cases. Heating pipes, tubes or ducts are buried in slabs of concrete or in plaster, or are formed into other flooring or wall material. Electrical cables for heating may be laid into flooring or fastened to the walls and buried in the material. Fabrics threaded with electrical resistance units have been used as part of the finished room-heating surfaces. Ordinarily the heated panel must be comfortable to the touch. Temperature at heating panel surfaces should never be more than 120° F.; preferably it should be held at 85° F., or a little less on floor panels.

In panel-heating systems, outer walls and floors directly above the basement must be insulated, so that heat is not lost to the outside or to the ground. Interior walls and ceilings between first- and second-story rooms are constructed without insulation and the heated surfaces on both sides radiate to the rooms exposed to the panel.

Although panel heating is a form of radiation heating, there is also a minor amount of heating by convection, due to air movement across the heated surfaces. Probably little convection heating is imparted by ceiling panels, since the warm-air temperature at ceiling level is little different from the temperature at the surface of the panel. Panel heating is slow in bringing up room temperature, since the large mass of panel material must first be-

Panel-heating unit for a one story house. The heating pipes, leading from the boiler and returning to it, are set in the floor; they are buried in concrete. The white lines in the diagram indicate the house's room layout.

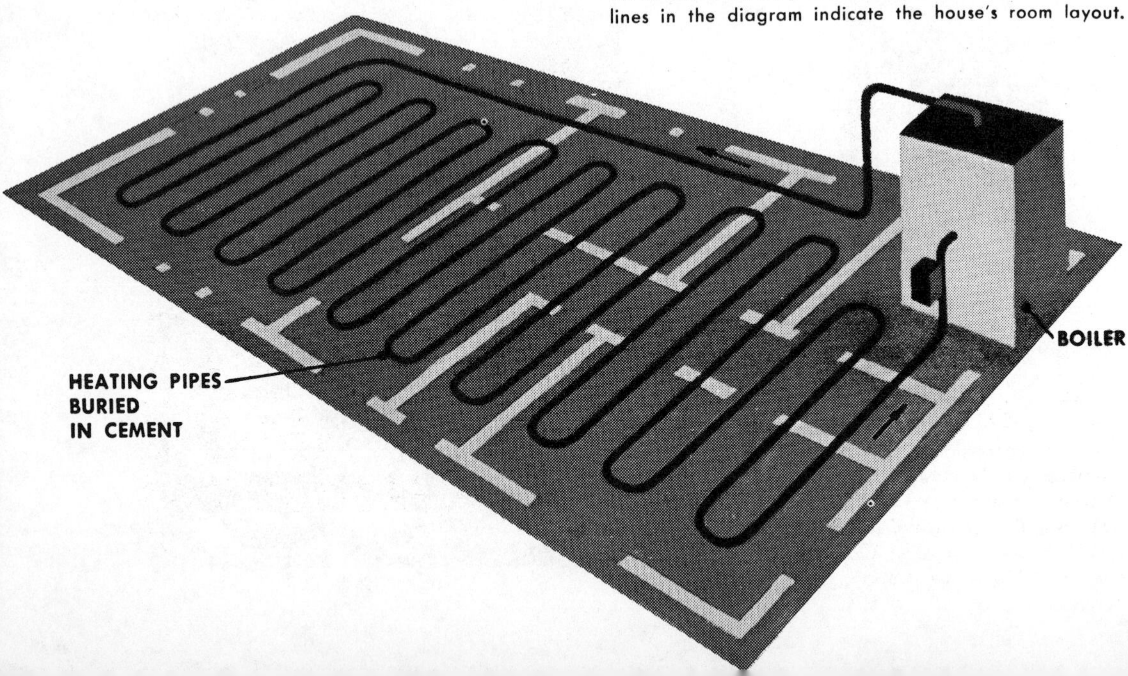

HEATING PIPES
BURIED
IN CEMENT

BOILER

come warm. When the floor, wall or ceiling has been completely heated, however, the heat dissipates slowly and the room temperature changes very little for hours after the heat has been turned off.

Heating by means of a heat pump

It is now possible, by means of the heat pump, to heat homes with warmth derived from the earth, or well water or air. For this kind of heating, no fuel is required. In summer the heating equipment can be reversed to cool the house.

The heat pump can take heat from the ground even when it is frozen over in the winter. A loop of one-inch pipe curves down about two hundred feet below the surface of the earth and back up again. Through this pipe circulates a liquid refrigerant which carries the heat from the earth into the house.

The heat pump operates in exactly the same way a refrigerator does. It takes heat from the ground, from well water or from outside air, just as the refrigerator removes heat from warm food placed inside it. As the liquid refrigerant travels down the pipe of the heat pump, it becomes increasingly hotter as it picks up more and more of the earth's warmth. On the trip back up to the surface none of this heat is lost because the upper part of the pipe is insulated. As the refrigerant enters the heat-pump unit in the house, the liquid is put under pressure. This forces its temperature even higher. Then, as the hot liquid passes through other coils of pipe, the air passing over these coils is warmed and in turn warms the house.

In summer the heat-pump system can, by the turn of a switch, be reversed to provide comfortable cooling. The heat from the air in the house is carried by the liquid in the pipes into the earth, which is then cooler than the air. The liquid in the pipes brings coolness from the earth back into the house. The only cost of operation is for the electricity to run the compressor and pump or blower motors.

The diagrams on this page show how a heat pump can be used to heat or to cool.

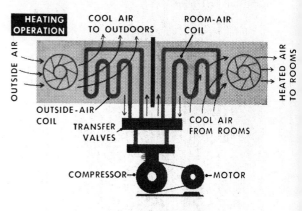

The heat pump shown in these two drawings can be used to heat or cool the rooms of a house. The heating operation is shown in the upper drawing. Liquid refrigerant goes through an expansion (transfer) valve into the outside-air coil as a cold, low-pressure gas. It extracts heat from outside air drawn over the coil and flows through the compressor. As a hot, high-pressure gas, it then enters the room-air coil. Here it gives up its heat to the air drawn over the coil from the space to be heated. The heated air passes into the rooms; the refrigerant condenses in the room-air coil from a gas to a liquid. It then passes through the expansion valve.

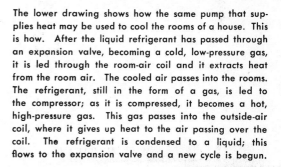

The lower drawing shows how the same pump that supplies heat may be used to cool the rooms of a house. This is how. After the liquid refrigerant has passed through an expansion valve, becoming a cold, low-pressure gas, it is led through the room-air coil and it extracts heat from the room air. The cooled air passes into the rooms. The refrigerant, still in the form of a gas, is led to the compressor; as it is compressed, it becomes a hot, high-pressure gas. This gas passes into the outside-air coil, where it gives up heat to the air passing over the coil. The refrigerant is condensed to a liquid; this flows to the expansion valve and a new cycle is begun.

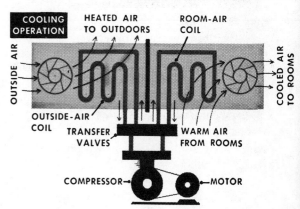

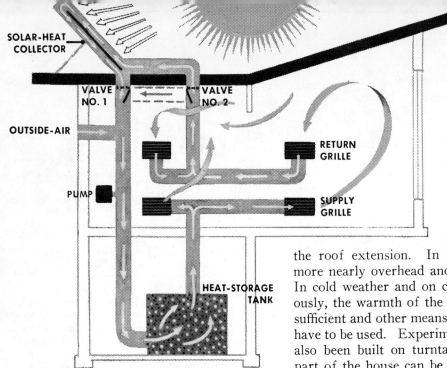

SOLAR-HEAT COLLECTOR

VALVE NO. 1   VALVE NO. 2

OUTSIDE-AIR

RETURN GRILLE

PUMP

SUPPLY GRILLE

HEAT-STORAGE TANK

In this solar-heating system, the sun's rays heat the air within a collector, set on the roof. This air is kept circulating by means of a pump. It is led to a heat-storage tank containing pebbles, which absorb heat. The air then goes to the supply grilles, heats the rooms and makes its way to the return grilles. As long as the sun is shining, Valves 1 and 2 are in the open position (indicated by solid black lines). When there is no sunlight, the two valves are closed (dotted lines). The air then returns from the rooms to the heat-storage tank by way of the duct indicated in the diagram by dotted lines.

Solar heating

The radiant heat of the sun has always warmed our houses to a great extent. Even in the coldest winter a room with a southern exposure is naturally much warmer than one that faces north. In recent years, engineers and scientists have developed new and more scientific ways of utilizing the sun's heat. Any one of several methods may be employed.

By drawing up appropriate plans, architects can provide homes with the greatest amount of natural warmth in the winter and the greatest amount of coolness in the summer. To accomplish this, houses are built with an overhanging extension of the roof. This admits the greatest possible amount of sunlight in the winter and excludes as much as possible in the summer. The sun is farther south and lower in the sky in the winter and thus shines in under the roof extension. In the summer it is more nearly overhead and cannot shine in. In cold weather and on cloudy days, obviously, the warmth of the sun would not be sufficient and other means of heating would have to be used. Experimental houses have also been built on turntables, so that any part of the house can be turned at a given time toward the sun.

Of course the solar-heating methods we have just mentioned are effective only during the hours of sunshine. Attempts have been made to install full-time solar-heating systems, by collecting and storing the sun's heat. In one such system the sun's rays are concentrated on the black or dark-green metal surfaces of a water jacket, usually on the roof. The heated water from the jacket flows into a storage unit, in which a substance such as Glauber's salt, a form of sodium sulfate, is used to absorb the heat. The salts become liquid as the heated water flows through them. They retain the heat, giving it off when required. The salts become solid again after the hot water has been released. This water runs through pipes for heating purposes. Air may be used instead of water as a circulating medium. With the air system a pebble-filled heat reservoir is sometimes provided to absorb heat. At the present time, solar heating is expensive and for this reason is not so widely used as it may be in the future.

Thermostats — devices that regulate temperature

The devices called thermostats maintain an almost constant temperature in a room by either activating or shutting off the heat-producing mechanism, depending upon the temperature. Practically all thermostats are based on the fact that when a substance is heated, it expands.

One of the most commonly used thermostats is the bimetallic type. Two metals are welded together to form a bimetallic ("two-metal") element. (See the diagram.) This element is joined to a steel blade, whose top holds an electric contact point. When this touches another contact point, an electric circuit is closed and the heating unit goes into operation. The device is set to the desired temperature; the room is heated to this temperature. As the temperature rises, the bimetallic element becomes hotter. One of the metals expands more than the other; as a result, the blade moves and the contact points no longer touch. This shuts off the furnace until the bimetallic element cools. The blade then returns to its former position, and the circuit is closed again.

The Bourdon-element type of thermostat is based on the fact that when a volatile liquid is heated, it changes into an expanding gas. The Bourdon element is a metal bellows, containing a volatile liquid. A compression spring at the top of the bellows exerts pressure on the liquid so that it does not change into a gas until the room is heated to the desired temperature. The heating unit supplies heat as long as the two contact points shown in the diagram touch. When the desired temperature is reached, the liquid is transformed into a gas and the bellows expands. As a result, the contact points move away from each other; the circuit is opened and the heating apparatus is shut off. The room becomes colder; the gas turns into a liquid again. The bellows contracts, the contact points touch again and the heating apparatus goes into operation.

Two types of thermostats, based on the fact that a substance expands when it is heated. Left: the bimetallic type. In this two metals are welded together to form a bimetallic ("two-metal") element, joined to a steel blade as shown. The top of the blade contains an electric contact point. When this touches another contact point, an electric circuit is closed and the heating unit is operated. The device is set to the desired temperature and the room is heated to this temperature. As the bimetallic element becomes hotter, one of the metals expands more than the other. Hence the blade moves (to the left in the diagram); the contact points no longer touch. This shuts off the furnace until the bimetallic element cools and the blade returns to its former position. Right: Bourdon-element thermostat. The Bour-

don element is a metal bellows; it contains a volatile liquid, which turns to a gas when the liquid is heated. A compression spring at the top of the bellows exerts pressure on the liquid so that it does not change to a gas until it is heated to the desired temperature. The heating unit supplies heat as long as the electric contact points shown in the diagram touch, thus causing the circuit to remain closed. When the desired temperature is reached, the liquid is transformed into a gas and the bellows expands. This causes the contact points to move away from each other, opening the circuit and also shutting off the heating apparatus. As the room grows colder, the gas turns into a liquid again. The bellows contracts, pushed down by the spring. The contact points touch again, and the heating apparatus goes into action.

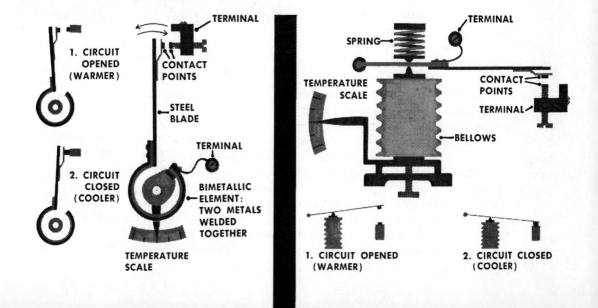

Ventilation

In warm-air, hot-water, steam and panel heating, leakage usually provides adequate ventilation through walls, window casings, doors and cracks. Forced warm-air systems are so constructed that ventilation with fresh air can be accurately controlled. When heating depends upon fuel combustion within a room, definitely planned ventilation is absolutely necessary.

Ventilation serves to remove excessive heat from closed spaces, as well as to replenish the oxygen supply. Human comfort and efficiency are greatly impaired by too high a room temperature and by the stuffiness and closeness that result from an insufficient supply of oxygen.

Ventilation also removes odors, smoke and contaminated air. Ordinarily, 15 to 20 cubic feet of fresh air per minute for each person is enough to accomplish this in the home. Schools, theaters, auditoriums and factories may require more fresh air, depending on the particular conditions and the number of persons occupying the enclosed space. Only in rare instances will 30 cubic feet of fresh air per minute per person be insufficient.

Natural
ventilation

Natural ventilation, as we have seen, is accomplished by leakage and by the inflow of fresh air through open windows and doors. To insure reasonable ventilation by natural means, most building codes require that living quarters have a window area equal to one eighth of the total floor area and that it must be possible to open at least half this window space.

Office buildings and factories take advantage of natural drafts of rising warm air. Roof openings allow warm air to escape; cooler air comes in at floor levels or through windows or specially constructed openings located to take advantage of the prevailing winds.

Shields or deflectors are sometimes placed across window openings in the winter. The cold air enters a small opening at the bottom of the window and is deflected upward into an upflow of air developed by some form of heating device under the window. The cold air becomes mixed with warm air before it strikes the occupants of the room.

Mechanical
ventilation

Mechanical ventilation includes any device or means of introducing a positively controlled flow of fresh air into the ventilating (heating) system. A forced warm-air heating system can supply ventilation; air inlets bringing outdoor air into such a system can be used. The air can be passed through the system without heating, to provide summer ventilation; in winter it can be warmed before passing to the rooms.

In large office buildings, theaters and other places where numbers of people gather, it is usual to require mechanical ventilation to insure that thirty cubic feet of fresh air per minute for each person is provided.

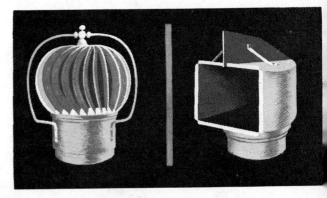

Two types of roof ventilation units. At the left is shown a wind driven rotary fan. It brings about a draft in a duct, and the stale air is drawn out at the top of the duct. Right: a vaned unit. It turns in the wind so that the air is exhausted in line with the wind flow.

The simpler forms of mechanical ventilation are attempts to aid natural ventilation. A wind-driven rotary fan brings about a draft in a duct and the stale air is exhausted, or drawn out, at the roof top. In another type of roof ventilation, a vaned unit turns so that the air is exhausted in line with the outside wind flow.

Positive ventilation may be obtained by installing fans of one type or another. They may be mounted in an opening in the wall and blow into a room, or they may remove air from the room by suction. The out-draft, or suction-type, fan is a common device for removing warm air from overheated space. It may be installed in a room vent, a wall ventilator or a duct system. Air is removed at a constant rate; fresh air enters the room from open windows, ventilators, doors or louvers or in other ways. Such fans are used commonly in homes to ventilate attics or even the entire house. Cool replacement air from the outside is quickly drawn into the house. If the fan is powerful enough the inside temperature will be only a little higher than that of the outside air.

Blower fans may be installed in windows or other kinds of openings. Outside air is picked up on the suction side of the fan and blown into the room. Deflectors are necessary if the fan air velocity is high. Blower fans are used in large industrial buildings when high volumes of air are required or when it is desirable to develop a slight positive pressure inside the building. Blowers also serve to direct a high-velocity air stream over a hot area, in order to disperse the heat rapidly.

Fans used in ventilating systems are of two basic types. The centrifugal fan is essentially an enclosed fan with blades moving across an opening. As the fan revolves, the air that comes through the opening is forced away from the center under high pressure. The air is discharged through an opening at right angles to the inlet opening. Such fans are used for high-pressure air flow in closed ventilation systems. In the axial fan the blades are mounted within a housing in such a way that the shaft is in the line of air flow. The blades take air from the inlet side and push it on to the outlet side. The propeller fan is the type mainly used in our homes. It consists of a number of blades mounted on a central hub; it is generally within a wire guard instead of a housing. It transfers air rapidly from one side of the blades to the other, either within a room or from the outside of a house wall to the inside.

In some industrial processes and in laboratories it is necessary to remove contaminated air from the work space before it makes workers ill or before a highly odorous material can pollute the atmosphere of a room. Local exhaust ventilation is required in such a case. Enclosures called hoods are built around the operation area and a mechanical exhaust system is installed. In bacteriological laboratories, for example, the entire room may be placed under negative pressure by an exhaust system. Then air can flow in one direction only, into the room and out of the exhaust duct.

In a typical local-exhaust ventilation system, there is a hood, an air duct connected to a fan, a blower and an exhaust duct. The hood is designed so that all of the harmful air is trapped by a current of air and is made to flow into the hood.

Humidity control

We must consider the effects of humidity — the moisture in the air — in both heating and ventilation, because the amount of this moisture greatly affects our comfort. We may feel almost comfortable even at a high temperature, when the air is fairly dry. When the air is saturated with moisture, most people feel uncomfortably warm. Air movement helps reduce the discomfort, but humidity control is more effective.

To understand why this type of control is so desirable, we must know something about the relation between temperature and humidity. Hot air can hold more moisture than cold air; when it can hold no more, we say it is saturated, or that the humidity is 100 per cent. This does not mean, however, that only hot air is humid. Cold air can also be full of moisture.

Why do we feel such discomfort when there is too much moisture, particularly when the temperature is high? The reason is that excess heat from the body must be given off in the form of moisture from the skin. If the air is already full of moisture, it cannot absorb any more. Therefore there is no way by which the moisture on our bodies can evaporate into the air around us. We therefore remain damp.

In the winter when rooms are heated to a high temperature, with windows closed, the humidity is apt to be too low. This condition also may cause considerable distress; the membranes of the nose and throat are likely to be uncomfortably dry.

If air can have some part of its normal moisture content removed as it enters a closed space, the relative humidity is lowered and a sensation of coolness results. The process of removing the moisture is called dehumidification.

The process of adding moisture to the air in living quarters or in offices is called humidification. Humidification sprays may be placed on the suction side of a forced-air system so that moister air will be conveyed to all warm-air outlets. In some old hot-water and steam-radiator systems, pans of water are hung on the heating units to add moisture to the air. This means of humidification is not very effective. In many homes the water in the pans is allowed to dry up and is not replaced.

The pan of water or the teakettle on the old wood or coal stove was a humidifier. The vapor jet from the spout added moisture to the air. Sometimes the moist air striking a cold windowpane would cool enough to condense on the pane. A rivulet of water would run down the glass when outside temperatures were very low and there were no storm windows.

Air-conditioning
systems at work

One purpose of air conditioning is to make enclosed spaces — rooms, auditoriums, stores, trains and even automobiles — more comfortable for human beings. Another purpose is to provide the most satisfactory type of indoor climate for various industrial processes.

The average person is likely to think of air conditioning as merely a cooling of the air in an enclosed space. Equally important, however, is the control of humidity. Air conditioning also regulates the movement and flow of air; it removes dust, bacteria and odors. In the broadest sense, air conditioning also includes the proper heating of enclosed spaces.

Air conditioning was first used commercially about 1906 in cotton mills. It served particularly to maintain the proper degree of humidity in the mills; it had been found that if the air was too dry the fibers would break. Two systems were developed — one by Stewart W. Cramer and the other by Willis H. Carrier. Both systems provided for humidification, humidity control and temperature control. It was Cramer who first used the term "air conditioning."

Air conditioning was used mainly in industry until about 1922, when the first motion-picture theater was air-conditioned. The process was soon applied in many other ways. Small air-conditioning units were first installed on railway coaches in 1930. At the present time the demand for individual air-conditioning units greatly surpasses the demand for industrial use. One has only to look at the outside of homes and apartment buildings to see how great a percentage of people today avail themselves of the advantages of cooled and properly humidified air.

In air-conditioning units used to cool rooms a forced-ventilation system blows

Air-conditioning unit used to cool a room. A refrigerant is compressed, while in the form of a gas, in the compressor and its temperature rises as a result. The gas is led to the outside-air coil; as it gives up its heat to the air from the outside, it condenses in the form of a liquid. It passes through an expansion valve and enters the room-air coil. The cool liquid refrigerant draws heat from the warm air from inside the room; the cooled air is then blown into the room by a fan. The refrigerant evaporates as it draws heat from the room air; it turns into a gas. The gas is led to the compressor and the cycle begins anew. The damper shown in the diagram is opened if it is desired to bring fresh air from the outside into the room.

warm room air across cooling coils, which form part of a mechanical refrigeration unit (see diagram). The warm air is cooled as it passes over the cold coils and it is then forced by the fan into the room. The sudden cooling causes air at the coil surface to become almost saturated with moisture at the cooler temperature and some moisture condenses out of the air and collects on the coil. The housewife sees this same sort of thing whenever she opens the refrigerator door on a hot day. The frost around the freezing unit is from water condensed from the atmosphere.

The cooler and now dryer air is delivered to the room and the temperature is reduced. If the outside air has a temperature of 90° F. and a relative humidity of 70 per cent — a probable condition in many eastern coastal states in the summer — the cooler may reduce the relative humidity to 60 per cent and the room air temperature to 85° F.

In desert areas of the western United States the air is hot and dry. Hot air can be pulled through moist layers of filtering material and the evaporation effect will lower the air temperature materially. If 100° air temperature is reduced to 90°, with 40 per cent relative humidity, the effective temperature (temperature as expressed in terms of comfort, not on a numerical scale) will be about 83° F.

Air-conditioning systems have been designed to cool large or small industrial buildings, theaters and office buildings and homes. Glass or fiber filters may be placed in the suction duct of an air conditioner to filter out dusts, pollens and even undesirable bacteria. If gases are to be removed, as is necessary in some industrial installations, it may be desirable to place adsorbent materials, such as activated charcoal, in filters. (An adsorbent material is one that holds to it, in a very thin film, molecules of gases or liquids.) Several units in combination can be made to produce air of the desired temperature and humidity — air that is practically free of all harmful gases, dust and bacteria. In the winter this same equipment can be used as a forced warm-air system by cutting off cooling units and passing fresh air over a hot heat-exchange unit.

See also Vol. 10, p. 277: "Heating and Ventilation."

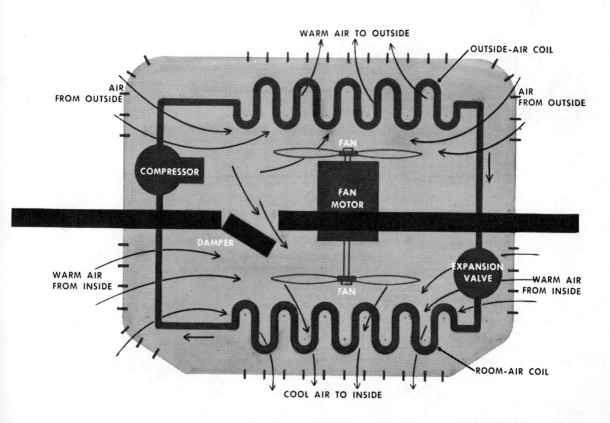

The male jumping spider (*Phidippus audax*) assumes this pose to threaten enemies or impress females.

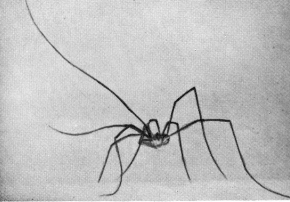

This is the familiar spider known as daddy longlegs. Note its long, wispy legs and its small body.

The scorpion brings its tail over its back when it is ready to thrust its sharp sting into a victim.

Unless otherwise indicated, all photos by Walker Van Riper, Denver Museum of Natural History

The female wolf spider (*Lycosa coloradensis*) is dragging her egg sac. She carries it about with her until young are hatched.

SPIDERS AND THEIR KIN

Fascinating Little Creatures of Field, Wood — and House

BY WILLIS J. GERTSCH

THE spider is commonly regarded as the very symbol of cold and malevolent cruelty. A fly or a mosquito hopelessly entangled in a web would certainly consider this reputation well deserved; but humans have little reason to think harshly of spiders. To be sure, some of them plague housewives by laying down their dragline silk on walls and ceilings; nor does anyone like tangled webs in basements or funnel webs that spoil the beauty of evergreens. It is true, also, that several species of spiders (very few and far between, fortunately) have a venom that is dangerous to man. On the other hand, spiders serve man (all unwittingly, of course) by destroying a vast number of bothersome insects — roaches, mosquitoes, flies and hosts of other unwelcome creatures. For certain peoples the spider is an article of food; it is cooked and eaten with great relish.

Spiders belong to the arthropods, or jointed-leg creatures — one of the most important and numerous groups of the animal kingdom. In addition to spiders, the arthropods include such familiar forms as insects, centipedes, millepedes, lobsters, crabs and shrimps. All have jointed legs and other appendages; all, too, have segmented bodies encased in stiff skeletons.

The spider is sometimes called an insect, but it is definitely not an insect. Insects have six legs; spiders have eight. Insects — and indeed most arthropods — have antennae, or feelers; spiders have none. Most insects have wings; there is no such thing as a winged spider.

The supreme accomplishment of spiders, perhaps, is the art of spinning silk made within their bodies. It is to this ac-

tivity that they and their kin owe the class name of arachnids (Arachnida). The story has it that Arachne, a mythical princess of ancient Lydia, in Asia Minor, was famed for her skill in spinning and weaving. She became so proud of her work that she rashly challenged Athena, Greek goddess of the handicrafts, to a test of skill. The goddess accepted the challenge, which proved to be disastrous to the Lydian princess. For Athena was enraged at the perfection of Arachne's handiwork and she tore it to pieces. In despair Arachne hanged herself; thereupon the goddess changed the rope into a cobweb and the maiden herself into a spider.

If we examine a spider at close range, we find, first of all, that its body is divided by a narrow waist, into two principal regions, the cephalothorax and the abdomen. "Cephalothorax" comes from the Greek words *cephalos:* "head," and *thorax:* "chest." As the name indicates, the cephalothorax is made up of the head and thorax (chest), which are fused together to form a single piece. The upper portion consists of a hardened and ordinarily rounded shield called the carapace, which bears the eyes at the front end. Most spiders have eight eyes; there are also six-eyed, four-eyed and two-eyed spiders. A few that live in caves have completely lost the eyes or retain only traces of them. The carapace shows considerable variations in some species; it may be ornamented with humps and projections.

Behind the cephalothorax is the abdomen, ordinarily a saclike structure joined to the cephalothorax, as we have seen, by a narrow waist. In nearly all spiders the

The garden spider guarding
its large and flimsy egg sac.

The wolf spider carrying its
tiny spiderlings on its back.

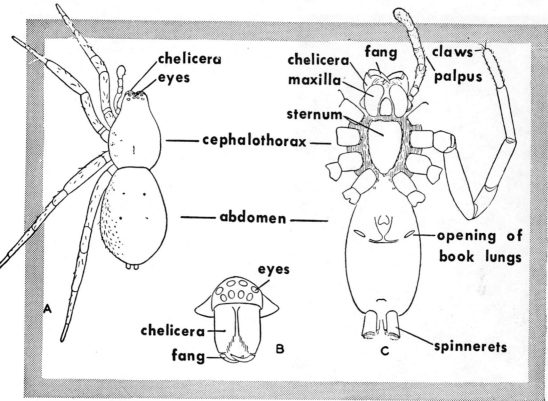

Labels in the diagram:
- chelicera
- eyes
- cephalothorax
- abdomen
- chelicera
- fang
- eyes
- B
- A
- fang
- chelicera
- maxilla
- sternum
- fang
- claws
- palpus
- opening of book lungs
- spinnerets
- C

From W. J. Gertsch, "American Spiders,"
D. Van Nostrand Co., Inc.

A generalized diagram of the body structure of the spider. In the left-hand drawing, the body is seen from above; in the
right-hand drawing, it is seen from below.
Note that the head and thorax are not separate but are fused together in one piece.

abdomen is in one piece and is rather soft.
The abdomen of some of the orb weavers,
or geometric spiders, is brightly colored,
hardened and armed with curious spines
and other outgrowths. Perhaps this armor
serves as a protective device against birds.
In some other spiders the abdomen is
drawn out into a long tail, giving the creature a wormlike appearance.

The underside of the abdomen bears
the openings to the breathing organs: the
tracheae, or air-conducting tubes, and the
book lungs, which are peculiar breathing
devices found only in arachnids. There
are usually two book lungs. Each is a sac
within the abdomen containing fifteen to
twenty shelves, suggesting the pages of a
book; the blood circulates through these
shelves. All spiders are air-breathing.
None of them are truly aquatic, though
certain species, living on the banks of
streams and lakes, run over the water and
dive into it.

Directly beneath the spider's cephalothorax, at the front end, are two jaws,
called chelicerae. Each has a stout fixed

segment and a sharp, movable fang, which
is the part thrust into the prey. Connected
with the jaws are a pair of poison glands
located in the fixed segment of the jaws
or in the head. These glands send their
venom coursing through a duct opening
near the end of the fang. The venom of
most spiders has only slight effect on warm-
blooded creatures; only in a few instances
can this venom cause severe bodily distress
to humans.

All spiders are predaceous, or preying,
animals; they eat insects almost exclusively,
subduing them with venom. With the aid
of their sharp jaws and the edges of their
maxillae — another pair of appendages lying immediately behind the jaws — they
cut and break the body of the prey. At
the same time they bathe it with digestive
liquids from glands located near the mouth

Fine filaments of silk are being emitted from spinnerets near the tail of this jumping spider and are being transported upward by an air current. Soon the spider will be flying, or "ballooning," in the air.

In this way the softer parts of the insect are predigested, and are then sucked into the spider's stomach by powerful muscles. The prey is rolled and chewed until only a little ball of indigestible matter remains, and this is finally cast aside. Several hours are often required to suck an ordinary fly completely dry.

The spider's eight legs are important, of course, as a means of getting from place to place. They are also useful to the spider because they are covered with extremely sensitive hairs and spines, which make it aware of its surroundings — fortunately for the spider, because it can neither hear nor smell. The spider has other sensory organs, called palpi. These are leglike appendages attached to the maxillae; like the legs, they are covered with hairs and spines.

The male spider is rather short-lived; it dies after a brief period of intense activity. It is generally much smaller than the female; it runs considerable risk in approaching its formidable mate, which may be hungry and interested only in satisfying its appetite. Males are sometimes killed and eaten by their females under these circumstances. In many cases males and females live together amicably.

Egg-laying activities of spiders, large and small

Each spider begins its life as an egg, which is usually one of many encased in a silken sac, or cocoon. The largest spiders lay a great number of eggs, sometimes as many as two or three thousand in a single mass. Smaller spiders produce fewer eggs; some lay only six to twelve and do not leave more than two or three in any one spot. In general the eggs in a sac produced in the fall hatch before winter. The spiderlings (young spiders) sometimes remain in the sac until spring, but in many cases they leave it and live under leaves during the winter. They are quite similar in appearance to the adult. Growth takes place through molting, a process of shedding the old skin at intervals as the creature grows. Most spiders molt from six to twelve times and cease molting after they become mature.

The spinnerets, or spinning organs, of spiders are fingerlike appendages, usually located near the rear of the abdomen on the lower surface. There are generally six spinnerets, and from them may be spun several different kinds of silk. The silk is produced as a liquid in various glands within the abdomen; this hardens to form the familiar silken line as soon as it issues from the tiny spigots on the ends of the spinnerets. Some spiders produce a viscous, or sticky, line that is used to entangle insects.

The copious use of silk by spiders sets them apart. Although some of the other arachnids and many insect larvae spin silk, they make only occasional and limited use of this product. But wherever a spider goes, it always leaves behind a dragline, or guiding thread, attached at intervals to the surface on which it crawls. This practice suggests the paying out of a rope when a man enters a deep cave or climbs a steep cliff. It accounts for the many silk threads, or cobwebs, we see on plants and in buildings and particularly on the walls and ceilings of our homes. A spider lines its retreat or burrow with silk; as we have seen, it encloses its eggs in a silken cocoon, often durably and beautifully made. Particularly interesting is the silken snare that certain spiders spin to capture their prey.

Spiders also use silk in the amazing activity called ballooning. On balmy days in the fall or spring, young spiders of many different species allow the breezes to pull out threads from their spinnerets; the tiny creatures are then raised aloft and wafted through the air. Tremendous distances can be covered in this way by spiderlings. The great English naturalist Charles Darwin recorded the arrival of ballooning spiders on the ship Beagle when it was sixty miles from land.

At one time spider silk was used widely for lines, or markers, in the lenses

of certain optical instruments. Silk that was to serve in this way was pulled from the spinnerets of the living spider and wound upon cards. Etched glass lines and platinum wire are now largely replacing spider silk in optical instruments.

The more than thirty thousand different kinds of spiders are divided into two major groups. One is made up of tarantulas and trap-door spiders; the other consists of the so-called true spiders.

The members of the former group are older and in many cases more primitive

than the true spiders; they are also much fewer in number, being restricted largely to the tropics and subtropics. Their jaws are parallel with the long axis of the body, are set side by side and move up and down. The spider lifts its body and jaws well up before it strikes. There is a swift downward thrust and the fangs pierce the prey, making two parallel punctures.

Some members of this group spin

Above is the orb web of *Cyclosa conica*, the tailed spider. Threads that extend from the surrounding framework meet at the center of the web. A sticky spiral is then laid down upon these threads.

The picture at the left shows us the web of the triangle spider (*Hyptiotes gertschi*, named after the author). The web of the spider roughly approximates the shape of a triangle, which accounts for its name.

sheet and funnel webs similar to those of the true grass spiders. Certain species are hunters; they have thick foot pads that enable them to climb steep surfaces with ease as they pursue their prey. The members of other species are skilled engineers, digging deep tunnels in the soil and covering the openings with hinged trap doors.

Giants among spiders are the hairy creatures called tarantulas by Americans and Canadians and bird-eating spiders by Europeans; they belong to the family of the Aviculariidae. The largest ones, which dwell in the steaming jungles of northern South America, attain a body length of three and one-half inches and a leg span of fully ten inches. By comparison, the species found in the southwestern part of the United States are pygmies, with bodies only about two inches long and legs that span only six or seven inches. Tarantulas

N. Y. Zool. Soc.

Left: a cross section of the burrow of a trap-door spider. Above: a California trap-door spider (*Bothriocyrtum californicum*) at the entrance to its burrow. Trap-door spiders are quite famous for their skill as small but efficient tunnel-builders.

Life photographer Andreas Feininger, (c) Time, Inc.

are longer-lived than most other invertebrates; some of them reach the age of twenty-five or even thirty years.

Most tarantulas live on the ground, making their homes in burrows that they line with heavy sheets of silk. They rarely go far from the mouths of these burrows but wait patiently for their prey to come close. Insects form a large part of their diet; they also subdue and devour frogs, lizards and small snakes. Some of the large tree-dwelling species occasionally feed on small birds; hence the name bird-eating spiders. The venom of tarantulas is deadly to cold-blooded animals but, ordinarily, harmless to man. The great size and hairy body of this spider make it appear to be more dangerous — that is, to man — than it really is.

Tarantulas have an odd protective device. They scrape the back of the abdomen with their hind legs when they are irritated

— an act that sends the fine hairs flying in a small cloud; some of them may lodge in the nose and eyes of a pursuer. This must cause a most unpleasant stinging sensation and must at least temporarily confuse the pursuer — perhaps some small animal that seeks to make a meal of the spider. Parasitic flies and wasps are the worst enemies of tarantulas. The great digger wasp (*Pepsis*) hunts them out and paralyzes them and then lays its eggs upon their bodies.

The trap-door spiders are nearly as well known as the tarantulas. They are stout and only moderately hairy creatures, famed for their skill in digging tunnels in the earth. Their digging instrument is a comb of stout spines on the margins of the jaws. After preparing their burrows, they waterproof the walls with saliva and earth, line them with silk and then cap the entrance with a hinged trap door. Some of the more active species construct what is known as a wafer door — a flimsy trap door of silk that lies loosely over the burrow. In some cases, the makers of wafer doors have a secret side burrow within the main chamber into which they can retreat when menaced by enemies; this burrow is closed with a second trap door.

The most expert artisans among the trap-door spiders build a thick door of alternating layers of soil and silk. It is beveled to fit into the burrow opening much as a cork fits into a bottle and, appropriately enough, is called a cork door. It is heavy enough to close of its own weight; it can be held firmly from within.

The true spiders far outnumber the tarantulas and trap-door spiders and are the common forms occurring in fields and woods in the temperate zones. The jaws of true spiders are set side by side, as in the case of the tarantulas; but the fangs of true spiders are turned inward and move toward each other as they pierce the body of the prey. Few of the true spiders live longer than one year. They may be conveniently grouped in two classes — the sedentary, or settled, web species and the more active wanderers, or vagabonds.

The sedentary webbuilders place great reliance upon silk throughout their lives. Their sense of sight is poor, but they make up for this deficiency by building large and efficient web-snares. The struggles of an insect in even the most remote recesses of the web are communicated to the spider, which has been patiently waiting for its meal to come to it.

Familiar to most of us are the tangled webs spun by the commonest of all house spiders, the species known as *Theridion tepidariorum,* which is as much at home in

the tropics as in the temperate regions. Males and females of this species live amicably together in the same web, thus disproving the popular belief that the female of the house spider always eats the male. A rather distant relative of the common house spider is the funnel-web spider which places its sheet web in the corner of

The full-grown female orb-web spider (*Argiope trifasciata*), as seen from above. The design of the web that this spider weaves is beautifully symmetrical and intricate.

a basement, rushing out to seize any insect that alights upon the web.

Quite closely allied to the common house spider is one that has become notorious throughout the world for its venom. This is the black widow, or shoe-button, spider, which spins a small, tangled net in some dark crevice and hides away during the day. The glossy black abdomen of the mature female does indeed resemble an old-fashioned shoe button; the rather long legs are only slightly less black. Red spots and dashes adorn the upper surface of the abdomen, especially in the males and in the immature stages; but mature females usually lose all bright upper markings. On the underside is a blood-red marking resembling an hourglass; this is visible in living specimens because these spiders al-

Lee Passmore

This wasp is inserting its paralyzing sting into a tarantula. The tarantula, a veritable giant among the spiders, reckons the wasp that deposits her eggs upon its body as one of its most formidable enemies.

ways hang back downward in the web. The female sometimes destroys the male, whence the name "black widow"; but she is quite as likely to live on friendly terms with her mate.

The venom of the black widow and of her close relatives throughout the world is an extremely potent one, fatal to small mammals and frequently serious in the case of man. Although few humans succumb to the bite, the symptoms are often most alarming and are accompanied by excruciating pain. Fortunately for man the black widow spider is a rather timid and retiring creature; furthermore, her striking markings make her easy to recognize.

The orb weavers, or
geometric spiders

The orb weavers, or geometric spiders, form a numerous group. They construct the familiar type of web known as the orb web — a roughly rectangular framework of silk from which extend threads that meet in the center, like the radii of a circle. A sticky spiral is laid down upon these radial threads. The web is usually placed at an angle; the spider hangs away from the sticky spiral lines and touches the others only with the claws of its feet.

The shimmering lightness and intricate symmetrical design of the orb web make it a thing of wonder and beauty. To the American Indians the orb web is a symbol of the heavens. The four corners of the framework point to the four cardinal points of the compass; the silky spiral represents, so it is firmly believed, the mystery and the power of the Great Spirit.

Vagabond spiders
pursue their prey

The vagabond spiders place much less reliance on silk than do their sedentary relatives; they use the substance chiefly to cover their eggs and line their retreats. They have fairly good eyesight and actively pursue their prey. The wolf spiders are swift hunters, living on the ground. They drag their egg sacs behind them; these look like white balls and are attached to the spinnerets. When the young hatch, they

climb upon the back of the mother and stay there until they are able to provide for themselves.

The name "tarantula" is given by Europeans to the largest of all wolf spiders, *Lycosa tarentula*. Many legends are associated with the name of this notorious creature, named after the city of Taranto, in Italy. According to one of these legends, accepted as gospel truth in the Middle Ages, the bite of the Italian tarantula brought on a nervous ailment called tarantism. The victims of this malady were inclined to be melancholy; they were often seized with an irresistible desire to dance. A sure cure for tarantism, it was said, was to whirl about in the rapid measures of the dance called the tarantella. Modern science scoffs at all this, for we know that the venom of the Italian tarantula, for all its ill repute, has little effect on man.

The lively fisher
spider, or pisaurid

Vagabond spiders also include the fisher spiders, or pisaurids. Some of them run over the surface of ponds and streams and dive and stay under water for long periods. They are known to capture small fishes and frogs, which they drag to the edge of the pond or stream and suck dry. The females carry large egg sacs around in their jaws. Later, at the tip of a plant, they spin a substantial nursery web in which the young hatch. The mother stands guard over the young until they are old enough to look out for themselves.

The water spider (*Argyroneta aquatica*) of Europe is able to live in the fresh water of streams for weeks, enclosed in a little diving bell of silk. This spider carries air bubbles beneath the surface to its retreat and keeps a supply of air imprisoned in the silken chamber. Even the eggs are laid and the family hatched out under water in the security of the nest.

Jumping spiders
have excellent eyesight

The jumping spiders are the most highly developed of all the vagabonds. Brightly colored and ornamented with tufts of hair, hanging scales and curious spines, these strongly built creatures run about actively on the ground and on vegetation. They have excellent eyesight. While courting, the little males dance and pose before the females, apparently to show off their bright colors.

Other arachnids, closely related to spiders, are the scorpions, harvestmen, or daddy longlegs, and mites. All of them differ quite markedly from their allies, the spiders, in appearance.

The scorpion has formidable weapons fore and aft. In front it is armed with a pair of powerful pincers; behind, the abdomen narrows to form a long tail, ending with a curved sting. When the scorpion is ready for the kill, it seizes its prey — an insect or a spider — in its pincers and then, bringing its tail over its back, it thrusts its sting in the victim and injects the latter with a dose of poison. The scorpion will fearlessly attack any animal that molests it, no matter what its size.

The sting of several Mexican scorpions (the most notable being *el alacran de Durango*) and of two Arizona species is

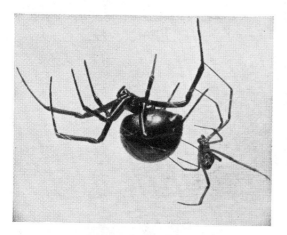

The tiny male black widow spider is shown courting the female. This picture exhibits the characteristic profile of the female.

Right: the female black widow spider is devouring her unfortunate mate. This type of cannibalism, however, is not always the rule.

Swarms of tiny black widow spiderlings are emerging from their egg sac.

dangerous to man and causes several deaths each year, generally among children. In the case of most species, however, the scorpion's sting is painful but not fatal. There is a legend that scorpions sometimes commit suicide by stinging themselves, but the fact of the matter is that they are not affected by their own venom.

The female scorpion often devours the male after mating. It brings forth its young alive and carries them on its back until they are ready to get along by themselves. Scorpions generally do their hunting at night. When dawn comes, they hide in some convenient place of refuge — under a stone or a rotting log or in a shoe of some unfortunate person.

The daddy longlegs is an odd creature, with long, wispy legs and a small egg-shaped body, fused into a single piece. It is a wandering scavenger; it has no burrows or nest but roves about the fields in search of its food, which consists of small insects, living and dead. Its chief protection against its natural enemies is the nauseating odor of its stink glands.

The mites are the smallest arachnids

The mites are the smallest of the arachnids. Their bodies are egg-shaped or round; the head, thorax and abdomen form a single unit. Many mites are reddish in color and live in soil or debris, or move freely over plants. Some of the most gaily colored species have taken to living in water and swim with the aid of long hairs on their legs. The tiniest mites are wormlike and suck plant juices, causing galls, spots and blemishes on some of our favored garden plants and trees. Other pygmies live in the air tubes of the honey bee and in the hair cavities of mammals, including man. The free-living forms feed on tiny animals or eat decaying vegetable or animal matter. About half the mites are parasitic and live on the bodies of invertebrates or vertebrates during all or part of their lives.

Mites hatch from eggs as six-legged larvae. After a certain period of feeding, the larva changes into a nymph, an eight-legged form that is not yet mature. It undergoes one or more nymphal stages and then becomes an adult.

Among the most troublesome of the mites are the larvae of the harvest mites. These larvae, more commonly known as red bugs, or chiggers, abound in grassland areas. They attach themselves to the skin of man, causing violent itching and irritation; their victims also include rats, rabbits, birds and other animals. Certain species transmit the bacterialike organisms that cause scrub typhus, often fatal to man.

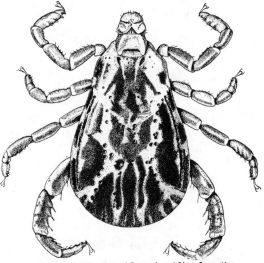

U.S.D.A.—Bur. of Entomol. and Plant Quarantine

The male American dog tick (*Dermacentor variabilis*). Dog ticks, which are the largest of the mites, are arachnids (Arachnida). They feed voraciously on the blood of canines.

Ticks are the largest of all the mites; when a female is swollen with food, it is sometimes almost an inch in length. The skin of a tick is leathery; its upper surface is provided with a tough plate, called the scutum. The beaklike mouth parts are forced into the skin of the tick's hosts. After a femal tick has become swollen with food, she falls to the ground and lays her eggs, which usually number several thousands. The six-legged ticks that emerge from the eggs climb plants; as a cow or other host brushes by, the ticks attach themselves to it.

Some ticks use the same host throughout their lives; others require two or three different kinds of hosts in order to complete their life cycle. Many ticks attack man and are a source of great annoyance because of their irritating bites. Among tick-borne diseases are Texas fever, which primarily affects cattle, and Rocky Mountain spotted fever, which is a very serious disease of man.

The many-legged arthropods known as millepedes (or millipedes) and centipedes are rather distant relatives of the spiders. They belong to the class of the myriapods ("countless legs"), a name referring to the many pairs of jointed legs. The head is not fused with the thorax (as it is in the case of the spider); it bears antennae and a pair of eyes. Below the head are jaws and accessory mouth parts similar to those found in insects.

The millepedes are sluggish animals

The millepedes ("thousand legs") are very sluggish animals that live under stones, debris and bark and in deep soil and humus — in fact, wherever it is sufficiently moist and dark. They feed for the most part on decaying vegetable matter. A few of them are pests in gardens and greenhouses, where they attack the bulbs and roots of plants. Each of the ringlike segments of the body bears two pairs of walking legs; for this reason the millepedes are also called diplopods, or "double-legs."

When millepedes hatch from eggs, they have three or four pairs of legs. They gradually add additional pairs as they molt; at maturity some of them have as few as nine pairs, while others have more than a hundred. Of course even this re-

spectable total is a far cry from the "thousand legs" indicated by their name. Some species of millepedes are very pretty creatures, with chestnut bodies margined in yellow or pink. The large, brown form found in the woods in the United States often exceeds two inches in length. It gives off a yellow secretion whenever it is menaced.

The centipedes ("hundred legs") are the wolves of the myriapod clan; they actively hunt small animals that live on or in the soil. They subdue their prey by poison from the first pair of legs, called the poison claws. Unlike the millepedes, each body segment of the centipedes has only a single pair of legs. Freshly hatched centipedes have six or seven pairs of legs, or even more. Adults commonly have fifteen pairs; certain species that dwell deep within the soil have nearly two hundred pairs, thus exceeding the quota of the millepedes. Some of the centipedes of the tropics are over a foot long and are able to inflict a very severe bite. Smaller species, found in temperate regions, bite viciously, but their venom causes only a disagreeable irritation.

The house centipede (*Scutigera*), which crawls on the walls of damp cellars, differs markedly in appearance from most of its relatives. It has fifteen pairs of very long legs, which drop off when they are touched. Most people find this centipede a repulsive creature; yet it should be hailed as an ally, for it feeds on insect pests.

See also Vol. 10, p. 276: "Spiders."

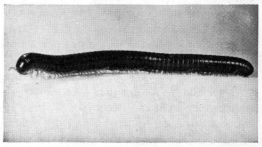

Above: a sluggish Ecuadorian millepede. It is native to the warm equatorial climates.

Left: a centipede. This many-legged hunter lives on tiny animals found in or on the soil.

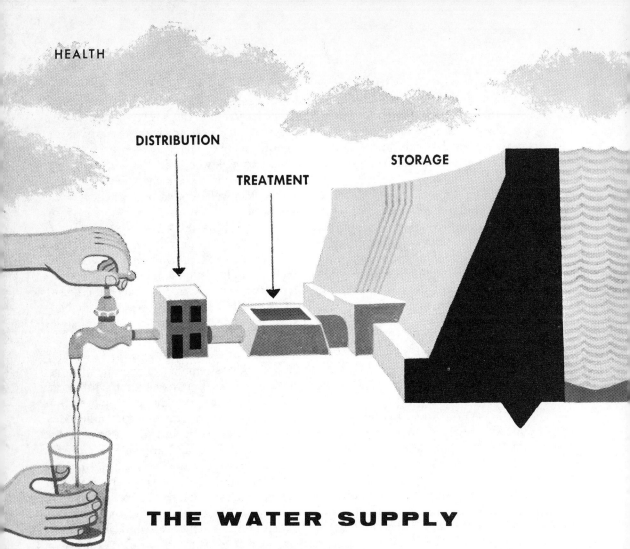

DISTRIBUTION

TREATMENT

STORAGE

THE WATER SUPPLY

How Water Is Collected, Transmitted, Treated and Distributed

BY WILLIAM S. FOSTER

WHAT is water? To the scientist it is the compound H_2O, combining two atoms of hydrogen with one of oxygen. It can take the form of a solid, liquid or gas. At atmospheric pressure (14.7 pounds per square inch), it solidifies when cooled to 32° F.; it boils at 212°. When pure, it is neither acid nor alkali. Water dissolves many substances; it is itself decomposed into its two constituents, hydrogen and oxygen, at 4,500° F. However, water is decomposed at ordinary temperatures when an electric current is passed through it.

The sanitary engineer sees water from a different viewpoint. He is interested particularly in the liquid form of water. The liquid must be transported from its source to homes, offices, factories and other places where it is to be used. It must be kept free from harmful bacteria. It should be colorless, relatively odorless, tasteless and moderately soft. Water-works men think of ice — water in its solid form — as a nuisance, causing trouble to river intakes, pipelines and hydrants. They consider water vapor only as water that has been lost from their reservoirs.

From the viewpoint of the public, water is an absolutely essential commodity. It makes up roughly 70 per cent of the total weight of our bodies. It must be replenished constantly as it evaporates from

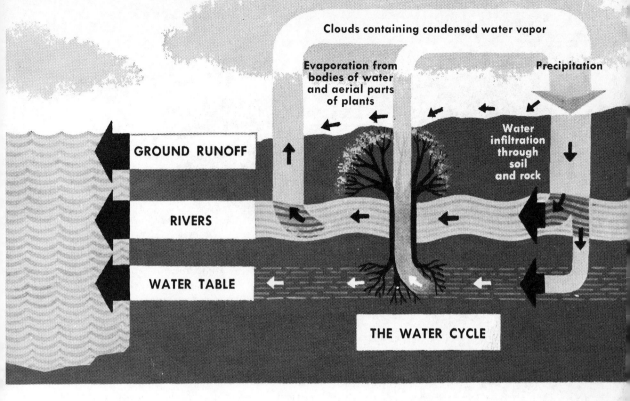

Clouds containing condensed water vapor

Evaporation from bodies of water and aerial parts of plants

Precipitation

Water infiltration through soil and rock

GROUND RUNOFF

RIVERS

WATER TABLE

THE WATER CYCLE

the lungs and skin and passes out of the body in the form of wastes. If we were denied water for a few days, we would die of dehydration. Water is also essential for our industries, which use vast quantities. For example, from 70 to 80 tons of this liquid are used in the manufacture of a ton of ingot steel. It requires 175 more tons of water to turn this ton of ingot steel into fabricated products.

Water dominates our history. The ancient Egyptians constructed an extensive system of reservoirs, storing up the waters of the Nile. There are many references to water supply in the Bible. For example, the 26th chapter of Genesis tells how Isaac's herdsmen fought with the inhabitants of the valley of Gerar for the possession of wells in the valley. Much later King Hezekiah "made a pool and conduit and brought water into the city of Jerusalem" (II Kings: 20, 20). Ancient Rome probably would never have attained its greatness without the assistance of its waterworks engineers. The waters of the Tiber had become too polluted to serve for drinking purposes. The engineers constructed nearly four hundred miles of aqueducts, which brought water into the city from various outside sources. In Arizona and New Mexico, archaeologists still explore irrigation projects built by ancient Indian engineers.

The treatment of water goes back to antiquity. Aluminum sulfate, a useful chemical coagulating agent, was employed by the ancient Chinese and Egyptians. A medical book written in Sanskrit, probably about 2000 B.C., pointed out that "it is good to keep water in copper vessels, to expose it to sunlight and to filter it through charcoal."

However, the distribution and treatment of water as we know it today is a modern development. Until comparatively recent times, only the extremely wealthy could afford to have water distributed to their houses. Most people were forced to carry it in containers from wells, or springs or central distribution points. House-to-house distribution became possible only through the development of steam-driven pumping machinery and cast-iron pipe strong enough to withstand high internal pressures. Modern water treatment began with the development of the slow sand filter by James Simpson in England in 1829.

Intake Tower in Reservoir

The turn of the century saw the introduction of the rapid sand filter, which made the slow sand filter almost obsolete. We shall discuss both types of filters later on in this article.

The sources of
our water supply

Water passes through a well-defined hydrological cycle, or water cycle. It falls to the earth's surface in the form of rain or some other form of precipitation. Some of it soaks into the ground, is absorbed by plant life and is returned to the atmosphere by transpiration from the aerial parts of plants. Some of the precipitation seeps through permeable and porous rocks and becomes part of the ground-water supply. (See the article Water in the Ground, in Volume 8.) Ground water makes its way to rivers, or comes to the surface in springs; sometimes it is brought to the surface by wells.

A good deal of the water that is precipitated flows along the surface of the ground in streams, large and small, or is collected in ponds and lakes. Much of this water is returned to the ocean. The sun draws surface water to the clouds by evaporation; from the clouds it is precipitated to the earth, and another cycle begins.

In the hydrological cycle, therefore, water passes from the atmosphere to the earth and then back again to the atmosphere. To obtain water for our water-supply systems we must draw it from rivers or lakes, or from wells, which tap the ground water beneath the surface.

When water is drawn from a river or other stream, the engineer must decide whether the river, when its level is lowest, will meet the maximum demands of the community. The heat of summer will reduce the stream by evaporation. At the same time it will increase the use of water for lawn sprinkling, air conditioning and other purposes. Suppose the engineer determines that the community will use more water than the river can supply during low periods. He will arrange to store a portion of the water when the river is high by building a dam in the stream. The waters that collect back of this dam will form an impounding (water-collecting) reservoir.

If the dam has been correctly designed, the water level in the impounding reservoir will be low before the spring freshets arise. The reservoir, therefore, will be able to catch and store the excess water that the freshets bring. As the summer goes on, the community will draw on this reservoir to compensate for the lack of adequate flow in the river.

Many problems arise from the use of impounding reservoirs. For example, in most parts of the United States the law does not permit a city to catch and store all the water of a stream. The court recognizes the rights of those below the reservoir to a part of the water. Generally, a community has to enter into an agreement with other communities concerning the amount of water that can be taken from a river and collected in an impounding dam.

When he builds a reservoir, the engineer must consider many important factors. The dam must have cut-off walls extending downward so that no seepage will occur under the dam. The slopes of earth dams must be moderate enough so that the earth will remain in place even when saturated. Earth dams must be provided with a core of impervious material, such as clay or concrete, so that water will not seep through. If the engineer builds a concrete dam, he must allow for expansion and contraction. The dam must be heavy enough so that it will not be overturned by the pressure of water against its face. In earth and concrete dams alike, there must be a spillway large enough to care for the greatest storm flow.

Water flows from the reservoir to the supply system through intake works. In reservoirs using earth dams, an intake tower is erected away from the shore. This tower is equipped with a series of ports at various levels; water flows through these ports into the intake-supply system. If the water is impounded by a masonry dam, the intake structure can be built in the dam itself.

Coarse screens are generally placed in the intakes to keep large floating objects, including ice, from entering the conduits. Inside the coarse screens, there are finer ones that intercept leaves, aquatic vegetation, fish and larvae. These screens must be cleaned frequently. In large systems, mechanical cleaning devices are often used.

Many of our streams carry silt washed from the soil. This silt often causes trouble to dams and reservoirs. In 1895, a reservoir was built across the Colorado River at Austin, Texas, with a capacity of 17,000,000,-000 gallons of water. Seven years later its capacity had been reduced to 8,600,000,000 gallons because of silt.

There are several ways of meeting this problem. Dredging is one; the use of silting basins is another. Such basins receive the water before it goes to the reservoir and trap the silt it contains. Of course the basins must be dredged from time to time to remove the silt. A third method is the use of low-level sluice gates, through which silt flushes out of the reservoir during times of flood. Sluice gates of this kind are not particularly useful on the larger types of reservoirs. A fourth method is to draw in clearer water from offshore areas by means of long intakes; this is no longer practiced very much at present.

The problem of evaporation

Evaporation causes open reservoirs to lose a great deal of water, particularly in the hot, dry Southwest, where the need for water is the greatest. For example, Lake Sahuaro, in Arizona, covering some 1,500 acres, will lose as much as five feet of water to evaporation during the year. Lake Hefner, covering 2,500 acres, and supplying Oklahoma City, Oklahoma, with water, will lose nearly two feet of water during the hot months of June, July and August. When we learn that there are roughly a million gallons of water in three acre-feet (three acres one foot thick or one acre three feet thick), we realize the tremendous volume of water that is involved here.

Progress has been made in solving the problem of loss of water from reservoirs by evaporation. To cut down such water loss, investigators have developed a thin chemical film, consisting of a mixture of hexadeconal and octadeconal. The film, only one molecule thick, floats on the surface of the water and makes it harder for water molecules to escape into the air. If the film is dispersed by wind, it forms again. Tests at Lake Sahuaro by the United States Department of the Interior have indicated a reduction of almost 15 per cent in evaporation. Even better results have been attained in tests conducted by Oklahoma City officials at Lake Hefner.

By inhibiting evaporation, the film causes the temperature of the water to rise somewhat and so stores the energy radiated into the water by the sun. Studies show that the film does not affect the physical and chemical qualities of the water nor harm the wildlife it contains.

A considerable part of the water supply is derived from ground water, which is contained in the openings of the soil and rock under the surface of the earth. To make this ground water available for water-supply systems, wells must be drilled, driven or even dug.

If we need only a relatively shallow well in soft material, we can drill it by hand or by power-driven augers. Most wells, however, are dug by cable-, or drop-tool, drilling machines. These consist of a tower, a motor and a large walking beam (a lever that swings up and down about a pivot). A rope or cable carrying the drill passes from one end of the walking beam over a pulley at the top of the tower and then down into the well. The motor then rocks the beam about the pivot, lifting and dropping the heavy drill. The operator does not allow the drill to drop freely to the bottom of the well. Instead, he lets the rope catch the drill near the bottom of the excavation. As the drill hits bottom, it stretches the rope and then springs back because of the rope's tension. The operator feeds out rope gradually as the hole becomes deeper.

Special conditions may require other types of drilling operations. For example, the California, or stovepipe, method is used to drill through gravel and loose rock materials. The operator uses a series of pipes, ranging from eight to thirty-six inches in diameter, depending upon the size of the well to be built. These pipes come in short lengths; they are telescoped like pieces of old-fashioned stovepipe as they go down. A small sand bucket, or bailer, is dropped down the piping; as the bailer scoops up sand and gravel, the pipe sinks deeper.

DRILLING A WELL WITH A DROP-TOOL DRILLING MACHINE.

Note the action of the walking beam, which lifts and drops the drill.

Walking Beam

For drilling deep wells in consolidated (hardened) rock formations, the hydraulic rotary method is preferred. This consists of rapidly rotating a bit on the bottom of a string of drill pipe. A mud fluid descending through the drill pipe and ascending outside the pipe removes the cuttings (rock pieces) produced by the bit. The pressure the mud exerts on the walls of the hole prevents them from collapsing; the mud also cools and lubricates the drill.

Drilled wells are enclosed with an impervious casing, with a tubular "screen" at the end to allow the entry of water from aquifers, or water-bearing strata. A screen of this type consists of slotted cylinders of durable metal. Often the outside of the screen is packed with gravel, a very permeable material, to increase the amount of water flowing into the well. This is called a gravel-wall, or gravel-packed, well.

In some cases, a well is excavated by means of a pointed pipe driven into the ground to the depth of the water-bearing stratum. This is called a driven well. It is not practical to dig such wells to a depth greater than seventy-five feet.

A large shaft has to be dug in the construction of the so-called radial well. The shaft has to be extended far enough down in order to intercept the most productive aquifer. From this shaft, a number of driven wells are extended in a horizontal direction. Heavy hydraulic jacks force these wells into place, driving them as far as two hundred feet into the aquifer. Under favorable conditions, the yield from such wells is very large.

Infiltration galleries are also used to capture ground water. These galleries consist of long pipes, laid through a water-bearing stratum that is often fed by streams. These pipes are laid like a huge drain tile, with the joints slightly open. The city of Des Moines, in Iowa, has a remarkable installation of this kind.

A centrifugal type of pump is often used to draw water from wells. This is known as a vertical turbine pump. It consists of a set of wheels, called impellers, mounted on a long shaft that extends into the well. The impellers rotate as the shaft

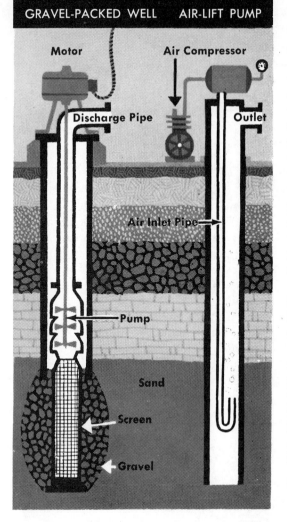

GRAVEL-PACKED WELL   AIR-LIFT PUMP

Motor   Air Compressor

Discharge Pipe   Outlet

Air Inlet Pipe →

Pump

Sand

Screen

Gravel

Two types of wells. Left: a gravel-packed well with a turbine pump. The pump, operated by a motor at the surface, is at the lower end of the discharge pipe, through which water is brought to the surface. Right: a well with an air-lift pump. Compressed air is conveyed through an inlet pipe to the bottom of the well. The air-and-water mixture forming at the bottom is lighter than water; it floats up the well and into a reservoir.

The wells will provide water even after an earthquake has struck.

A very simple pump used to draw water from wells is the air lift. This consists of a fairly large pipe called an eductor, which fits inside the well casing. Set within the eductor is a smaller pipe, which is used to convey compressed air to the bottom of the eductor. The mixture of air and water that forms at the bottom is much lighter than water itself. It floats up the eductor pipe and finally out into the pipeline or reservoir. This type of pump has the advantage of operating without any moving parts submerged in water. It also serves to aerate water. The eductor can draw water from practically any type of well hole, even if it is not straight. Its main disadvantage is that its efficiency is low, especially in deep wells.

Other types of pumps, such as the familiar lift pump (see Index), are used primarily on very small farms. The lift pump depends upon atmospheric pressure for its operation. It cannot raise water higher than thirty-four feet under ideal conditions. As a matter of fact, the limit is generally from twenty to twenty-five feet.

**How water is
transmitted**

Very often a community has to obtain its water from a distant source. The water supply of Boston is derived from a lake in a river valley fifty miles away from the city. New York gets over half of its water from the Catskill Mountains, more than a hundred miles away. Los Angeles goes all the way to Parker Dam — a distance of more than 240 miles — for part of its water supply. Cities such as these have much the same problems as the old Roman engineers faced when they built the aqueducts leading into the city of Rome. Of course the modern engineer has much better materials at his disposal.

The connecting links between the water source and the distribution system consist of aqueducts, also called transmission mains. The water in most aqueducts flows by gravity. In such structures the slope down which the water runs (the hydraulic gradi-

turns. Water entering the center of the rotating impellers is forced upward and enters the pipeline. Generally an electric motor in the pumphouse at the top operates the shaft.

It is not necessary to use a long shaft, however. Engineers have developed a small, powerful, completely sealed motor, which can operate the pump even when it is submerged. Wells with this type of pump and motor have many advantages. Since they require no pumphouse, there is no danger of stoppage because of flooded pumphouses.

ent) must be steep enough so that there will be a continuous flow. It must not be so steep as to bring about excessive pressures. In some cases siphons carry water over mountains, under rivers and across valleys. Pumps may force the water through the transmission mains in places where it will not flow by the force of gravity.

Water-transmission lines usually take the form of closed conduits or pipes, although in certain cases open flumes are used. Generally engineers do not like open flumes for water-supply purposes because of the danger of contamination.

To carry water efficiently, the transmission main should offer the smallest amount of surface for the volume of water carried. Obviously a circular pipe answers this requirement best. In large sizes, however, such piping is very expensive. In such cases engineers often select the more easily constructed type with a cross section suggesting the shape of a horseshoe. (See the diagram on this page.)

Concrete pipe makes a good conduit because of its smooth interior surface. To enable it to carry water under pressure, it is often "prestressed." Very strong wire is wound tightly around the concrete pipe and then concrete mortar is sprayed with a pneumatic gun onto this wire-wound core. This keeps the inner core in compression. When water enters the pipe under pressure, the strong steel wires carry the load instead of the concrete.

Another fine material for transmission mains is cast iron. It has a long life, requires little maintenance and can be cast to withstand heavy pressures. Difficulties may arise if corrosive water is sent through an untreated cast-iron pipe. These difficulties can be overcome by providing an inner lining of cement or bitumen.

Steel pipe can withstand high pressures. Expansion joints must often be provided to accommodate changes in water pressure. Generally the steel is protected by inside and outside linings. Engineers have learned how to make good pipe of asbestos and cement; pipe of this kind is smooth, withstands corrosion and is easily installed.

Occasionally transmission mains are made of wood slats bound together by iron bands. Pipe of this kind is so smooth that it offers little resistance to water flow. It will not require much maintenance if the wood remains wet and the bands are protected. Cities in Alaska often use this sort of transmission main.

The purification of the water supply

Once water has been collected, it must be made safe for use in our communities. Sanitary engineers take no chances; they remove from the water everything that they even suspect may be harmful. Their most reliable index of pollution is the coliform bacterium, or *Escherichia coli*. ("Bacterium" is the singular form of "bacteria.") As the name indicates, this bacterium is associated with human body wastes from the colon, a part of the large intestine. Engineers are quite ready to admit that the coliform bacterium is not necessarily harmful in itself. However, where it exists, harmful bacteria can also exist. At the same time that we eliminate *Escherichia coli,* we also do away with harmful bacteria.

We pointed out that there are two sources of water — surface supplies and ground-water supplies. The treatment of water will depend to some extent on which source we use. Let us see first how surface waters are treated.

Whenever water is stored in surface reservoirs, we face the problem of the plants called algae, which may cause water

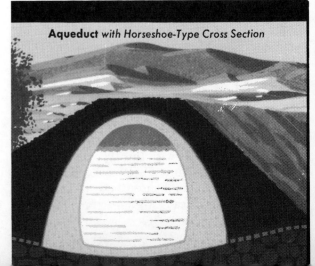

Aqueduct *with Horseshoe-Type Cross Section*

to acquire an objectionable taste. It is true that certain algae impart to water a flavor suggesting that of watermelon, which is a delicacy to many people. However, when we drink water, we usually do not want it to have any taste or odor, no matter how pleasant it may be. Hence the water-works man does what he can to remove algae from the water supply.

The algae found in reservoirs are minute cellular organisms. Most of them have the beneficial effect of introducing oxygen into the water; they also reduce the carbon dioxide content. However, these plants are quite short-lived. After their death their bodies decompose and create difficult water-treating problems.

Water-works men combat algae by introducing the chemical copper sulfate into the water in minute quantities throughout the year. This is generally done by putting crystals of the chemical in a gunny sack and towing the sack around the reservoir behind a boat. The copper sulfate treatment kills the algae before they grow numerous enough to cause trouble.

In a small reservoir, the growth of algae is checked by covering the reservoir. Algae cannot survive this treatment, since they need sunlight to live. Occasionally algae have been eliminated by a heavy dose of activated carbon. This darkens the water and blots out the sun.

Although algae give water a bad taste, they are not harmful. It is particularly important to remove disease-causing bacteria. The slow sand filter process was the first to be used for this purpose. It has been replaced by the more efficient rapid sand filter method for most water-supply requirements.

The slow sand filter works well enough. In this method, water is run into a large basin. The filter consists of a 24- to 36-inch layer of relatively fine sand laid on top of a layer of gravel. As the water sinks through the sand and gravel, suspended particles settle on the top layer of the sand, forming a schmutzdecke, or slime mat, which acts as a filter. The schmutzdecke becomes thickly matted after a time and is removed.

The slow sand filters still in operation do an excellent job. They treat water at an average rate of two million to four million gallons a day per acre of filter bed. There are certain objections to these filters, however. For one thing, they are not particularly effective in treating water that contains more than a hundred parts per million of silt or other suspended solids.* Besides, the removal of the schmutzdecke is a slow and expensive process. Workmen have to skim it off with shovels, rakes and other hand tools.

Today almost all water-filter plants use the rapid sand filter. This device represents only one stage in a series of treatment processes. Much of the objectionable matter has already been removed before water passes through the rapid sand filter.

* Sanitary engineers often use the term "parts per million," referring to the ratio between a given substance and the water in which it is contained. When we say "a hundred parts per million of silt," we mean a million gallons of water contain a hundred gallons of silt.

WATER TRANSMISSION LINES

Siphon

Open Flume

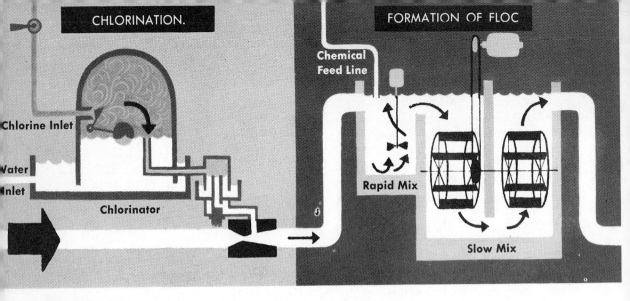

Chemical Feed Line

Chlorine Inlet

Water Inlet

Chlorinator

Rapid Mix

Slow Mix

Water is led into a chlorinator, where it is mixed with chlorine gas. The concentrated solution formed in this manner is fed from the chlorinator into the water main.

Water is mixed with chemicals, called coagulants, in such a way as to form a floc — a light, loose mass that will combine with impurities and precipitate with them.

Purifying water by chlorination and aeration

The first phase of water treatment is chlorination — the addition of chlorine. Like oxygen, chlorine is a chemically active gas that readily combines with many other kinds of substances, forming different compounds. Waterworks men use chlorine for two primary purposes — to kill harmful bacteria and to destroy objectionable organic matter. In a surface supply of water, this organic material may come from dead leaves, algae cells, human refuse, dilute amounts of sewage and various other sources.

In large water-supply systems, chlorine is normally fed to the water as a gas. Many times the taste that appears so objectionable in chlorinated water is not from the chlorine but from partially altered inorganic and organic compounds. These compounds can be eliminated by increasing the chlorine dosage.

Offensive tastes and odors are often removed by aerating surface water — that is, by mixing it thoroughly with air. The oxygen in the latter combines with, or oxidizes, the various materials in the water that may cause the foulness. We usually aerate water by letting it flow over steps or spray out of nozzles like a fountain. Often water is allowed to trickle over trays filled with coke; this helps absorb any objection-able odors. Aeration is particularly effective in eliminating disagreeable tastes and odors when these are caused by gases formed as organic matter decomposes. Water from wells can also be improved by aeration, particularly if they contain carbon dioxide, hydrogen sulfide or iron. Aeration releases the carbon dioxide and hydrogen sulfide. It oxidizes the iron, causing it to precipitate as an insoluble compound that filters later can remove.

Removing impurities from water by coagulation

The next important step in the purification of water is to mix it with chemicals so as to form flocculence, or floc — a light, loose mass that will combine with impurities and precipitate with them. The more solid kinds of impurities (such as sediment) are usually removed in this way. Flocculating chemicals of this type are called coagulants. The coagulant most generally used today is aluminum sulfate, or alum. If it is dissolved in water and is given time to react, the alum produces an aluminum floc, which looks very much like a large snowflake. The floc is sticky and carries an electrical charge opposite that of the sediment; therefore, it attracts the sediment. Later, in the settling basin, the combined floc and sediment will drop to the bottom of the basin and will be removed.

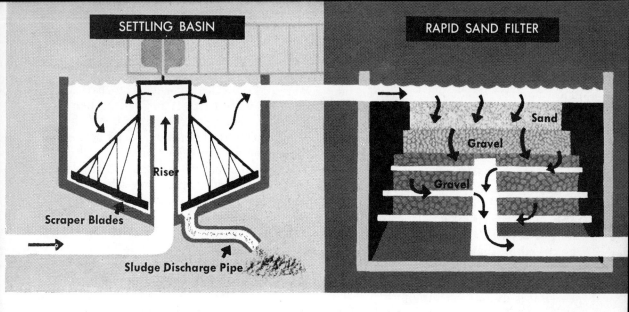

SETTLING BASIN

Riser

Scraper Blades

Sludge Discharge Pipe

RAPID SAND FILTER

Sand

Gravel

Gravel

Water flows into the tank through a riser. The sludge settles at the bottom of the tank and is pushed by rotating blades into a well, from which it is piped away.

This filter finishes the purification operation. Coarse sand is set on a layer of gravel. After the water has passed through the sand and gravel, it is drained off.

At the same time that a floc is formed, a weak form of sulfuric acid is produced. Generally, there is enough alkalinity to neutralize this acid. If not, lime or soda must be added to the water in order to make it fit to drink.

Other coagulants besides aluminum sulfate are quite effective. Among these are ferric sulfate and ferric chloride, which react to form an iron-hydroxide floc. They also release an acid that can be neutralized.

In most plants activated carbon is added to the water together with the chemcals that serve as coagulants. Activated carbon is not used as a coagulant but to absorb offensive tastes and odors. It is later removed by the rapid sand filter, together with the combined floc and sediment. In small plants, water may be run through a filter of carbon. This will become exhausted in time and will have to be replaced.

After coagulants have been added to the water, they must have time to react and to form a floc. This is done by passing the water through a mixing basin. Some basins consist of tanks provided with baffles. These are plates that deflect the water, forcing it from one side of the tank to the other, as it passes through. Certain mixing basins use mechanical mixing paddles and propellers in order to stir the water thoroughly and thus bring about the desired chemical reactions.

When the mixing operation has been completed, water is led into settling basins. Here the sediment contained in the water is allowed to sink to the bottom. Water is kept in these basins from an hour and a half to six hours, according to the needs of a particular plant. The capacity of the basin will depend on the quantity of water that the plant treats every day. If this quantity is 240,000 gallons, 10,000 gallons will have to be treated in a single hour. If you want a settling tank that will keep the water for two hours, you must make it large enough to hold 20,000 gallons.

Sediment is sometimes removed in another type of basin—the upflow, suspended-solids contact unit. Water, mixed with coagulating chemicals, enters the lower part of the basin. As it flows upward, it passes through a layer of suspended flocculent material (material made up of flocs). The fresh chemical reacts more readily in the presence of this blanket. The sediment and floc are filtered instead of settling to the bottom (as is the case in the settling basins described above).

Purifying water by rapid filtration

The water is now ready for the rapid sand filter. By this time most of the undesirable matter in the water has been removed. The filter simply puts the finishing touches on the operation; it retains any suspended matter that may not have settled out. Obviously water can pass through this kind of filter much faster than it does through the slow sand filter, which receives untreated water.

Comparatively coarse sand is used in the rapid sand filter. It is usually set thirty inches deep upon a layer of gravel. The gravel particles range in diameter from a sixteenth of an inch to three inches; the larger sizes are at the bottom. After the water has passed through the sand and gravel, it is drained off through pipes. The sand in the filter can be replaced by finely ground anthracite coal. Many feel it does a better job; however, sand is generally cheaper.

The operators clean the filters by backwashing — that is, by directing a stream of water upward through the filter through the same pipes that carry off the purified water. The accumulated solid matter in the filter is discharged together with the backwash into a sewer. Backwashing must be done carefully. If it is too violent, the coarse gravel particles at the bottom of the filter will work their way to the top.

Many modern filter plants also use a surface wash to help clean the filter. Normally the surface of the filter will become dirtier than any other part. If backwashing does not remove all the sediment, accumulated mud will form into balls and will cause difficulty. To insure thorough cleaning at the surface, designers have supplied small pipes with $1/4$-inch nozzles. Jets of water are directed through the nozzles to the surface area. By stirring up the surface thoroughly, they free it from silt.

The final step in the purification process is to see to it that there is a proper amount of "free" chlorine in the water, in order to guard against contamination in the distribution system.* The chlorine that was added to the water at the outset may have been used up, during coagulation and filtration, in oxidizing organic matter. If this is the case, the operator will have to add

more. As a rule, he will try to have not more than one part per million of chlorine in the water as it leaves the plant. If there is too much at this stage, he reduces the content by adding sulfur dioxide.

Chlorine may have to be added to the water again and again. In such cases, it is considered good practice to blend the chlorine with ammonia. This germ-killing combination has more lasting effects than chlorine alone, although it is not so strong.

So far we have been dealing with the purification of surface water. The treatment of ground water is simpler in certain respects. This water has already been "filtered" as it seeped through the ground, and it is generally free from harmful bacteria. However, another problem is involved. As ground water has passed through different strata of rock, it has dissolved various minerals contained in the rock. These remain in solution as water is brought to the surface in wells. Such water is "hard."

The most objectionable of the minerals that make water hard are the calcium and magnesium carbonates and the calcium and magnesium sulfates. Water-works men refer to the hardness produced by these two groups of minerals as "carbonate hardness" and "noncarbonate hardness." Water containing either group of minerals will not form a lather when soap is added. The soap combines with the calcium and magnesium to form a scummy precipitate, which will ultimately sink to the bottom of the sink or washbowl.

There are various ways of treating hard water in a water-works plant. In one method — the lime-soda ash process — the calcium and magnesium compounds are removed by a series of chemical reactions. Lime is used for the carbonates; soda ash for the sulfates. In either case, after a short active mixing period, a precipitate is formed. After this has settled, the water goes to the filter to remove any precipitate that may still remain. Before filtering takes place, carbon dioxide gas is generally added to the water. This is done to neutralize the excess alkalinity that will have developed, since both lime and soda ash are highly alkaline.

---

* Actually the chlorine in the water is not free; it has combined with water to form hypochlorous acid ($HClO$).

The lime-soda ash process has certain disadvantages. For one thing, an excessive amount of sludge is produced when the calcium and magnesium are precipitated. Besides, it is costly to reduce the hardness much below eighty parts per million. However, this amount is satisfactory in most cases.

In some instances hard water is treated by substituting some less objectionable compound for the calcium and magnesium carbonates and sulfates. An ion exchange material, such as zeolite, is used. Zeolite is a complex sodium compound. When it comes in contact with hard water, it exchanges the calcium and magnesium for sodium. Thus it forms sodium carbonates and sulfates, which are soluble and do not prevent water from forming a lather. The water still contains a mineral — sodium — but this is not objectionable.

After a time, all the sodium in the zeolite will be replaced by calcium and magnesium derived from the hard-water minerals. The sodium content of the zeolite is then renewed by an ingenious method. A supply of salt brine is flushed back through the filter. This salt is sodium chloride (common table salt), a compound in which sodium is combined with chlorine. The sodium contained in the brine is exchanged for the calcium and magnesium now present in the zeolite. The zeolite will have a renewed store of sodium and can again go about the task of softening the water. The calcium and magnesium are flushed away as a waste in the form of calcium and magnesium chloride.

This process has many advantages. Small household units can be built conveniently and operated without difficulty. There is no sludge to dispose of, as in the case of the lime-soda ash process. The zeolite will remove all the hardness, if desired; generally, however, this is not necessary. As we have seen, operators are content to soften water so as to bring the total hardness to a figure somewhere near eighty parts per million. The zeolite process has certain disadvantages, it is true. It will not remove sediment, even though it

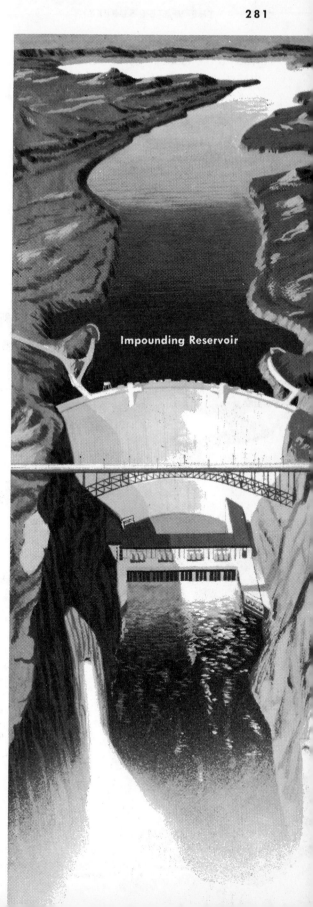

Impounding Reservoir

appears to act like a filter. Many people object to the taste after the water has been softened by zeolite.

Zeolite has been used by the United States Army and Navy in order to make sea water fit to drink. This is the reverse of the softening process. The zeolite replaces the sodium in sea water with another element that does not harm the human system.

Water containing the minerals iron and manganese must be treated. If such minerals are present even in the tiny proportion of less than one part per million, a stain will be produced in sinks and on laundered clothes. The annoying iron bacteria, which thrive in darkness and in the presence of iron, are likely to be found in such water. Iron and manganese can generally be removed by aeration. They are oxidized and precipitated, and then removed by sand filters. Sometimes, however, special treatment is required.

For reasons of dental health, compounds called fluorides (combinations of various elements with fluorine, a gas akin to chlorine) may be added to the water supply. See the Index, under Fluoridation.

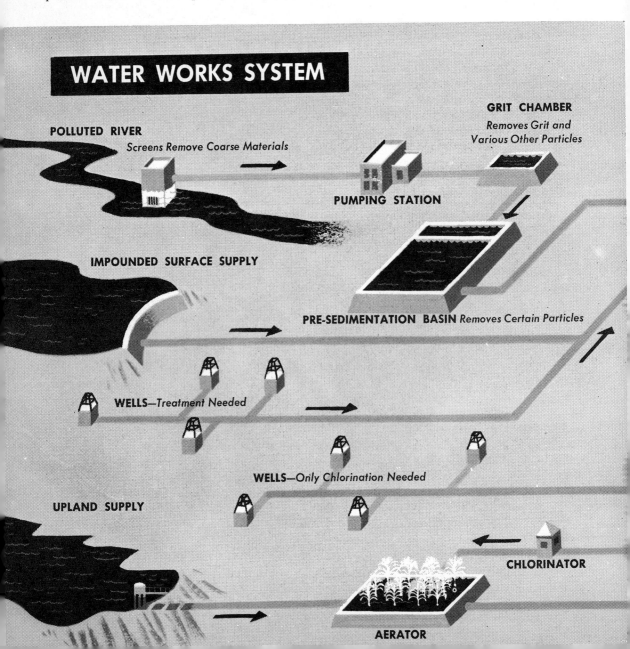

WATER WORKS SYSTEM

POLLUTED RIVER *Screens Remove Coarse Materials*

GRIT CHAMBER *Removes Grit and Various Other Particles*

PUMPING STATION

IMPOUNDED SURFACE SUPPLY

PRE-SEDIMENTATION BASIN *Removes Certain Particles*

WELLS—*Treatment Needed*

WELLS—*Only Chlorination Needed*

UPLAND SUPPLY

CHLORINATOR

AERATOR

Fresh water
from salt water

Scientists and engineers are developing inexpensive ways of making saline water fresh and suitable for drinking and other purposes. It will be difficult, however, to devise processes that can operate cheaply enough for farmers to use the water for irrigation, where the need is greatest. Nevertheless, salt water is promising for cities and industries in dry regions. The Sheikhdom of Kuwait (Arabia) has a plant converting over 4,700,000 gallons of water from the Persian Gulf into drinking water daily. On the Caribbean island of Aruba, a plant transforms 3,500,000 gallons of sea water into fresh water. At Mandalay Beach, California, a large electric generating plant distills 100,000 gallons of Pacific Ocean water for use in power generation. Other plants are operating in Arabia, Gibraltar and Bermuda. The island of Guernsey in the English Channel has a reserve plant for the occasional years when rainfall is inadequate to support its crops.

One should be able to produce a thousand gallons of pure water from the ocean by

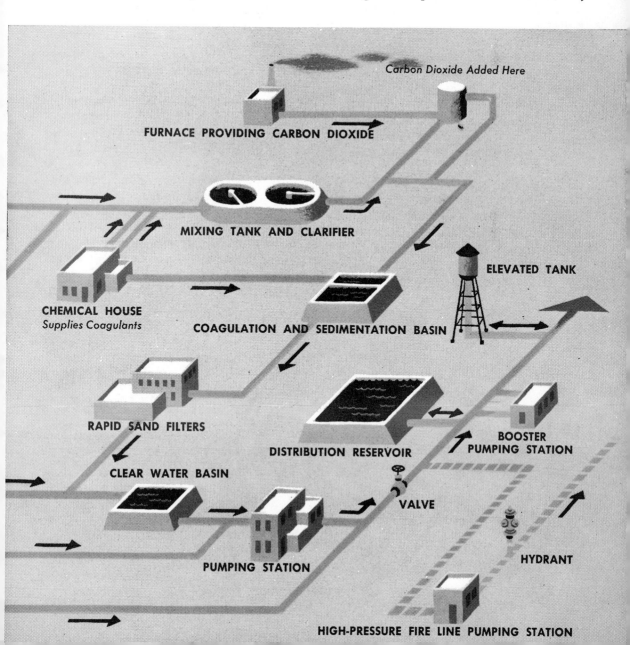

Carbon Dioxide Added Here

FURNACE PROVIDING CARBON DIOXIDE

MIXING TANK AND CLARIFIER

ELEVATED TANK

CHEMICAL HOUSE
Supplies Coagulants

COAGULATION AND SEDIMENTATION BASIN

RAPID SAND FILTERS

DISTRIBUTION RESERVOIR

BOOSTER
PUMPING STATION

CLEAR WATER BASIN

VALVE

PUMPING STATION

HYDRANT

HIGH-PRESSURE FIRE LINE PUMPING STATION

using 2.8 kilowatt hours of electrical energy. Actually, it requires much more energy with present methods. Most conversion costs run from $1.25 to $2.25 per thousand gallons of water. The basic water-conversion methods now being studied are: (1) distillation or evaporation; (2) electrodialysis; (3) freezing. The first one is also the oldest; Julius Caesar obtained drinking water for his troops by using solar evaporators to distill water from the Mediterranean Sea. Almost all of the systems currently in use employ some form of distillation.

The second one is an interesting procedure that takes advantage of the fact that saline water is an electrolyte — that is, it conducts electricity. Therefore, salt water may be demineralized, or "desalted," by having an electric current passed through it (electrolysis). If an electric current is passed through a saline solution, the cations, or positively charged atoms, of the solution move toward the cathode, or negative pole of the electrical apparatus. The anions, or negatively charged atoms, move to the anode, or positive pole. Membranes that have the property of passing either cations or anions, but not both, are placed in the saline solution. There these membranes sift out, or dialyze, the electrically charged salt atoms and produce desirably salt-free water. Electrodialysis is used in Coalinga, California, to purify brackish water from a well. Prior to this, the city had to import water by tank car.

The third method, freezing, is still under development. It takes advantage of the fact that salt water, when it freezes, forms into fresh-water crystals. These crystals of ice can be separated from the solution and can then be melted in order to produce salt-free water.

The distribution of the water supply

After water has been purified, treated to remove objectionable taste, odors and suspended matter and softened to make it suitable for general domestic use, it is distributed throughout the community. In the great majority of cases it flows through cast-iron pipes. Sometimes pipes of steel and reinforced concrete are used, especially in large-diameter installations. Asbestos and cement pipes are also employed; they are particularly desirable when corrosive water is to be distributed. However, even cast-iron pipe can be used to carry corrosive water if the pipe is lined with cement.

In some cases, water flows from the source to the ultimate user through the force of gravity. Generally, however, pumps are required to send it through the distributing system. The earlier pumps were of the piston type. A large piston would draw water into a cylinder; on its return stroke it would force this water out into the pipeline. Piston-type pumps were almost always powered by steam.

Left: a motor-driven pump sends water through the distribution system. Right: an elevated storage tank. During the night, when the demand for water is low, the pumping rate is greater than the demand and water is forced up into the storage tank. In the morning, when the demand for water becomes greater than the pumping rate, water flows out from the tank, as a result of the force of gravity, into the distribution system.

Pump

They were efficient devices, which could be operated without difficulty at various pumping rates. But they were huge and costly; they were so tall that they had to be housed in large buildings. Of course steam-driven pumps required boilers. These were often inefficient; it was costly to keep them in repair.

About 1915, water-works men began to adopt the small, powerful centrifugal pump. Today it has made the old piston pump almost obsolete. A centrifugal pump consists of a wheel, called an impeller, rotating in a casing. The water enters

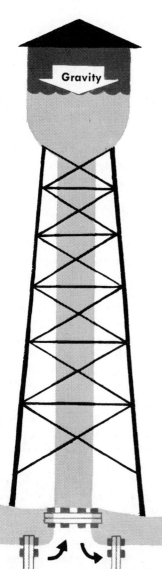

through the center of this rotating wheel and is thrown violently to the outside; it leaves the pump under a pressure of about fifty pounds per square inch. This pump is efficient, economical, simple and quite small, requiring only a limited amount of housing. It can be built to furnish almost any amount of water against pressure heads * of up to 250 feet.

Centrifugal pumps can be driven by electric motors or internal combustion engines, such as gasoline or diesel engines. Large units are sometimes operated by steam turbines. Such pumps are low in cost, simple in operation and easily repaired. Their only disadvantage is that their rate of flow cannot be regulated easily.

Reservoirs form an essential part of most water-distribution systems. Some of these reservoirs serve primarily to store water. Others are intended to equalize the rate of water flow. These consist of elevated tanks, which may be built on high ground or set on towers. Such elevated storage tanks "float" on the distribution system. This means that a tank has a single riser pipe connected with the supply main. Through this one riser pipe, water may enter the tank or may be discharged from it.

When such elevated tanks are provided, water-works pumps operate twenty-four hours a day at a steady rate. During the night, when the demand for water is very low, the pumping rate is greater than the demand. Water is then forced upward into the storage tank. In the morning, when household activities begin, and later, when the city's industries start operating, the demand is greater than the pumping rate. Water then flows out of the

* "Head" measures the height to which water is raised by the pressure causing it to flow. One pound per square inch supports a column of water 2.3 feet in height.

Main to Consumer

storage tank, through the force of gravity, and into the distribution system.

Why overhead storage tanks are useful

Without overhead storage tanks of this type, a city would have to pump directly to the mains as much water as would be needed for any particular part of the day. This means that the pumps would have to be big enough to supply heavy emergency flows such as would be required for fire fighting. The pumping rate would have to vary to meet the changing demand for water throughout the day. Elevated storage tanks keep a large volume of water in reserve. This will be available under pressure to meet normal variations in water requirements or any emergencies that may arise.

Distribution systems must provide adequate water for fire protection. The figures for the number of gallons per minute and the total number of hours the water is re-

Often, in the case of tall buildings, a pump in the basement forces water up to a tank on the roof. From this tank, water is distributed to the upper stories.

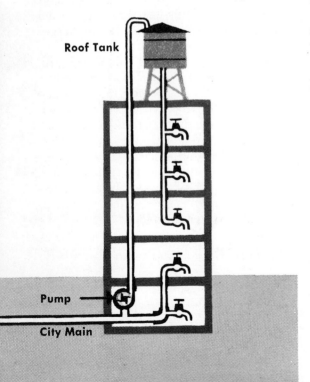

Roof Tank

Pump

City Main

quired to flow in fighting fires vary, depending on the size of the town or city in terms of population. For large urban areas, the quantities of water needed are tremendous — thousands of gallons a minute for hours at a time.

The spacing of fire hydrants is also an important factor in the fighting of fire. Many cities space their hydrants so that no line of hose will exceed a length of five hundred to six hundred feet. At least half the streams needed at any point should require hose lengths considerably less than the above figure.

Water distributed by systems of mains

All well-designed water-distribution systems make use of a network of mains — pipes of large diameter running underground. A single water main serving a large area is undesirable. In such a pipe, called a dead end, the water gradually loses oxygen and becomes stale and objectionable. Furthermore, it is dangerous to rely on a single water main. If it should be put out of operation, the water supply of the entire area will be cut off.

Very often, when a city is located on a hillside, it is necessary to divide the distribution system into two or three sections. This is to prevent excessively high pressures in the lower portions of the system. There are as many as five or six of these sections in some cities.

Water mains are provided with valves, which permit the flow of water to be shut off completely in the event of a break or some other emergency. From the main, water flows through a network of pipes to the individual buildings of a community. If a building is very tall, the operating pressure may not suffice to raise water to the upper stories. In such cases, a pump in the basement of the building forces water up to a tank on the roof. From this tank, water is distributed to the upper stories. The lower stories are supplied by pipes leading from the main. The operating pressure in the main suffices to raise water to the required heights.

See Vol. 10, p. 279: "Water Supply."

EXPERIMENTS WITH AIR

Examining the Properties of the Ocean of Air Around Us

BY M. F. VESSEL

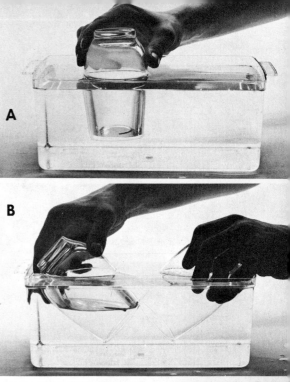

AIR is the ocean of gases (oxygen, nitrogen and several others) in which we live. We are seldom conscious of its presence. Only when a strong wind blows or when the air becomes polluted and foul-smelling do we become aware that it is a real substance — as much so as water, or a boulder or the crystals of sugar or salt.

Showing that air occupies space and has weight

We can show that air occupies space by a simple experiment in which we "pour" air from one glass to another. Pour water into a large pan to a depth of six inches. Drop a wooden matchstick on the surface of the water and then cover the stick with a drinking glass, holding the glass upside down. Force the glass straight down into the water; the matchstick will show the water level in the glass (Figure 1A). Water will not enter it because something — that is, air — is already there. Put a second glass in the water in a sideways position and keep it under the surface until it is entirely full. Holding the two glasses as shown in Figure 1B, you can "pour" the air from the first glass into the second one. The bubbles you see and the gurgling sound you hear indicate the passing of air from one glass to the other. When you straighten out the glasses again and raise them so that their mouths are only an inch or two below the surface, note that the water level has been raised in the first glass and lowered in the second because of air transfer (Figure 1C).

If air can occupy space it must also have weight. We can weigh air just as we do any other substance. Suspend a dowel

All photos, Kellner Associates—D. Krueger

1. A demonstration of the fact that air occupies space. For a detailed explanation, see the text on this page.

stick about two feet long as shown in Figure 2; this will serve as a balance. Provide yourself with a fully inflated balloon and a small weight — a one-ounce fishing weight will do very well. Suspend the balloon at one end of the dowel and place the weight at the other end. Then move the weight along the dowel until the latter remains horizontal when both the balloon and the weight are in position. The weight is now to be firmly attached to the dowel.

When the balloon was inflated, air was forced into it under a certain amount of pressure. As a result, the air in the balloon is much more concentrated than it would ordinarily be. Now carefully let the air out

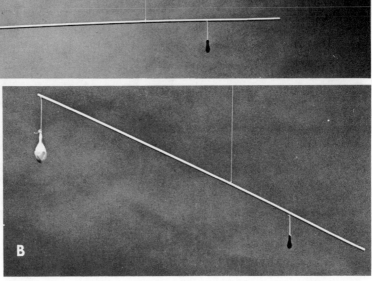

2. A balloon is set at one end of a dowel; a small weight near the other end is so adjusted that the dowel will remain horizontal. When air is let out of the balloon, the weight will pull it down because now the balloon is lighter. This shows that air has weight.

of the inflated balloon. The weight will pull down the balance because the balloon has become lighter. This proves, of course, that air has weight.

What we mean by
atmospheric pressure

It is true that air is not very heavy, compared, say, to iron or even water. Yet because the ocean of air in which we live has weight and there is so much of it, it presses down upon us with a very noticeable effect. Scientists have measured the pressure of the atmosphere and have found it to be about 14.7 pounds for each square inch of surface at sea level. We do not feel this atmospheric pressure because our bodies contain air at the same pressure pushing outward in all directions. As we climb to the top of a mountain or go up in an airplane, the pressure decreases because there is less air above us pushing downward.

In 1654, a German physicist, Otto von Guericke, gave a striking demonstration of how great a force can be exerted by atmos-

pheric pressure. He provided himself with two hemispheres of metal, which fitted together very snugly. He exhausted the air from the sphere formed in this way. Then he attached a team of horses to one hemisphere and another team to the other. The horses were not able to pull the hemispheres apart because the atmospheric pressure on all sides of the sphere held them together. But when air was admitted to the sphere, and the inside pressure became equal to the outside pressure, the two hemispheres were easily pulled apart.

You can perform a somewhat similar experiment (Figure 3). Provide yourself with a drinking glass and a sturdy piece of cardboard (such as one would find in a shoebox), with a diameter greater than that of the lip of the glass. Rub some greasy substance, such as vegetable fat or Vaseline, liberally around the lip of the glass. Set fire to a crumpled piece of paper and drop it into the glass. Then at once press the cardboard firmly in place over the lip of the glass. If you have provided an

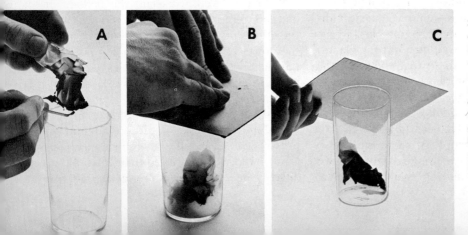

3. After the lip of a drinking glass has been greased, a piece of paper is set on fire and is dropped in the glass (A). A piece of cardboard is pressed over the lip of the glass (B). If the cardboard is lifted up, the glass will remain firmly attached to it (C).

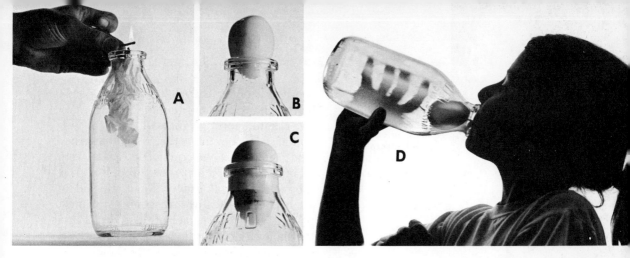

A B C D

adequate seal (that was the reason for applying the greasy substance), the glass will remain attached to the cardboard after you lift up the latter. Set the glass down again after a few seconds, as it will not remain attached to the cardboard very long. Why did the cardboard and the glass stick together? The burning piece of paper in the glass heated the air and made it expand, and some of it escaped before you capped the glass with the cardboard. There was now less air pressure inside the glass than outside. The outside air pressing against the cardboard kept it and the glass together because of the lessened pressure within the glass.

The same principle is involved in a favorite trick: getting a peeled, hard-boiled egg into a milk bottle. The egg will not quite go through the mouth of the bottle at first (Figure 4). Set fire to a piece of paper and drop it into the bottle. Then immediately place the peeled egg on the bottle neck; the egg will soon plop into the bottle. The next thing to do is to get the egg out of the bottle. Tilt the bottle bottom side up so that the egg rests in the neck. Blow as hard as you can into the bottle, and then quickly pull it away from your mouth; the egg will pop out. By blowing hard into the bottle, you compressed the air within it. When this compressed air was released as you pulled the bottle away from your mouth, the air pushed the egg out of the bottle.

Some effects of atmospheric pressure

Partly fill a glass tumbler with water and cover the top with a piece of stiff cardboard, which should extend beyond the lip of

4. How to get a peeled, hard-boiled egg into a bottle and out of it again. Set fire to a piece of paper and drop it into the bottle (A). At once put the egg on the bottle neck (B). The egg will be forced through the bottle neck by atmospheric pressure (C) and will plop into the bottle. To get the egg out again, you must first blow into the bottle just as hard as you can (D). When you pull it away from your mouth, the egg will pop out.

the tumbler. Hold the card on top of the tumbler and then quickly turn the tumbler upside down (Figure 5). Remove your hand from the card. The air pressing upon the card will hold it in place despite the downward pressure of the water due to the force of gravity. Try the same experiment with a tall bottle, such as an olive bottle. Will the air hold up this taller column of water?

Here is a spectacular demonstration of atmospheric pressure at work. You will need a large empty can with a screw cap. For safety's sake, use a can that has held some nonflammable liquid. Wash out the inside of the can; then pour about one-half

5. Partly fill a drinking glass with water and cover it with a piece of cardboard (A). Hold the cardboard firmly and turn the glass upside down. The cardboard will remain in place because of atmospheric pressure (B).

A

B

6. Insert a piece of glass tubing in a one-hole stopper that fits tightly in an ordinary soda bottle containing soda. What happens when you try to suck up liquid from the bottle?

cup of water into the can and heat the liquid until it boils. Then, using two potholders, remove the can from the source of heat and set it down. Quickly put the cap on and screw it tightly. As the can cools, the steam inside it will gradually condense, forming a partial vacuum. The inside air pressure will now be less than the outside pressure; and this outside pressure should cause the sides of the can to cave in. If nothing happens in a reasonable period of time, sprinkle the can with cold water. This will hasten the condensation of the steam. If a large can is not available, a smaller one will do, provided it has a screw cap.* Only about a half-inch of water at the bottom of the can will be needed.

Obtain a piece of clean glass tubing, fire-polished on both ends. Insert it in a

* Automobile polish often comes in such a can.

one-hole stopper that fits tightly in a soda bottle (Figure 6), containing soda or any other liquid for that matter. Try to suck up the soda from the bottle. What happens? The fact is that you cannot sip soda from a bottle through a straw or through a glass tube such as you used without the aid of atmospheric pressure: the outer air must press against the surface of the soda. Put a two-hole stopper in the bottle and insert the glass tube through one of the holes. Do you have any difficulty now in sucking up the soda?

You can use atmospheric pressure to remove debris from the water in an aquarium without disturbing its occupants unduly. Provide yourself with a dip tube, which you can buy in most pet shops; any long and narrow tube of glass or plastic will also do. Place your finger over one end of the tube and lower it into the water of the aquarium (Figure 7). The air remaining in the tube will prevent the water from rising in it. When the tube is just over a speck of debris in the aquarium, remove your finger from the end of the tube. The atmospheric pressure upon the surface of the water will force water up in the tube, bringing the speck with it, and will push out the air formerly contained in it. Again place your finger over the top of the tube and lift the tube out of the aquarium. The water will not flow out of the tube until you have removed your finger from the top.

Atmospheric pressure in the process of respiration

Atmospheric pressure plays an important part in the vital process of respiration. In man, the mechanical act of respiration is brought about by alternately decreasing and increasing the volume of the chest cavity. When the dome-shaped diaphragm, at the base of the chest cavity, is drawn downward toward the abdomen, and the ribs are pulled upward and outward, the volume of

7. How to use a dip tube. Placing a finger over one end of the tube, lower it into a fishbowl (A). When the tube is just over a speck of debris, remove your finger from the end of the tube. The water will rise in the tube, bringing the speck up with it. Again put your finger over the top of the tube and lift it out of the bowl (B).

the chest cavity is increased. Air is then drawn into the lungs through the force of atmospheric pressure. The muscles that brought about the intake of air then relax; the ribs are moved downward and inward, the diaphragm expands, moving upward, and the volume of the chest cavity decreases. The lungs then contract and expel air.

You can duplicate some of the essential factors in the mechanics of breathing by means of the apparatus illustrated in Figure 8D. This experiment should be supervised by an adult or a teacher. Provide yourself with a good-sized glass bottle. You are to cut off the bottom part as follows. First make a cutting frame from two boards and an end piece, as shown in Figure 8A. Cut a groove in the bottom board and set a glass cutter in position in the groove (Figure 8A). Place the bottle between the two boards and the end piece and slowly turn it against the glass cutter (Figure 8B). Prop the bottle against a wooden support, as in 8C; then heat the area slightly below the etched line with a Bunsen burner, turning the bottle rapidly as you do so. Dip the part below the etched line in a pan of cold water. The bottom part will then snap off, or will break off if tapped. If any jagged pieces are left, bend them back and forth with a pair of pliers toward the upper part of the bottle and they will break off. The sharp edges where the glass has been cut should be filed smooth or covered with adhesive tape.

Get a one-hole stopper for the bottle and insert a Y-shaped plastic tube through the hole of the stopper as shown in Figure

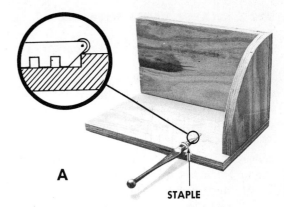

A

STAPLE

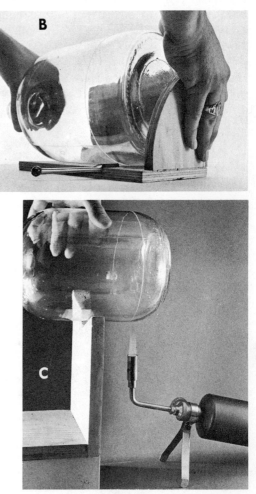

B

C

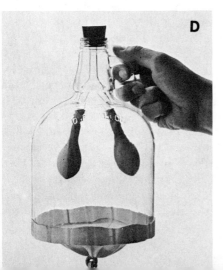

D

8. In the text on this page, we explain how to prepare a piece of apparatus that will show the mechanics of breathing. The illustrations show four stages in the construction of the apparatus. A. A glass cutter is in position on a cutting board. B. A glass bottle is turned against the cutter, producing an etched line. C. The bottle is heated just below the etched line. The bottom of the bottle is then removed. D. A one-hole stopper with "lungs" (really, toy balloons) is in place; a rubber sheet has been fastened to the bottom of the bottle. To demonstrate inhalation, the sheet is pressed down; the "lungs" then become partly filled with air. When the sheet is pressed in, the "lungs" collapse (exhalation).

8D. Fasten a balloon tightly to each fork of the Y; these balloons will represent the lungs. Spread a rubber sheet across the bottom of the bottle and fasten it in place, either by tying it securely or by cementing it. The rubber sheet will be the diaphragm of your apparatus; the inside of the bottle represents the chest cavity. You can use the upper half of a large toy balloon instead of a rubber sheet.

When you pull down the rubber sheet at the bottom of the bottle, you increase the volume of the "chest cavity." Air will be drawn in through the Y-shaped tube and will partially fill the balloons. When you press the rubber sheet in, the "chest cavity" will contract. Air will be forced out of the balloons, and they will collapse.

Illustrating the
principle of the siphon

If you have ever used a siphon, you have made water flow uphill. This, too, is an effect of atmospheric pressure. The siphon is a device with which you lift a liquid and then deposit it at a lower level. You can siphon gasoline from the tank of your car to a can resting on the ground, but you could not siphon water out of a well nor out of a leaky boat at sea.

To prepare a siphon (Figure 9), put a container nearly full of water on top of a box, set on the table; put an empty con-

9. A siphon in operation. Water is being transferred from the container on the box to the lower container.

tainer on the table beside the box. Then fill a rubber tube full of water; stop one end with your finger and hold up the other end so that the water will not escape. Place the free end in the water of the upper container, and the other end in the lower container as shown. When you remove your finger from this end of the tube, the water will flow in a steady stream from the upper container to the lower one. If you do not fill the tube full of water to begin with, you can start the water flowing by sucking at the end of the tube that is to be put in the lower container.

The principle of the siphon is quite simple. When water is set flowing out of the tube into the lower container, the atmospheric pressure upon the surface of the water in the upper container forces water up the tube to replace the water that has flowed out. Of course once the long arm of the siphon is under the surface of the water in the lower container, the same atmospheric pressure is exerted on this surface and tends to keep the water from flowing out of the upper container. But since the pressure on the two surfaces is the same, the greater weight of water in the longer column keeps water flowing into the lower container.

What we mean by
Bernoulli's principle

When a current of air moves more rapidly than the air that surrounds it, it lowers the atmospheric pressure in the area through which it passes. The greater the speed of the current, the less the pressure. This law is called Bernoulli's principle, after the name of the Swiss scientist who discovered it, and it applies to liquids as well as to gases. We can illustrate the principle by several interesting experiments:

With a drop of cement attach threads to two Ping-Pong balls; then suspend the balls so that they will hang about two inches apart, as shown in Figure 10. Now blow through a large straw between the two balls. You would expect that they would be blown apart by the miniature blast of air that you have created; instead, they come closer together. The rapidly moving current of air between the two balls has reduced the at-

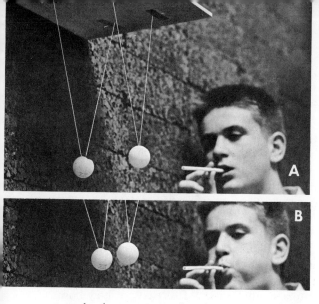

A

B

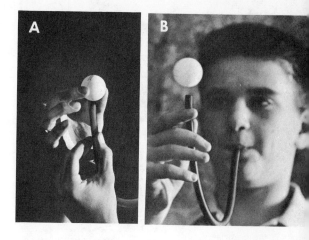

A   B

11. A Ping-Pong ball is set on one end of a rubber tube (A), the other end being in your mouth. Blow through the tube (B) and see what happens.

12. Insert a funnel at one end of a rubber tube and point the tube straight downward. Will you be able to blow a Ping-Pong ball away from the funnel?

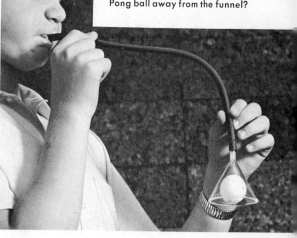

13. The girl is trying to turn over the index card by blowing under it. All the pictures included on this page show Bernoulli's principle in operation.

mospheric pressure in the area between them. Therefore they are drawn together as the air outside this area presses against them.

Provide yourself with a length of rubber tubing. Put one end in your mouth; hold a Ping-Pong ball over the other end, as in Figure 11A. When you blow through the tubing, the ball will remain suspended in the air (Figure 11B). The reason, of course, is that the ball is held in the area of lessened atmospheric pressure created by the rapidly moving air current; the air beyond this zone presses against the ball, forming a sort of invisible wall beyond which the ball cannot pass.

Here is a somewhat similar experiment. Insert a funnel at the end of your tubing and hold it with the large end downward, as in Figure 12. If a Ping-Pong ball is placed in the funnel while air is being blown through the tube, the ball will be suspended instead of being blown away from the funnel as you would expect. It will continue to remain suspended in the air as long as you keep blowing. Can you explain why?

Bend an index card into the shape shown in Figure 13 and place it on a table. Ask somebody to turn the card over by blowing under it. It cannot be done. Since there will be an area of lessened pressure under the card, the pressure of the atmosphere against the top of the card will keep it firmly in place.

Perfume atomizers and small hand sprayers operate because rapidly moving air brings about a decrease in air pressure. You can set up a small atomizer, using two

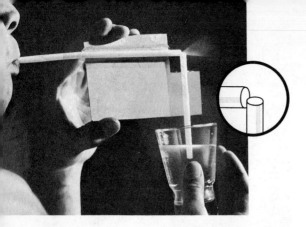

14. An atomizer that anyone
can make. It really works!

then forces the liquid up the tube and out
of it. As the current of air hits the jet of
water emerging from the tube it breaks it
up in the form of a spray.

The force exerted
by compressed air

Ordinary air pressure is great, but
even greater force can be obtained by compressing the air — that is, by squeezing it
into a smaller space. It is easy to show how
great this force is. Place a paper bag under
a heavy book. Blow into the bag, compressing the air in it; the book will be lifted.

Compressed air can be made to move
water out of a bottle, producing a miniature
fountain (Figure 15). Procure a one-hole
stopper that will fit tightly in a flask. A
glass tube is to be inserted through the hole
of the stopper in such a way that it will
extend almost to the bottom of the flask
and will protrude an inch or so above the
stopper. Attach a two-inch piece of rubber
tubing to the protruding part of the glass
tube. Then insert a medicine dropper, small
end up, in the open end of the rubber tubing. Pour water in the flask only to a depth
of about an inch. Now put the stopper in
place and blow into the medicine dropper.
Pinch the rubber tubing tightly just before
you take your mouth away from the dropper. When you release your pressure on
the tubing, the air compressed in the flask
will force the water out in a fountainlike
stream. You can regulate the flow by alternately pressing on the rubber tubing and
then releasing the pressure.

Compressed air has many uses. You
have probably seen men operating a pave-
ment breaker, which is a drill used to break
up concrete or other solid materials in a
street or sidewalk. A rubber hose brings
air under pressure into the device, and
it is this air that operates the drill. The
force exerted is greater than could be produced by men using sledge hammers. Compressed air in a garage is used to fill tires;
torpedoes are operated by compressed air.
See also Vol. 10, p. 289: "Physics, Experiments in."

15. How to produce a
miniature fountain. A
rubber tube is set be-
tween a glass tube and
a medicine dropper (A),
as described on this
page. Blow through
the medicine dropper,
pinching the rubber
tube. Release your
pressure on the tube; a
fountain will spout (B).

straws, a card about the size of a postcard
and a glass of water. Cut out a section from
one corner of the card and set the straws
in place, as shown in Figure 14. You can
hold the straws in position by means of
thread; push the thread through the card
with a needle and then tie the ends together.
When you blow hard on one straw, as
shown, you create an area of lessened pressure above the other straw. The atmospheric
pressure directly over the straw is reduced;
the pressure upon the water in the glass

THE MIDDLE AGES (450-1450)

BY JUSTUS SCHIFFERES

THE EARLY PERIOD

THE name Middle Ages is commonly given to the long period from the collapse of the Western Roman Empire in the fifth century to the invention of printing, about 1450. There was a time when this period was considered to be a sterile interlude in the story of mankind — "a long Gothic night," as Rabelais put it. We realize today that this view was not justified. The men of the Middle Ages created great literature — BEOWULF, THE SONG OF ROLAND, the romances of Chrétien de Troyes, the lyrics of the Provençal troubadours and the German minnesingers, Dante's DIVINE COMEDY and Petrarch's SONNETS. The Middle Ages produced those marvels of architecture — the Gothic cathedrals — that we can still admire at Amiens, Reims, Chartres, Paris, Canterbury, Cologne and Burgos. There were great philosophers, too, in those days: Albertus Magnus, Thomas Aquinas, Duns Scotus, William of Ockham. Yet, on the whole, as we shall see, the Middle Ages represented a period of stagnation in the history of science.

In the first few centuries of the Middle Ages there was turmoil in the Western world, as new kingdoms and principalities rose and fell. It seemed indeed, at one time, that the Frankish King Charles the Great, or Charlemagne (742–814), might bring about a new era. He united much of Europe in a mighty empire and he sought to restore law and order in his realms; but after his death his empire fell to pieces.

Learning was in a sorry way in the West after the Roman Empire fell. There were exceptional cases, indeed. Thus, in Ireland, the great St. Patrick (389?–461?) had stoked fires of culture which made the Emerald Isle one of the most civilized countries in the Western world during the fifth and sixth centuries; in Rome, the scholar Boethius (480?–524?) wrote books on arithmetic and geometry and music which remained standard for many centuries.

Learning in the early Middle Ages was cultivated chiefly in the monasteries. As Latin was the official language of the Church, certain classical Latin writings continued to be studied; among these were the NATURAL HISTORY of Pliny and the NATURAL QUESTIONS of Seneca. Few men had any knowledge of Greek, and the wonderful Greek heritage was all but lost. However, a few Greek works were still available in Latin translations, such as those of the philosopher Boethius.

The record of the scientific achievements of antiquity was available chiefly in a series of compilations. In the fifth century Martianus Capella wrote a curious Latin allegory called SATYRIKON, or ON THE NUPTIALS OF PHILOLOGIA AND MERCURY AND ON THE SEVEN LIBERAL ARTS. The work begins with an account of the marriage of the god Mercury to the nymph Philologia, patroness of learning. It then goes on to discuss the seven liberal arts — grammar, dialectics, rhetoric, geometry, arithmetic, astronomy and music — which are represented as courtiers of Mercury and Philologia. The SATYRIKON, for all its allegorical trappings, is really an encyclopedia of the arts and sciences.

Bishop Isidore of Seville (570?–636) summed up the learning of his time in an

An outstanding example of medieval architecture — the cloister of the Cathedral of Saint-Trophime. It is in Arles, France.

Bildarchiv Foto Marburg

encyclopedic work called ETYMOLOGIES, or ORIGINS, from the title of one of its sections. The ETYMOLOGIES takes up almost everything under the sun: the seven liberal arts, medicine, libraries, the law, church doctrine and lore, language, history, men, beasts, birds, geography, building construction, road building, metals, agriculture and a great variety of other topics. Isidore

Saxon cleric Alcuin (735–804), was attended by the children of the Emperor, the sons of nobles and a few other carefully selected children.

The palace school was discontinued after the death of the great Emperor, but the cathedral schools continued to flourish; they helped to preserve such learning as was still available in those days.

In the early Middle Ages, learning was cultivated chiefly in the monasteries.

was a man of wide learning, but he was not very critical; he tended to accept all kinds of fanciful legends at face value.

Compilations like these were available only to a small number of learned men. The general ignorance of "book learning," even among the so-called ruling classes, was appalling.

Disturbed by the low stage of knowledge in his realms, Charlemagne sought to bring about educational reform. He ordered schools to be set up in cathedrals for the education of those who wished to enter the clergy. He also established a palace school at the capital city of Aix-la-Chapelle. This institution, which was under the direction of the learned Anglo-

ARAB STANDARD-BEARERS OF SCIENTIFIC LEARNING

The Roman Empire had been divided up in the fourth century, as we have seen, into western and eastern parts. In the Eastern Roman Empire, which came to be known as the Byzantine Empire, the general intellectual level was somewhat higher than in the West during the Dark Ages. Since the language of the Eastern Empire was Greek, scholars never lost contact with the works of Plato and Aristotle and other great representatives of Greek thought. But the Byzantine court was particularly interested in theological studies. Science did not flourish there, though scholars continued to make compilations of

earlier scientific writings — chiefly medical works.

The cause of science was now to be served by a group of heretical Byzantines, called Nestorians. They followed the teachings of Nestorius (died about 451), the patriarch of Constantinople, who had been dismissed from his post and exiled because of his unorthodox views. His followers eventually settled in southwestern Persia, where they developed an outstanding intellectual movement. The Nestorians wrote in Syriac. They translated into this language a number of ancient classics, including works by Aristotle, Hippocrates,

Euclid, Archimedes, Ptolemy and Galen.

In the seventh century a new force entered upon the world scene — the religion of Islam, or Mohammedanism, founded by the Arab prophet Mohammed (570–632). The Arab followers of the prophet began to spread their master's teachings by fire and sword; in a few years they conquered Egypt, Syria, Armenia and Persia. The Nestorians came to terms with the Arab conquerors, who were greatly impressed by the learning of these heretical Christians.

In the years that followed, Greek learning was transmitted to the Arabic world chiefly through the agency of the Nestorians. At first Syriac was the language of science and learning in general in the Arabic empire; then Arabic began to replace Syriac for this purpose. The works of Aristotle, Ptolemy, Galen and other Greek notables were translated into Arabic, which proved to be well adapted to scientific writing.

In the ninth century the Arabs became the chief standard-bearers of science and philosophy. The golden age of Arabic science lasted for about two centuries, from roughly 900 to 1100 A.D. It is true that many of the best "Arab" scientists were neither Arabs nor Moslems; they were Syrians, Persians and Jews who had Arabic names and wrote in the Arabic language. Yet the world owes a great debt of gratitude to the Moslem caliphs for their support of learning.

The Arabs made important contributions to mathematics. The outstanding Arabic work in this field, perhaps, was the ARITHMETIC of the Persian Al-Kwarizmi (ninth century). In this treatise the author introduced a striking innovation — the number system that we use today and that we call "Arabic numerals." (The Arabs called them *gobar* numbers.) In this system, which Al-Kwarizmi derived from the Hindus, the value of a digit depends upon its *position* in a series of digits. Thus 2 by itself stands for 2; in the series 21, it stands for 20 $(21 = 20 + 1)$; in the series 215, for 200 $(215 = 200 + 10 + 5)$. The zero

sign — 0 — has no value of its own; it simply indicates the position and, consequently, the value of the preceding digit, or digits. For example, the two zeros in 200 show that the first digit (2) has a value in the hundreds instead of in units, tens or thousands. It is far easier to calculate with Arabic numbers than with the cumbersome Latin numerals that were generally used in Western Europe until the end of the Middle Ages.

Al-Kwarizmi derived the system of so-called Arabic numerals from the Hindu mathematicians of India. They had worked out the system as early as the third century B.C.; the first reference to it outside of India is found only in the seventh century A.D., a thousand years later. The Hindus also introduced the idea of negative numbers, which they illustrated in problems having to do with assets and debts.

The name "algebra" comes from the Arabic

Al-Kwarizmi wrote a treatise ON ALGEBRA, based to a certain extent on Hindu sources. The name "algebra" is of Arabic origin; it comes from *al-jebr*, meaning "the union of broken parts." The word meant a certain type of algebraic computation as well as the science of algebra as a whole. It also was used as a surgical term; it referred to the setting of broken bones.

Another famed Persian mathematician was Omar Khayyam, who lived in Nishapur in the twelfth century. He solved mathematical problems and wrote enduring poetry. The English translation of his poem THE RUBAIYAT, by the nineteenth-century English scholar, Edward Fitz-Gerald, is one of the best-known poems in any language. (Many mathematicians have been poets and writers; best known to English-speaking people, perhaps, is the author of ALICE IN WONDERLAND, Charles Lutwidge Dodgson, whose pen name was Lewis Carroll.)

The Arabs were greatly interested in astronomy. The caliph Ma'mun built a splendid observatory in Bagdad in the year 829, and his astronomers made regular observations of the heavens. An Arab scholar translated the GREAT COMPOSITION of Ptolemy (see the Index) under the title of the ALMAGEST. This work became the standard textbook of astronomy for the Arabs.

One of the greatest of the Arab astronomers was Al-Battani (died 929). He accepted the teachings of Ptolemy in the main, but, instead of following the master blindly, he worked over the Alexandrian astronomer's observations and in many cases he obtained more accurate values. He pointed out that the apparent movements of the sun in the heavens do not correspond to those indicated in the Ptolemaic system. But he did not realize that this was because the system itself was extremely inadequate.

The pseudoscience of alchemy had many devotees among the Arabs. These alchemists believed that the primary chemical elements were sulfur (fire), mercury (liquid) and salt (solid). They held that these elements were present, in different proportions, in all the metals, ranging from base metals, like lead, to noble metals, like gold. By changing the mixture of elements in a base metal, it was possible, they thought, to transmute a base metal to a noble one.

The name alchemy itself is of Arabic origin, but its exact derivation is not clear. *Al* is the Arabic article meaning "the"; but the form "chemy" is puzzling. Some think it is derived from the Greek *chymeia* (mixture); others trace it back to the Greek *chyma* (molten metal); still others to the Egyptian *kem-it* (black).

The foremost Arab alchemist was Jabir or Jaber (Geber in Latin), a Syrian physician who lived in the eighth or ninth century. Scholars disagree about the nature of Geber's contributions to alchemy. Certain treatises by Geber, in Arabic, still exist; there are also Latin translations of works that are attributed to him. It is not certain that these are genuine translations. Some suspect that the supposed translator was really the author but that, since al-

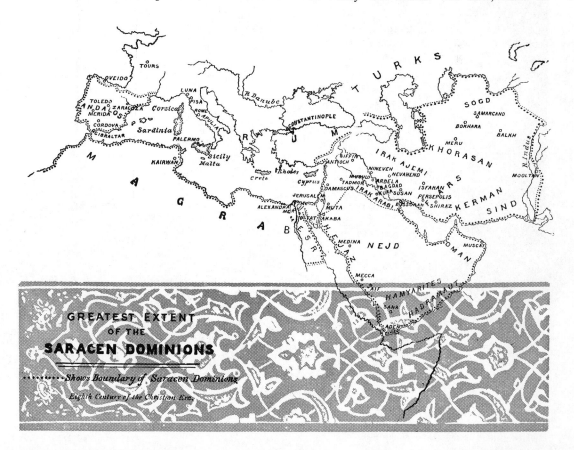

GREATEST EXTENT
OF THE
SARACEN DOMINIONS

········ Shows Boundary of Saracen Dominions

Eighth Century of the Christian Era.

chemists were often persecuted in Western Europe, he preferred to attribute his own work to an Arab. If the Latin works are genuine, they show that Geber perfected new methods of evaporation, filtration and crystallization, and that he was able to prepare a considerable number of chemical substances, such as alums, alkalis, saltpeter and mercuric oxide.

The Persian-born physician Rhazes (865?–925?) also contributed to the literature of alchemy with his BOOK OF THE ART. He has given a clear account of the apparatus and the processes that he employed. He classified all substances as animal, vegetable and mineral—a distinc-

tion that still prevails, of course, in our popular speech. There were other Arab writers on alchemy. Most of them were decidedly inferior to Geber and Rhazes; they were often willfully obscure, since they did not wish to reveal their secrets to the public at large.

The foremost Arab physicist was Alhazen (965?–1038?) of Basra. His chief works were THE TREASURY OF OPTICS and ON THE BURNING SPHERE. Alhazen worked out the laws of reflection; he experimented with spherical and parabolic mirrors and with magnifying glasses. He discussed atmospheric refraction (which causes the mirages that are sometimes seen in the desert); he studied the refraction of light-rays as they pass through air and water. His theory of the process of vision marks a definite advance over Euclid and other ancient Greek

Above: a Moorish astrolabe, used to determine the altitude of celestial bodies. It consisted of a disk, which could be suspended from a ring, and a pointer, which pivoted at the center of the disk.

writers, who had taught that the eye sends out rays to the object that is beheld. Alhazen maintained that vision results when the form of the perceived object passes into the eye and is transmitted by the lens.

The Arabs numbered many excellent physicians. Among the best known was Rhazes who, as we have seen, was an alchemist as well as a medical man. His chief medical work was the COMPREHENSIVE BOOK; in this he set forth not only the medical lore of the ancient Greeks, Nestorians and Arabs but also the fruits of his own extensive experience. Rhazes was the first to distinguish between smallpox and measles.

Avicenna (980?–1037) of Bokhara was both a distinguished Arab philosopher and an eminent physician. He was the author of a huge medical textbook called the CANON OF MEDICINE. Like Rhazes, Avicenna summed up the knowledge of medicine inherited from the Greeks, and he added to it the contributions of the chief Arab writers on medicine. The translation of his CANON OF MEDICINE became a favorite medical textbook in Western Europe; it was still used in certain universities as late as the seventeenth century.

Thus far we have been dealing with the Arab scientists who flourished in the eastern part of the Moslem world. In Spain an equally enlightened but somewhat different type of Moslem culture had developed. The Mohammedans of Spain were mostly Moors, whose ancestral homeland was in northern Africa. The Moors had conquered most of the Iberian peninsula (Spain and Portugal) in the early part of the eighth century; they were not driven from the last of their possessions in the peninsula until 1492. With the help of the Sephardic Jews, to whom they had given refuge and opportunity, the Moors developed a high type of civilization in Cordova, Toledo and Seville. Industry flourished in their realms: Cordovan leather and Toledan blades became famous.

The foremost representative of Moorish culture in Spain was Averroës of Cordova (1126–98). He was proficient in theology, law, mathematics, medicine and philosophy; he was a practicing physician and a judge of high repute. He idolized Aristotle and prepared a series of extensive commentaries on the works of the great Greek philosopher. These commentaries were not pure Aristotle by any means; they bore traces of Neoplatonism (see Index, under Neoplatonic school).

Averroës believed, like Plotinus, that the human soul is an emanation of the divine world soul. The world, he said, is eternal; it did not come into being as the result of a single act of creation. Instead, there is a constant process of creation, resulting in a constantly changing world. The only stable element in the world is the Prime Mover, who is eternal and changeless. This viewpoint was directly opposed to the tenets of the Islamic faith, and

Averroës incurred the hostility of conservative theologians. His works were publicly burned and he was in official disgrace during the latter part of his life.

The Jewish physician, philosopher, mathematician and astronomer Moses ben-Maimon (1135–1204), better known as Maimonides, combatted the Averroist idea of constant creation. In his philosophical treatise, The Guide for the Perplexed, Maimonides set forth his belief in a single creative act, which reflected the divine design of the Creator. Maimonides was a truly remarkable man. He was the personal physician of Saladin, King Richard the Lion Hearted's chivalrous foe; he was also the greatest rabbinical authority of his time. He wrote treatises on medicine and hygiene in which he showed considerable independence of thought. He even made so bold as to criticize certain opinions of Galen, the Greek physician who was still considered to be the supreme authority in medicine.

In the twelfth century, conservative Moslems began to turn against the learned men who had brought such glory to the name of Islam. The flame of learning began to sink low in the Moslem world; it was now to be kindled anew in the West.

THE FLOWERING OF MEDIEVAL THOUGHT

In the ninth and tenth centuries it was very generally predicted that the year 1000 A.D. would mark the end of the world. Of course this calamity did not come to pass as scheduled. A change in the mood of Western Europe made itself felt as the spirit of doom and foreboding that had been so widespread was gradually dissipated.

There was renewed interest in learning as the lore of the Arabs penetrated into the West by way of Spain and The Two Sicilies. We saw that Spain, which geographically formed a part of the Western world, had been almost entirely conquered by the Moslems in the early part of the eighth century and was not entirely freed from Mohammedan rule until 1492. The Two Sicilies, a region including Sicily and part of southern Italy, remained under Saracen

domination from the eighth century to the eleventh. The Normans, under Count Roger, then succeeded in driving out the Moslems; but Arabic culture remained strong in the area for many years to come. Despite the natural hostility of Christians and Moslems, there were many contacts between them in Spain and The Two Sicilies.

By the end of the twelfth century, translations into Latin had made available to European scholars a good many Arabic scientific works, as well as Greek scientific works which had been translated previously into Arabic. There were the Physics and the biological writings of Aristotle; mathematical works like the Elements of Euclid, On the Quadrature of the Circle, by Archimedes, and the Algebra of Al-Kwarizmi; astronomical works like the

Comprehensive Book of Rhazes and the Canon of Medicine of Avicenna.

Many of the translations from the Arabic were prepared by Jewish scholars in Moslem Spain. They were unusually well equipped for their task; not only did they know the Arabic tongue very well, but they were also thoroughly familiar with Arabic works on astronomy, alchemy, mathematics, theology and the like. There were also many Western translators. The greatest of these was Gerard of Cremona (1114?–87), who had spent a number of years in Toledo and who had acquired a thorough knowledge of Arabic. Gerard is said to have translated ninety-two Arabic works into Latin, including the Almagest of Ptolemy and the Canon of Medicine of Avicenna.

All translators from the Arabic were handicapped by the lack of technical terms in Medieval Latin; certain Western translators had an imperfect understanding of the meaning of certain Arabic words. A number of these words, therefore, were taken over more or less intact into Latin. Many of them later found their way into English: chemical terms like alcohol, alkali, alembic and camphor; astronomical terms like nadir, zenith and almanac; names of stars like Aldebaran, Betelgeuse and Vega; mathematical terms such as algebra, cipher

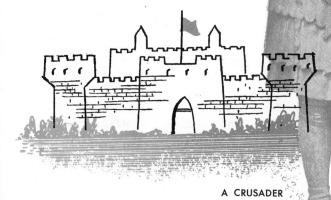

A CRUSADER

and zero; botanical terms like artichoke, coffee, lemon and sumach.

The translations from the Arabic revealed a new world of thought to the men of the West and brought about a quickening of the sense of wonder. The Crusades contributed to the growing ferment. These military campaigns, in the course of which the Christian knights of the West wrested the Holy City of Jerusalem from the infidel and lost it again, extended over a period of something like two hundred years (roughly, 1090–1290). The Crusades brought many men of the West in contact with the more advanced civilization of the East — with its literature, its philosophy, its science, its architecture, its arts, its industries. The returning crusaders brought back with them from the East a host of new impressions and also of new wants.

The rise of
European universities

The growing thirst for learning was soon reflected in the rise of universities. In part these institutions were the outgrowth of the cathedral schools that had been set up at the bidding of Charlemagne. Some of the earliest universities, like that of Bologna, were corporations or associations of students who banded together for study and also for mutual protection against hostile townspeople. (In those early days, too, there was rivalry between "town" and "gown.") Other universities, like that of Paris, were originally guilds of masters, or teachers.

The course of study included the seven liberal arts, which were divided into two groups — the trivium and the quadrivium. The trivium (three-division course of study) consisted of grammar, rhetoric and dialectic; the quadrivium (four-division course of study), of arithmetic, music, geometry and astronomy. After a student obtained both his Bachelor of Arts and Master of Arts degrees, he was eligible for the higher courses of theology, law and medicine.

The universities were profoundly influenced by two new religious orders: the Franciscan order, founded by the Italian St. Francis of Assisi in 1209, and the Do-

minican order, which the Spaniard St. Dominic of Galaroga established in 1215. Both orders provided a great many outstanding university teachers. Albertus Magnus and St. Thomas Aquinas were Dominicans; Robert Grosseteste and Roger Bacon were Franciscans.

Great stress was laid in the universities on a penetrating kind of philosophy called scholasticism, which had arisen in the cathedral schools. The schoolmen, as the scholastic philosophers were called, often displayed a keenness of logical reasoning that has rarely been surpassed.

Aristotle's influence
on medieval thought

The schoolmen were greatly influenced by the writings of Aristotle. By 1225 almost all the works of the great Greek philosopher were available in Latin translation. The scholastic philosophers were dazzled by the tremendously wide range of Aristotle's pronouncements on philosophy and literature and science. They girded themselves for the task of squaring the doctrines of Aristotle with the tenets of Christian dogma.

Among the schoolmen who tried to interpret and systematize the rediscovered works of Aristotle was Albertus Magnus (1206?–80) of Cologne. He was considered to be the most learned man of his time. Into his elaborate commentaries on Aristotle he wove all that was then known about astronomy, geography, botany, zoology and medicine. In his scientific writings Albertus sometimes showed considerable powers of observation.

The greatest pupil of Albertus Magnus was St. Thomas Aquinas (1225?–74), who has been called the "Christian Aristotle." Born near Aquino, in southern Italy, he joined the Dominican order when he was eighteen. He journeyed to Cologne to study under Albertus Magnus; later he taught at Paris and at Rome. His greatest work was his SUMMA THEOLOGICA (The Sum and Substance of Theology), in which with faultless logic he combined Aristotelian learning with the teachings of Christian theology.

St. Thomas rejected Aristotle's doctrine of the eternity of the world, because Holy Scripture required a creation in time; he also modified certain other doctrines. But, on the whole, the Greek philosopher was accepted as the authority in philosophy and in science.

It was the aim of St. Thomas to construct a complete system of thought that would show that the universe was in logical accord with divine revelation and "spiritual fact." The supreme goal of all learning, therefore, was theology (the study of God's ways), the "queen of the sciences." ("Sciences" then meant simply "branches of knowledge.") Philosophy, including natural philosophy — the study of the physical world — was considered to be the handmaid of theology.

In one respect St. Thomas and other schoolmen made a valuable contribution to the development of modern science, for they held firmly to the belief that ours is an ordered universe that can be comprehended by the light of reason. Modern science is based upon this faith in reason (rationalism) and this belief that events can be coupled with causes in a definite and orderly manner.

St. Thomas's teachings were not universally accepted in the years that followed; Duns Scotus and others disputed the master on various points. But the authority of Aristotle was now firmly established. Thenceforth few ventured to challenge either his philosophy or his fragmentary and sometimes inaccurate scientific views. Together with Aristotle, the astronomer Ptolemy and the physician Galen were accepted as supreme authorities whose word was law except for certain minor details. This viewpoint was entirely hostile to the spirit of free investigation.

A DARING FRIAR OF OXFORD

The hampering restrictions laid upon free investigation by authority were seriously challenged by a friar of Oxford, Roger Bacon (1214?–94), the greatest figure in medieval science. Born in the second decade of the thirteenth century at Ilchester, Somersetshire, of a wealthy and

Roger Bacon, the greatest figure in medieval science.

respected family, Bacon was sent to Oxford to study. There he came under the influence of the learned Franciscan Robert Grosseteste (1175?–1253), chancellor of the University of Oxford and, later, Bishop of Lincoln. The good bishop was particularly interested in literature; but he was also no mean mathematician and he conducted many experiments with mirrors and lenses. Bacon said of him: "But one alone knows the sciences — the Bishop of Lincoln."

After receiving the degree of Master of Arts at Oxford, Bacon went to Paris for further study about 1235. He received a master's degree at Paris; according to some accounts, he also became a Doctor of Theology. He was back in Oxford by 1251 and he became a friar of the Franciscan order. He lectured at Oxford; he also performed many experiments in alchemy and optics, spending large sums of money for books and instruments. His interest in the experimental method, his advanced views and also his supposed dabbling in magic caused him to be regarded with suspicion. He was forbidden to lecture at Oxford; later, he was sent to Paris and kept closely confined in a Franciscan monastery for ten years, 1257 to 1267.

He had the good fortune, however, to meet a liberal-minded cleric, Guy de Foulques, who appreciated his genius. When De Foulques became pope in 1265, taking the name of Clement IV, he ordered Bacon to set down in writing the ideas that he had been forbidden to teach. In 1267, after eighteen months of feverish work, the friar completed his task and sent to the Pope the three manuscripts upon which his scientific reputation chiefly rests. They were an Opus Maius (Greater Work), outlining at length his views on mathematics, physics, philosophy, logic, grammar and philology (the study of languages); an Opus Minus

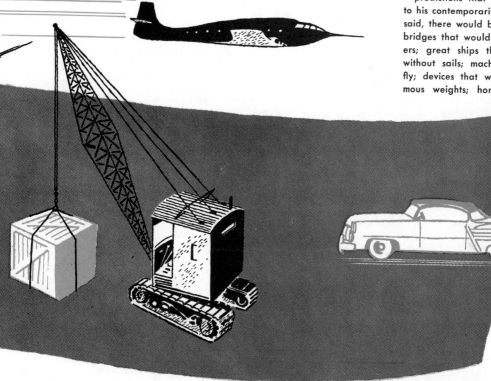

Bacon made a number of startling predictions of future developments — predictions that seemed fantastic to his contemporaries. Some day, he said, there would be big suspension bridges that would span broad rivers; great ships that would move without sails; machines that would fly; devices that would raise enormous weights; horseless carriages.

(Lesser Work), summarizing the Opus Maius; an Opus Tertium (Third Work), which he sent to the Pope for fear that the other works might be lost in transit.

Bacon was released from custody and he returned to Oxford. In 1277 he was again in hot water; his works were denounced and he was condemned to renewed imprisonment in the Franciscan house in Paris. He was not released until 1292; he died two years later.

Bacon believed
in experimentation

Bacon was one of the very few men of his age to appreciate the value of experiment in science. "Since this experimental science," he wrote, "is wholly unknown to the rank and file of students, I am therefore unable to convince people of its utility unless at the same time I disclose its excellence and its proper significance. This science alone knows how to test perfectly what can be done by nature, what by the effort of art, what by trickery . . . This science investigates by experiment the notable conclusions of all science . . . which must employ its principles . . . I give as an example the rainbow and the phenomena connected with it. Neither Aristotle nor Avicenna in their Natural Histories has given us a knowledge of phenomena of this kind, nor has Seneca, who composed a special book on them. But experimental science attests them." *

Bacon explained many optical phenomena with rare clarity. He understood the nature of the rainbow and described many of the optical properties of lenses; he was among the first in Europe to suggest the use of lenses for spectacles. He is said to have developed a formula for making gunpowder in the course of his alchemical experiments. (His popular reputation rests on this so-called invention of gunpowder.) He studied the calendar and pointed out

* From English translation of *Opus Maius* by Robert B. Burke (1928, University of Pennsylvania Press).

that the reckoning of 365 ¼ days a year produced an error of one day every 130 years. He criticized the astronomy of Ptolemy. He startled the men of his time with his seemingly fantastic predictions of things to come — horseless carriages, ships that would move without sails, machines that would fly through the air; other machines that would raise great weights; suspension bridges that would span rivers. Of course, these marvels came to pass; for today we have automobiles, steamers, airplanes, cranes and suspension bridges.

Bacon never completely cast off the shackles of the age in which he lived. He was a firm believer in alchemy and considered its study a *must* for all students worthy of the name; he believed just as firmly in astrology. Yet in his attitude toward experimentation as the acid test of truth he was truly a man of science. Unfortunately for him, he was centuries ahead of his time.

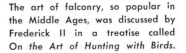

The art of falconry, so popular in the Middle Ages, was discussed by Frederick II in a treatise called *On the Art of Hunting with Birds.*

SCIENCE WEDDED TO TRADITION

Bacon's contemporaries did not heed his call to put scientific theories to the test of experiment. The voice of authority remained supreme; medieval science, for the most part, remained fettered to the past. However, as we shall see, it developed a considerable body of useful knowledge in the fields of astronomy, biology, primitive chemistry (alchemy) and hygiene.

The Ptolemaic system of the universe was almost universally accepted; it formed the basis of the most popular medieval textbook on astronomy, by the Englishman John of Holywood, who was also known as Sacrobosco (died 1250). The chief advances in astronomy were in the nature of more exact observations. Thus, under the patronage of King Alfonso the Wise of Castile (1226?–84), a group of scholars worked out a new set of astronomical tables — the ALFONSINE TABLES — which remained the finest work of its kind for several centuries. Among other things, the TABLES calculated the length of the year with considerable accuracy.

Astronomy, throughout the medieval period, was hardly to be distinguished from the pseudoscience of astrology. Most astronomers, learned or otherwise, believed that human affairs and natural events were influenced by the heavenly bodies. A com-

Page of a medieval bestiary preserved in the Cambridge University Library. The drawing shows the fabulous tree Peridexion. The dragons cannot touch the doves while the latter are either on the tree or else in the shadow that is cast by its branches.

prehensive astrological system was worked out. According to this, the fixed stars rule the natural events that occur in regular and orderly succession — such as the seasons and day and night. The planets and the signs of the zodiac, on the other hand, are supposed to control the variable phenomena of nature; they are also thought to exer-

cise a direct influence upon the bodies of men.

There was considerable interest in natural history in the Middle Ages, as was attested by the great popularity of the bestiaries (beast books). These works described the habits of living creatures and drew from them farfetched moral and religious lessons. The bestiaries contained a vast amount of misinformation about animals that actually existed to say nothing of such legendary creatures as sirens, dragons, unicorns, basilisks and mantichoras (lions with human heads). A number of herbals (plant books) were also prepared. The herbals described plants and gave their medical uses as drugs. They were probably the first of the so-called popular "doctor books" for home treatment.

A more authentic account of the animal world was furnished by the SUMMA DE CREATURIS (Compendium of Living

Things) by Albertus Magnus (see Index). Perhaps the outstanding biological work in the medieval period was the treatise ON THE ART OF HUNTING WITH BIRDS, by the versatile Frederick II (1194–1250), King of Sicily, Holy Roman Emperor, soldier and patron of the arts and sciences. The Emperor, a keen observer, wrote most entertainingly. His observations on bird migration were particularly interesting and surprisingly modern. "With a prophetic instinct for the proper time to migrate," he wrote, "birds as a rule usually anticipate the storms that prevail on their way to and from a warmer climate . . . The slower migrants begin their departure early . . . When the winter threatens to set in early, they migrate much sooner than usual."

The Middle Ages contributed little to the advance of mathematics. Perhaps the most significant mathematical development of this period was the introduction of Arabic numerals to Western Europe. The pioneer in this field was Leonardo Fibonacci (1180?–1250?) of Pisa, who was a merchant and also a learned mathematician. Leonardo was educated in Barbary, on the north African coast, where his father was a commercial agent. The youth learned the numerals used by the Arabs, and he was greatly impressed with their usefulness in calculation. When he returned to Italy, he published a book of reckoning — THE BOOK OF THE ABACUS — in which he urged the adoption of Arabic numerals. It was the first book by a Christian of Western Europe in which this system of calculation was employed. The system was also advocated in a far more popular book — the

An alchemist at work, from a painting by Teniers.
Bettmann Archive

ALGORISMUS, or ARITHMETIC, of John of Holywood. For some reason or other, however, the people of Western Europe were slow to adopt Arabic numerals, and they did not come into general use until the close of the Middle Ages.

Perhaps the most romantic science — or rather pseudoscience — in the medieval period was alchemy, adapted from the Arabs (see page 299). It probably originated with certain Greek metalworkers of Alexandria; but most alchemists attributed the discovery of their art to Hermes Trismegistus, who was sometimes identified with the Egyptian god Thoth. Alchemy was often called the hermetic art; its devotees set the seal of Hermes upon their vessels. (This is the origin of the phrase "hermetically sealed," which is frequently applied to airtight vessels.)

The goals of
the alchemists

With unflagging zeal some alchemists sought the secret of the "philosopher's stone," which would change base metals into gold. Others tried to perfect a universal remedy (panacea) that would cure all human ills; still others sought an "elixir of life" that would keep a man forever young. The laboratories of the alchemists were crammed with furnaces, stills, crucibles, alembics, bellows, jars and a thousand and one other pieces of equipment. In their endless experiments they used every conceivable kind of material — flowers, herbs, blood, flesh, manure, urine, the eyes of toads, the hearts of salamanders. They crushed these materials, burned them, distilled and redistilled them, fused them.

In the main, the endless quest of the alchemists was a monument to human folly. The alchemists themselves were generally held in disrepute; time and time again church and state authorities forbade them to continue their researches or to publish any books. Yet the alchemists numbered some outstanding men of learning, including Albertus Magnus and Roger Bacon, and their labors were not entirely without fruit. They discovered new and important substances — nitric acid, sulfuric acid, hy-

drochloric acid, ammonium chloride, silver nitrate, borax, cream of tartar, plaster of Paris. Some of the apparatus they developed — such as stills, retorts and water baths — still serve in modern chemical laboratories. In the years to come alchemy was gradually to develop into genuine chemical science.

Medicine was wedded in the Middle Ages to the teachings of Galen; few physicians dared to depart from his doctrines. Yet there were certain indications even in this undistinguished period of the future greatness of medical science.

The school of
medicine at Salerno

One of the most promising developments was the founding of a school of medicine in the eleventh century at Salerno, a little seaside resort some thirty miles southeast of Naples. Arabic, Greek, Moorish and Jewish physicians were included among the early teachers. They began anew, like Hippocrates, to study diseases at first hand instead of from books handed down from the past. They believed in dissection in order to acquire information about the human body; but, bowing to the prejudices of the time, they cut up pigs instead of human corpses.

The masters of Salerno had quite sensible ideas about diet and hygiene. The sum total of their ideas on these vital subjects was set down in a long doggerel poem in Latin — the HEALTH REGIMEN OF SALERNO. It became immensely popular; it passed through some 250 separate editions and was translated into many other languages, including English, Gaelic and Hebrew. The teachings of the school of Salerno are aptly summarized in the opening lines of the REGIMEN, in the spirited translation of Sir John Harrington:

"The Salerno School doth by these lines impart
All health to England's king * and doth advise
From care his head to keep, from wrath his
 heart. . .
Use three physicians still: first Doctor Diet
Next Doctor Merryman and Doctor Quiet."

The medical school of Salerno did not fulfill its early promise; it began to go

* Robert of Normandy, son of William the Conqueror.

The hospital known as the Hôtel-Dieu of Paris consisted of a hall in which beds for the sick were placed.

downhill when Frederick II set up a rival university at Naples in 1224. It became notorious in the later Middle Ages as a "diploma mill," where students received degrees for medical work that they never did.

The study of medicine flourished in other medieval universities. Unfortunately medicine, like the law, was considered to be a "learned profession," and the professors of medicine laid stress upon bookish learning rather than upon experimental research or surgical work. The result was a cleavage between medicine and surgery. Surgery was generally left to barbers, who combined haircutting with bloodletting and other simple operations. The white and red peppermint-striped barber pole of today is a relic of the barber-surgeon of the past. The white stripe of the pole represents the bandages used in bloodletting; the red represents the blood of the patient.

The Middle Ages saw the organization of many hospitals for the care of the sick. Charity hospitals under Christian auspices go back to the fourth century; one of the first was established by Helena, the mother

of the Roman Emperor Constantine the Great. The famous Hôtel-Dieu in Paris was founded by a bishop of Paris probably in the seventh century. The hospital idea had become well established by the last years of the eleventh century. But a hospital was essentially a place of refuge, not a place for operations and other medical treatment.

The leper houses (leprosaria) of the Middle Ages were really special hospitals providing nursing care and lodging. There were also hospitals for the aged, for foundlings and for poor and infirm pilgrims. During the thirteenth century hospitals gradually passed from religious to municipal control. The art of nursing began to decline and fall into disrepute; it did not regain a respectable status in society until the nineteenth century.

The Black Death, or plague, which ravaged Europe at intervals in the fourteenth century and later, was responsible for the introduction of the medical practice known as quarantine. The Black Death had been carried by trading ships from Turkey and the Crimea to Genoa and Venice and thence along the trade routes to western and northern Europe. The doctors of that day were baffled by the plague, and millions died of it.

In 1374 the guardians of public health in Venice took steps to keep the dread disease from their city. They excluded from the port of Venice all ships infected with the plague or suspected of carrying it. Three years later the city of Ragusa decreed that all travelers from Asia Minor must be isolated for thirty days in a deten-tion hospital or on shipboard, outside the harbor, before being permitted to enter the city. The period of detention was later increased to forty days in both Marseilles and Venice. This forty-day period, known as *quarantina* in Italian, has given us the word "quarantine." Nowadays quarantine no longer refers to a specific forty-day period; it is applied to any forced stoppage or isolation destined to ward off infection.

PROGRESS IN THE PRACTICAL ARTS

The contributions made by the Middle Ages to pure science were comparatively insignificant, but there was considerable progress in the application of science to the industrial arts and, in general, to the affairs of everyday life. Glassmaking, which had been developed in antiquity, flourished in medieval times; large glass works were established in Germany, Italy and Spain. Spectacles were introduced, probably in northern Italy, possibly in Holland, in the thirteenth century. New iron foundries were set up; new mines were developed in Bohemia, Germany and Hungary. By the middle of the fourteenth century, the art of papermaking, brought in from Moorish Spain, had spread through France, Italy and Germany. Gunpowder was introduced in this same century. The development of sturdy metal casings made it possible to use gunpowder in cannon and gradually brought about a revolution in the art of warfare. Clocks with elaborate trains of wheels were developed. The compass, which may have been introduced into Europe as early as the twelfth century (see Index, under Compasses) removed much of the guesswork from navigation.

Perhaps the outstanding industrial development in the Middle Ages, from the standpoint of science, was the invention of printing from movable type. Credit for the discovery is generally given — though not without dispute — to Johann Gutenberg (1397?–1468?) of Mainz on the Rhine; he was aided by the wealthy Johann Faust. By 1450 Gutenberg had developed a method of printing from movable type.

Before Gutenberg's day, books were few and costly. Most of them existed only in manuscript form; they were laboriously copied by hand, chiefly by industrious monks. A few books had been printed on paper from blocks of wood, on which the letters for the whole page had to be cut. Gutenberg's chief innovation was the use of movable type, locked into place in a chase, or frame. With this system, any number of combinations of letters could be set up rapidly and cheaply, at least by comparison with copying by hand. Further-

Train of wheels of a large clock formerly in Dover Castle. The clock was built in Switzerland in 1348.

Johann Gutenberg at his press. The three letters that we show here are specimens of the Gothic lettering he employed.

more, the letters, once carved in wood or stone or cast in metal, could be used over and over again.

The first complete book printed from movable type was an edition of the Bible (completed about 1455); this is known now as the Gutenberg Bible. The art of printing spread rapidly. William Caxton (1422?–91) brought the printing press to England in 1476; other pioneers set up presses in Holland, France and Italy. Refinements in the art of fine and rapid printing have been constantly introduced ever since. Today a rotary press can turn out from 800 to 1,000 copies of a complete newspaper in a minute.

It would be difficult to overestimate the importance of printing in spreading and preserving knowledge. Formerly ideas had been circulated only among a small and select group of learned men; with the development of printing, they became available to an infinitely larger circle of readers. Our problem today is no longer how to circulate scientific information; it is how to catalog and abstract all the scientific information that gets into print.

The mariner's compass, gunpowder and printing "changed the whole face and state of things throughout the world," to quote Sir Francis Bacon. Science profited immensely by this upheaval. The grip of authority upon men of science was not immediately loosened; a stern, uphill fight lay ahead. But conditions were far more favorable than before for the ultimate triumph of free scientific investigation.

Continued on page 361.

THE FORCE OF GRAVITATION

BY LOUIS M. HEIL

How All Things Attract One Another

ONE of the first things a very young child learns is that any object (including himself) will fall to the ground if it is free to fall. He will note, later, that any object tends to bend in the direction in which it would fall if it were dropped. For example, a rope that is hung between two vertical poles will sag.

Observations such as these led the ancients to believe that the earth is the natural resting place of all objects. They held that a ball dropped from a height will fall to the ground and that a rope hung between two poles will sag because the ball and the rope are trying to get to their natural resting places. Scientists now have a much more satisfactory explanation. It was worked out in the seventeenth century by the great English philosopher and mathematician Sir Isaac Newton.

Newton was trying to find out why Mars, Venus, Jupiter and the other planets of our solar system keep moving in very definite orbits around the sun. We can compare the paths they take to the path described by an object that a boy swings at the end of a string. There is one important difference, however. There is a mechanical connection — the string — between the boy's hand and the object that he is whirling. Obviously, there is no mechanical connection between the sun and the planets. Newton came to the conclusion that a planet keeps revolving around the sun because the two bodies attract one another. This type of action-at-a-distance he called gravitation.

He made a careful analysis of the action-at-a-distance, and he developed his famous law of universal gravitation. According to this law, every particle in the universe attracts every other particle with a force which is proportional to the product of their masses and inversely proportional *

---

* Inverse proportion involves switching the numerator and denominator of a fraction. For example, let us assume that the ratio between A and B is 2 to 1. We could set down this relationship as

$$\frac{A}{B} = \frac{2}{1}$$

To bring about an inverse proportion in this case, we would switch the 2 (numerator) and the 1 (denominator). The new proportion would be

$$\frac{A}{B} = \frac{1}{2}$$

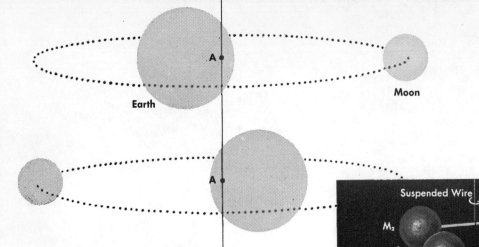

1. The earth and its satellite, the moon, drawn to each other by gravitational force, move around a common center of gravity, located within the earth (A, above). In the upper diagram, we see the earth and the moon at one point in their respective orbits. The lower diagram shows the relative positions of the earth and its satellite approximately fourteen days later. They are now on the opposite side of their orbits around the common center of gravity. You will observe, in the diagram, that not only the moon but also the center of the earth have moved around A

2. The Cavendish gravity experiment. He suspended two lead balls, M_1 and M_2, at opposite ends of a torsion balance. When a third ball, M_3, was brought close to M_2, mutual attraction caused M_2 to approach M_3, thus twisting the suspended wire.

to the square of the distance between the various particles.

Let us give a simple illustration. Suppose that two bodies are set at a given distance from each other. We assume that one body has a mass of 4 tons and the other a mass of 8 tons and that the gravitational force acting on each is 1 pound. The product of the two masses is 32 (4×8). We now double the mass of the first body, leaving the distance between the two bodies unchanged. Since the first body now has a mass of 8 tons, the product of the two masses is 64 (8×8). This product is twice the former one. Therefore the gravitational force between the two bodies is doubled; that means that it is increased from 1 pound to 2 pounds.

We now consider again the two original masses of 4 and 8 pounds. Suppose we reduce the distance between the centers of the two bodies by ½. Since the gravitational force between the bodies is inversely proportional to the square of the distance between them, this force will now be increased 4 times (²⁄₁ squared). It will be 4 pounds. If the distance between the two bodies was doubled, the force would be reduced to ¼ its original value (½ squared). It would therefore be ¼ pound.

It is important to note that the force resulting from gravitational attraction acts on both bodies involved. The earth, whose mass is much greater than that of the moon, attracts the moon through the force of gravitation; but the moon also attracts the earth. We assume that both the earth and the moon are moving about a common center (Figure 1). This is much closer to the center of the earth than to the center of the moon because of the difference in their masses. Actually, as the diagram shows, the common center around which both the earth and the moon move lies within the earth.

The force of
gravitation is universal

Gravitational attraction applies to all masses, regardless of where they are located. It explains why a baseball falls to the ground when it is dropped from the hand, why a rope sags when it is slung between two poles and why planets keep whirling in their orbits around the sun. We are able to analyze the forces involved with such accuracy that we can confidently predict the motions of the planets. We can tell in what part of the heavens a planet will be at a given time.

It was because the orbit of a planet did *not* follow exactly the law of gravitation that another, hitherto unknown, planet was discovered. For many years the orbit described by Uranus had puzzled astronomers, because this planet should have

the ends of the balance. Then he brought up an equally massive lead ball, M_3, until it was close to M_2. If the law of gravitation held true, the attraction between M_2 and M_3 should make M_2 move slightly, thus causing the suspended wire to be twisted somewhat.

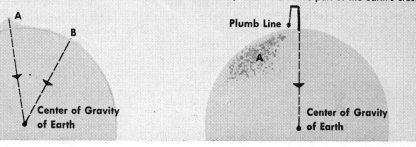

3. The pull of gravity is not so strong at the mountaintop, A, as it is in the plain, B. The reason is that A is farther away from the center of gravity of the earth than B.

A

B

Center of Gravity of Earth

4. The plumb line shown in the diagram does not point exactly to the earth's center of gravity because it is attracted to A, which is a dense part of the earth's crust.

Plumb Line

A

Center of Gravity of Earth

followed a somewhat different course if the law of gravitation held true. Two astronomers — the Englishman John Couch Adams and the Frenchman Urbain-Jean-Joseph Leverrier — found the true cause. Uranus apparently was attracted not only by the sun but by some other heavenly body, hitherto unknown. In the 40's of the nineteenth century, the two astronomers, working independently, calculated the orbit of the unknown body, applying the law of gravitation. In 1846, a German astronomer, Johann Gottfried Galle, discovered this body — the planet now called Neptune — in the position predicted by Leverrier. Pluto, lying beyond the orbit of Neptune, was discovered in much the same way. We give more details in the article The Outermost Planets, in Volume 5.

The law of universal gravitation was accepted at first by scientists because it seemed to give the right answers. Then an eccentric English scientist, Henry Cavendish (1731-1810), put the law to the test in a famous laboratory experiment.

His apparatus (Figure 2) consisted of a torsion balance * capable of supporting a large mass. He suspended two massive lead balls, M_1 and M_2 in the diagram, from

* A torsion balance is one that can turn around the point from which it is suspended.

This is exactly what happened. Cavendish then changed the masses M_2 and M_3 as well as the distance between their centers. He found that M_2 and M_3 attracted each other in accordance with Newton's law of universal gravitation. Experiments like the one performed by Cavendish have been carried out by other scientists since his time.*

The force of attraction between the earth and a baseball dropped from the hand is so strong because the mass of the earth is so very great. Every particle on the earth acts on every particle of an object on or above the surface of the earth. The result of all these little forces is a single large force directed toward the center of our planet.

However, the force of attraction between two ordinary masses of about equal size is exceedingly small. Suppose that a one-pound iron object is located so that its center is one foot from the center of another one-pound iron object. The gravitational attraction acting on both masses is about 3 billionths of a pound. This would be

* As is pointed out in the article The Theory of Relativity, in Volume 4, Albert Einstein showed that Newton's law does not apply exactly when we deal with speeds approaching the speed of light (over 186,000 miles per second). In such cases, we must use the calculations of the relativity theory. However, for calculations that do not involve such fantastic speeds, Newton's law still holds.

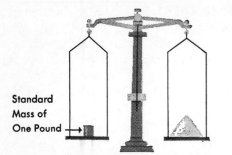

5. To measure out a quantity of sugar with a mass of one pound, we put a standard mass of one pound on one pan of a balance and some sugar on the other pan. If the two pans balance, the mass of the sugar is equal to one pound.

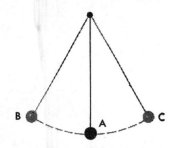

6. A simple pendulum. As the bob, A, swings to and fro between B and C, it is acted on by the force of gravity.

approximately the weight of a very small cube of iron with an edge about equal to the thickness of a sheet of paper.

When the earth attracts a certain quantity of sugar, say, the result is always a definite force, which we call weight. Suppose this force is one pound; in that case, we say that the sugar weighs one pound at the surface of the earth. Weight is not the same thing as mass. *Mass* is a quantity of a substance — the amount of matter it contains. The *weight* of a body is the force acting upon it due to the gravitational attraction of the earth.

This attraction brings about a downward acceleration (a constant increase in the rate of speed) of all objects toward the center of the earth. The acceleration in question is called gravity. It is the same for all objects, regardless of their mass, at a given point on the earth's surface, if air resistance is small.* The acceleration due to gravity is called "g." It

* If the air resistance is considerable, it will affect light objects more than heavy ones; the acceleration of the lighter objects will not be quite so great. We discuss acceleration in detail in the article How Things Move, in this volume.

is approximately 32 feet per second per second, or 980 centimeters per second per second. This means that if an object is accelerated toward the earth's center, it will travel 32 feet per second faster at the end of the first second than at the beginning of the first second. It will travel 32 feet per second faster at the end of the second second than at the beginning of the second second and so on.

The words "gravity" and "gravitation" are sometimes used as if they meant the same thing. Strictly speaking, gravitation refers to the acceleration of any two objects in the universe toward each other, while gravity, as we have just seen, represents the gravitational acceleration toward the center of the earth. The word "gravity" has also been applied to the gravitational acceleration toward the center of other heavenly bodies. Thus we can speak of the force of gravity on the planet Mars.

The value of g has been accurately measured at many different places on the earth's surface and has been found to vary, as shown in the table on this page. The variation is due to several factors. One of these is distance from the center of the earth. The nearer an object is to this point, the greater the earth's attraction for it and the greater the value of g. If two places are at approximately the same latitudes, the one at a higher altitude will show a lower value of g than the other one (Figure 3).

Another factor affecting the value of g is the uneven distribution of the mass

Values of g, the acceleration due to gravity	
Place	Value of g
	(centimeters per second per second)
Cambridge, Massachusetts	980.398
Denver, Colorado	979.609
Eagle City, Alaska	982.183
Galveston, Texas	979.272
Greenwich, England	981.188
Honolulu, Hawaii	978.946
Madras, India	978.281
New Orleans, Louisiana	979.324
Ponta Delgada, Azores	980.143
Reykjavik, Iceland	982.273

on the earth, particularly in the crust. This contains very dense substances in some locations and less dense substances in others. There are certain places where the bob, or weight, at the end of a plumb line does not point toward the exact center of the earth because of the attraction exercised by dense masses in a nearby area (Figure 4).

The weight of an object on the earth's surface will differ, therefore, from place to place, because the gravitational attraction varies from place to place. Yet the mass of an object never changes. A standard mass of one pound and a balance (see Figure 5) can be used to measure a pound of mass anywhere on the earth's surface, or for that matter on the surface of any planet. The difference between the two ends of the balance is so small that there is no difference in the gravitational attraction upon them; this is because the earth's radius is much longer than the balance arm.

A standard one-pound mass may be used with a balance in Cuba to measure a one-pound mass of sugar. Suppose this same one-pound standard and the pound of sugar are taken to Iceland. They will be in equilibrium on a balance located there even though the actual force acting on both the standard and the sugar in Iceland will be greater than the force acting on both in Cuba.

How to measure the acceleration due to gravity

An accurate measurement of g, the acceleration due to gravity, can be made with a pendulum. A simple pendulum (Figure 6) consists of a small sphere, called a bob, suspended from a fixed support by means of a long, thin thread. The bob is set moving by a slight sideways push. As it swings upward it will be acted on by the force of gravity until finally its upward course will be halted. Then the force of gravity will cause the bob to swing downward in the opposite direction to the first one. Its momentum will carry it past the starting point and then upward. Again it will be slowed down by gravity until its upward course will be halted, and it will swing downward in the opposite direction, as before.

The path the pendulum describes as it moves from one high point of its course to the other and then back again to the first one is called a complete vibration. The time required for a complete vibration is known as the period. Of course the length of the period will be affected by the force of gravity. The stronger the gravitational pull, the shorter the path of the pendulum and the shorter the period will be. If we know the period and the length of the pendulum, we can calculate the pull of gravity — that is, the value of g. With a simple pendulum, such as the one we described, the margin of error would be about 1 per cent. Using more complicated pendulums, scientists are able to determine the value of g to six significant figures.*

* If, for example, we calculate the value of g at a given place as 982.183 centimeters per second per second, the six significant figures would be 9, 8, 2, 1, 8 and 3.

7. If the bar shown in the diagram below and the earth were comparable in size, the gravitational forces acting on the bar, all pointing downward toward the center of gravity of the earth, would differ markedly in direction.

8. Here the bar and the earth's surface (of which only a few inches are shown) are drawn to exact scale. The center of gravity of the earth is so far from the bar that the gravitational forces shown are practically parallel.

Why should scientists want to make such very accurate measurements of g? For one thing, you will recall that the attraction depends on the mass of the particles on the earth as well as their distance from the object on which they exert a gravitational force. Hence, an accurate measurement of g gives definite clues concerning the density (mass per unit volume) of the substances immediately below the earth's surface. These clues are useful to the geologist in determining how movements of the earth's crust take place. They also serve to detect the presence of oil deposits in the earth's crust, because the value of g definitely changes near the region of such deposits. Large oil companies have spent vast sums of money in measuring g in many regions of the earth's surface.

In the case of the horizontal bar or any other object, for that matter, there is always one point at which the combined forces of gravity will be centered. This point is located at what is called the center of gravity. We may think of it as the point where all of the weight of the body is concentrated.

In the case of solid bodies with regular geometric shapes, the center of gravity is always at the geometric center of the body — that is, if the density is the same throughout. We show some bodies of this kind in Figure 9. Note that the center of gravity of a cube or of a sphere is at the exact center of these solids. For a cone, it is on the axis and at a point a fourth of the way from the base of the cone to its vertex, or tip.

11. Finding the center of gravity of an irregularly shaped cardboard.

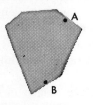 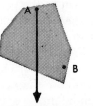 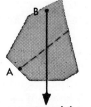 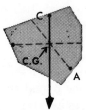

To find the center of gravity of the piece of cardboard shown above, we punch holes A and B at different places near the edge.

The cardboard is suspended at A from a nail. A vertical line, drawn with a plumb line guide, will pass through the center of gravity.

We now suspend the cardboard at B and draw the vertical line from B. The center of gravity is where the lines from A and B cross.

We make another hole at C and hang the cardboard at this point. A vertical line from C will likewise pass through the center of gravity.

This great expense has been amply rewarded. (See the article Modern Methods of Prospecting, in Volume 7.)

**The center
of gravity**

The gravitational force acting on each bit of mass of a substance, as the earth attracts it, is generally directed toward the center of the earth, as we have seen. Suppose the earth were comparable in size to a horizontal bar, such as the one shown in Figure 7. In that case, the gravitational forces affecting the different parts of the bar would differ in direction, as shown in the diagram. But since the earth is so very much larger than the iron bar, the forces of attraction are to all intents and purposes parallel (Figure 8).

If a body is in the form of a sheet, the center of gravity corresponds to the center of the area (Figure 10). If the sheet is rectangular in shape, the center of gravity is located at the point where the two diagonals intersect. In the case of a triangle, it is one third of the distance from the middle point of any of the three sides to the opposite point. For a circular sheet, it is at the center of the circle.

Even if a body is irregular in shape, the center of gravity can be determined. Suppose we want to locate it in the case of the piece of cardboard shown in Figure 11. First we punch two holes, A and B, at different points along the edge of the cardboard. Then we hang the cardboard at point A from a nail driven into a post, say. When the cardboard comes to rest, its

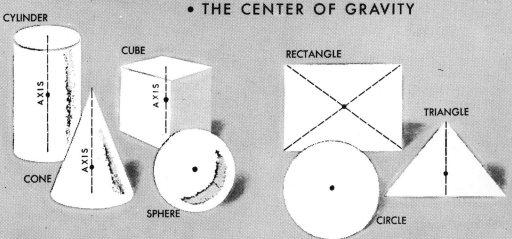

9. Center of gravity of four types of solid bodies having regular geometrical shapes.

10. Center of gravity of three kinds of regularly shaped areas in the form of sheets.

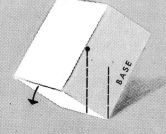

12. The left-hand block of wood is in a state of stable equilibrium. If we lift up one end of it somewhat (right-hand drawing), the center of gravity will be raised. When we let go of this wooden block, it will return to its former position.

13. If we were to tip a block of wood so that a vertical line from its center of gravity were to fall outside of the base of the block, it would fall over.

14. If we tip the long stick at the left, we lower its center of gravity and as a result it will fall. Before it is tipped, the stick is said to be in unstable equilibrium.

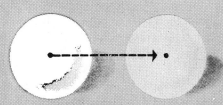

15. If we roll a ball along a table, the center of gravity will be neither lowered nor raised. The ball is said to be in neutral equilibrium.

center of gravity will be located on a vertical line extending from the point of support. To find the vertical line, we hang a plumb line from the same nail. Using it as a guide, we draw the vertical line on the cardboard. Then we hang up the cardboard at point B and repeat our procedure. The vertical line from B will cross the one from A at the center of gravity. We can prove that this is so by making another hole, C, in the cardboard and suspending the cardboard at point C. A vertical line from C will pass through the center of gravity.

The three types of equilibrium

The location of a body's center of gravity will determine how stable it is — that is, to what extent it resists any effort to disturb its equilibrium, or balance. Generally speaking, there are three states of equilibrium; they are known as stable, unstable and neutral.

A body is said to be in stable equilibrium if we raise its center of gravity when we tip it or lift one end. If we release the body, it will fall back to its former position. A square block of wood resting on the floor (Figure 12) is a good example of a body that is in stable equilibrium. If we lift up one end of the block slightly, the weight of the body, concentrated at the center of gravity, will make it return to its original position. However, if we were to tip the block so that a vertical line from the center of gravity would fall outside the base of the block (Figure 13), it would tip over. It would be in a state of stable equilibrium in its new position. To keep a body as stable as possible, it is advisable to provide a wide base and a low center of gravity. This is done in designing automobiles, boats, furniture and the like.

If we lower the center of gravity of a body when we tip it, the body is in unstable equilibrium. Suppose we set a pointed stick in a vertical position on a horizontal table, as shown in Figure 14. Any slight tipping of the stick will lower the center of gravity and will make it fall over suddenly.

If the center of gravity of a body is neither raised nor lowered when the body is displaced, we say that the body is in a state of neutral equilibrium. A ball on a table (Figure 15) is in a state of neutral equilibrium, because any force that moves the ball sideways neither lowers nor raises the center of gravity. It will continue to remain in equilibrium, no matter how we move it along the table.

Gravitational attraction on the moon

It appears likely that man will land on the moon in the not too distant future. Will he find that the same forces of gravitational attraction will hold for the moon as for the earth? If he drops a ball from a height on the moon, will it fall to the moon's surface? If he strings a heavy wire between two high places, will it sag downward? The answer is "Yes." However, a traveler from the earth would find that the forces of gravitational attraction would not be nearly so great on the moon as on the earth, because the mass of the earth is so much greater.

The acceleration due to gravity at the surface of the moon would be about 6.7 feet per second per second, as against 32 feet per second per second on the earth's surface. In 3 seconds, an object dropped from a height on the earth would travel a total distance of 144 feet. The same object dropped from a height on the moon would fall a total distance of only about 30 feet in the same period of time.

Because of the lessened gravitational force on the moon, our traveler would be able to perform feats that would be quite impossible on the earth. He would be able to carry with ease objects that on the earth would tax the powers of a champion weight-lifter. He would be able to run like a deer and to jump to fantastic heights. The world's record for the high jump is about 7 feet. Even without any kind of athletic training, our traveler would be able to clear the 25-foot mark on the moon without any great effort. He would be able to do other remarkable things.

See also Vol. 10, p. 280: "General Works."

A striking insect fossil — an ant that has been preserved in amber. The latter substance is a hardened, translucent fossil resin.

Amer. Mus. of
Nat. Hist.

THE AMATEUR FOSSIL HUNTER*

How to Collect and Interpret Fossils

BY JOHN W. SHRUM

IF YOU like to hike in the country, visit new places, study plants and animals or collect unusual things, join the ranks of amateur fossil collectors. Few hobbies offer as much fun and satisfaction for such a modest investment of time and money. As a fossil hunter, you can work with your hobby throughout the year. In good weather you will want to visit places where fossils may be found; in cold or rainy weather you can work at home with the fossils you have already collected.

You will find it a source of great satisfaction to be able to identify the specimens you locate. It will be interesting for you to learn whether those collected in a particular location have ever been found there before. Perhaps some day you might discover a previously unknown plant or animal fossil.

What is a fossil? The word "fossil" is applied to the remains or other evidence of plants and animals that lived before the beginning of recorded history. These remains have been preserved in the earth's crust by natural processes. Most common-ly they are found in rocks or in finely divided rock particles, such as dust, mud, sand and soil. Under unusual circumstances, plants and animals have been preserved as fossils by being frozen, or dried out, or "pickled" in a brine solution, or embedded in amber or trapped in tar pits. Among the commonest fossil remains are shells, bones and impressions of leaves or other parts of plants and animals. In some cases, the entire organism is preserved. Fossils also include footprints, tracks and trails, burrows of worms and rodents, eggs and gastroliths, or "stomach stones." The latter are thought to be smooth, polished pebbles from the gullets of prehistoric reptiles.

You will recognize many fossils by their similarity in form to living plants and animals that you have seen. Snails, clams, oysters, fish, ferns, tree limbs, roots and leaves, for example, are well represented in the fossil record. You will also notice that these fossils may differ in form from living representatives of the same type. By studying these differences you will begin to see how living organisms have changed through a long period of time.

Ways in which fossils are preserved. When a plant or animal dies, it may be devoured by various living animals. If this does not take place, the remains will usually decay through bacterial and chemical action. However, suppose the organism is quickly buried after death in mud, sand, or stagnant or brackish water. Under such conditions, the remains are not in contact with the air and the usual decay processes cannot take place. Freezing of an organism will also ward off decay. In the course of time, organic remains that have escaped total decay will become fossils.

* Editor's note: We wish to acknowledge the co-operation of the author in the search for illustrative materials for the article. Valuable help was also provided by Dr. Horace G. Richards, Chairman of the Department of Geology and Paleontology at the Academy of Natural Sciences of Philadelphia. Among other things, he enlisted the services of two young members of the Delaware Valley Amateur Paleontological Society — Michael Gibson and David Govoni — in setting up materials for photographs.

Chicago Nat. Hist. Mus.

At the left, in the left-hand photo, is a limestone mold with the surface markings of a trilobite, whose remains had dissolved away. Mud settled into the mold cavity, producing the cast at the right in the photo.

Shells, bones, teeth and other hard materials may be preserved without any change taking place in the fossil when the sediments in which burial has taken place are lithified (changed into rock). These are known as unaltered fossils since they have not been changed from their original condition. There are, however, various processes that commonly affect the plant or animal once it has been buried or otherwise prevented from decaying.

Suppose that groundwater seeps through the sediment containing a buried fossil. If, as is often the case, the water is a weak acid solution, it will dissolve shells and other hard parts containing the minerals calcite and aragonite. If the fossil is completely dissolved, an impression of the original material will be left in the sedimentary rock. This impression is called a *mold*. Other sediments or different minerals may fill the mold and produce an exact copy of the exterior of the original fossil — a duplicate known as a *cast*. The fossil hunter sometimes makes a cast by pouring plaster of Paris into a mold that he has found. He can also reverse this process by making a mold of a fossil specimen in molding clay. Then he can pour molding plaster or plaster of Paris into the clay mold to produce several casts of a specimen for study or trading purposes.

Some shells and most bones and plants are porous — that is, there are air spaces between the solid materials. Mineral matter carried in groundwater may be deposited in these air spaces. When this happens, the fossil is said to be *permineralized*. One clue you can use in determining if a fossil has been permineralized is that it will be heavier than normal because of the additional mineral matter filling the air spaces. Minerals that commonly fill the spaces of permineralized fossils are calcite, silica (quartz) and pyrite (fool's gold).

Groundwater may also dissolve a fossil bit by bit while compounds in the water replace the dissolved materials. This is known as *replacement*, since the dissolved original materials are replaced by new compounds. In the fossil remains known as petrified wood, the internal structures have been beautifully preserved as cells have been replaced with minerals.

Soft-bodied animals, fish and leaves are sometimes preserved as fossils by the process known as *carbonization*. In this case, only a thin film of carbon remains in the rock.

Where fossils are to be found

Most fossils (about 99 per cent of them) occur in sedimentary rocks. These are made up of particles eroded from other rocks, or derived from organic materials, such as corals and plants, or deposited by minerals dissolved in water. The particles in question have been compacted or cemented together and have been formed into such sedimentary rocks as shale, sandstone and limestone. It is important for the fossil collector to be able to distinguish such sedimentary formations from either igneous rocks or metamorphic rocks.*

The chances are very good that you live in or close to a region where the bedrock is sedimentary. Geologic maps for different areas indicate where sedimentary rocks may be found. You can obtain such maps from your state Geological Survey or from the United States Geological Survey, Washington, D. C. You will find helpful general information about fossil-collecting

* Editor's note: These three major classes of rocks — sedimentary, igneous and metamorphic — are discussed in the article The Crust of the Earth, in Volume 3. The article Mineral and Rock Collecting, in Volume 9, contains useful information on identifying the three kinds of rocks.

Above: petrified forest, twenty miles east of Holbrook, Arizona. In the logs shown here, the dissolved original materials have been replaced by minerals. Right: a carbonized ray from the Eocene Green River formation in Wyoming. This unusual fossil is in the Academy of Natural Sciences of Philadelphia.

locations — and methods, too — in FOSSILS; AN INTRODUCTION TO PREHISTORIC LIFE, by William H. Matthews III (No. 280, Everyday Handbook Series), Barnes and Noble Inc., New York, 1962.

Do you happen to live in or close to a region of sedimentary materials? Do you plan to visit other parts of the country where there are sedimentary rocks? If your answer is "Yes" to either question, you can begin to plan trips into the field to look for fossils.

Once sedimentary deposits are located, is it likely that they will contain fossils? The answer is that it is possible for any sedimentary rock to contain fossils, but that some sedimentary formations contain many specimens while others have practically none. Rocks. formed from sediments deposited in a body of water, especially a shallow sea, are the source of many good fossil specimens. Thus, if you can determine that a rock is a marine sandstone, shale or limestone, the chances that you will find fossils are quite favorable. Lake and swamp sediments are good sources of fossils also. Sediments deposited by streams on land such as floodplains, sandbars and alluvial fans (see Index) often contain fossils of land animals and freshwater animals. In general, however, fossils are less well-preserved and not as numerous in stream deposits as in marine and lake deposits.

In most places, sedimentary rocks are covered by the regolith — that is, by the loose materials, such as sand and gravel, that overlie bedrock. Fossils may be found in the regolith, but not so frequently as in bedrock.

Good natural exposures of bedrock occur where a stream has cut down through the regolith and into the bedrock. Along the valley wall of such a stream, one or more strata may be studied to determine if fossils are present or not. Chunks of rock that have broken off the bedrock layers may be found downslope from the formation and, frequently, in the stream itself. Often it is possible to identify the layer of rock from which the chunk has come. This identification is important when you begin to interpret the fossils that you find.

Other good exposures occur in stone quarries, either currently in operation or no longer in use. If you wish to collect in quarries, bear in mind that most of them are privately owned. You will need the permission of the owner or a caretaker before doing any exploring or collecting. A site similar to a quarry but available for only a short period of time is an excavation for a new building. Since, like quarries, excavation sites are private property, you will need permission to collect fossil specimens there.

The construction of highways has exposed sedimentary bedrock in many localities. These roadcuts may be excellent sites for fossil collecting. Be sure, however, that you take safety measures if you are working close to a busy highway. If the road is under construction, you should obtain permission from a representative of the construc-

Young fossil collectors in the field. A. A member of the Delaware Valley Amateur Paleontological Society has just uncovered a fossil snail which had been embedded in Pleistocene clay along the Potomac River at Cornfield Harbor, Maryland. This specimen is now in the fossil collection of the Academy of Natural Sciences of Philadelphia. B. Collecting in a sandstone quarry near Lyons, Colorado. C. A promising fossil site: an eroded hillside near Boulder, Colorado, with shale outcrop and cobbles and gravel brought down from above.

Photo A, H. G. Richards

Photos B and C, John W. Shrum

tion company before collecting fossils. Even with such permission, you will need to be very careful to avoid being in the way of the men and machines. You may have to collect when the men are not working.

All the sites we have just mentioned may be good for fossil collecting. Certainly there are other good locations that you will notice as you begin to explore areas near your home. Each new location that you find holds a promise of more, better or different specimens to add to your collection.

How to collect fossils

To collect fossils you will have to have proper equipment and you will have to employ proper field techniques.

Equipment. This will vary slightly with the kind of specimens and the nature of the rock with which the fossil collector is working. For collecting fossils of animals without backbones (invertebrates), small vertebrates and plants, you will need a hammer for breaking and trimming rocks; a collecting bag; one or more chisels; a notebook and pencil; and paper for wrapping and labeling specimens. All of these items can be obtained in hardware stores or in the hardware section of department stores. A regular mason's or bricklayer's hammer is excellent for fossil collecting. You will find a canvas hunting bag, knapsack or bookbag with a shoulder strap is quite satisfactory for carrying equipment, specimens and lunches. A notebook with hard covers about five by seven inches in size will be convenient and useful in recording where each specimen is found and in keeping a record of all the observations that you make. The chisels can be regular stonecutter's chisels or good-quality metalworking chisels. Both a small and a large chisel will be useful in chipping specimens out of the rock. Paper for wrapping specimens may be newspapers, various sizes of paper sacks and tissue paper for delicate specimens. Small sheets of plain paper containing an identifying number can be wrapped with each specimen.

Certain additional items of equipment are also desirable. You will find a five- to

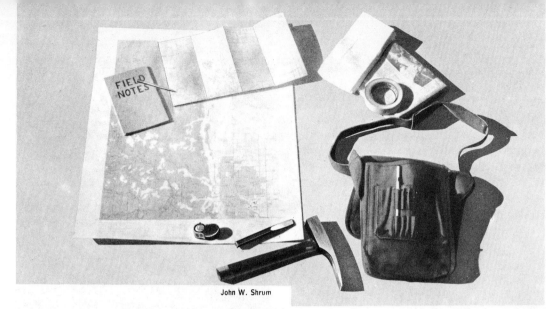

A fossil hunter's equipment. At the top left are field notes (with a pencil), a road map (folded) and a topographic map. At the bottom of the topographic map are magnifying lenses and a cold chisel, with a mason's hammer just below the latter. At the right, from top to bottom, are tissue paper, newspaper, masking tape and knapsack, with pen and pencils attached to its side flap.

ten-power lens useful in getting a better look at specimens in the field. String, rubber bands and small boxes will be useful when you work with small or broken specimens. You can measure the thickness of strata and formations with a six- or ten-foot tape. A small shovel, such as the folding "foxhole" type available in army-surplus stores, will remove clay, sand and soil.

You will find various types of maps useful in your work in the field. We have already mentioned the value of geologic maps for the areas in which you work. Topographic maps are also very helpful. They show the location of roads, railroads, houses and other buildings, and features of the land surface, such as streams, lakes, hills and valleys. You may obtain these maps from your state Geological Survey or from the United States Geological Survey, Washington, D. C. Road maps of different areas will be useful in locating specific localities and in recording where collections have been made.

The same equipment that is used in the field will be useful in working with the specimens at home. Additional tools will improve the quality of your work in your home laboratory. We discuss these tools later on in this article.

Field techniques. A variety of techniques must be used in the field in order to do a satisfactory job of collecting fossils. The object of any technique is to obtain the best specimen possible and as much information about it as you can. Sometimes this amounts simply to picking up specimens that have weathered out of the bedrock, wrapping them for safe transport and identifying the location where they were found. No matter how the specimens were obtained, wrapping and identifying techniques are similar. Each fossil should be wrapped individually in newspapers or a small sack. Then all specimens from the same location should be wrapped in a larger bundle. Place a slip of paper containing a record of your finds in the large bundle. You may want to make a separate record for each specimen.

The record may be written out in detail or else it may consist only of a code word or number referring to the record made in your notebook. The complete record should include the geographic location, where the fossil was found in the rock formation and the name and age of the rock formation, if this can be determined. It might be well to add other observations, such as the characteristics of the rocks exposed, the relative abundance of fossils and the variety of fossils in the formation.

Good specimens are frequently those that have weathered out of the bedrock. These may be found in thin layers or soil overlying the bedrock, in the accumulation

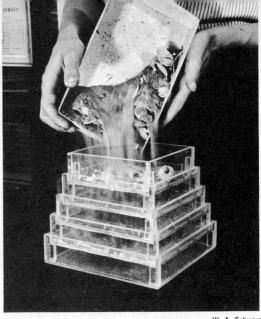

Fossil mollusks of various sizes in dry sand are being sifted here through a set of wire screen sieves. Each one of the sieves has a finer mesh than the one above it.

of rocks that have weathered and fallen or slid from a cliff or steep valley wall and in beds of clay between rock layers. Where fossils occur in this manner, you may need to sift through the soil or rock fragments or wash the fossils out of the material in a nearby stream.

Where fossils occur in solid rock, the task of removing them is somewhat more difficult. You will have to use a hammer or chisel or both. *Caution: when working with hammer or chisel always wear safety goggles in order to protect your eyes from flying chips of stone.*

The chunk of rock containing the fossil can be pried loose and broken with the hammer in some cases. Sometimes you will have to remove the part of the rock you want by chiseling around the fossil. Experience will show you the best way to do this for different fossils and rocks. Generally you should chisel a groove around the specimen, being careful to stay far enough away from it so that it is not damaged. Chisel deep enough to split the rock underneath the fossil. Never try to trim a speci-

W. A. Schwarz

men closely in the field. Wait until you get home where you can use the right tools to do the job.

Techniques for collecting vertebrate fossils, such as large fish, dinosaurs, birds and mammals, are involved and require specialized equipment. Should you happen to find vertebrate fossils, report your find to the nearest geology department in a college or university or to your state Geological Survey. A skilled paleontologist (see Index, under Paleontology) will probably be glad to examine your find and either help or advise you in the removal of the fossil.

The preparation of specimens at home

Fossils brought in from the field need to be prepared for further study, identification and storage or display. Remove excess rock with a hammer, using a chisel if necessary. If you have several sizes of chisels and hammers, you will be able to select the best one for working with each specimen. *Remember to use safety goggles when working with either hammer or chisel.* A hacksaw can be used to saw through the rock in some specimens. Remove only small pieces of rock at any one time, so as to avoid breaking the fossil. When a large part of the rock

In *A*, a collector has just dug a fossil cephalopod out of rock. *B* shows a striking assemblage of small fossils. They had been embedded in shale and had become exposed after the shale, being softer than the fossils, had been washed away. The fossils include gastropods and corals; the collector holds a gastropod shell in his hand.

Photo A, John H. Gerard, from Nat. Audubon Soc.; photo B, Socony-Mobil Oil Co., Inc.

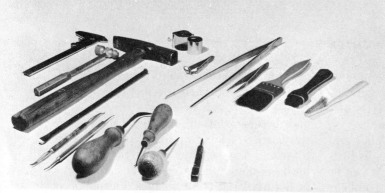

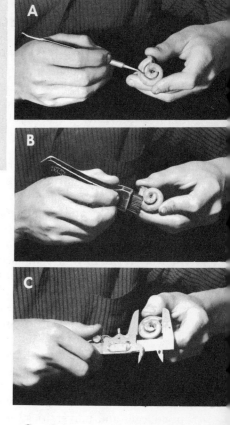

Photos, W. A. Schwarz

Above: basic equipment for preparing fossil specimens at home. Shown here are calipers, ball-peen hammer, geologist's hammer, chisel, high-power magnifying glass, curved tweezers, small paint brush, short stiff-bristle brush, toothbrush, dental probes and awls of various sizes. Photos A-C, at the right, show a collector preparing a gastropod fossil specimen. He picks out or loosens clay or other earthy material from the fossil (A). The loosened particles are then removed with a short stiff-bristle brush (B). Finally the fossil is carefully measured with calipers (C). It is now ready to be catalogued and will be placed in a collection or on display.

has been removed, you can chip the remaining material away with small chisels, ice picks, wire brushes, pliers and knifeblades. Hat pins or similar strong, sharp-pointed instruments will be useful in removing bits of rock from the specimen. Small paint brushes (both hard- and soft-bristle varieties) and a wire brush can be used in cleaning up your fossils.

Soaking in water will sometimes soften the rock enough so that it can be readily removed from the specimen with the use of the tools mentioned above. Dilute hydrochloric acid will be useful in dissolving limestone from some fossils. Extra care is necessary in using acid. Be careful not to get any of it on your skin; wash your hands frequently while working with it. Remember, too, that the acid will dissolve the fossil as well as the limestone if the fossil is composed of calcium carbonate (calcite). Put a drop of dilute acid on an inconspicuous spot of the specimen. If the acid reacts by starting to dissolve the fossil, you will see gas bubbles in the acid. Immerse the specimen in a bucket of clean water to stop the action of the acid.

The object of preparing the fossil is to remove as much of the rock material as possible so that the fossil itself can be studied in detail. Remember that many fossils are millions of years old; hence we are interested in obtaining all the information we can about them. Careful preparation of your specimens will reveal significant details.

Identifying fossil specimens

If you can identify the fossils that you find, your collection will have added value and interest. You should begin by acquiring a good understanding of the classification system used in the study of plants and animals. The system in use today is based on one proposed by the Swedish biologist Carl von Linné, better known by the Latinized form of his name — Carolus Linnaeus. His system has been modified as paleontologists and biologists have learned more about the relationships among plants and animals. The article The Roll Call of Living Things, in Volume 1, explains and illustrates the classification system.

To identify fossils you will have to compare your specimens with those described in reference books. An excellent one to start with is THE FOSSIL BOOK, by C. L. Fenton and M. A. Fenton, Doubleday and Company, Inc., New York, 1958. This book is well illustrated and contains excellent descriptions of the plants and animals that are found as fossils. It will probably be in your school library or public library, or perhaps in both. Another good reference is INDEX FOSSILS OF NORTH AMERICA, by H. W. Shimer and R. R. Schrock, John Wiley and Sons, Inc., New York, 1944. This book is comprehensive, though technical. It can be found in the larger public libraries, college libraries and museum libraries.

In addition to these reference books, numerous books and pamphlets contain information that will help you identify fossils found in various localities in the United States. Write to your state Geological Survey, located in the state capital, for a list of the fossil publications available for the area where you live. These publications are usually inexpensive; yet they may rank with your best sources of information.

Further information may be obtained from museums, state Geological Surveys, the United States Geological Survey, Washington, D. C., and the geology departments of colleges and universities. In many communities there are clubs whose members are active amateur fossil collectors; you will usually find them very cooperative. You may also be able to obtain information from a professional geologist in your community.

The important task
of labeling your finds

If a collector has a good system of labeling his specimens, he can locate individual specimens when needed, maintain a permanent record and keep the identification of each fossil clearly in mind. There are various ways of labeling fossils.

One or more specimens of the same fossil can be stored in a small box along with an identifying label. Such a label should be made from good-quality paper or lightweight cardboard. The record on the label should include the identification of the specimen, the name of the rock formation and of the geographic location in which it was found and its geologic age. You can also add the date the fossil was found, page references to your notebook, the sources used in identification and various other notations of special interest. Use a permanent ink, such as India ink, in printing labels.

Often it is desirable to have an identifying mark on each specimen. One way is to glue a small label onto the specimen and then to print an identifying number on the label. A label of this type may come loose and may be lost. Hence the following marking method is preferable. Place a spot of light-colored paint about a quarter of an inch in diameter on each fossil. Put the spot where it will not obscure any of the features that you may want to study. Quick-drying enamel, fingernail polish and airplane-model enamel and dope all can be used for this purpose. When the paint spot is dry, write an identifying number on the paint with India ink. A coat of clear nail polish or colorless airplane dope will protect the numbered spot, thus making a permanent record.

Whatever system you may use in marking your fossils, you should keep a permanent record, giving detailed information for each numbered specimen. This permanent record can be entered in a notebook, on index cards or on lists stored with each group of fossils.

Storage
and display

Fossils are relatively easy to store and display, compared with other kinds of scientific collections. No special care is needed, as would be the case with ordinary plant and insect collections. Your chief concerns will be to prevent breakage and to keep the specimens free from dust.

For the beginning collector, cigar boxes with homemade cardboard dividers can serve effectively for storage. The boxes can be labeled or numbered according to the particular system that you have adopted. For example, you can store together specimens from the same locality, or of the same kind, or of the same geologic age or of the same rock formation. The important thing is to arrange your specimens so that you can find what you want when you want it.

Wood or metal cabinets with divided drawers of various depths are ideal for storage. The purchase of new cabinets of this type involves a sizable investment in your hobby. Until you wish to make such an

Shown here are a compartmented box for a fossil collection, a fossil squid from the collection, a page from the collector's notebook and a card index file. The open notebook contains information about the squid; further information about the specimen is contained in the card set atop the others.

investment, old furniture can be adapted with the use of a little imagination and work on your part.

Fossils can be attractively displayed in a variety of ways. Single specimens can be embedded in clear plastic now available in hobby shops. Such specimens can be formed into paperweights, bookends, lamp bases and other useful articles. Remember, however, that if they are mounted in this way, they will no longer be available for close study.

Display space in bookcases, "whatnot" racks and glass-front cabinets will attract attention to your hobby and arouse interest in it. The specimens on display are readily available for further study. The display can be changed as frequently as you wish.

The interpretation of fossil specimens

The study of fossil specimens can reveal much about the prehistoric plants or animals that lived in various periods of geologic time. Even though only the hard parts are preserved, the anatomy of an animal can often be inferred from muscle scars on the bone or shell and through the comparison of the skeletal parts with those of similar living organisms. It may be possible to determine the life habits of a given organism from the inferred anatomy, together with such evidence as other fossils found in the same location, the number and arrangement of fossils in the rock and the kind of rock.

The interpretation of fossils also helps determine the age of rocks. As is pointed out in the article The Geological Time Scale, in Volume 6, geologic time is based on the fossil record. Certain organisms lived only at certain times; hence when the fossils of these organisms are identified, the geologic age of the rocks can be determined.

Much can be learned about the environment of the past from the kinds of fossils found in a given locality. For instance, it is known that certain organisms living today thrive best in a particular environment. Corals, as an example, live in warm shallow seas; antelopes live in plains areas; pine trees grow in large numbers at higher elevations; thick-leaved plants are common in tropic regions. The kinds of fossils found can provide information as to whether the environment was marine or terrestrial and what kind of climate existed.

The condition of the fossil itself may give us information about conditions in the past. If there are a large number of single valves of brachiopods and clams * or broken pieces of shell in a given site, they were probably transported and broken by wave and current action. Fragments of shells and bones in terrestrial deposits indicate probable transportation by streams. On the other hand, if the fossil is a whole shell or organism or if it is fairly large, the chances are good that the organism lived right in the area where it was fossilized.

From such information you can begin to see how the earth has changed through geologic time. The fossil record provides evidence for seas where there are now mountain ranges, deep lakes where there is now dry land and even tropical forests where there are now ice sheets. Your fossil collection will help you see the relationship of life and places in the past to the life and places of the present.

* *Editor's note*: The valves in this case are the two parts of a brachiopod or clam shell.

GEORGE WASHINGTON BRIDGE

THE STORY OF BRIDGES

Vital Links in Land Transportation

BY JOSEF SORKIN

MOST modern bridges serve as links in land-transportation systems. They span natural and man-made waterways (rivers, canals and the like) and deep depressions in the ground level, such as ravines and canyons. Thus they make it possible to extend footpaths, roads, highways and railway tracks across and beyond such obstacles. Certain bridges, known as aqueducts, carry water-supply conduits over streams or hollows. This use of bridges has been rather limited in modern times.

The very first bridges that served man were made by nature. The bridge might be a natural arch, caused by erosion *; or else

* *Editor's note*: See Index, under Natural bridges.

In the New Stone Age, some bridges consisted of logs that had been lifted and hauled into place across a stream.

a chasm or stream might be spanned by a fallen log or a vine extending from one tree to another. The earliest man-made bridges, which imitated those fashioned by nature, go back to the New Stone Age. In many places, these structures consisted of logs or stones that could be lifted and hauled into place. For wider bridges over rivers, intermediate supports, called piers, were provided by piling up stones in several places in the stream. Then beams made of wood or stone were set upon the piers in such a way as to form a continuous bridge. In warm climates, fibers derived from grasses or vines or stems were woven into ropes and these were strung across chasms or streams to form primitive suspension bridges. Such bridges are still in use in Tibet, India, Peru and other places.

By the year 4000 B.C., men had learned how to set stones in place so that they would span a given space by forming an arch. A number of fine arch bridges were built by the ancient peoples of Mesopotamia, Egypt and China. The masonry arch enjoyed its greatest development under the ancient Romans, who were the greatest bridgebuilders in antiquity. A number of Roman arch bridges still exist. Among them are the Pont du Gard Aqueduct at Nimes, France, built about the time of Christ, and a bridge at Alcántara, Spain, which goes back to about the same period. The Romans also erected many timber bridges.

For centuries after the fall of the Western Roman Empire about A.D. 500, few new spans were constructed in Western Europe, and many of the older ones failed because of the lack of proper maintenance. Beginning with the twelfth century, the art of bridgebuilding was revived and a number of fine masonry arch bridges were constructed. A particularly famous one was the Thames River Bridge at London, popularly known as the Old London Bridge. Completed in 1209, it was in use for rather more than six centuries. Another notable stone arch bridge of the Middle Ages was the Ponte Vecchio (Old Bridge) over the river Arno in Florence. It is said that the structure was originally built in 1177 and that it was rebuilt in 1345; it is still in use.

Some outstanding bridges were erected during the Renaissance. The Rialto Bridge, spanning the Grand Canal in Venice, was built in 1591 by Antonio Da Ponte and still serves. The Santa Trinità (Holy Trinity) Bridge over the Arno in Florence was completed in 1569. It was a particularly beautiful structure, with three spans of white marble. Unfortunately, it was destroyed in World War II.

There were few notable advances in bridgebuilding until the eighteenth century. It was then that scientific analysis, rather than traditional practice, began to be applied. The French architect Hubert Gautier wrote a trail-blazing treatise on bridges in 1714. In 1747, the first engineering school in the world was founded in Paris; it was the renowned Ecole des ponts et chaussées (School for Bridge and Highway Construction). The introduction of iron in bridge-building was another striking development of the eighteenth century. The first all-iron bridge was the hundred-foot span over the river Severn in Coalbrookdale, England; it was designed by Thomas Pritchard and was completed in 1779. Many covered timber bridges were built in Europe and America in this century and the following one.

Iron became a favorite material for bridgebuilding in the course of the nineteenth century — particularly for the construction of large bridges. The development of the railroad in the first half of the century created new engineering problems, since locomotives and trains weighed much more than the vehicles that had previously crossed bridges. Spans had to be made much stronger and more rigid than before.

Methods for economically producing steel were developed about the middle of the nineteenth century, and this alloy was used increasingly for bridges in the years that followed. Since 1900, steel has almost completely supplanted iron in bridge construction. Reinforced concrete has also played an important part in the building of bridges in the present century.* The foundations and piers of almost all big present-

* Plain concrete is relatively weak in resisting tension forces. Reinforced concrete has embedded steel rods to resist tension forces.

The Roman aqueduct now called the Pont du Gard ("Gard Bridge") was built across the Gard River in southern France in 19 B.C.; it supplied Nemausus (modern Nîmes) with water. It is in an excellent state of preservation; the lowest of its three tiers now serves as a road bridge.
Ewing Galloway

The beautiful Rialto Bridge, which spans the Grand Canal in Venice, Italy, was built by Antonio da Ponte in 1591. Along both sides of the roadway shops were constructed, and in them jewelers displayed their wares. The bridge and the shops that line it are still in use.
Italian State Tourist Office

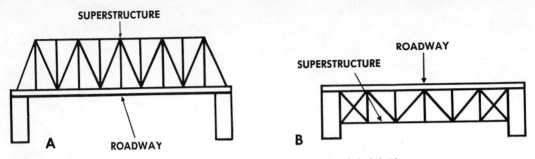

These two diagrams show the basic difference between through bridges and deck bridges. In the through bridge (A, above), the principal elements of the superstructure have been set above the roadway, while in the deck bridge (B) the superstructure is below the roadway.

day bridges are made of reinforced concrete. This material has also been used in the construction of arch and pontoon bridges.

The bridges of today show remarkable variety. Some consist of a single span extending between end supports, called abutments.* Others may have a number of spans. In such cases, there are not only end supports (abutments) but also the intermediate supports known as piers. Bridges differ, too, in the position of the roadway with respect to the superstructure — that is, the part of the bridge resting upon abutments or piers. In *through bridges*, the main elements of the superstructure extend above the roadway; in *deck bridges*, the superstructure is below the roadway. The bridge floor (also called the deck) of highway bridges usually consists of reinforced concrete slabs. Where weight has to be reduced to the minimum, as in movable bridges, an open-grid type of flooring is generally used.

All bridges fall in one or the other of three main groups: (1) fixed, or stationary; (2) movable; (3) floating. We shall take up each one of these groups in turn in the paragraphs that follow.

FIXED BRIDGES

Most bridges are of the fixed type. As the name indicates, they are intended to remain permanently in the position in which they were originally constructed. Fixed bridges over navigable waterways are erected at a height that will enable ships to pass under them. If the waters that they span are not navigable, the lowest point of the superstructure is set above the highest point that the stream will ever reach.

Fixed bridges are constructed of steel, concrete or timber. There are limits to the span length (distance between supports) that each of these materials can attain. With certain exceptions (notably arch bridges*), spans exceeding a hundred feet are built of steel. For spans up to a hundred feet, either steel or concrete can be used. Occasionally, under favorable conditions, wood can be utilized for spans shorter than twenty-five feet.

There are four different classes of fixed bridges: (1) beam and girder bridges; (2) truss bridges; (3) arch bridges; (4) suspension bridges.

Beam and girder bridges. A beam is a horizontal structural member that spans two supports; it may be of different materials, such as wood, concrete or rolled steel. A plate girder, sometimes called simply a girder, is a built-up steel beam. It consists of two horizontal components, called flanges, joined together, either by riveting or welding, by a vertical member called a web. Riveted angles or welded plates are attached to the webs to provide added stiffness. Girders may also be of concrete.

In bridge construction, two or more parallel beams or girders are set on common supports and are connected by crosswise members. Beam and girder bridges may be *simple* — that is, they may rest on only two supports. They may also extend without interruption over three or more supports; in that case they are said to be *continuous*.

The single-span length of beams made of rolled steel is generally limited to approximately 125 feet. However, the load-carrying capacity of the beams may be increased by composite construction. In

---

* The length of a bridge is measured from abutment to abutment.

* Arch bridges ranging up to a thousand feet in length have been constructed of concrete.

GIRDER BRIDGE

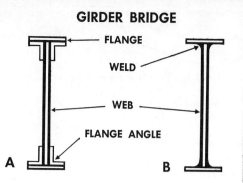

FLANGE

WELD

WEB

FLANGE ANGLE

A   B

Two types of plate girders. A plate girder has two horizontal components — flanges — joined together either by riveting (as in A) or by welding (as in B).

TRUSS BRIDGE

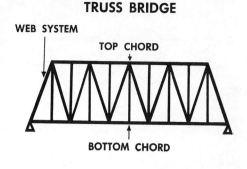

WEB SYSTEM

TOP CHORD

BOTTOM CHORD

A typical truss bridge. The top members form the upper chord; the bottom members, the bottom chord; the vertical or diagonal members, the web system.

Ewing Galloway

This girder bridge is a road bridge. It spans the West Virginia turnpike at Milepost No. 1, in Mercer County.

Paducah Chamber of Commerce

A fine example of a truss bridge: the Irvin Cobb Bridge between Paducah, Kentucky, and Brookport, in Illinois.

this, the tops of the beams are rigidly connected to the concrete roadway slab so that the two members act together.

Steel girders can be made quite deep and correspondingly strong; hence they may provide extraordinarily long bridge spans. The continuous-girder bridge across the Niagara River at Niagara Falls, New York, has a span of 450 feet. The world's record is held by the Save River Bridge in Yugoslavia, with a main span 856 feet long. Such extreme spans are made feasible only through the use of high-strength steels and lightweight ribbed steel decks.

Truss bridges. Trusses are framed structures extending between supports; they show a pattern of interlocking triangles. There is a sound reason for the use of the triangle as the unit in this case. It is that a three-sided figure of given dimensions can have only one shape; consequently a construction built in the form of a triangle will be rigid.* The top members of a truss

---

* *Editor's note*: This point is discussed in Volume 3, pages 431–32.

are called the upper chord; the bottom members, the lower chord; the vertical or diagonal members, the web system. The two parallel trusses forming a truss span are tied together by crosswise members.

The advantages of this type of construction have long been recognized. Andrea Palladio, a famous Italian architect of the sixteenth century, designed several truss systems to be applied to bridgebuilding. For several centuries thereafter, the sizes of truss members and their arrangement were governed by rule-of-thumb methods based on previous experience. Only within the last hundred years or so has there been a clear understanding of the precise stresses in trusses.

As in the case of beam and girder bridges, truss spans may be simple or continuous. The truss principle makes it possible to construct simple-span bridges of considerable length. By way of example, the Metropolis Bridge, which spans the Ohio River, is 720 feet long. Engineers have attained still greater lengths

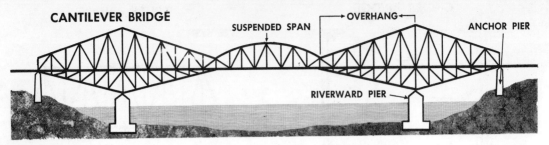

CANTILEVER BRIDGE

SUSPENDED SPAN · OVERHANG · ANCHOR PIER · RIVERWARD PIER

This diagram shows a familiar type of three-span cantilever bridge. Each end span is attached to an anchor pier and extends beyond a riverward pier. The extension, or overhang, constitutes a cantilever arm. The two cantilever arms are connected by a suspended span.

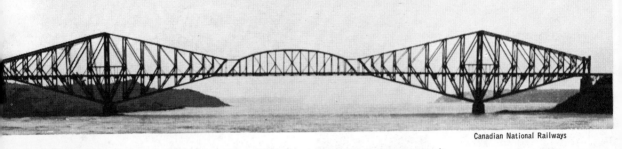

Canadian National Railways

The Quebec Bridge over the St. Lawrence River at Quebec, in Canada. Construction work on this cantilever bridge was begun in 1904; the bridge was not completed until 1918.

than this with continuous-span structures; for example, the continuous span of the Julien-Dubuque Bridge at Dubuque, Iowa, is 845 feet long.

Truss bridges lend themselves to the cantilever arrangement. In this, there is an extension, or overhang, of a truss beyond its support; the overhang is called a cantilever arm. There are various kinds of cantilever bridges. In a familiar type, there are three spans, resting on two anchor piers and two riverward piers. Each end span is attached to an anchor pier and extends beyond a riverward pier. The extensions, or cantilever arms, are connected by a span known as a suspended span. The Mississippi River bridges at Greenville, Mississippi, and East St. Louis, Illinois, are good examples of this kind of cantilever bridge.

One of the best-known cantilever truss bridges is the Firth of Forth Bridge over the Firth (Estuary) of Forth at Edinburgh, Scotland. It extends over two wide stretches of water and an island in the middle of the Firth. Its main span is 1,710 feet long.

It is interesting to note that in simple and cantilever truss spans, when the supports — abutments or piers — settle to a limited extent, they do not affect the stresses in the trusses. If the supports of continuous-span bridges settle, however, there is a redistribution of stresses in the truss members and this may lead to trouble. Hence such bridges are constructed at sites where foundation conditions are especially favorable, so that there will be a minimum amount of settlement of either abutments or piers.

Arch bridges. The arch-bridge principle has been utilized for some six thousand years. The load-carrying element in this type of construction is the curved arch rib. The loads are delivered to the foundations on either side of the bridge by compression in the arch rib, producing an outward thrust at the ends of the span. When the foundations are such that the horizontal thrust of the arch can be easily resisted, as for instance in deep, rocky gorges, the arch bridge is one of the most economical types of bridge construction.

Steel is a favorite modern material for this type of bridge. Steel arches may have solid ribs, or they may have open ribs, made up of trussed members. The rib may be rigidly fastened to its abutments, or it may be "hinged" — that is, it may be built so that a certain amount of end rotation is allowed. In some steel arches, the roadway is carried on columns resting on the arch

ARCH BRIDGES

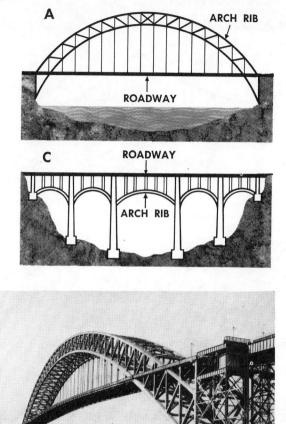

A — ARCH RIB — ROADWAY

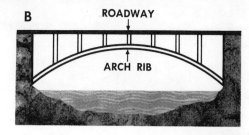

B — ROADWAY — ARCH RIB

C — ROADWAY — ARCH RIB

The diagrams at the left and above illustrate three different types of arch bridges. A and B are steel arch bridges. In A, the roadway is suspended from the arch rib, while in B it is carried on columns that rest on the arch rib. C shows a concrete arch bridge, in which the roadway is supported on vertical columns resting on a series of arch ribs. Other concrete arch bridges, such as the one shown in the photograph below, have a single arch rib.

Standard Oil Co. (N. J.)

The American Swedish News Exchange

The Bayonne (Kill van Kull) Bridge, from Bayonne, New Jersey, to Staten Island, New York — the longest steel-arch span in the world. It extends 1,652 feet.

The Sando Bridge (Sandöbron), in Sweden, is one of the largest concrete arch bridges in the world, with a span of 866 feet. The bridge was completed in the year 1943.

rib; in others, it is suspended from it. In certain cases, a horizontal tie, usually at the level of the roadway, connects the ends of the arch rib, and resists the horizontal portion of the arch thrust. Spans of this type exert only vertical forces on their substructure. They are built where foundation conditions make it impossible to construct the conventional arch type.

There are many outstanding examples of steel-arch construction. The Bayonne, or Kill Van Kull, Bridge in New York City has the longest arch span — 1,652 feet. The Hell Gate Bridge, also in New York, is designed to carry the heaviest load; it is a railway bridge with four tracks. The Sydney Harbor Bridge, at Sydney, Australia, with an arch span of 1,650 feet, is almost as long as the Bayonne Bridge; its clearance to the water is 360 feet. It has been esti-

mated that the present limit for a steel-arch bridge span is 2,500 feet. As stronger steels are developed, this limit will undoubtedly be extended.

Reinforced concrete is used extensively in modern arch-bridge construction. A number of "plain" or unreinforced concrete arches were erected during the period of transition from stone to reinforced-concrete construction. However, the advantages of concrete reinforced with embedded steel rods made unreinforced concrete obsolete for bridgebuilding. In recent years, prestressed concrete has also proved most satisfactory. In preparing this material, embedded steel rods are placed under tension (stretched) while the high-strength concrete sets.

In some concrete arch bridges, the roadway is carried on earth or rubble fill

SUSPENSION BRIDGE

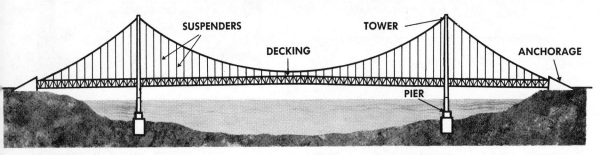

A suspension bridge. Support for the roadway is provided by cables strung between towers and attached to anchorages. Vertical components—anchorages—hang down from the cables.

Mackinac Bridge Authority

An outstanding suspension bridge — the Mackinac Straits Bridge, in Michigan. This is one of the longest bridges of the suspension type in the world; its span extends 3,800 feet.

placed directly on the arch. This form of construction is used only for bridges of small span. The roadway of larger bridges is supported on vertical columns resting on the arch rib.

One of the chief difficulties in long-span concrete arch construction has been the necessity of supporting the very heavy concrete ribs during erection. This drawback has been partially overcome in recent years by the use of cellular, or box arch, ribs. They are made up of slender top and bottom slabs, connected by thin vertical webs.

Suspension bridges. These bridges are notable for their extraordinary length of span, far exceeding that of any other bridge type. As we have pointed out, the earliest suspension bridges go back thousands of years. Iron was first used in this type of construction in 1741, when the Wynch Bridge was built over the Tees River in England. The cables of this bridge were made of iron chains; the flooring rested directly on the cables. The first sus-

pension bridge with level flooring suspended from overhead cables was built in 1801 over Jacob's Creek, in Pennsylvania, by James Finley. In the years that followed, the suspension bridge attained its fullest development in the United States; it may be called the brain child of the American engineer. This type of bridge proved to be the most economical in spanning the many deep and wide rivers of the United States.

The structural principle of the suspension bridge is not unlike that of the household clothesline. In place of the clothesline rope, from which laundry hangs, the bridge has a cable, which consists of a number of high-strength wire strands and which supports the suspended roadway. At the ends, the cable is attached to anchorages, which resist its pull. Anchorages are usually of masonry or concrete; sometimes it is possible to anchor the cables in natural rock. Between the anchorages there are two towers, which support the weight of the cable and also the weight of the entire superstructure. Modern towers are built of steel,

BASCULE BRIDGE

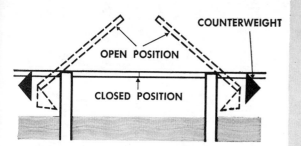

Double-leaf bascule bridge. Each leaf is counter-weighted; it can be turned on its axis so as to assume a nearly vertical position. In the closed position, the single-leaf spans act as a continuous span.

Standard Oil Co. (N. J.)

A double-leaf bascule bridge being raised for a big barge near the Phoenix Oswego Canal, in New York State.

SWING BRIDGE

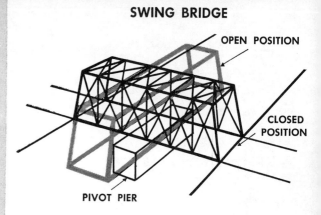

Swing bridge. The superstructure, which may be either a truss or a girder, rests on two end piers and a central pivot pier. It can be turned on the pivot pier, so as to become perpendicular to its former position.

Amer. Institute of Steel Construction

A swing bridge in the open position. This is the Victory Bridge between Perth Amboy and Sayreville, N.J.

supported by masonry and concrete piers. Hanging down from the cables are vertical components, called suspenders; the floor system, or decking, is suspended from them. In some suspension bridges, there is a series of towers, each resting on a pier.

For a given span and a given load, the resulting stress on the cable is inversely proportional to its sag; the greater the sag, the less the stress. It is generally considered desirable to have the sag amount to approximately one-tenth of the span length.

Because of the flexibility of the cable, it is usually necessary to provide a stiffening truss or girder for the decking. This distributes the load imposed by traveling vehicles and thus reduces or minimizes the swaying of the bridge. In some instances, where the cables are particularly large, the stiffening members are omitted. This was the case with the George Washington

Bridge over the Hudson River in New York City, when it had but one deck. A second deck has now been added; trusses have been provided to support it.

Disaster may result when adequate measures are not taken to counteract the inherent flexibility of the suspension bridge. A noteworthy example was the collapse of the Tacoma Narrows Bridge at Tacoma, Washington. This structure had a 2,800-foot main span and a two-lane roadway; it had an eight-foot stiffening girder. Because of its relatively narrow width and unusually shallow stiffening, the structure was extraordinarily flexible and at times swayed noticeably in the wind; it received the not very flattering name of "Galloping Gertie." Its stability was inadequate, and it did not have the necessary resistance to forces brought about by the wind. In November 1940, four months after its completion, it

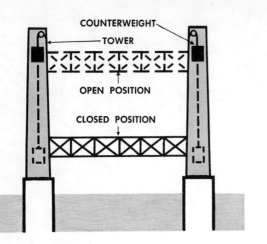

Vertical-lift bridge. In this structure, a single span is set between two towers. Counterweights are provided, one at each tower. The bridge is operated by a power unit, which is generally located in the center of the span.

Amer. Institute of Steel Construction

Portage Lake Lift Bridge at Houghton-Hancock, in Michigan, in the open position. Bridges of this type have gradually replaced railway swing-span bridges, and they have also been used extensively for railway bridges.

collapsed in a 42-mile-an-hour gale. A new Tacoma Narrows Bridge was erected on the old piers in 1948-50.

When well designed and suitably constructed, suspension bridges are safe and stand up well. A fine example is New York City's Brooklyn Bridge, completed in 1883. This graceful structure has a 1,595-foot main span. Modified and strengthened to accommodate heavy motor traffic, the bridge still gives satisfactory service.

The longest suspension bridges are to be found in the United States. The Golden Gate Bridge at San Francisco, California, the Mackinac Straits Bridge in Michigan and the George Washington Bridge in New York City all have spans exceeding 3,000 feet. In no other country do existing bridges of the suspension type approach this length. However, the Firth of Forth suspension bridge, now under construction, will compare with the longer American bridges; it will have a span of 3,300 feet. It has been estimated that the maximum span length for suspension bridges is about 10,000 feet.

MOVABLE BRIDGES

In many cases, it is uneconomical or otherwise undesirable to construct a fixed bridge high enough above a navigable waterway to meet the vertical-clearance requirements. Under such conditions, movable-span bridges are constructed. The three principal types are swing bridges, bascule

bridges and lift bridges.* The movable span of a swing bridge turns about a vertical axis; that of a bascule bridge swings upward about a horizontal axis; that of a lift bridge moves vertically. Since weight is an important factor in the cost of operation of all these bridges, movable spans are constructed of steel rather than concrete, which is heavier. Also, open grating or other lightweight types of construction are generally used for the bridge flooring.

Swing bridges. The superstructure of a swing bridge consists of a truss or girder resting on two end piers and one central pivot pier. In its closed position, the superstructure, together with the live load upon it, is supported by all three piers. To operate the swing bridge, the superstructure is disengaged from the two end piers and is turned on the pivot pier in such a manner as to be ultimately perpendicular to its former position. All operating machinery is located on the pivot pier. Swing spans were particularly popular in the late decades of the nineteenth century and in the early years of the twentieth. They are gradually being replaced by bascule and lift bridges.

Bascule bridges. In recent years, bascule bridges have been used extensively, particularly for automobile traffic. In the

* There are various other minor types. Retractile bridges move horizontally. In transporter bridges, there is a moving platform suspended from an overhead fixed span. Pontoon bridges are sometimes constructed so that a span can be swung aside, permitting boats to pass through.

usual arrangement, the bascule span, also known as a leaf, is counterweighted, so as to reduce the power requirements for operation. Through a system of gears and pinions, the leaf can be turned about its axis so as to assume a nearly vertical position. There are single-leaf and double-leaf bascule bridges. A double-leaf bridge consists of two single-leaf spans, which meet at the center of the bridge and are locked to act as a continuous span when in the closed position. To provide an opening in the channel, each leaf is rotated at the piers to assume a near-vertical position.

Lift bridges. During the past seventy years, the vertical-lift bridge, because of more rapid operation and greater horizontal span, has gradually displaced the railway swing-span bridge and has also been used extensively for highway bridges. The typical lift bridge consists of a span with towers at each end. To counterbalance the dead weight of the span, there are usually counterweights — one at each tower. Each counterweight and the end of the span it counterbalances are connected by continuous steel wire ropes, which are extended over sheaves (pulleys) set on top of the towers. Usually four sheaves are utilized, one at each corner of the span. Thus the dead weight of the span is virtually suspended from the sheaves by means of the counterweight ropes. In the down position, the span rests on shoes which are adequate to support the live load. Therefore, the motive power required to move the span either up or down is relatively nominal, as

it needs only to overcome the frictional resistance of the operating machinery and journals.*

Vertical-lift bridges may be classified as span drive or tower drive. In the span-drive arrangement, the power unit and the machinery are usually located in the center of the span. Power is generally transmitted to the ends of the span by means of operating ropes wound on drums at the center of the span and extending to sheaves at its ends. In recent years, power has also been transmitted by means of a solid shaft extending from the machinery at the center of the span to each end.

In the typical tower-drive arrangement, the power machinery and other equipment are located in each of the towers. Of course this means that there will be less load to lift when the bridge is in operation. Likewise, the span itself can be made lighter, since it does not have to support the weight of the machinery. The resulting savings compensate partially or wholly for the greater cost of the electrical equipment that is required to synchronize the movement of the ends of the tower-drive span.

FLOATING BRIDGES

Floating bridges, or pontoon bridges, have been used extensively for military operations since ancient times. For temporary military use, they ordinarily consist of pontoons or boats, set in position so that their centers are approximately fifteen feet

* *Editor's note*: A journal is a rotating part that turns in a bearing.

FLOATING BRIDGE

The Lake Washington Bridge at Seattle, Washington; we show two views of the floating structure at the east side of the navigation channel. In the left-hand photo-

graph, the draw is half open; in the right-hand photograph, it is closed. The bridge is the world's largest permanent pontoon bridge. It was completed in 1940.

Both photos, Seattle Chamber of Commerce

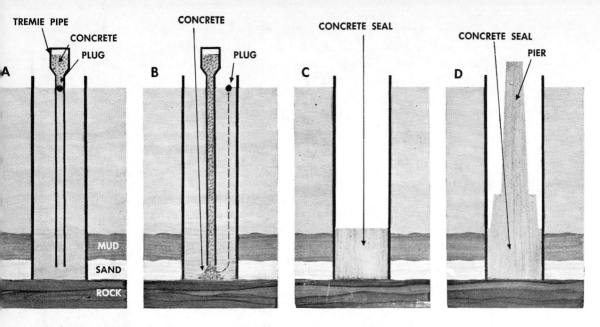

A | B | C | D

TREMIE PIPE
CONCRETE
PLUG
CONCRETE
PLUG
CONCRETE SEAL
CONCRETE SEAL
PIER

MUD
SAND
ROCK

It is sometimes necessary to put a concrete seal in place before water can be pumped out from a cofferdam. A long steel pipe — the tremie pipe — is lowered almost to the bottom of the cofferdam. A wooden plug is set in the pipe and concrete is poured on top of the plug (A). The plug prevents the concrete, as it makes its way downward, from mixing with the water. When the concrete reaches the bottom of the pipe, it pushes out the plug, which rises to the surface and is retrieved. The concrete settles on the bottom of the excavation (B). The tremie pipe is moved about so as to spread the concrete effectively. As more concrete is poured, the pipe is raised, though still kept embedded in the concrete. At the end of the pour, there is a concrete block, the seal, at the bottom of the cofferdam (C). The water is pumped out; the reinforced concrete pier is built up on the seal (D).

apart. Beams span the boats and form a support for the deck. Each pontoon is held in place by a system of anchors that can withstand the forces produced by currents.

Floating-type bridges have also been used to handle normal motor traffic. The Lake Washington Bridge in Seattle, Washington, is a good example. This structure, completed in 1939, is 6,566 feet long; it has a four-lane roadway and can handle the heaviest modern trucks. It consists of a number of concrete pontoons, rigidly joined end to end; a central draw span provides an opening for ships. The buoyancy of the structure is such that approximately $7\frac{1}{2}$ feet of each pontoon is above water. The riding surface is set directly on top of the pontoon decks. Cables extending from each side of the pontoons are connected to anchors buried in the bottom of the lake at some distance from the bridge. The anchor cables have sufficient slack so that there is virtually free up-and-down movement of the bridge, corresponding to variations in the lake level to the extent of approximately 4 feet. The chief advantage of a floating bridge such as this is that the cost of con-

struction is considerably less than that of a fixed bridge. For one thing, it is not necessary to build deep foundations, such as would be required for a fixed bridge extending over a wide expanse of water.

BRIDGE CONSTRUCTION

In bridge construction, the type of bridge to be built and the number and kinds of spans it will have will depend on various considerations. The bridge engineer has to take into account the materials that are readily available, the foundation conditions and the clearances required. All bridges must be designed to withstand the different kinds of loads they will have to endure as well as the different forces to which they will be subjected, such as winds, temperature changes and, in certain parts of the world, earthquakes.

The ideal foundation for a bridge is bedrock. If this is within a reasonable depth below the bed of the stream or the surface of the ground, the bases of piers and abutments are placed directly upon it. It often happens, however, that the depth to bedrock is excessive. In such cases, foundation piles are often used; the bases of the piers and abutments are placed upon them. Piles may be of steel, precast concrete reinforced with steel bars, cast-in-place concrete or wood.

Where the foundation is to extend below the ground-water level, on land, or below the surface of a waterway, a cofferdam is prepared. This is a boxlike temporary structure, whose dimensions correspond to those of the proposed base. It is built up in various ways. Sometimes interlocking steel sheets are driven into the ground, so as to form a more or less watertight continuous structure.

When the cofferdam has been driven to the desired depth, the earth inside it is removed and internal bracing is set in position as required. After the earth material has been excavated to the desired depth in the cofferdam, the water inside it is pumped out and concrete for the base is poured into it. In porous material, it is sometimes necessary to place a concrete seal underwater before the water inside the cofferdam can be pumped out. Concrete for the base is then poured on top of the seal and subsequently the shaft is constructed on the base. After the shaft is completed, the cofferdam is removed.

If it is not feasible to construct open cofferdams, caissons are utilized. A caisson is essentially a hollow box made of concrete or steel. After it is sunk to the desired depth, it is filled with concrete and it becomes the base upon which the pier shaft is constructed. The caisson may be floated into place or may be constructed on top of a sand-filled cofferdam. The bottom of the caisson is open and the weight of the structure rests on the sharply beveled edges of the walls, forming the so-called cutting edge. The earth material inside the caisson is excavated with a clamshell bucket, and this permits the caisson to sink under its own weight. As it sinks, its walls are extended vertically, increasing the weight and causing the sinking to progress even farther.

If some obstacle, such as a large boulder, a log or a thin, hard stratum, prevents the open caisson from sinking, it is sometimes necessary to seal the top of the caisson hermetically, thus converting it into a pneumatic caisson. Air is pumped into the sealed caisson to a sufficient pressure to force the water from it. Workers called "sand hogs" enter the caisson through airlock chambers and excavate at the cutting edge, permitting the caisson to resume its downward progress. Pneumatic-caisson construction is limited to a depth of approximately 100 feet below the water surface. At this depth, an air pressure of 45 pounds per square inch is required, and this is the practical limit under which effective human effort is possible.

There are many bridge sites where the depth to bedrock is so great that the cost of founding piers on bedrock would be prohibitive. Sometimes, in such cases, a caisson is lowered below the stream-bed level until it reaches a stratum where the pressure of the surrounding material will provide adequate support. The depth to which the caisson will be sunk will depend on the character of the earth material that is penetrated and on various other factors, such as the anticipated depth of erosion. Bridges along the lower Mississippi and elsewhere are supported on caissons in this way. A typical example is the Mississippi River Bridge at Greenville, Mississippi. Here the piers are supported on caissons set approximately 200 feet below water level.

Bridge superstructures are erected on their foundations in various ways. If the spans are short and accessible from the ground beneath, they may be lifted into place with large cranes. Longer and heavier spans are often assembled in their final position on temporary scaffolding, called falsework. Occasionally, in rivers or lakes, a span may be erected on scaffolding supported by large floating barges. The span may then be floated into position and lowered onto the piers.

Over deep and swift streams, spans are erected by cantilevering out from supports. Temporary struts may be extended from the pier base, or a falsework pier may be used to steady the construction across the top of the pier. The erection then proceeds progressively each way so that a balance is maintained. This procedure is

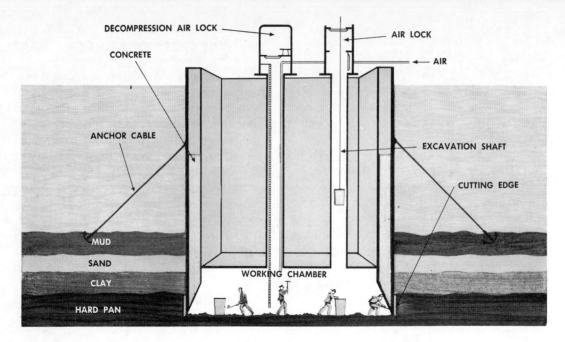

DECOMPRESSION AIR LOCK

AIR LOCK

CONCRETE

AIR

ANCHOR CABLE

EXCAVATION SHAFT

CUTTING EDGE

MUD

SAND

CLAY

WORKING CHAMBER

HARD PAN

Pneumatic caisson used in the construction of a large offshore foundation. The bottom section of the caisson — the working chamber — is roofed over and has hollow outer walls, with a cutting edge at the bottom. Two shafts extend upward from the roof of the working chamber and provide access to the latter. One shaft is for the workers and has a decompression air lock at the top. The other, also provided with an air lock, is for excavated materials. The caisson is sunk in place on the stream bed. Compressed air is forced into the working chamber to keep out water. Workers entering the decompression air lock stay there while the air pressure is gradually increased. When it approximates the pressure in the working chamber, the men go down a ladder at the side of the shaft and into the working chamber. Excavated materials are hoisted up through the excavation shaft. When workers come up from the working chamber, they remain in the air lock while the air pressure is gradually brought down to the normal pressure of the outer air, to prevent the "bends" (see Index). The caisson sinks as material is removed and as the hollow walls of the caisson are filled with concrete. The walls are extended upward as required, thus remaining above water. When bedrock is reached, the entire caisson is filled with concrete.

continued until the cantilevered construction from each support is joined at the center of the span.

Steel arch bridges are often erected on falsework. When this is not possible, temporary tie-back cables may be attached to the arch ribs so that erection may proceed by cantilever methods.

Concrete arch bridges and other large concrete bridges which must be built in their final position are poured on form work supported by scaffolding. Smaller concrete-slab and precast-beam bridges may be set directly in place with cranes.

Suspension bridges require special construction techniques. The towers and anchorages at the ends of the bridge are constructed first. For shorter suspension bridges, the wire-rope cable strands are cut to their precise required lengths and anchorage sockets are attached to them. The cable strands are then pulled across the towers and individually attached to the end anchorages. For longer suspension bridge spans, a procedure of cable spinning is employed. In this procedure, a traveling pulley carries a loop of wire from one anchorage up across the towers and down into the other anchorage. At the anchorage, the two wires in the loop pass around an anchor sheave, and the traveling pulley carries the loop of wire back across the towers to the other anchorage. This procedure is repeated until a cable of the desired size is spun.

Individual strands of wires of the cable are then compacted into a round shape with a hydraulic press, and the cable is wrapped tightly with wire. Bands are clamped around the cable at intervals. A wire rope suspender cable is then extended down from each band to support the stiffening trusses or girders and the floor system.

See also Vol. 10, p. 285: "Bridges."

IMPORTANT BRIDGES OF THE WORLD

Type of bridge	Name of bridge	Location	Main Span (feet)	Completed
Suspension	Golden Gate	San Francisco, Cal.	4,200	1937
"	Mackinac Straits	Michigan	3,800	1957
"	George Washington	New York City	3,500	1931
"	Tacoma Narrows	Puget Sound	2,800	1950
"	Transbay*	San Francisco Bay, Cal.	2,310	1936
"	Bronx-Whitestone	New York City	2,300	1939
"	Delaware Memorial	Wilmington, Del.	2,150	1951
"	Walt Whitman	South Philadelphia, Pa.- Gloucester City, N. J.	2,000	1957
"	Seine River	Tancarville, France	2,000	1959
"	Ambassador	Detroit, Mich.	1,850	1929
Steel arch	Bayonne (Kill van Kull)	New York City	1,652	1931
"	Sydney Harbor	Australia	1,650	1932
"	Birchenough	Southern Rhodesia	1,080	1935
"	Saikai	Nagasaki, Japan	1,042	1955
"	Hell Gate	New York City	977.5	1917
"	Rainbow	Niagara Falls	950	1941
"	Askero Fjord	Sweden	912	1960
"	Duisburg-Rheinhausen	Germany	838	1951
"	Volta River	Ghana, Africa	805	1956
"	Henry Hudson	New York City	800	1936
Concrete arch	Douro Porto	Portugal	886	1957
"	Sando	Sweden	866	1943
"	Plougastel	Brest, France	612	1929
"	Antas River	Brazil	612	1929
"	Traneberg	Stockholm, Sweden	585	1934
"	Albert Louppe	France	567	1930
"	La Roche-Guyon	France	528	1937
"	Svinesund	Sweden	509	1946
Cantilever	Quebec	St. Lawrence River	1,800	1917
"	Firth of Forth	Scotland	1,710	1887
"	Howrah	India	1,500	1942
"	New Orleans	Mississippi River	1,575	1958
"	Transbay*	San Francisco Bay, Cal.	1,400	1936
"	Tappan Zee	Hudson River	1,212	1955
"	Longview	Columbia River	1,200	1930
"	Queensboro	New York City	1,182	1909
Continuous truss	Julien-Dubuque	Mississippi River	845	1943
"	Earle C. Clements	Shawneetown, Ill.	825	1956
"	St. Louis	Mississippi	804	1944
"	Kingston-Rhinecliff	Hudson River	800	1956
"	Sciotoville	Ohio River	775	1918
"	Chain of Rocks	Mississippi	699	1929
Simple truss	Metropolis	Ohio River	720	1917
"	Paducah	Ohio River	716	1929
"	Tanana River	Alaska	700	1922
"	MacArthur	St. Louis, Mo.	668	1911
"	Henderson	Ohio River	665	1933
"	Louisville	Ohio River	644	1919
Continuous girder	Save River	Belgrade, Yugoslavia	856	1956
"	Duesseldorf-Neuss	Rhine River, Germany	676	1951
"	Bonn-Beuel	Rhine River, Germany	643	1949
"	Cologne-Deutz	Rhine River, Germany	605	1948
"	Speyer	Rhine River, Germany	537	1958
"	Britannia	Menai Straits, Wales	460	1850
Movable	Arthur Kill (Vertical lift)	New Jersey	558	1959
"	Cape Cod Canal (Vertical lift)	Massachusetts	544	1935
"	Fort Madison (Swing)	Mississippi River	525	1927
"	Willamette River (Swing)	Oregon	521	1908
"	Sault Ste. Marie (Bascule)	Michigan	336	1914
"	Erie Avenue (Bascule)	Lorain, Ohio	333	1940
Floating bridge	Lake Washington	Seattle, Wash.	6,566	1940

*The figures for the Transbay Bridge are for each of the main suspension spans (identical in length) and the cantilever span.

TRANSFORMATIONS OF WATER VAPOR

Rain, Snow, Sleet, Hail and Other Precipitation

THE rain that supplies welcome moisture to parched fields or brings terrible floods in its wake is the end product of a process that is going on constantly in the atmosphere. This process is the transformation of the invisible gas called water vapor into liquid or solid form.

There is always a considerable amount of water vapor in the atmosphere. Much of it comes from the water that has evaporated from the ocean and from lakes and streams. Water vapor is derived from other sources, too. It passes into the air from the leaves and other aerial structures of plants, and it is one of the waste products exhaled by men and the lower animals. The atmosphere can hold a certain amount of water vapor at a given temperature; the higher the temperature is, the more vapor the air can hold. When it can take up no more, it is said to be saturated.

When the air is chilled, it gradually approaches the saturation point. If this point is reached, some of the water vapor will condense, in the form of tiny droplets, upon the dust and salt particles and the ions (electrified particles) that are always present in the atmosphere. The droplets will become visible — as fog and mist at low levels and as clouds at heights of a half mile and more above the level of the sea. In some cases, when the temperature is below the freezing point, water vapor passes directly into the solid state and is converted into ice crystals. Some clouds are made up entirely of water droplets; others of ice crystals; still others of a mixture of these two forms of condensation of water vapor.

The particles of water or ice crystals in clouds are small and light, and so the cloud of which they form a part resists the pull of gravity and floats in the air. But a great many of the individual droplets in the cloud keep falling toward the earth. They are so light that the resistance of the air holds them back greatly as they drop, and they evaporate long before they reach the ground.

If there are strong ascending air currents within a cloud, the droplets will continually bump into one another; they will stick together and thus will grow in size and weight. The heavier they become, the more slowly they will rise through the ascending air currents, and the faster they will fall when these currents can no longer support them. The droplets have now become full-fledged drops. If they are heavy enough and there are enough of them, they will reach the earth in the form of rain. As we shall find later in this chapter, condensed water vapor may also fall to earth as snow, sleet and hail.

The distribution of rainfall depends not only on climate but on the physical features of the land. In a general way, the following rules may be laid down.

There is likely to be more rainfall in tropical climates than elsewhere. The reason is that as we approach the equator the increasing heat causes more water to evaporate — that is, to be transformed into water vapor.

Other things being equal, there is more rain near the sea than there is inland. For one thing, a wind from the sea is likely to contain a great deal of water vapor. Again, the land and the sea are often at different temperatures. Suppose the sea is warm, while the land is relatively cool; the water vapor in a wind blowing from the sea will be condensed as the wind passes over the land.

As water vapor has condensed, it has formed a cloud on the cold slope of this mountain.

Other things being equal, the rainfall increases with the height above sea level, up to heights not exceeding ordinary cloud level. This is due to the action of mountains in condensing the water vapor contained in the winds that blow over them. The average rainfall of the plains of Europe is 22.6 inches per year; in the mountainous districts it is over 50 inches. Along the western slope of the Continental Divide in the United States, the precipitation is abundant, reaching a total of some 135 inches a year in certain localities. In the interior of the United States it is much smaller. It is less than 15 inches a year in some states.

The rainiest regions of the world are probably the lower slopes of the Himalayas. The village of Cherrapunji, in the Khasi Hills of India, south of the main body of the Himalayas, has a rainfall averaging 426 inches. A record-breaking twelve-month rainfall of 1,041.78 inches occurred at Cherrapunji from August 1860 through July 1861. No less than 150 inches of rain fell in a five-day period at this village in August 1841 — the equivalent of almost four years of rainfall in New York State.

347

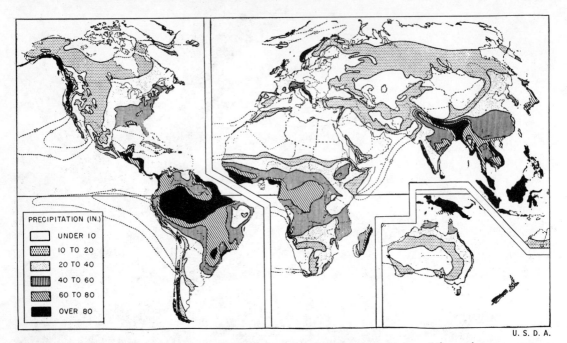

PRECIPITATION (IN.)

UNDER 10

10 TO 20

20 TO 40

40 TO 60

60 TO 80

OVER 80

U. S. D. A.

Diagram showing how precipitation (rain, snow, hail and so on) is distributed over the face of the earth.

The ascent of moist air blowing across a mountain range also accounts for the heavy rainfall in the Pacific Coast region of British Columbia and for the average annual rainfall of 462.93 inches near the top of Mount Waialeale, in central Kauai, Hawaiian Islands. This type of precipitation is known as orographic rainfall (from the Greek word *oros,* meaning mountain). Because time must elapse between the beginning of the lift of the vapor-laden air masses and the actual fall of rain, the greatest orographical rainfalls are generally found part way up the mountain slopes. If the mountains are low, rain may fall in great quantities beyond the crests of the ranges; there may be as much rain on the far side as on the near side. If, however, the ranges are high, precipitation is greater along the windward slopes.

The heavy rainfalls in the tropics are due not so much to condensation of moisture by mountain ranges as by the effect of cold winds pouring in from cooler regions. The line of meeting moves north and south with the movement of the sun. When the sun is north of the equator, the cloud belt is in the Northern Hemisphere; when the sun is south of the equator, the cloud belt is in the Southern Hemisphere. The French geographer Jean-Jacques-Elisée Reclus said of this cloud zone: "It is undoubtedly visible from the nearest heavenly bodies and must resemble those whitish bands which our telescopes discover on the planet Jupiter." The forward and backward movement of the great girdle of clouds brings about the alternation of wet and dry seasons in the tropics.

In the temperate zones there are no clearly defined wet and dry seasons. The lifting of moist air by revolving storms, or cyclones, may bring about precipitation in these areas. Cyclones form an eccentric pattern on the weather map as they advance; hence the rainfall patterns resulting from them show far more variation than those of orographic rainfall. When rainfall results from the lifting of moist air by convection, it is apt to be spotty. The same rainfall may drench one community and barely settle the dust a few miles away.

In certain regions of the globe there is almost no rainfall. Very seldom does it rain in the districts to the south and east of the Caspian Sea, in the Karroo (a plateau area in the Union of South Africa), in the southern part of Australia and in

U. S. Forest Service

A well-watered region — the Snow Basin, near the town of Ogden, in the northern part of Utah. Note the lush vegetation that flourishes in this section of the big state.

spell; the mortality among sheep and other animals is great. When the rains come, the response of vegetation to the moisture is almost miraculous. The French geographer Reclus gave a graphic account of the effects of the dry and rainy seasons upon the soil of the Colombian llanos (plains). "The watercourses," he wrote, "become exhausted [in the dry season]; the lakes change into pools and then into sloughs. . . . The clayey ground shrinks and cracks; the plants wither and are torn to shreds by the winds. The cattle [are driven] by hunger and thirst. . . . and multitudes of their skeletons lie bleaching in the plains. . . . All at once the storms of the rainy season inundate the soil. Multitudes of plants shoot out from the dust, and the yellow expanse is transformed into a flowery meadow."

The sad effects of deforestation

It has been maintained that trees bring rain and that the felling of forests decreases the rainfall. There is no doubt that deforestation diminishes the permeability of the soil, and diminishes its capacity for catching and holding water. Trees hinder the evaporation of water because of their foliage. A road overshadowed by trees, for example, takes longer to dry out after a heavy rain than a road running through a treeless expanse.

What part do trees play in precipitation? It is well known that trees — particularly leaf surfaces — release water vapor to the atmosphere by the process known as transpiration (see Index). In an area that is heavily wooded, transpiration is the source of much of the water in the atmosphere — water that may fall to the earth in the form of precipitation.

Temperature and the process of precipitation

Temperature plays an important part in the process of precipitation. According to R. Brown, "the slightest difference in the temperature of the soil over which a vapor-laden cloud is sailing may determine whether its moisture will be condensed

the canyon region of Arizona. Various parts of Peru and Chile are also quite rainless. There is practically no precipitation in a belt of land, about ten degrees wide, which extends across Africa (it includes the Sahara and Libyan deserts), crosses the north of Arabia into Persia and ends near the western border of Afghanistan. Rain never falls in vast areas of the Gobi, in central Asia.

If there is only a small amount of rainfall, it may be vitally important. In the forbidding table lands of the Karroo, vegetation dies when there is a protracted dry and precipitated, or whether the misty vapor will float away without the thirsty earth obtaining the benefit of its contents, here more grudgingly bestowed than in the cooler regions near the poles." Certainly trees do not retain heat, and they are usually cooler than the soil.

Whether by favoring condensation, whether through the high electrical tension of the tops and tips, there seems a fair amount of evidence that forests directly attract rain, and that deforestation leads to drought. The cutting down of trees in St. Helena was followed by a decrease in the rainfall; a replanting of trees was followed by increased rainfall.

Drought brings with it the ever present danger of forest and prairie fires. After weeks of dry weather, grass and shrub and tree are like tinder, ready to catch fire, and a very small spark may kindle a destructive blaze. Sometimes even the friction of two branches against each other may suffice to kindle a flame. Forest and prairie fires sometimes spread for many miles. In 1923 whole towns were wiped out in the southern part of the state of California.

Rain plays a very important part in molding the face of the earth. Its action in this particular process is partly chemical and partly mechanical.

In considering the chemical action of rain, we must bear in mind that it is not pure water. In the atmosphere it absorbs atmospheric gases — oxygen, nitrogen and carbon dioxide. These are found to be absorbed in the following average proportions: nitrogen 64.47; oxygen 33.76; carbon dioxide 1.77. The absorbed gases are not found in the same proportion as in the atmosphere; the carbon dioxide occurs in proportions thirty to forty times greater than in the atmosphere. Besides these natural atmospheric gases, rain also absorbs a certain amount of nitric acid, sulfuric acid and salts. It also carries down with it germs and dust. As soon as it touches the earth it adds to its chemical contents.

Rain, accordingly, contains various more or less active chemical substances and has a varied chemical action on the rocks and soil on which it falls. Owing to its oxygen, it oxidizes or rusts various minerals, such as iron, which it passes over.

Soil Conservation Service

An odd erosional formation in soft sandstone in the land of the Navahos, near Gallup, New Mexico.

Owing to the organic matter it contains, it deoxidizes other minerals such as gypsum. And owing to the carbonic acid it contains, it dissolves limestone and marble, carbonate of magnesia and other minerals. The so-called "pipes" and "swallow holes" found in limestone rock are funnel-shaped cavities corroded in the limestone by rain. If there is no soil on the surface to fill up these holes, they deepen and may eventually become caverns.

The Carso district in Yugoslavia is honeycombed with these holes, which are locally known as *doliniens* or *dolinas.*

U. S. Geological Survey

This strange, statuelike formation offers a most striking example of the way in which rain sometimes carves rock.

Some of them are deep (the deepest is 525 feet); some shallow. At the bottom is found a red earth — the insoluble iron-oxide residue of the limestone. In northern Bohemia and Saxony hollows 3 to 30 feet deep, known as *karren* or *sehratten,* are found, and these doubtless are also formed by rain eroding the limestone rock.

Even granite is rotted by water, so that it becomes loose and can be dug into with a spade. It is mixed with clay and sand. In the District of Columbia granite has been found decomposed to a depth of as much as 80 to 100 feet. Near St. Austell, in the English county of Cornwall, huge pits, as big as skyscrapers, have been dug into the granite by miners in search of tin and china clay.

In some cases when rain is absorbed by rock, the latter forms a chemical compound with the water and undergoes the change known as hydration. Anhydrite, for instance, is converted into gypsum, and it increases in bulk at the same time about 33 per cent.

The mechanical action of rain is quite obvious. Every heavy shower of rain scours and scars the roads and paths with its runnels; and when the rain comes down in sheets it carries away the soil as effectively as a river. Where there are trees and vegetation to shield the soil and to hold it together, the rain may fail to remove much of it, but where the soil is unprotected it may be quickly carried away. The destruction of forests, accordingly, is bound to increase greatly the destructive effect of rain, and many parts of Syria, Greece, Asia Minor, Africa and Spain have first been denuded of trees by men, and then of soil by the rain. "If," wrote Reclus, "some modern Attila, traversing the Alps, made it his business to desolate these valleys forever, the first thing he should do would be to encourage the inhabitants in their senseless work of destruction."

In some cases torrential rain produces floods of mud; a catastrophe of this kind occurred near the volcano of Vesuvius, in Italy, in September 1911.

"The torrential rains which fell caused a huge volume of mud and lava to flow down the sides of the mountain, and this, dividing into several branches, swept over the entire countryside, destroying everything in its path. The town of Resina was completely engulfed in it, and the mud gradually reached the height of the first-floor windows of the houses. To describe the horror of the scenes that ensued one would be obliged to have recourse to the most awesome incidents in Dante's IN-FERNO. The floating corpses of people who had been overtaken by the terrible

The gullies shown here were all produced within a period of several days by heavy rains near Bethany, in Missouri.

flood presented a dreadful spectacle. . . . Farming utensils and furniture, together with cows, horses and various other domestic animals, were also caught up and borne along by the stream. The district of Miglio di Oro, one of the most enchanting parts of the commune of Resina, has been flooded with mud and totally ruined. The onrush of the stream was such that many houses were swept away bodily.

"The impetuous torrent rushed down the mountainside and burst with great force against the walls of the houses. The doors crashed in and the thick stream . . . flooded the lower floors. . . . In many cases, the mud inside the houses flooded the stairs and the upper floors. . . . Many persons, particularly women and children, were so terrified by the unusual sight that they had not even sufficient energy left to save themselves, and they were consequently drowned by the awful torrent."

How rain helps
bring about landslides

In many cases rain destroys, not by causing deluges of mud, but by producing landslides, in which large masses of earth and rock slide bodily downhill. Rain contributes to landslides in various ways. It causes the disintegration of soil and adds immensely to its weight. It creates new debris on slopes by penetrating into crevices and cracks in rock; when freezing takes

place, the ice expands and causes the surface rock to be broken up. Water also acts as a lubricant for landslides. Some landslides involve only the regolith, the mantle of loose material that lies above bedrock. In other cases, the descending material includes quantities of rock fragments that were broken off from the underlying layer as the slide passed over it.

The mass movement of weathered material on slopes may be very slow. This material will begin to descend after it has been saturated by particularly heavy rains or by melting snow. The movement may continue for many years and may cause practically no destruction. Trees may continue to grow on a slope on which a slide of this type is taking place; they are likely to be tilted at various angles.

In some instances great masses of rock fragments, large and small, move downhill at a very rapid rate and may create havoc. One of the most destructive slides in recent centuries occurred in Italy in 1855. A mass of rock debris 3,500 feet long, 1,000 feet wide and 600 feet high, roared down into the valley of the Tiber River, in the vicinity of the village of San Stefano. The debris completely dammed up the valley, converting the Tiber into a deep lake. San Stefano, which nestled in the valley, was submerged under fifty feet of water; there was a great deal of property damage and many persons lost their lives.

Another devastating slide took place in 1903 at Frank, in the Canadian province of Alberta. A huge volume of rock, estimated at 40,000,000 cubic yards, slid from the top and side of Turtle Mountain and went crashing into the valley floor below. Such was the momentum of the slide that its front advanced two miles across the valley and 400 feet up the opposite side. The entire movement lasted less than two minutes. The mass of rubble that covered the valley wiped out the town of Frank and killed seventy persons.

The Gros Ventre Valley in Wyoming was the scene of a memorable slide in 1925. About 50,000,000 cubic yards of loose debris descended some 2,000 feet on an underlying layer of saturated clay. As in the case of the Alberta slide, the front of the mass of debris made its way across the valley and then up the other side.

A slide (or slides) probably accounts for the curious blocks of quartzite that fill many of the valleys in the Falkland Islands. The blocks are covered with white lichen and from a distance look like small glaciers. Since they have the same structure as the quartzite ridges on the hills above the valley, it is believed that they were detached somehow, probably through the action of rain, and slid down the slope.

Other land movements caused by rain are less dramatic, but play an important part in molding the landscape. As the loose soil masses that often form the banks of rivers are saturated by heavy rains, they sometimes slump. This type of action accounts for a great deal of the river-bank erosion that takes place in areas where rainfall is abundant.

In regions where there is little or no rain, rivers do not carve out gentle valleys, but cut steep gorges with perpendicular banks, as in the canyon country of Arizona. If this area were subjected to rainfall such as deluges Cherrapunji, its contours would soon be completely altered.

Rainfall produces the odd formations known as earth pillars or pyramids — tall pinnacles of earth capped by stones. They are simply columns of hardened clay; protected by their stone capping, they have resisted the eroding power of rain, while the clay that was not so protected has been washed away. If the stone falls off, the pillar will soon be eroded to the surface of the ground. Earth pillars of this type are to be found in the Tirol, the Himalayas and various other places.

California hillside orchard, ruined by heavy rains that carried off the topsoil and created a series of gullies.

Both photos,
Amer. Mus. of Nat. Hist.

The two photographs above show the exquisite patterns that can be formed by snow crystals. Each crystal has six points or sides. No two of them are exactly alike.

Snow is not
frozen rain

The popular idea of snow is that it consists of frozen raindrops. This notion should be discarded, together with the belief that lightning cannot strike twice in the same place. It is true that sometimes raindrops freeze in their passage from the mother cloud to the earth; as we shall see, we call such frozen raindrops sleet or hail. But snow is something else again. It is made up of water vapor particles that have been transformed into crystals, without first passing through the liquid state. Such crystals can form only when the dew point is below 32° F.* Once the crystals have been produced, they may enlarge by combining with other crystals or with water droplets. Large flakes are generally combined in this way when the temperature is not much below the freezing point; they are never formed at very low temperatures.

Snowflakes are still a good deal of a mystery to scientists. For instance, why should every perfect crystal of snow always have six sides or six points? Why should it be flat and not round like a hailstone or

* The dew point is the temperature at which a mass of air becomes saturated, when it is cooled with no change in either the air pressure or the amount of water vapor it contains.

raindrop? How long does it take a crystal to form? Why are no two crystals exactly alike? Wilson Bentley, of Jericho, Vermont, photographed and examined snowflakes for over fifty years, and he never found two identical flakes.

Snow can fall from almost any kind of low or middle cloud. It may come when the barometer is rising and the air pressure is increasing, or when the barometer keeps going down. There may be snow when the thermometer outside your window reads 37° F. above; if it goes above that mark, the flakes will probably melt and fall to earth in the form of rain. It may also snow when it is 50° below; but that does not happen very often.

To a poet snow is the subject matter for a lyric. To youngsters it means coasting and snowball fights; to their elders, skiing and tobogganing. But snow is not the exclusive property of poets and lovers of sports. For one thing, it is a valuable resource of mankind. The snow that accumulates in mountainous areas during the winter and gradually melts during the spring and summer is an important source of water supply. Snow also serves as a blanket that prevents the heat of the soil from escaping into the air. It keeps the roots of perennial plants and the seeds of

Striking winter scene in the woods at Banff, Alberta, Canada. Snow has mantled all things with spotless white.

Canadian Pacific Railway

annuals from freezing. In this way, it assures the permanence of vegetation.

Of course, a heavy snowfall can often be disagreeable or even dangerous. Heavy snow comes when warm air masses ride up over colder air masses lying in their way. If the rising air is very moist and if the wedge of cold surface air remains nearly stationary, the stage is set for snow-making on a very large scale. It will continue to snow as long as the supply of warm, moist air lasts and as long as it is forced to ride up over the colder air mass. Under such circumstances, a rate of more than one inch of snowfall an hour is not uncommon. When this goes on hour after hour, it adds up to a good deal of snow.

In the United States a heavy snow with violent winds is known as a blizzard. Perhaps the most famous one in the history of the country struck New York on March 12, 1888. The city was buried in snow; drifts reached second-story windows. All street-car and elevated traffic stopped. Electric wires collapsed; rail and wire communication was cut off. The cost ran into many millions of dollars. Even more snow fell upon the city on December 26, 1947 — 25.8 inches in less than twenty-four hours. But this snowfall was not a blizzard, since the winds were moderate.

How sleet and glaze are formed

Sometimes newly formed raindrops freeze on their way to the earth; they may be mixed with snowflakes that have melted and then frozen again. This formation is called sleet in the United States. (In England the word sleet applies either to a mixture of snow and rain or to a mixture of snow and hail.)

Some raindrops freeze *after* they have reached the earth. Many people refer to this sort of deposit, too, as sleet; but the official name given to it by the United States Weather Bureau is glaze. Glaze on a large scale is called an ice storm; it is a menace to man and beast. It often comes unannounced; and then the weatherman comes in for his share of criticism. He had predicted a harmless shower or snow-fall only to find that glaze had converted the streets into a vast skating rink.

As a matter of fact, the dividing line between snow-making and glaze-making is difficult to determine. Glaze is produced under much the same conditions as snow. A moist air mass is pushed up over a wedge of colder air. If the air aloft is cold, there will be snow. If it is warm, rain will start to fall.

Effects of an ice storm in Denison, Texas, on January 7, 1949. Sleet and freezing rain turned to ice, which built up on sagging telephone lines. Finally, the weight snapped wires, poles and cross-arms.

Bell Telephone System

The Hartford Fire Insurance Co., Hartford, Conn.

Left: typical hailstones. The top ones have been cut in two to show the alternating clear ice and snowy ice. Below: unusually large hailstones. Some are about as big as the baseball in the foreground. Right: damage caused to a small church building in Rayville, Missouri by big hailstones blown by a gale.

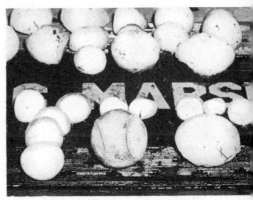

Shoopman — Gen. Adjustment Bureau, N. Y. C.

Suppose now that the wedge of underlying cold air is shallow and that the raindrops have only a short distance to fall before reaching the ground. In that case the chances are that the drops will not begin to freeze until they hit something cold, such as the limb of a tree, or a telegraph line or the ground itself. Every exposed object gets a coating of ice. Given time, the coating process may go on until the layer of ice that has formed will be thick enough to weigh down and break the branches of trees. Humans and animals will flounder helplessly on the icy surface of the ground. Small birds may have their feet frozen to the branches of trees; the wings of others may be frozen solid.

The ice storm that swept over New England in November 1921 did almost as much damage in certain places as the hurricane that struck the area in September 1938. The damage to trees was particularly heavy. Orchards were ruined and forests were badly mutilated. Nor did the immediate effects of the storm tell the whole story of disaster. The wounds inflicted on the surviving trees made them vulnerable to the fungus and insect enemies in the neighborhood. The litter of broken branches paved the way for forest fires the following summer.

Really bad storms like this are comparatively rare, both in Europe and North America. The most frequently affected area in North America runs westward from the New-England-mid-Atlantic coast through the Central Lowlands to Nebraska, Kansas and Oklahoma.

The formation of hailstones

A particle of sleet and a hailstone may look much alike; but there is a difference just the same. Sleet is simply frozen water; but as we shall see, a hailstone is a much more complicated object, with alternating layers of snow and clear ice. There are other differences. Hail forms inside thunderclouds instead of underneath warm air fronts. It is a summer visitor, while sleet is more apt to fall in the winter months.

Hail may form as water droplets freeze in the upper air. As the hailstones fall, they grow by congealing the cooled water drops through which they pass lower down and collecting them as additional ice layers. According to another theory, hail is created as raindrops, instead of falling, are carried by strong winds into the upper atmosphere, where they are covered with snow. When the winds fail to hold

International Newsreel photo

their increasing weight, the pellets start to fall. They tumble back into the above-freezing cloud levels and get a coating of raindrops. The stones, which have now become hailstones, may be caught up in another upcurrent and blown back into the snow region again. There the newly acquired water coating freezes into clear ice and the stones get another wrapping of snow.

Under favorable circumstances, this shuttlecock movement can go on for a long time. Of course the hailstones get bigger with every completed up-and-down movement. Hailstones have been found with as many as twenty-five alternating layers of snowy ice and clear ice. Just cut open a newly fallen stone sometime and see for yourself. If you divide the number of layers by two, you will have the approximate number of up-and-down journeys made by the stone.

Only a thunderstorm can produce hailstones but very few actually do; the figure is something like one out of four hundred. We may be thankful for that, for hail is a troublemaker. A single hailstorm can cause several million dollars' worth of crop damage when it comes, as it generally does, about midsummer. All this damage is likely to be concentrated in a strip of land seldom more than twenty-five miles long and five to ten miles broad. You can easily see why some farmers speak of "hell-storms" and why they are such firm believers in hail insurance.

Most of the damage done in a hailstorm is done by pellets no bigger than peas. Occasionally hailstones are as big as baseballs. (A baseball is a little less than three inches in diameter.) When such hail falls, greenhouses and roof tiles are smashed to bits and men and animals may be literally stoned to death. The records tell us that on July 10, 1923, hailstones killed twenty-three people and many cattle near Rostov, in the Soviet Union.

Under particularly favorable circumstances, hailstones may become as big as good-sized grapefruit. Stones of this kind fell on the town of Potter, Nebraska, on the afternoon of July 6, 1928. One of the giant stones was weighed, measured and photographed immediately after it had fallen. Its weight was found to be 1½ pounds, and it had a diameter of about 5 inches. This was the largest hailstone of which we have definite record. Imagine how many times it must have been tossed up and down in order to attain its imposing size!

See also Vol. 10, p. 271: "Weather and Climate."

COMMUNICATION SATELLITES*

Promising End Products of the Space Program

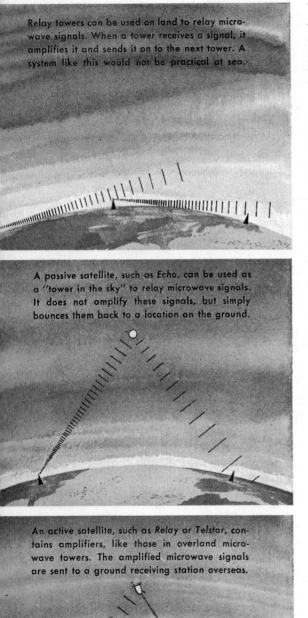

Relay towers can be used on land to relay microwave signals. When a tower receives a signal, it amplifies it and sends it on to the next tower. A system like this would not be practical at sea.

A passive satellite, such as *Echo*, can be used as a "tower in the sky" to relay microwave signals. It does not amplify these signals, but simply bounces them back to a location on the ground.

An active satellite, such as *Relay* or *Telstar*, contains amplifiers, like those in overland microwave towers. The amplified microwave signals are sent to a ground receiving station overseas.

THE communication systems of the world — telephone, radio, television, high-speed data transmission and the like — have been expanding with amazing rapidity. Existing transmission facilities are taxed as never before, and microwave radio has been called on increasingly to provide added pathways of communication. Microwaves are very short electromagnetic waves. The broad-band radio systems** in which they are employed can handle all types of communication, including telephone and television.

A striking property of microwaves is that, generally speaking, they travel in a straight line. Unless they are intercepted in some way, they soar off into space instead of following the curvature of the earth. To channel them properly, a series of relay towers must be provided. Each tower intercepts a given microwave signal and, after amplifying it, sends it on to the next tower. The system of relay towers for microwave transmission has proven very effective over land areas. Today, for example, a large proportion of Bell Telephone System long-distance messages are carried on microwave.

Up to now, however, microwave transmission has not been possible over wide bodies of water. It is not practical to erect a system of relay towers at sea, so that there is no way to intercept and relay the microwave signal. For overseas microwave transmission, a special kind of tower is needed — a tower in the sky: that is, a satellite.

Satellites that can serve as relay towers are of two kinds — active and passive. Passive satellites are large balloons or other types of reflectors that "mirror" a signal without adding to its power. *Echo I*, launched under the auspices of the Na-

* Article prepared with the assistance of the Bell Telephone System, the Radio Corporation of America and the National Aeronautics and Space Administration.
** "Broad-band" refers to the range of frequencies. All electromagnetic waves have the same speed — about 186,000 miles per second — but they have an immensely wide frequency range.

Telstar I, an experimental satellite built by the Bell Telephone System and launched in July 1962. It sent live television from North America to Europe within 15 hours after its launching. It weighs 170 pounds; its diameter is 34½ inches.

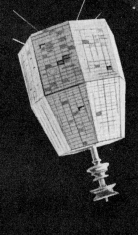

Relay I, built by the Radio Corporation of America for the National Aeronautics and Space Administration, is an eight-sided prism, 51 inches high and 27 inches in diameter at its broad end. Its exterior panels contain over 8,000 solar cells. This satellite was sent aloft in December 1962.

Above is an artist's conception of the *Syncom* satellite. This long-range active satellite is placed in orbit around the earth at a distance of 22,300 miles from our planet.

If either *Telstar* or *Relay* is to provide a true worldwide communication system, fifty or more satellites, orbiting the globe at carefully calculated intervals, will have to be put into use.

It is believed that three high-altitude *Syncom* satellites, at appropriate intervals over the equator, would provide microwave transmission for every region on earth except remote polar areas.

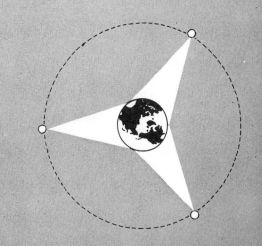

Randolph Churchill reading a message from his father, Sir Winston Churchill, in the presence of President Kennedy outside the White House on April 9, 1963. The elder Churchill was declared an honorary American citizen by President Kennedy in a ceremony telecast and transmitted to Great Britain via the *Relay* satellite.

tional Aeronautics and Space Administration (NASA) in August 1960, is a good example of a passive satellite. An aluminum-coated plastic balloon, it serves as a backboard. Signals from the ground are bounced off its reflective surface to another location on the ground. Since *Echo I* has no amplification equipment, its capacity and band width are very limited.

Active satellites contain amplifiers, similar to the amplifiers in overland microwave towers. Signals are received in the satellite from a ground transmitter. The signals are amplified by the satellites, then sent to a ground receiving station overseas. Many more circuits can be provided with active satellites than with passive ones.

Already several active communication satellites have been placed in medium-range orbits, with apogees (points farthest from the earth) of several thousand miles. All have been built under the auspices of NASA. The first of these satellites, *Score*, was constructed by the Radio Corporation of America and was launched in December 1958. It carried President Eisenhower's radio greetings to the world in Christmas of that year. The *Relay I* satellite — also built by RCA, was launched in December 1962. The Bell Telephone System placed *Telstar I* and *Telstar II* in orbit; the former in July 1962 and the latter in May 1963.

The *Relay* and *Telstar* satellites have transmitted short "live" television programs with outstanding success. Basically, how-

ever, these satellites are experimental devices. With them, scientists are trying to find out more about the conditions under which communication satellites must operate. Special equipment on the *Relay* and *Telstar* satellites measures the radioactivity that is encountered; the effects of collisions with tiny meteoroids; temperatures at the exterior and in the interior of the satellites; the amount of sunlight received; and so on.

To be effective in a worldwide system as relay towers in space, a number of medium-range satellites — fifty or more — would have to be provided. This would ensure that as one would disappear over the horizon, another would move within the range of ground communication stations.

Another type of active-satellite system, called Syncom (from "Synchronous Communication") is being developed. The satellites to be used would be known as "synchronous" because their speed in orbit would be synchronized (matched) with the speed of the earth's rotation. This would be brought about at an altitude of about 22,300 miles above the earth. Each satellite would be in a fixed position in relation to a given point on our planet. It has been calculated that three of these high-altitude satellites, stationed at appropriate intervals over the equator, would provide adequate microwave transmission facilities for every region on earth except for remote polar areas. The Syncom active-satellite system shows great promise indeed.

RENAISSANCE (1450-1600)

BY JUSTUS SCHIFFERES

THE NEW LEARNING

SCIENCE stirred to new life in the Renaissance, that tremendously exciting period in which there was a rebirth of literature and art in western Europe. The Renaissance took some of its inspiration from the masters and the works of classical antiquity. In these masterpieces men rediscovered, or thought they rediscovered, a rational approach to knowledge, a free spirit of inquiry and a great zest for life. It was an age of self-expression, often beautiful, sometimes violent. It was several centuries in the making, but by the end of the fifteenth century, the period was in full swing.

The Renaissance drew its first breath in sunny Italy. There were various reasons why this was so. For one thing, the

Alinari

The great poet and scholar Francesco Petrarca, or Petrarch, was a forerunner of the Italian Renaissance.

Italian peninsula had been the seat of the old Roman Empire, the mightiest in antiquity. The Italians of the Middle Ages stood in close contact with the vanished glories of Rome; everywhere there were relics and ruins of the glorious past — stately temples, long viaducts, statues, busts, coins. Small wonder, then, that Italians took pride in the heritage of their past glory.

Furthermore, in Italy the political and social conditions of the time favored the rise of a new spirit. There was considerable political liberty in most of the Italian city-states. A flourishing commerce, begun in the eleventh century, put the inhabitants in contact with other peoples and other ideas. The wealthy upper classes spent more time in the city than upon their country estates; this favored the development of centers of culture where intellectual pursuits were fostered.

The herald of the Italian Renaissance was the scholar and poet Francesco Petrarca (1304–74), more commonly known to English-speaking people as Petrarch. He brought the men of his own age into sympathetic contact with the authors and the ideas of the classical world. He collected books and old coins, urged the preservation of ancient monuments, edited classical manuscripts.

Though Petrarch knew no Greek, he appreciated the importance of learning this language. His friend, Giovanni Boccaccio (1313–75), the author of the DECAMERON, laid the foundations for the study of Greek. The new study of Greek science and philosophy was to become the starting point of modern science in the following years.

Alinari

Leonardo da Vinci and four of his "projects": flying machine, cannon, parachute and military engine.

In the early years of the fifteenth century a number of Greek scholars from the Byzantine Empire came to Italy to teach classical literature. The fall of this Empire in 1453 to the Ottoman Turks brought about an increased influx of these scholars, who brought priceless manuscripts with them. To find other manuscripts men eagerly ransacked the libraries of Italian monasteries and cathedrals.

These companies of scribes (manuscript copyists) were set to work turning out new copies of the Greek and Latin masters. For a time there were not enough copies to meet the demand, in spite of the busy hands and pens of copyists. But the discovery of printing from movable type, about 1450, and improvements in the art of papermaking in time solved the problem of providing books for all who wanted them.

The devotees of the new learning became known as humanists (the word comes from the Latin *humanitas:* education in the liberal arts). For some, humanism meant merely a great increase of interest in classical studies. Others, however, were greatly influenced by the boldness with which the ancients had discussed the vital problems of life and death; they were fascinated by the ancient poets who sang of the beauty and joy of life. Humanists like these drew a new concept of everyday living. For them personal freedom became the highest goal — freedom to express themselves without reserve; freedom to live one's life to the full.

At the same time that a renewed love of classical learning was sweeping Italy, there was also a rebirth in the arts — particularly in architecture, sculpture and painting. The art of the Renaissance was vigorous; it was full of motion and feeling. The artists learned from the ancients and from each other; they eagerly studied nature and man; they were insatiably curious.

The restless and many-sided activity of the Italian Renaissance is best illustrated in the life and achievements of the great Leonardo da Vinci. Born in the small town of Vinci, near Florence, in 1452, he became the pupil of a Florentine goldsmith, Verrocchio. He soon turned to painting and he became wonderfully proficient in this art and in many other fields. In 1482 he entered the service of Ludovico Sforza, the Duke of Milan, as a painter, sculptor, musician, engineer and architect. Among the other notables who became his patrons in later years were Cesare Borgia and the French kings Louis XII and Francis I. He died in France in 1519.

Leonardo was an outstanding painter, though he left few canvases to posterity; his masterpieces are Mona Lisa and The Last Supper, which are known and admired the world over. He was also an eminent sculptor, architect, engineer, philosopher and scientist. We have already met such "men of many talents" — polymaths — in the history of science, foremost among them Aristotle and Archimedes. We shall meet many more in the pages that follow — Cellini, Benjamin Franklin, Hermann von Helmholtz and Goethe, among others.

The range of Leonardo's remarkable powers of thought and observation, his incredible energy and his ingenuity are fully revealed in his notebooks. These were unsystematically arranged and written, often ungrammatically, in reversed, mirror-image writing. They looked so unpromising on the surface that for centuries no one thought of publishing them. And yet they are a treasure-trove for the historian of science. In them we find definite contributions to scientific knowledge as well as the seeds of inventions which were perfected centuries later — the airplane, the breech-loading gun, the parabolic compass, the military tank and the parachute.

Leonardo thought incisively about the laws of the lever and of freely falling bodies. With his painter's eye, he studied the laws of optics and perspective as well as the structure of the human body. He was vitally concerned with a great many other scientific matters, from hydraulic machines to the nature of fossils.

Leonardo did not attempt to formulate a complete, definite system of philosophy, as so many of his medieval forebears had done. He preferred to investigate particular problems in the true spirit of modern science. Like the ancient Greek geometer Archimedes, whose works he eagerly studied, he was often forced to be a practical man. As an engineer, he concerned himself with building solid bridges, walls and canals rather than with carrying on discussions bearing on abstract principles.

He experimented endlessly. "While nature begins with the cause and ends with the experiment," he wrote, "we must nevertheless pursue the opposite plan, beginning with the experiment and by means of it investigating the cause." For "those sciences are vain and full of errors which are not born from experiment, the mother of all certainty."

Another noted artist-scientist was Benvenuto Cellini (1500–71), a native of Florence. Cellini's famous autobiography reveals him not only as a profligate "man about town" and as a consummate artist in gold and bronze but also as an authority on metals. He was greatly interested in the texture, structure and composition of the materials with which he worked. He inserted many penetrating passages on metals — especially alloys — in his autobiographical writings.

The new learning worked its way north from Italy and found many enthusiastic followers. One of the earliest of these was the German Johann Mueller (1436–76), sometimes called Regiomontanus, after the Latin name for his birthplace Koenigsberg, or King's Mountain. He made a digest of Ptolemy's ALMAGEST, built an observatory and provided useful nautical tables for practical navigators. Another outstanding

Metropolitan Museum of Art

A drinking bowl fashioned by Benvenuto Cellini

northern scholar was Nicholas of Cusa (1401–64), who became a cardinal. This liberal churchman was particularly interested in astronomy, mathematics, physics and calendar reform. He came to believe that the earth moves and that the universe is boundless. The outstanding figure of the northern Renaissance was the Dutchman Desiderius Erasmus (1467?–1536), a learned and witty man; as Drummond put it, he fought "the battle of sound learning and plain common sense."

THE AGE OF DISCOVERY

The Renaissance marked a new development in literature and art; it was also an age of great geographical discoveries, when the two Americas and vast areas in Asia and Africa were revealed to the people of Europe.

The Portuguese opened the age of discovery under the leadership of Prince Henry the Navigator (1394–1460). They discovered the Azores in 1419; then they pushed down along the west coast of Africa, first as missionaries, then as hunters of gold and of slaves. Toward the end of the century the Portuguese captain Vasco da Gama rounded the Cape of Good Hope and sailed directly across the Indian Ocean to India, reaching the city of Calicut in May 1498. This exploit was immortalized by the Portuguese poet Camoëns in the epic THE LUSIADS.

The most dramatic event of this pioneering era, of course, was the discovery of the Americas — a New World. It was, in a way, an accident — the result of a false concept of the globe that went back to the days of the ancient Greeks. In the third century B.C., Eratosthenes, believing that the earth was round, had suggested that by sailing due west from Spain one could reach the coast of India. Of course he had no idea that two continents — North and South America — lay in the way.

In the fifteenth century a number of intelligent men were convinced that a ship could reach the coast of Asia by tracing a westerly course from Europe. Among them was the Florentine physicist and mathematician Paolo dal Pozzo Toscanelli (1397–1482). In the year 1474 he prepared a map and sailing directions showing how, by crossing the Atlantic, one could reach Cathay (China) and India — "those regions most fertile in all kinds of spices and jewels and precious stones." Cathay had been reached from Europe by travel overland and was known by the reports of such famous travelers as Marco Polo (1254?–1324?). According to some, the Genoese sea captain Christopher Columbus (1451?–1506) was familiar with Toscanelli's map. He determined to be the first to reach Asia by sailing westward.

Columbus tried unsuccessfully to get the King of Portugal to outfit an expedition for a westward voyage. At last, after many rebuffs, he persuaded the sovereigns of Spain, King Ferdinand and Queen Isabella, to equip an expedition of three small ships. Columbus set sail from Palos, Spain, on August 3, 1492; ten weeks later (October 12) he landed upon what he thought was one of the islands of the East Indies. Ac-

tually, he had set foot on one of the Bahamas. Columbus made three more voyages from Spain to the New World. He died in the year 1506, still firmly convinced that he had traced a new route to the Far East.

Other explorers now followed in the wake of the great Columbus. Among these

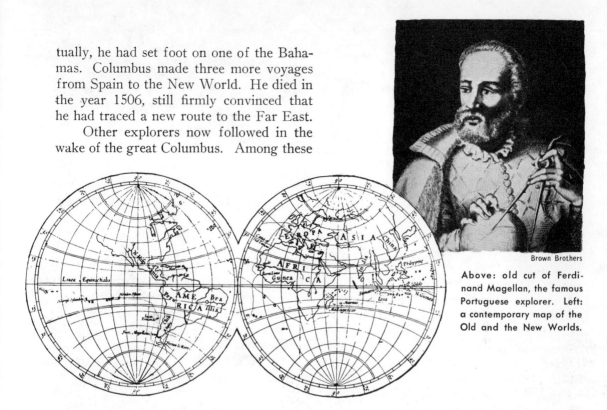

Brown Brothers

Above: old cut of Ferdinand Magellan, the famous Portuguese explorer. Left: a contemporary map of the Old and the New Worlds.

pioneers was the Florentine pilot Amerigo Vespucci (1451–1512), better known as Americus Vespucius (the Latinized form of his name). We know of Vespucius' explorations through two letters of his, one written in 1503 and the other in 1504. If we are to accept the statements made in these documents (many scholars do not), Vespucius took part in four transatlantic voyages in all and was the first to discover the continent of South America. He thought that this was a hitherto unknown part of Asia; he called it the New World, because it had not been seen before by any European. The learned German geographer Martin Waldseemueller took Vespucius' claims at their face value. In his INTRODUCTION TO COSMOGRAPHY, published in 1507, Waldseemueller suggested that the new land to the west be called America, "because Americus discovered it."

The Italian navigator Giovanni Caboto (1450–98), who had settled in England and had changed his name to John Cabot, made several voyages to the New World under letters patent issued by Henry VII of England. Cabot discovered Cape Breton Island, St. Pierre, Miquelon and Baffin Land. Like Columbus and Vespu-

cius, he was convinced that he had reached the eastern outposts of Asia.

The conviction grew, however, that the westward route to the Orient was barred by a continental barrier. Many attempts were made to find a way through or around this barrier. In search of such a route, the Spaniards explored the Gulf of Mexico and the Isthmus of Panama. In the year 1513, Vasco Nuñez de Balboa discovered the mighty Pacific Ocean, which he called the Southern Sea (Mar del Sur). Of course the Spaniards found no water route through the narrow neck of land that separated the two Americas. It was not until the Panama Canal was dug, some four centuries later, that this barrier was pierced.

The Spaniards now sought a more southerly route to the Far East. A Spanish fleet of five ships, captained by the Portuguese nobleman Ferdinand Magellan (1480?–1521), sailed in 1519 from San Lúcar de Barrameda. Reaching the coast of South America, Magellan turned southward and then west, sailing through the strait at the southern tip of South America that now bears his name. He then crossed over into a calmer sea, which he called the Mar Pacífico (calm sea) — the Pacific

Henry Hudson was set adrift with a few companions in a small boat by his mutinous crew.

Ocean. Continuing westward, the fleet was reduced to three ships. Short of water and food, they reached the Philippine Islands; here Magellan was killed by the natives. One of the five ships of the original fleet managed to round the Cape of Good Hope and return home. It had sailed completely around the world; thus it had furnished conclusive proof that the earth is round.

In the course of the years that followed, the Spaniards discovered and conquered vast tracts of land in the New World: Mexico, Central America and most of South America. The immense area that is now the country of Brazil was taken over by Portugal.

During the sixteenth century English, French and Dutch navigators sought to find a Northwest Passage to the Orient around the north coast of North America. The Frenchman Jacques Cartier sailed up the St. Lawrence River in 1535 but got no farther than the present site of Montreal. Later, French explorers pushed on to explore the Great Lakes regions and the upper Mississippi Valley.

Among the English seekers after the Northwest Passage were Martin Frobisher, John Davis and Henry Hudson. On his third journey, made for the Dutch East India Company in 1609, Hudson discovered the Hudson River and sailed up it as far as Albany. On his last voyage, two years later, he took a more northerly route and reached Hudson Bay. He and eight companions were then set adrift in a small boat by a mutinous crew and were never seen again.

Mutinies were always among the hazards that the intrepid sea captains of the age of discovery had to face. The reasons are clear enough. The living conditions aboard sailing ships were frightful. Fresh food was lacking; scurvy decimated crews; water was always a problem. The common sailor, more than likely impressed into service against his will, was always ready to turn about and sail back home.

After further exploration by navigators Baffin, Button and Bylot, the "companies of merchant adventurers" who financed most of these expeditions came to the conclusion that there was no practicable Northwest Passage to the East Indies. (Today air routes provide a practical Northwest Passage.) But all this time a more accurate idea of the coastline and interior of North America was being formed.

The Pacific Ocean was explored in the sixteenth and early seventeenth centuries. Sir Francis Drake touched the California coast in 1578 on his famous journey around the world. William Dampier landed in Australia and New Guinea and later wrote a famous DISCOURSE ON WINDS. Dutch pilots and others explored the South Pacific in search of Terra Australis (Southern Land), a huge continent which was supposed to lie in that area.

There was also considerable exploration in Asia. Much of it was accomplished by Catholic missionaries, traveling overland with traders. The Portuguese and, later, the Dutch opened to trade various regions in southern Asia, including Siam, Burma and Indochina. The coastal areas of Africa were pretty thoroughly explored, but the interior of that continent remained a sealed book for the most part. Yet one missionary, Pedro Paez, reached the headwaters of the Blue Nile in 1613; he solved the mystery of the Nile floods, upon which early Egyptian civilization and science had been based.

With all this exploration going on, men's notions about geography were radically revised, and new maps had to be drawn up. Foremost among the cartographers, or map-makers, of the age were Mercator and Ortelius.

Gerardus Mercator is the Latinized version of the name of the Fleming Gerhard Kremer (1512–94). Unable to make a living as a teacher, he became first an instrument-maker and then a map-engraver. Mercator's maps were soon recognized as the best of their time; since they included the new data reported by explorers, they were extremely valuable to navigators. Mercator was most thorough; he made many personal surveys. In 1585, he published the first part of a collection of maps called ATLAS, OR COSMOGRAPHICAL MEDITATIONS ABOUT THE STRUCTURE OF THE WORLD. It was completed after Mercator's death by his son Rumold (1595). In this work, the word "Atlas" was used for the first time in the sense of a collection of maps.

Mercator introduced the projection that is still known by his name. A projection is a method of representing the rounded surface of the globe upon a flat-surface map. Many different kinds of projections are possible. In the Mercator projection the equator is drawn as a straight line, with the meridians of longitude at right angles to it and the parallels of latitude parallel to it. In this type of projection the meridians are much more widely spaced toward the polar regions, north and south, than is actually the case. Of course this results in a considerable amount of distortion upon a map; Greenland, for example, is represented as being much larger than it really is. The chief advantage of the Mercator projection was, and still is, that it provides a convenient way of mapping a ship's course and steering it by compass from point to point. On the map the ship *appears* to be sailing in a straight line; actually it is following a curved line on the sphere of the earth.

Abraham Ortelius (1527–98) ranks second only to Mercator among the geographers of this period. He was born at Antwerp, of German parents; his family name, Wortels (Oertels, according to some), was later Latinized to Ortelius. He traveled extensively as a merchant. He became interested in cartography through the influence of Mercator, and in 1570 published his THEATER OF THE WORLD, an atlas containing fifty-three maps. Taken in large part from other cartographers, these maps were carefully edited by Ortelius, who also supplied a commentary. Ortelius later became geographer to Philip II of Spain.

The geographical discoveries of the Renaissance played an important part in the development of science. They helped to release men from the restrictions of medieval thinking and gave a fresh impetus to the study of the physical world. New places, new peoples, new animals, new plants were constantly revealed by explorers. Curiosity was whetted; the old explanations no longer sufficed. Science flourished in this atmosphere.

FIRST FRUITS OF THE NEW SCIENCE

The progress in scientific thinking in the Renaissance — its first fruits — can be traced in the careers of five outstanding men — Fracastoro, a physician and poet; Paracelsus, an odd combination of charlatan and man of science; Agricola, a physician turned mining expert; Gesner, an editor; and Gilbert, a court physician.

Girolamo Fracastoro (1478?–1553) was the father of epidemiology — the study of epidemics. Born at Verona, in Italy, he studied at the University of Padua, long famous for its medical instruction. There he was a fellow student of Copernicus. He practiced medicine most of his life at Verona and was one of the first men of his time to engage in the specialized study of disease.

He is most famous, perhaps, for his strange poem on syphilis, called SYPHILIS, OR THE FRENCH DISEASE. The name of the dread malady is an invention of Fracastoro; he derived it from Syphilus, one of the characters in the poem. Written in elegant Latin and first published in 1530, SYPHILIS was the least scientific of all Fracastoro's works.

His most important contribution to

science was his treatise ON CONTAGION, published in 1546. In this work he discounted the prevalent idea that epidemics were caused by foul air. ("Malaria," for example, comes from the Italian equivalent of "foul air": *mala aria*.) Fracastoro perceived, more clearly than anyone else for centuries to come, that epidemics in communities are the result of infections in individuals. He suggested that there were "essential seeds" of infection which propagated themselves. Fracastoro pointed out that disease could be transmitted in three ways: (1) by direct contact, (2) by clothing or other articles contaminated by the sick person and (3) from a distance. Unfortunately his correct theories about the transmission of disease did not make great headway until four centuries later, with Pasteur.

Paracelsus was a man of quite different stamp from the elegant and quiet-mannered Italian physician Fracastoro. A braggart and a nomad, he led a stormy and difficult life. He was born in 1493 at Einsiedeln, near Zurich, in Switzerland. His name was really Theophrastus Bombastus von Hohenheim; he later assumed the name Philippus Aureolus Paracelsus, by which he is commonly known. He studied medicine at the University of Basel for a time; he also ferreted out the secrets of alchemy under the guidance of the learned Trithemius, the abbot of Sponheim. Paracelsus traveled widely and picked up a good deal of folk medicine from the gipsies, barbers, midwives and fortunetellers who were his companions. He spent some time in the mines of Tirol, where he studied the nature of minerals, the technique of mining and miners' diseases.

Armed with this strange intellectual baggage, Paracelsus came to Basel in 1526 and became town physician and professor of medicine at the university. He began his professorship by burning the medical books of Galen and Avicenna; he promptly announced that he would replace their antiquated teachings with the doctrines of the "divine Paracelsus, the marvel of the age." He lectured in German, instead of in Latin, the language then usually employed in med-

ical teaching. Paracelsus was popular as long as his innovations had the charm of novelty. Gradually, however, his extravagant claims and his quarrelsome nature aroused general hostility. At last, in 1528 (some say 1529), he left Basel and resumed his wanderings, practicing medicine in a number of different cities. He died in Salzburg in 1541.

Paracelsus made certain genuine contributions to science. He studied the physical and chemical properties of ores and mineral waters. He knew how to prepare various chemical substances; thus, his "receipt for extract of vitriol" actually yields ether. He used chemical substances for the rational treatment of disease; chemotherapy (curing by chemistry), which he established in the sixteenth century, became one of the great props of medical science in the twentieth. He added opium, mercury, sulfur, lead, iron, arsenic and copper sulfate to the collection of drugs available to the physician. He introduced mineral baths; he was the first to write on miners' diseases.

Paracelsus' teachings
contained much folly

Unfortunately, his teachings contained a great deal of folly. He was a firm believer in astrology and maintained that the stars have a direct bearing upon disease. As a confirmed alchemist, he believed that man's body, like all other things, is a compound of salt, sulfur and mercury. When the "Archaeus," a vital force located in the stomach, fails to function properly, he taught, the salt-sulfur-mercury compound is broken up and sickness results. Paracelsus believed in mystic forces, in gnomes and sprites. He did not believe in dissection; the only surgical operation he sanctioned was "cutting for the stone" — that is, the removal of stones in the kidney.

The mining country of central Europe furnished material for the first important treatise on mining: CONCERNING METALS, by Georg Bauer, better known as Agricola. (Agricola is the Latinized form of the German *Bauer*: farmer.) The best English translation of this masterpiece, which was written in Latin, was made by Herbert Hoover, a mining engineer, and his wife. Hoover was later to become president of the United States.

Agricola was born in Saxony in 1494. He studied medicine in Italy and obtained a medical degree. He then returned to Germany and began the practice of medicine in the Joachimsthal, in Bavaria, one of the most important mining areas in central Europe. Agricola became greatly interested in mining operations; he made a careful study of the various methods of extracting, smelting and refining metals. In the course of his study of mines, he made many interesting findings about the structure of the earth. Among other things, he noted that the earth through which mine shafts were sunk was marked out in definite and often regular layers.

Agricola wrote ON THE NATURE OF FOSSILS, published in 1546 and containing ten volumes on minerals, including metallic ores. Minerals are for the first time systematically classified and described. Agricola's CONCERNING METALS

(1553), in twelve parts, deals with the mining and metallurgy of sixteenth-century Europe. Agricola here takes up techniques of surveying and prospecting for ore; he rejects the use of the forked stick, or divining rod, as useless magic. He discusses the methods of laying out and reinforcing shafts and tunnels; of constructing such equipment as windlasses, pumps and gear wheels; of assaying and smelting ores in various kinds of furnaces. He also considers the arts and sciences, including law, medicine and astronomy, which he thinks a mining engineer ought to know.

Agricola's work linked scientific observation with improvements in technology — that is, the application of scientific method to the work of the world. It laid the foundation for practical improvements in metalworking. Finally, it furnished striking proof of the importance of the printing press. For the author of CONCERNING METALS spread far and wide a mass of technical information that might otherwise have been known only to a few local artisans in different communities.

Two illustrations from Agricola's Concerning Metals. Below is a whim (hoisting machine).

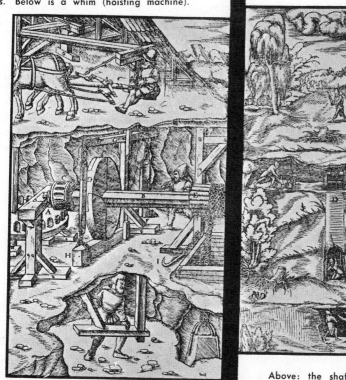

Above: the shafts of a sixteenth-century mine.

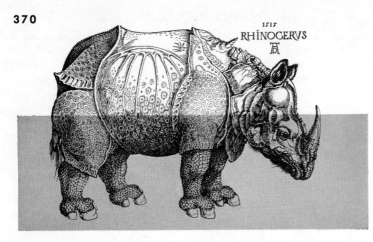

1515
RHINOCERVS

This fine picture of a rhinoceros, drawn by the German artist Albrecht Duerer in 1515, appeared in Gesner's *History of Animals*.

Much of the usefulness of books as a means of advancing science depends upon their being properly catalogued, so that the scientist can put his finger on the exact information that he wants. About a century after the invention of printing from movable type, a German-Swiss editor, Konrad von Gesner (1516–65), published a UNIVERSAL BOOK CATALOGUE, which undertook to catalogue in Latin, Greek and Hebrew all the books that had ever been written. This work laid the foundations of bibliography — the systematic study of manuscripts and books. Another book of Gesner's, MITHRIDATES, furnished the starting point of another science — comparative linguistics. MITHRIDATES gives an account of 130 languages and translates into 22 languages the Lord's Prayer.

The author of the UNIVERSAL BOOK CATALOGUE and MITHRIDATES was a learned and conscientious man, whose life was a constant struggle against poverty. He studied medicine at the University of Basel. After receiving his medical degree, he obtained an ill-paid appointment as city physician of Zurich and lecturer in physics at the university. He died of the plague in 1565 while caring for victims of that dread disease.

Gesner made many valuable contributions to biology; because of the all-embracing nature of his interest he has been called the "German Pliny." His 4,500-page HISTORY OF ANIMALS described and pictured every animal then known in Europe; this book is considered a basic text in the development of modern zoology. He also published a HANDBOOK OF THE HISTORY OF PLANTS and a CATALOGUE OF PLANTS.

Gesner had a surprisingly modern view of the value of co-operation in scientific research. "One man is nothing," he wrote. "But if each one makes known his observations for the general welfare, then some day one complete and comprehensive work can be completed from these initial steps." He thus anticipated the scientific "teams" of the present day.

Probably the most distinguished English scientist of the sixteenth century was William Gilbert (1544?–1603). Born at Colchester of an old Suffolk family, he was educated at Cambridge and received the degree of Doctor of Medicine in 1569. After a period of travel on the continent, he returned to England and became a practicing physician. He won many honors for his medical accomplishments; he became president of the Royal College of Physicians and court physician under Queen Elizabeth I and her successor, James I. Yet, throughout his career, he had an overwhelming interest in the researches on magnetism and electricity to which he owes his chief fame.

In the year 1600 he published the results of these studies in one of the greatest classics of scientific literature: OF THE MAGNET AND MAGNETIC BODIES AND THE GREAT MAGNET, THE EARTH; A NEW PHYSIOLOGY. This work was the fruit of seventeen years of independent researches, carried out at the author's own expense. To be sure that the reader fully realized the importance of his contributions, Gilbert marked his discoveries with asterisks set in the margins of the book. Large asterisks denoted important discoveries; small ones, minor discoveries. There were 21 large asterisks and 178 small ones in all!

The magnetic properties of the lodestone had been known ever since antiquity; for several centuries before Gilbert's time, the magnetic compass had guided ships at sea. But the subject of magnetism remained shrouded in mystery; all kinds of fanciful properties were attributed to magnets. Some doctors used them as a purge for melancholy; that eminent physician-quack Paracelsus made poultices out of ground lodestones.

Gilbert's OF THE MAGNET was the first serious, scientific work on magnetism since the LETTERS ON MAGNETISM, written by Peter the Stranger in the thirteenth century. Gilbert placed the study of magnetism on a scientific basis. He experimented with *terrellas,* spheres made of lodestone, and with small needles, set on pivots. He would put a needle at various places on a *terrella* and then note the direction in which it pointed. He observed that the needle traced out lines of force and that these lines of force passed through two opposite points on the *terrella* — the magnetic poles.

He concluded that the earth is a spherical magnet, like the *terrella,* with magnetic north and south poles. The needle of a magnetic compass points north because its north-seeking pole is attracted by the earth's North Pole. Gilbert also pointed out that the Magnetic North and South Poles do not correspond to true north and south, and that a magnetic needle free to move up and down dips toward the earth at many places.

Unfortunately Gilbert was not content to let his experiments speak for themselves; he constructed an entire system on the basis of his theories of magnetism. He assumed that not only the earth but also the sun and the moon and the other heavenly bodies possess magnetic properties. He attributed not only their rotation but likewise their movements in the heavens to the "magnetic virtue that is poured out on every side."

Gilbert's great book contains a short digression on the properties of amber. It had been known for more than two thousand years that if a piece of amber is rubbed on a woolen cloth it attracts small pieces of straw or woody fiber. Gilbert coined the word "electricity" (*vis electrica,* in the original Latin of the treatise) for this strange property; he derived it from the Greek word for amber: *elektron.*

To study electrical phenomena, he used a light needle of metal, pivoted like a compass on a pin. With this "electroscope" he tested the electric properties of various substances and found that many things besides amber could be so electrified by friction that they would make his needle move when brought close to it. And so the sage of Colchester became not only the founder of modern magnetic theory but also the father of electricity.

THE REVOLUTION IN ASTRONOMY

1543 is one of the great dates in the history of science. In that year the Polish-German astronomer Nicolaus Copernicus published a treatise called ON THE REVOLUTIONS OF THE HEAVENLY BODIES. He thus set the stage for a truly Homeric struggle between the spirit of free scientific inquiry on one hand and the forces of tradition on the other.

In the REVOLUTIONS Copernicus maintained that:

The earth is not the center of the universe.

All the planets revolve around the sun; *the sun, therefore, is the center of the solar system.*

What appear to us to be motions of the sun arise not from its motions but from the motions of the earth. The earth revolves around the sun like any other planet.

These propositions, which no educated person would deny today, ran counter to the beliefs of the generality of mankind. The Christian world had come to accept the earth as the center of the universe because the earth was the stage on which the great drama of human life was acted. The Copernican system upset this idea, and consequently the new theory met with stormy resistance.

Nicolaus Copernicus (the Latinized version of Niklas Koppernigk) was born in 1473 at Thorn, on the Vistula River. His father was a Polish merchant of Cracow, who had migrated to Thorn; his mother was a German woman of good family. Nicolaus' father died when the boy was ten years old. Thereafter his uncle, Lucas Watzelrode, a man of the church, sponsored his education and paved the way for his career. Watzelrode later was named Bishop of Ermeland.

When Copernicus became a student at the University of Cracow, he was particularly interested in astronomy and mathematics. He became acquainted with the use of astronomical instruments under the keen tutelage of Albert Brudzewski. Later he spent a number of years in Italy, attending the famous universities of Bologna, Ferrara and Padua. While continuing to devote himself to astronomy, he branched out into law, medicine and painting.

When he returned home, Copernicus went to live with his uncle, the Bishop of Ermeland, at the latter's palace at Heilsberg. He remained there until the Bishop died in 1512. Copernicus then took over the duties of canon at the cathedral of Frauenberg and continued to fulfill these duties for the next thirty years. His life, on the surface at least, was uneventful;

besides his ecclesiastical duties, he dabbled occasionally in politics and he gave free medical advice to the poor of the district.

Yet during these years Copernicus was formulating his world-shaking heliocentric theory (the theory that the sun — *helios,* in Greek — is the center of the solar system). He had become dissatisfied with the Ptolemaic theory while at Bologna and had frankly discussed the errors of the AL-MAGEST with Domenico di Novara, professor of astronomy at the university. Copernicus might have found the germ of his own theory of the heavenly bodies in several ancient writers. Philolaus the Pythagorean had maintained in the fifth century B.C. that the earth and the other planets and the sun, too, revolved around a central fire. Two centuries later Aristarchus of Samos, the "Copernicus of antiquity," had hit upon the truth with his guess that the earth moves around the sun.

Copernicus had worked out the essentials of his theory by 1530. In that year he circulated his conclusions among his friends in a little tract called the COMMEN-TARIOLUS (Little Commentary). He continued to work away at the more complete account of his theory that was to be presented in ON THE REVOLUTIONS OF THE HEAVENLY BODIES.

By the time this great work was completed, Copernicus was ailing; he had to leave the details of publication to a young friend, the German astronomer and mathe-

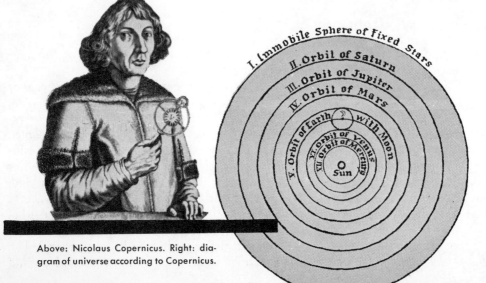

Above: Nicolaus Copernicus. Right: diagram of universe according to Copernicus.

matician Rheticus, whose real name was Georg Joachim. Rheticus, for his part, turned over the task to Andreas Osiander, a local Lutheran clergyman. Osiander was afraid that the work might offend the religious authorities, and so he stated that the theory of Copernicus was only a method for calculating the motions of the heavenly bodies and that it was not to be taken literally. As soon as the REVOLUTIONS,

to verify the heliocentric theory until more complete and authentic data could be provided. This essential material was soon provided by the Danish astronomer Tycho Brahe, one of the greatest observational astronomers — star-gazers, if you will — who ever lived. Brahe did all his work before the telescope had been developed. We can only conjecture what he could have accomplished if he could have utilized this

with its disarming preface, was off the press, a copy of it was sent to Copernicus. When it reached him, he was on his deathbed. He died on May 24, 1543.

Copernicus' account of the heavens left many problems unsolved. It was inaccurate, too, in certain respects; for Copernicus, whose eyesight was bad, was a poor observer. Yet he had certainly provided a far simpler and in all respects more satisfactory explanation than Ptolemy for the movements of the sun, moon and planets.

Copernicus realized that the earth wobbles a little as it rotates, like a spinning top. He traced out the route of the earth around the sun, and calculated the length of the year correctly to within 28 seconds. He diagrammed the planets then known — Mercury, Venus, Earth, Mars, Jupiter and Saturn — in their correct order and determined the approximate period of revolution about the sun for each. He recognized a basic principle of relativity, for he remarked that "all change in position is due to a motion either of the observer or of the thing observed."

Copernicus had provided a set of planetary tables with his REVOLUTIONS. Unfortunately these tables were based on insufficient and inaccurate observation and they gave an inadequate idea of the true motion of the planets. Little could be done

indispensable instrument in his work.

Brahe was born in 1546 of a noble Danish family and attended the University of Copenhagen. While there, he observed an eclipse of the sun and was greatly impressed by the fact that the time of this eclipse had been accurately predicted. Determined to devote himself to astronomy, he traveled to many northern European universities, including Leipzig, Wittenberg and Basel, so that he might study with eminent astronomy professors.

Upon his return to Denmark, sharp-eyed Brahe created a sensation by discovering, in November 1572, a bright new star shining in the constellation of Cassiopeia. He traced its course almost nightly for eighteen months thereafter. The appearance of this brilliant visitor astonished all the astronomers of the time; it cast doubt upon the teaching of Aristotle that the stars in the fixed sphere of the heavens were immutable.

In 1576 the King of Denmark became the patron of Tycho, granting generous funds to the young astronomer and setting aside the island of Hven, between Copenhagen and Elsinore, for his observations. On this island Brahe erected the most elaborate astronomical observatory of the time. He called it Uraniborg, or Castle of the Heavens; it was complete with living quarters, observation towers, laboratories, printing press and paper mill. Brahe's astronomical instruments, most of which he created himself, were the best available. Under these ideal conditions he made the most complete and accurate astronomical observations that had ever been carried out up to that time.

Brahe mercilessly prodded his corps of assistants and even the members of his family in carrying forward the endless task of scanning the heavens. Besides being a harsh taskmaster, he was unbearably arrogant. Eventually he alarmed the Danish court by his unbridled extravagance. At last he was forced to leave Uraniborg (1597).

In 1599 the Holy Roman Emperor Rudolph II invited Brahe to come to Prague and promised to build a new observatory for him. Brahe hired a corps of assistants and prepared for a new series of observations. But he died in the year 1601, before he could carry his new projects forward to any great extent. The following year saw the publication of his masterpiece, the PRELIMINARIES FOR THE RESTORATION OF ASTRONOMY. In this work the positions of 777 stars were given with hitherto unapproached accuracy.

Brahe bequeathed the priceless collection of astronomical observations that he had made at Uraniborg to his favorite assistant, Johannes Kepler. He had exacted a deathbed promise from the younger man that this data would be used to bolster up Brahe's own strange theory of planetary motion. For Brahe held the strange belief that, while the planets moved around the sun, the earth itself remained stationary and the sun moved around the earth! Today we realize that Brahe's great contributions to astronomy and to science in general were not his theories, but his amazingly accurate observations and the instruments that he developed.

One of the early converts to the doctrines of Copernicanism was the Italian monk Giordano Bruno (1548?–1600), a philosopher who rejected Church dogma and worked out his own philosophy. Expelled from the Dominican order because of his heretical ideas, he made his way to France and then to England. At Oxford he expounded the Copernican theory and upheld it in debate with supporters of the Ptolemaic system. He went further than Copernicus; without benefit of astronomical observations he made some astonishingly accurate guesses about the heavenly bodies. He maintained that the so-called fixed stars were suns scattered throughout the infinite universe and surrounded, perhaps, by planets like our own. He also held that the sun rotates, that the earth was flattened at the poles and that there were more planets in our solar system than had yet been found. Bruno later returned to Italy. He was arrested, tried for heresy and burned at the stake on February 17, 1600, as a heretic — not, as is often held, for his strictly scientific opinions.

THE REDISCOVERY OF ANATOMY

In 1543, the year when Copernicus' ON THE REVOLUTIONS OF THE HEAVENLY BODIES appeared, a Flemish physician, Andreas Vesalius, published another epoch-making book — THE ANATOMY OF THE HUMAN BODY. It marked the high point in the history of anatomical studies.

For many centuries anatomists had parroted the teachings of Galen, an ancient Greek physician who lived in the second century A.D. (see the Index). In the Preface to his ANATOMY Vesalius pointed out that "those who followed Galen . . . if they handed on anything worth while, borrowed it from him. . . . And so completely have all surrendered to his authority that no doctor has been found to declare that in the anatomical books of Galen even the slightest error has ever been found, much less could be found." Vesalius could not brook this spirit of slavish devotion. By dint of careful dissection and examination of the human body itself — a practice generally forbidden by law — he exposed many of the errors of Galen and revealed the true structure of the human body.

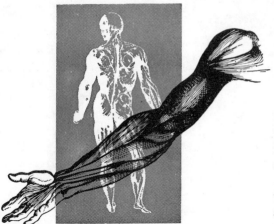

anatomy, Vesalius did not reject all of the master's doctrines. In fact, he became an adept in the medical lore of Galen, and to the end of his life he followed some of Galen's teachings.

The learned doctors of Louvain resented Vesalius' innovations and quarreled with him. Determined to seek his fortune in Italy, he betook himself to the University of Padua and studied medicine there for several years. In 1537, at the age of twenty-two, he was appointed to a professorship of anatomy in that venerable institution.

Vesalius brought about a complete reform in the teaching and understanding of human anatomy. Instead of leaving dissection to barber-surgeons, he always performed this task himself; and his lucid explanations of the structure of the body delighted his students. He was immensely successful; he gave lectures and demonstrations to as many as five hundred students at a time.

Vesalius published THE ANATOMY OF THE HUMAN BODY when he was only twenty-eight. It appeared in a large folio

According to some accounts, he had to steal corpses for dissection from the gallows where criminals were hanged.

Vesalius was born in Brussels in 1514. Descended from a long line of physicians, he decided at an early age that he would become a doctor. While a mere lad, he pored over the books on anatomy in his father's library and dissected the bodies of animals. He became a medical student at the University of Paris and, later, at the University of Louvain.

The anatomical teaching in these renowned seats of learning was based, of course, on the writings of Galen. Human dissection was carried on, indeed, but in a very ineffective way. "The detestable procedure now in vogue," writes Vesalius in the previously quoted Preface, "is that one man should carry out the dissection of the human body and another should give the description of the parts." The dissectors were barber-surgeons, who would generally botch their task; the lecturers would "drone out information that they had committed to memory from the works of others . . . Thus everything is wrongly taught . . . and less is offered to the onlooker than a butcher in his stall could teach a doctor."

Goaded by the inadequacy of these methods, Vesalius took in his own hands the task of dissecting cadavers and explaining their structure to his fellow students, both at Paris and Louvain. In the course of these dissections he came to realize how wrong Galen often was. But, though he was aware of Galen's shortcomings in

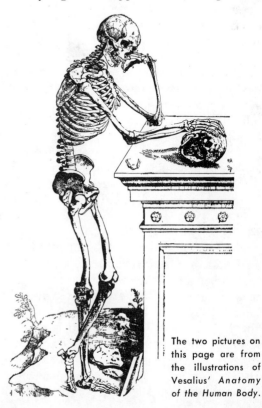

The two pictures on this page are from the illustrations of Vesalius' *Anatomy of the Human Body.*

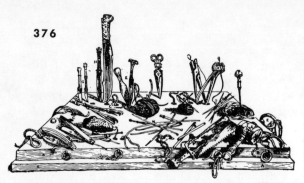

This striking drawing, taken from Vesalius' *Anatomy of the Human Body*, shows the many dissecting instruments that he used.

volume, beautifully and accurately illustrated by a pupil of Titian. The work is arranged in seven parts; the author takes up in turn bones and cartilages, ligaments and muscles, veins and arteries, nerves, internal organs of digestion and reproduction, heart and lungs, brain and sense organs. The ANATOMY provides a surprisingly complete account of the structure of the human body; it has been said that all later writings on anatomy are "mere commentaries upon it." The work is as important for what it leaves out as for what it includes. There are no references to astrology, no suggestion that the movements of the stars in the heavens may control the shape or function of the human body. The author adopts a matter-of-fact approach; he sticks to observed facts.

The publication of Vesalius' ANATOMY aroused a storm of protest from the followers of Galen; Jacob Sylvius, who had been the author's teacher at Paris, was particularly violent in his denunciation. The most preposterous charges were made against Vesalius; he was accused, among other things, of having dissected living human beings.

The year after the publication of the ANATOMY Vesalius left Padua for Spain, where he remained for nearly twenty years as court physician, first to the Holy Roman Emperor Charles V and then to his son Philip II. In 1563 he set out on a pilgrimage to the Holy Land. On his return he fell ill, and he died shortly afterward.

Other able anatomists followed Vesalius at Padua. Gabriel Fallopius, or Fallopio (1523–62), was particularly famed for his discovery of the Fallopian tubes leading from the ovaries to the womb. Long-lived Hieronymus Fabricius (1537–1619) also taught at Padua; his most famous pupil was the Englishman William Harvey, who later discovered the circulation of the blood. Fabricius made a fortune as a surgeon; he used this money to build a magnificent anatomical theater at Padua. His most important contributions were his studies in embryology (growth of the embryo and fetus before birth) and his discovery of the valves of the veins.

Advances in the study of anatomy brought about improvement in the quality of surgery, for safe surgery is impossible without an adequate knowledge of anatomy. The greatest surgeon of the sixteenth century was the Frenchman Ambroise Paré, an admirer of Vesalius. He made a thorough study of the ANATOMY OF THE HUMAN BODY and wrote an abstract of the work in French.

Paré, born about 1510, came to Paris as a barber-surgeon's apprentice. He rose in his profession to the rank of dresser at the hospital called the Hôtel-Dieu and later went off to the wars as an army surgeon. He learned as a result of his wide experience that the best way to stop bleeding was to tie off the bleeding blood vessel with a ligature thread, not to cauterize it with a hot iron; that gunshot wounds should not be treated with boiling oil but with simple dressings; that better surgical instruments made for better surgery. He understood the healing force of nature, which he summed up in the famous saying: "I dressed the wound; God healed it." He wrote many books on surgery and obstetrics. So popular was this able, courageous and kindly surgeon that, although he was a Protestant, his life was spared at the Massacre of St. Bartholomew in 1572. He died in 1590.

Thus in the sixteenth century medicine began to cast off the shackles of authority. But the rediscovery of human anatomy, unhappily, did not immediately affect most other branches of medical science. Medicine was still to be a happy hunting ground for pedants and charlatans for several centuries to come.

Continued on page 1, Volume 3.

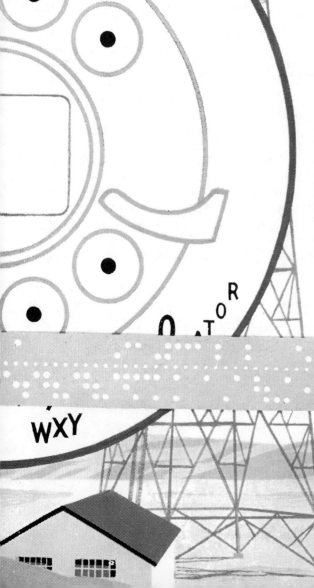

TELEGRAPH AND TELEPHONE*

Two Vital Methods of Communication

IN THE course of his long history, man has used various methods of signaling through space. Some of them have been described in detail in ancient writings; others have been mentioned casually. The Scriptures contain various references to smoke signals. Cyrus the Great of Persia set up a series of stations using signal fires; by means of these stations he was able to send a message in one day from one end of the Persian Empire to the other — a distance that could not be covered by a mounted messenger in less than thirty days. The Greeks and Romans sometimes sent signals by flashing polished surfaces like mirrors or shields in the sunlight. The American Indians built a smoke fire on a hilltop and covered it at intervals with a blanket. In this way they produced a succession of smoke plumes, which could be interpreted by a distant observer.

*Article prepared with the assistance of the International Telephone and Telegraph Company, the Western Union Telegraph Company and the Bell Telephone System.

In the latter years of the eighteenth century, two French brothers, Claude and Ignace Chappe, developed a semaphore system of communication. The semaphores consisted of movable arms set on top of long poles; words or letters were represented by different positions of the arms. Semaphores were erected at a series of stations, which were so located that the signals sent out by one station would be visible to observers at the next station of the series. It is said that messages could be sent in this way 150 miles in a quarter of an hour. The semaphore system of communication, which was also called the telegraph, was used rather extensively in France; it also served in England and in some of the German states.

The semaphore signaling method, of course, could not be used at night; it was unreliable during the daytime when visibility was poor. For example, when Wellington was fighting the French in Spain, the city of London was thrown into a panic by a semaphore message sent from Portsmouth to the Admiralty. The message read "Wellington defeated." Some time later, two more words — "the French" — came through; the transmission of these words had been delayed by a sudden fog.

Signal lamps were sometimes used to transmit messages at night. The British Navy used to send night signals by raising or lowering a lantern in a bucket. Signal lamps set in the tower of Boston's Old North Church revealed to Paul Revere that the British were leaving Boston by sea, in order to seize the stores amassed by the minutemen at Concord.

The distance to which signals could be sent directly by any of the methods that we have mentioned was limited by the sensitiveness of the eye and also by the nature of the intervening obstructions, to say nothing of the weather. Men naturally sought for a means of communication that would not be affected by darkness or by weather conditions. In the eighteenth century a few inquiring souls began to wonder whether such a means of communication might not be provided by the newly discovered force of electricity.

The fact that electricity could be sent through a wire of considerable length was first demonstrated by Stephen Gray in 1729. Apparently it did not occur to him that his discovery furnished the means for the rapid transmission of signals. The earliest suggestion that electricity could be used in this way appeared in an anonymous letter to THE SCOT'S MAGAZINE in 1753. It was probably written by a Scottish physician, Charles Morrison.

In Morrison's method, as in other early ones, there were as many wires as there were letters to be transmitted. By charging the wires successively with an electrostatic machine (there were no batteries or dynamos in those days), bits of paper could be attracted to the other ends

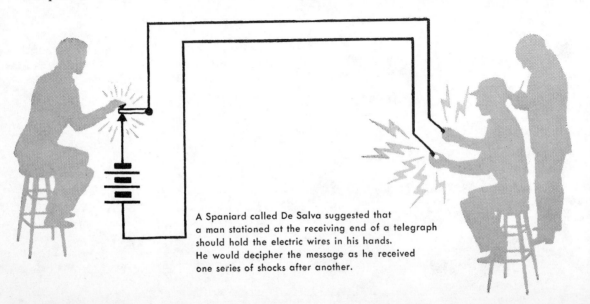

A Spaniard called De Salva suggested that a man stationed at the receiving end of a telegraph should hold the electric wires in his hands. He would decipher the message as he received one series of shocks after another.

of the wires and they would signify letters. In this way, messages could be sent over a mile or two at considerable speed.

The development of the modern electric telegraph from these primitive beginnings required many years of discovery and invention. It was first necessary to provide better insulators for the conductors so that higher currents could be carried with less leakage. The use of glass insulators on wooden poles was not adopted until later. More important still was the invention of a source of electricity that would send a steady current through the wires. While the first battery had been constructed by Volta in 1800, a battery of sufficient strength for telegraphic communication was not invented until the year 1836. In the early part of the nineteenth century, a number of inventors suggested the use of electric telegraphic systems that required only two connecting wires. This was an improvement over the old system.

Oersted's discovery of electromagnetism in 1820 was a culminating episode in the development of the electric telegraph. It was well known that varying impulses could be sent over a wire for a considerable distance, but no satisfactory way had been found to recognize the pulses at the receiving end of the wire. Many crude methods had been suggested for the purpose. For example, a Spaniard, De Salva, had suggested that a man stationed at the receiving end of the line should hold the different telegraph wires in his hands. He would decipher the message as he received one electric shock after another!

Oersted discovered that an electric current flowing through a wire set up a magnetic field that would deflect a needle placed near the wire. The needle would align itself with the field. André-Marie Ampère, the French mathematician and physicist, suggested that the deflection of a magnetic needle should be utilized for the reception of electric signals. However, a practical needle telegraph system was not devised until 1837 by Wheatstone and Cook.

Joseph Henry made important contributions to the knowledge of electromagnetism between 1828 and 1831 while he was a professor at Princeton. He demonstrated that the magnetic effect of an electric current could be amplified many times by winding a coil of wire on some soft iron. Henry explained to his classes how it would be possible to ring church bells at a distance through the use of his electromagnet. It is indeed strange that this gifted man, who had an unsurpassed knowledge of electricity and magnetism, did not appreciate the commercial importance of his electromagnet, which was to serve in a great many useful devices.

It would appear that the invention of the modern telegraph by Samuel F. B. Morse in 1837 resulted, in part at least, from a chance conversation between Morse and Dr. Charles T. Jackson of Boston aboard ship on a voyage from Le Havre to New York in 1832. When Morse was required to defend his patents before the Supreme Court in 1850, Dr. Jackson claimed that he had suggested most of

SAMUEL F. B. MORSE, who constructed the first really practical electric telegraph.

the elements of the invention in his conversation with Morse during the voyage. The court decided that this was an exaggeration; it upheld the validity of Morse's patent. It seems likely, however, that the conversation with Dr. Jackson turned Morse's attention to the possibilities of the electric telegraph.

Morse succeeded, by patience and perseverance, in constructing an electric telegraph that was better than any other devised up to that time. His first telegraph line was constructed under an appropriation of Congress between Baltimore and Washington in 1844. The basic principles of Morse's first telegraph were used in all telegraphic devices for a good many years.

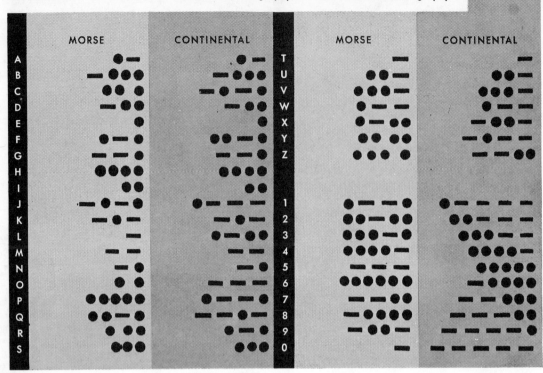

When the key at the sending station was pressed down, the battery sent a current through the coils of an electromagnet at the receiving end of the telegraph. A strip of iron, originally held away from the electromagnet by a spring, was pulled against it with a sharp click when the current was turned on. The iron strip was drawn away from the electromagnet again, because of the action of the spring, whenever the key at the transmitting end was released by the operator.

In Morse's first telegraph, a pen was attached to the end of the iron strip. As the strip moved to and from the electromagnet, the pen alternately made contact

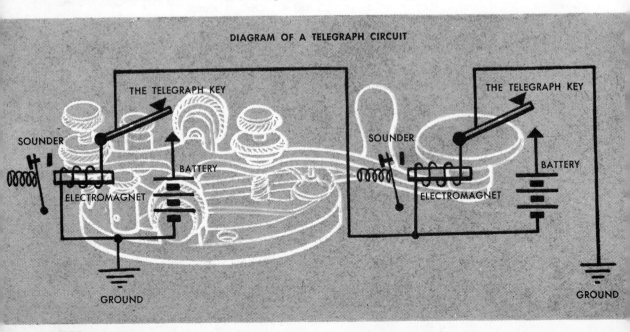

DIAGRAM OF A TELEGRAPH CIRCUIT

with a moving ribbon of paper and broke off contact. The result was a series of straight lines on the paper; their length was determined by the length of time that the transmitting key was held down. Short lines represented dots and longer lines dashes, forming the Morse code.

Later, operators became so expert in receiving messages by sound that the printing method was abandoned. The receiving device was then used as a sounder; the dots and dashes of the Morse code were retained. This code is still in use, though to a limited extent, in the United States and Canada. A rather similar code, called the Continental code, is used in other countries for hand-operated telegraphic devices, as well as for ocean-cable telegraphy and radio telegraphy. Both of the codes are shown on the preceding page.

In his early machines, Morse noted that the current was much weaker at the receiving end than at the sending end, because of current leakage and the resistance of the wire. To overcome this serious difficulty, the inventor set relays, or repeaters, in the telegraph line at intervals. A relay consisted of an electromagnet which, as it attracted a strip of iron, connected a fresh battery with the next section of the line. Messages could now be sent with no appreciable loss in current strength.

Simple diagram of a manually operated telegraph circuit. When the sending key is pressed down, it closes an electric circuit and energizes an electromagnet. This attracts the sounder, which clicks as it is pulled down. As current passes through the circuit to the electromagnet at the other end, this magnet is also energized and the sounder at that end is also pulled down. When the sending key is released, the current is broken; the electromagnet is no longer energized and the sounder is released making another clicking sound. A corresponding click is then heard at the other end of the line. In this way a pattern of clicks is transmitted, and is arranged to form a code. A long key contact represents a dash; a short contact, a dot.

The first telegraph message — "What hath God wrought!" — was sent from Washington to Baltimore on May 24, 1844. By 1848, Americans had become enthusiastic about the new communication device, and many new lines were built in the East and the Midwest. The telegraph was soon adopted by foreign countries. Today, telegraph lines form a network extending through all the civilized lands of the world.

Hand-operated devices, using transmitting keys and sounders and sending out their messages in code, have been gradually replaced by automatic equipment. They are still to be found in limited numbers at certain railroad telegraph offices. Manual methods of operation require that the person transmitting read the message and actuate a telegraph key to convert each letter into a code group of short and long pulses (dots and dashes). The receiving operator must listen to the code groups, translate them into letters and typewrite the letters onto the message blank to be delivered. Errors are possible at each of these stages. The use of automatic equipment reduces greatly the chance of human error. Manual telegraphy began to be replaced by printing telegraphy before World War I and by facsimile telegraphy in the early 1930's.

In automatic transmission by the printing method, a device called a teletypewriter, or perforator, is used. It looks like a typewriter with three rows of keys. As each key is pushed down in turn, it punches a certain number of holes, forming a distinctive pattern, in a narrow paper tape passing through the machine. The tape is then passed into a transmitting machine. Sometimes the tape passes directly into the transmitter from the perforator; sometimes the operators feed it in at their convenience when a certain number of messages are to be sent.

Little pins in the transmitting machine press lightly against the tape paper. As the pins come to the holes in the tape, they move down into them just enough to operate small electric switches. The switches cause current impulses to be transmitted over the telegraph wire; the impulse pattern corresponds to the arrangement of the

SENDING A MESSAGE BY TELETYPEWRITER

The operator types a routing symbol at the beginning of each telegram and then types the message which appears in the form of a perforated tape. As the tape passes through the automatic transmitter at the left, the coded symbol causes an electronic "brain" at the distant high-speed message center to route and flash the message.

How the facsimile transmission device called the DeskFax operates. The telegram to be transmitted is wrapped around a cylinder. Light is concentrated through a lens upon a small area of the telegram. Light reflected from the illuminated area is permitted to pass to a photocell which causes a current of electricity to flow when it is exposed to the light. The amount of current is proportional to the amount of light falling on it. As the cylinder upon which the telegram is wrapped revolves, the light moves along the message until the entire telegram has been covered or "scanned." The current is sent over the line to the distant receiver, in phase with the transmitter and operating at the same speed. The photoscanning feature is replaced by a needlelike stylus, which produces a facsimile of the original message.

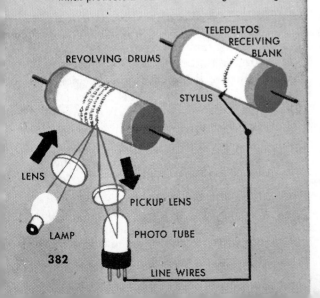

holes in the tape. The impulses operate an automatic typewriter, called a teleprinter, at the receiving end of the line. The messages appear in capital letters on long strips of paper, which are then cut and pasted on telegraph blanks.

In preparing a message, the operator types a routing symbol at the beginning of each telegram. After she has typed the message on the perforated tape, it passes through an automatic transmitter. The coded symbol causes an "electric brain" at the high-speed message center to route the message to its destination area. Here the automatic teleprinter receives the message and typewrites it.

Many industrial firms and public agencies use some form of teletypewriter or teleprinter exchange service, such as Western Union Telex. Each Telex subscriber is provided with a teleprinter, an associated dial unit and a nationwide directory of other subscribers with their Telex numbers. A subscriber can get in touch with another subscriber by dialing his number; the connection is completed automatically in eight seconds anywhere in the United States. Canadian and Mexican subscribers can also be dialed. Subscribers in seventy-nine countries overseas can be reached through interconnection with overseas Telex networks that are compatible with Western Union Telegraph transmission speeds.

Facsimile transmission plays an important part today in telegraphy. Facsimile transmission machines, based on the photoelectric cell, can send and receive pictures of telegrams automatically. (See article on Facsimile Transmission, in Volume 7.)

In the original Morse system, only one message could be sent at a time over a wire in either direction. Since even a skilled operator can tap out at most only about thirty words a minute, telegraph transmission often could not keep pace with the great number of messages to be transmitted. More than one message can now be sent over the same wire at the same time through the use of multiplex systems.

In the time-division multiplex system, the transmission path is divided among several sets of transmitting and receiving devices. We show how the system works in the diagram on this page.

Frequency-division multiplex is based on the generation of electric waves of different frequencies and on the ability of the receiving set to select one desired frequency and to reject all others. Through this method, hundreds of messages can be sent simultaneously over a single pair of wires. The electrical properties of the wires may be improved by shaping one wire into a tube and running the other one through the center of the tube. The structure produced by this arrangement is known as a coaxial cable because the two conductors have a common axis.

Microwave radio beam networks represent an important advance in telegraphic communication. The first commercial network of this type was installed by Western Union in 1945 between New York and Phil-

adelphia. A transcontinental microwave network now exists. Radio towers about thirty miles apart are substituted for the familiar pole lines. Antennas equipped with parabolic reflectors transmit radio-telegraph signals in a narrow beam from tower to tower. Unattended repeater stations automatically and instantaneously send the radio-telegraph signals on their way. Thousands of messages can be sent out at the same time over a microwave radio beam.

Telegraphic systems are being used on an ever-increasing scale in combination with electronic digital computers. (See the article Electronic Computers, in Volume 9.) The messages are in the "language" of the electronic computer (or "brain," as it is popularly known)—that is, extremely brief pulses sent with great rapidity. Input information is usually presented to the machines as punched tape and the output appears as typed tape. The punched tape can be made to operate a transmitter at one end of a telegraph line, the other end being connected to a central electronic data-processing device. In this way, information from electronic computers in widely separated areas can be transferred to the central electronic "brain" in a form that it can use immediately. A computer network of this type was set up in 1963 for the United States Department of Defense. It is called AUTODIN, from the phrase "AUTOmatic DIgital Network." Of course the word "digital" in this case stands for "digital computer."

The modern telegraph company even provides for voice or record communication. Thus, in a recently established service called "broadband switching," Western

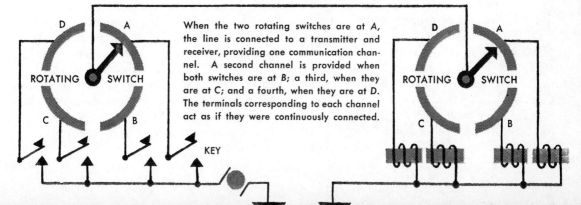

SIMPLIFIED DIAGRAM OF A TIME-DIVISION MULTIPLEX SYSTEM.

When the two rotating switches are at A, the line is connected to a transmitter and receiver, providing one communication channel. A second channel is provided when both switches are at B; a third, when they are at C; and a fourth, when they are at D. The terminals corresponding to each channel act as if they were continuously connected.

ROTATING SWITCH

D A C B KEY

Union offers customer-to-customer connections for voice as well as for data, facsimile and other types of communication.

The transmission of
messages by submarine cable

The transmission of telegraph messages by submarine cable involves special difficulties. The laying of a cable is a time-consuming and expensive task. Every inch of the interior copper wire must be perfectly insulated from the surrounding salt water. The cable must be strong enough to resist the action of underwater currents; it must be protected from damage by marine animals and dragging anchors.

The credit for the laying of the first transatlantic cable is due primarily to an indomitable American business man, Cyrus W. Field. After he had retired with a large fortune at the age of thirty-three, he had met the Canadian inventor Frederick N. Gisborne, who had had considerable experience in laying deep-sea cables. Gisborne had already laid one such cable between Prince Edward Island and New Brunswick and he was planning to connect Cape Ray and Cape Breton. As a result of his meeting with Gisborne, Field became interested in the idea of a transatlantic cable. In 1856, he organized the Atlantic Telegraph Company, supported almost entirely by English capital.

Using two ships, he first attempted to lay a cable between Ireland and Newfoundland in 1857. The cable parted 335 miles from the Irish coast and was abandoned. In 1858, a second attempt was made; the two ships started in midocean and sailed in opposite directions. After the cable had broken several times, the ships returned to port with their mission unaccomplished. Later in the year, however, a third attempt, following the same procedure, proved successful. The first message was sent from Newfoundland to Ireland on August 7, 1858. The cable ruptured less than a month later and was abandoned, with great financial loss to the promoters.

Another cable, laid in 1865, broke at a distance of 1,200 miles from Ireland. The next year a new cable was laid successfully, and the cable abandoned in 1865 was picked up and completed. One of these cables failed in 1872 and the other in 1877; but four other cables that had been laid in the meantime continued in service. In the years that followed, many other cables were set in place. By 1955, the various parts of the world were connected by 1,221 submarine cables with a total length of 344,966 miles.

The feeble nature of the signals sent through a long cable necessitated the invention of more sensitive receiving equipment. The siphon recorder developed by William Thomson (later Lord Kelvin) in 1867 solved the problem of sensitivity and was used for many years. The instrument consisted of a light coil of fine insulated wire, suspended between the poles of a powerful magnet. Current from a cable was sent through this coil. It represented a dot, in the Continental code, when sent in one direction; a dash, when sent in the other. When current from the cable passed through the coil, it twisted one way or the other, depending upon the direction of the current. A thread attached to one part of the coil pulled a glass tube containing ink across a moving paper tape; thus it produced an undulating line, representing changes in cable current. The glass tube was fed with ink by an inkwell placed higher than the tape, so that the ink was conveyed by siphon action. This ink recorded the message.

The coaxial cable has been adapted to submarine use in recent years. In conjunction with vacuum-tube amplifiers acting as relays, it provides hundreds of telegraph channels and dozens of telephone channels. A cable of this type has been laid across the Atlantic. It contains dozens of vacuum-tube amplifiers, inserted in the cable at regular intervals. They are built into cylindrical housings slightly larger than the cable itself and are, of course, submerged as part of it. Power for the amplifiers is carried over the cable with the signals. The vacuum tubes and other elements of the amplifiers are designed and carefully built to give many years of life before being replaced.

LAYING A DEEP-SEA CABLE

A cable plow, drawn by a tow line, makes a furrow in which the cable will be laid. The cable is kept stored on the ship in cable tanks. Engines pull it out of the tanks and control its speed and tension during the laying operation. The cable passes over a dynamometer, a device that measures the tension on the cable before it goes over the sheaves located at the bow of the boat.

DYNAMOMETER   BOW SHEAVES

MESSENGER CABLE

CABLE TANK

SUBMARINE CABLE

TOW LINE

CABLE PLOW

THE DEVELOPMENT OF THE TELEPHONE

In 1854, a French inventor, Charles Bourseul, published an article in which he described a method for transmitting speech electrically. He proposed to connect a diaphragm with one of a pair of contacts in a telegraph line. Suppose that a series of sound waves struck the diaphragm. The vibrations of the diaphragm as it opened and closed the circuit would produce pulsating currents corresponding to the frequency of the sound waves. If a similar diaphragm were placed near an electromagnet at the other end of the line, it would vibrate by magnetic attraction and would reproduce the original sound. Bourseul had at least approximated the basic idea of the modern telephone; but he made no practical application of his idea.

Six years later Philipp Reis, in Germany, constructed an instrument based on much the same idea. Reis called his machine a "telephone" ("far-sounder"). He succeeded in transmitting continuous musical tones with a fair measure of success; however, he was not able to transmit human speech, with its constant changes in pitch and its many subtle overtones.

The first practical telephone resulted from a series of experiments in telegraphy. In 1873, Alexander Graham Bell, professor of vocal physiology at Boston University, became interested in the study of multiple telegraphy. He conceived the idea of what he called a harmonic telegraph, a device capable of sending several messages over a single wire simultaneously by means of several pairs of steel springs. This is how the device worked.

If a telegraph key were closed at the transmitting end, a spring at that end would be attracted by the electromagnet of the transmitter. The spring would be so attached that as it made contact with the electromagnet, it would cause the circuit to be broken. The spring would then return to its original position. As it did so, the circuit would again be closed and the spring would again be attracted to the electromagnet. As the current would be alternately opened and closed in this way, the spring would vibrate continuously at its natural frequency; it would do so as long as the key would be held down. The current in the telegraph line would pulsate at

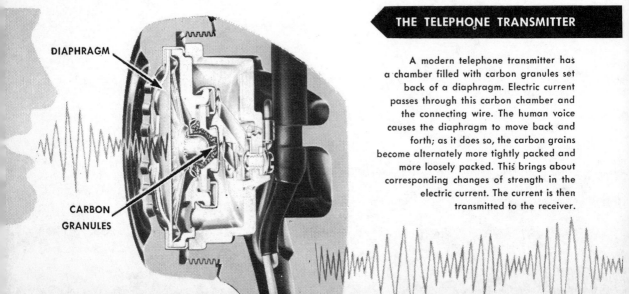

DIAPHRAGM

CARBON GRANULES

THE TELEPHONE TRANSMITTER

A modern telephone transmitter has a chamber filled with carbon granules set back of a diaphragm. Electric current passes through this carbon chamber and the connecting wire. The human voice causes the diaphragm to move back and forth; as it does so, the carbon grains become alternately more tightly packed and more loosely packed. This brings about corresponding changes of strength in the electric current. The current is then transmitted to the receiver.

the same frequency as the vibrating spring, since it would be turned on and off and on again as the spring vibrated.

Another spring would be set at the receiver at the other end of the line. It would be attracted to the electromagnet of the receiver as current flowed through; it would spring back as the circuit was broken and would again be attracted to the electromagnet as the circuit was closed again. The two springs would vibrate in unison at opposite ends of the telegraph line.

Bell believed that a number of these spring units could be connected to the ends of a single telegraph line and that several messages could be sent at the same time if each pair of springs were tuned to a different frequency of vibration. He built several models of the harmonic telegraph, but he was never able to make any of these models work satisfactorily.

While these experiments were going on, Bell had suggested to several friends the possibility of transmitting speech electrically. His friends advised him to continue with his telegraph experiments and he decided to do so.

On the afternoon of June 2, 1875, Bell's assistant, Thomas A. Watson, was working on the transmitting spring of a short-line telegraph in an attic on Court Street in Boston, while Bell was adjusting the springs at the receiving end. One of the transmitting springs had stopped vibrating; Watson kept plucking it to get it started again. Suddenly Bell rushed into the room and cried: "What did you do then?" Bell had heard the sound made by the plucked spring at the receiving end of the line.

This is what had happened. The make-and-break points of the transmitting spring had become welded together. When Watson snapped the spring, the circuit had remained unbroken. As the spring, of magnetized steel, vibrated over the pole of the magnet, it generated a current of electricity that varied in intensity as the air varied in density near the spring.

Bell realized the full significance of this unexpected development. He replaced the spring with a diaphragm that vibrated in accordance with the varying air pressure produced by a human voice. After experimenting with various diaphragm shapes, he developed a transmitter and receiver that transmitted speech fairly well. The first telephone patent was issued on March 7, 1876; it has been called the most valuable patent ever issued in any country.

Bell was soon involved in extensive patent litigation over the question of pri-

THE TELEPHONE RECEIVER

In the telephone receiver, an electromagnet, with many turns of thin wire wound around it, is so arranged that it exerts a force of attraction on a thin iron diaphragm. The electromagnet will attract the diaphragm more or less strongly, depending on the strength of the current passing through the wire. As a result the diaphragm will move to and fro rapidly. It will cause the air in its vicinity to vibrate in such a way as to reproduce the sound of the human voice.

ELECTROMAGNET

DIAPHRAGM

ority. Reis claimed that the priority was his, because the "telephone" he had invented could transmit musical sounds. The United States Supreme Court ruled against the German inventor because his device, unlike that of Bell, was based on alternately making and breaking a circuit and could not transmit human speech. "To follow Reis," said the Court, "is to fail, but to follow Bell is to succeed."

The American inventor Elisha Gray claimed priority for a telephone that he had invented. He had filed a caveat (an application for the protection of his idea) in the United States Patent Office only a few hours after Bell had applied for a patent. Still others claimed to have invented the telephone; it is said that 600 separate suits in all were filed against Bell. However, after many years of litigation, the validity of his telephone patents was confirmed by the courts.

Various improvements were made in the construction of the telephone. The most important one was the substitution of a permanent magnet for the soft iron core that had formerly been used. Other alterations were made in the telephone, resulting in a much simpler and more compact instrument. Bell now began a series of lectures in various cities;·he described his improved telephone before large audiences, and aroused great interest in it.

However, when Bell and other owners of Bell patents organized the Bell Telephone Company and began to lease telephones for private use at ten dollars per year, the public response was anything but encouraging. Small exchanges were set up in a few cities, but there were few subscribers. At first the telephone was used chiefly on private lines — two telephones connected by private wire. Those wishing to communicate over long distances used the telegraph.

The Western Union Telegraph Company entered the telephone field in 1877. Since Western Union controlled most of the telegraph lines in the country, it became a serious competitor of the Bell Telephone Company, which started suit against its rival. There was a bitter fight between the two companies; ultimately, however, Western Union acknowledged the validity and priority of the Bell patents and withdrew entirely from the telephone field.

In 1885, the American Telephone and Telegraph Company was organized. Its particular purpose was to build long-distance lines that would connect the city exchanges of local companies licensed under the Bell patents. In 1889, this organization absorbed the American Bell Company and became the headquarters of the system of interconnected Bell companies.

In the meanwhile, a large number of other local companies were organized at the expiration of the original Bell patents. In March 1958, there were some 4,000 of these companies. Their lines interconnect with those of twenty-three Bell companies that have evolved from the original licensees. The total of about 64,146,000 telephones thus interconnected is further linked by radio telephony and submarine telephone cable with millions more in foreign countries and island possessions. The American telephone user, therefore, can reach any one of some 114,550,000 telephones, or 96 per cent of all the telephones in the world.

In some nine decades of telephone research, the telephone engineers have overcome one by one the barriers to speech transmission. From the very beginning, the progress of the art has been marked by epoch-making advances due to inventions and improvements in apparatus and equipment. Some of the more notable achievements have been as follows:

The development of the switchboard, without which no interconnecting group of telephones would be possible. This was the beginning of the telephone exchange.

The discovery of the process of hardening copper wire and its application to telephone circuits, thus improving transmission and making long-distance open-wire telephone circuits possible.

The substitution of a pair of wires for a single wire with ground return, thus reducing the disturbance caused by adjacent power circuits or other telephone circuits and greatly improving transmission.

Development of automatic switching systems, opening the way for tremendous expansion in the fields of local and long-distance telephony.

The development of radio relay as a supplement to wire communication to the extent that such routes by mid-1958 provided over 13,000,000 miles of telephone circuits all over the United States, or a quarter of the Bell System's entire long-distance telephone-circuit mileage.

Development in the late 1940's by the Bell Telephone Laboratories of the transistor. The small size and low power requirements of this electronic device opened the way for more compact and efficient telephone systems.

The transposition of telephone circuits, thereby minimizing the interference of other telephone circuits and of electric light and power wires.

The development of the underground cable, making possible the removal of pole lines from the main thoroughfares of cities; and the aerial cable, reducing the number of crossarms and the size of the poles.

Improvement in the designs and methods of manufacture of cables for local exchange use, thus making it possible to increase greatly the number of wires that may be placed within a cable sheath of given size. By employing smaller wires, the maximum number of wires carried in a single cable has been increased to 2,121 pairs.

The development of magnetic alloys permalloy and perminvar. Permalloy, a magnetic alloy composed of approximately 80 per cent nickel and 20 per cent iron has revolutionized the submarine telegraph cable art by permitting speeds five times greater than before. The use of permalloy has also made possible a reduction in the sizes of telephone cables and a decrease in the cost of the loading coils required, and has brought about savings in a great many other types of telephone apparatus.

Developments in telephone submarine cables, including the use of coaxial structures and submerged repeaters capable of operating under deep-sea pressures.

How telephone calls are made

In the earliest telephone systems, one person could call another only if the two phones were directly connected by a separate wire. Nowadays central exchanges permit calls to be placed anywhere in the world with only one line leading from the subscriber's phone to the exchange. A vast network of trunk lines joins the exchanges in different cities and countries, spanning continents and oceans.

Today the vast majority of telephones in the United States are dial-operated. Various types of automatic switching equipment are used. The subscriber spins a dial on his telephone in accordance with the letters and figures of the number desired. As the dial is released, a mechanism connected to it alternately opens and closes the circuit a certain number of times. The number depends on how far the dial has been turned. For example, if the subscriber has inserted his finger in the number 5 position and turned it as far as it will go, the circuit will be opened and closed five times when the dial is released. The electrical impulses are transmitted to dial apparatus in the telephone central office.

Various types of dial equipment are in use. The most common type, called "step-by-step," is found mostly in smaller locations, where switching arrangements are fairly simple. When the user lifts the receiver, equipment in the office connects his telephone line to a device called a selector switch. The caller hears a dial tone and begins dialing. Other selector switches advance the call as each successive letter or figure is dialed. When the final number is dialed, the bell on the called telephone begins ringing. Step-by-step equipment was introduced in 1892; extensive use began about 1919. At about the same time the panel system was developed for heavily populated areas. Although succeeded by the faster, more efficient crossbar system in the late 1930's, many panel installations are still in service.

In crossbar systems there are two kinds of apparatus: the control equipment

THE SWITCHBOARD

In a nondial central office, your line ends in a "jack" or hole in a switchboard. When you lift the receiver, a light glows above your jack on the switchboard, attracting the attention of the operator. She turns a switch, picks up a cord with a plug at either end and inserts one of the plugs in the jack below the glowing light. Then she says: "Number, please." When you give her the number you want, she tests the jack corresponding to the desired number, using the free plug of the cord. If the line is not busy, she inserts the plug into the jack and rings the number, thus completing the connection.

THE DIAL SYSTEM

Step-by-step dial equipment. When you lift your receiver, your telephone line is automatically connected to a device called a selector switch. You then hear a dial tone and you begin dialing. Your call is advanced by a series of selector switches as you dial each successive letter or figure. When the final number is dialed, the bell on the called telephone begins ringing.

and the switching network. The latter network sets up talking paths under the direction of the control equipment.

On a call dialed through some types of crossbar equipment, connections are not set up until the complete number is dialed. On other types, the called office is selected after the first three digits are dialed. At that time the control apparatus in a split second determines the correct path the call must take to reach the desired telephone. Once the path has been determined, the equipment closes the appropriate switches and the call goes through instantaneously.

If the call is to an out-of-town point, the control equipment places it on a circuit to the distant office. Control apparatus in that office sets up the appropriate circuits over which the call can be completed. Since many such calls are usually charged for individually, Automatic Message Accounting equipment comes on the line. It records on tape details such as the number from which the call is made, the called telephone, the time of answer and the time the call is ended. This information is transcribed automatically and later translated by other accounting equipment to the simple details that later appear on the telephone bill.

The automatic accounting equipment has made it possible to extend the range of customer dialing in many cases far beyond the range of nearby cities. By 1958, more than 5,000,000 telephone users could dial their long distance calls direct to 30,000,000 telephones from coast to coast. Another 10,000,000 customers could dial nearby towns and cities.

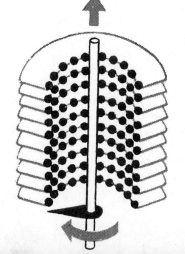

In a manual telephone system, the connections are made by operators instead of machines. The vertical part, or panel, of each switchboard holds rows of small sockets, called jacks, each of which is a terminal of a subscriber's line. A tiny signal light is located near each jack. Protruding from the horizontal part, or bench, of the board are pairs of flexible cords tipped with brass terminals, which are known as plugs. The members of a pair are connected to each other underneath the bench. A pair of signal lights on the bench is linked to each pair of plugs through automatic relay switches. Power for the exchange and the subscribers' lines is supplied from a battery at the exchange plant.

Every subscriber's line is wired to a number of jacks which reappear at intervals along the bank of switchboard positions. This makes connections between any two lines easy, and allows a subscriber's call to be answered at any one of the switchboards, by whichever operator happens to be free at the moment.

When a subscriber lifts his receiver off the hook, all the lamps next to his jacks in the switchboard are automatically lit up. Seeing one of the signals, an operator picks up a plug and inserts it into the jack; the signal lights then go out. The operator presses a key that connects her telephone to the subscriber's and says, "Number, please?" Upon hearing the number, she inserts the free plug of the pair into one of the jacks on the desired line, lighting the signal lamp for this plug on the bench. Then the operator presses a key that rings the bell of the called subscriber's telephone.

As soon as the person who is answering the call lifts up the receiver, the lamp adjacent to the cord is extinguished; this indicates to the operator that the desired connection has now been made. When the subscriber replaces the receiver after having completed his conversation, the lamp adjacent to the corresponding cord flashes; the operator withdraws the cord, thus extinguishing the lamp, and then returns the plug to the bench. In a busy telephone exchange, the switchboard lamps are constantly flashing on and off.

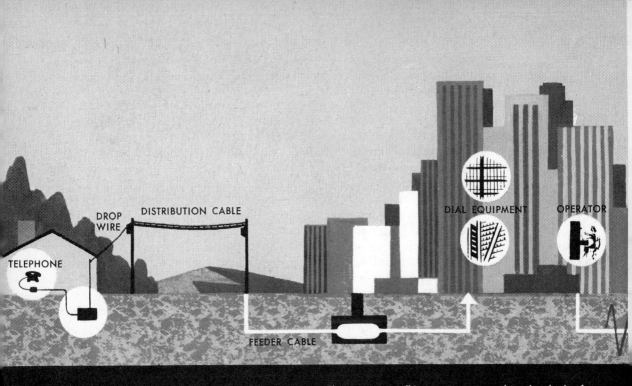

When you lift up your receiver, current flows up a drop wire and along a distribution cable and feeder cable to a telephone office. Here your call will be put through by automatic dial equipment or by an operator.

Then you start talking to a person perhaps hundreds of miles away. The vibrations of your voice as you talk into the receiver are converted into electric current of varying strength. This voice current, as it is called, is then trans-

Improvements in
long-distance lines

For many years after the invention of the telephone, speech transmission over lines more than a few hundred miles in length proved impossible. Even over shorter lines it was frequently difficult to transmit speech clearly. In ordinary speech we recognize syllables, words or voices by the special blend of high and low frequencies in the sound waves the speaker produces and by the order in which they follow one another. If this balance is altered, making some frequencies stronger and some weaker (frequency distortion), or if the sequence is changed (delay distortion), the character of the voice is changed. Individual words may become unintelligible and even whole phrases may be quite difficult to understand.

Frequency distortion was a major problem in long-distance transmission. As voice currents passed along a great stretch of wire, the higher frequencies were attenu-

ated, or weakened, more rapidly than the lower ones. At the end of a long line, what the listener often heard was only an unrecognizable remnant of the original sound.

The cause of this distortion was well known. Two insulated electric wires, lying very close to each other, behave somewhat like a capacitor, or condenser (see Index, under Condensers). This capacitor is continuously being charged and discharged for each half-cycle of voice current transmitted. The charging current is drawn through the line wires. Because the line wires have resistance, a certain amount of heat is produced. Each time the capacitor is charged, the same amount of electricity is required. But the higher the frequency, the shorter the charging time and the greater the current that must flow to provide the charge. The greater the current, the more the heat loss produced in the line wires. Thus the higher frequencies are not transmitted as well as the lower ones.

In 1900, a physicist at Columbia University, Michael I. Pupin, managed to

RADIO RELAY STATION

REPEATER STATION

counteract the capacitor effect by placing inductance coils (see Index) in the lines at certain calculated intervals. The voice frequencies were then all transmitted about equally well, with almost no distortion. Pupin's idea, known as coil loading, was adopted by the telephone companies and increased the range of transmission by three or four times.

There were many other problems in long-distance transmission. Coil loading had greatly extended the range of telephone transmission, but still greater ranges were needed, and better voice transmission was also required.

Telegraph companies used mechanical "repeater" elements in their lines to restore the energy of signals. These were actually electromagnets; they were too sluggish and inefficient to reproduce the broad range of frequencies used in telephony.

The problem was solved in the early 1900's. After years of experimentation, special equipment was finally developed for adapting the audion (three-electrode) electron tube for use as a telephone repeater. Here was a flexible instrument that would amplify the energy of electrical currents while maintaining the original frequency patterns with remarkable fidelity. Energy for the tube could be drawn from any source of direct current. (The operation of electron tubes as telephone repeaters is similar to their function as amplifiers in radio broadcasting. This subject is taken up in the article An Introduction to Electronics in Volume 6.) To a large extent, repeaters made possible the opening of the first transcontinental telephone line, in 1915, between New York and San Francisco.

The same improved electron-tube amplifier that made transcontinental telephone possible in 1915 made it possible to extend telephone service to distant overseas points. In 1927, radiotelephone service to London was inaugurated and grew rapidly. Service at first was provided by means of long-wave radio; later, short-wave channels were utilized. By mid-1958, telephone subscribers in the United States could reach more than 120 countries or areas by means of a number of radio and underseas telephone cables.

The early 1950's saw the development of an amplifier that would operate under deep-sea pressure for long periods of time without attention. This breakthrough paved the way for the first deep-sea ocean telephone cable system to be laid across the Atlantic between North America and Europe in 1956. A second cable was laid the same year from Port Angeles, Washington, to Alaska. In 1958, a deep-sea cable was placed between California and Hawaii. A fourth was installed between Europe and the United States mainland in the year 1959, and a fifth to the island of Puerto Rico in 1960.

The deep-sea sections of these transoceanic telephone cable systems are constructed according to similar engineering designs. These sections are made up of two coaxial cables, transmitting in opposite directions. Built into each cable, at 40-mile intervals, are amplifiers which obtain their operating power from direct current transmitted by the center cable conductor. The amplifiers are expected to operate more than twenty years, on the average, without replacement. Each cable system forms a path for a carrier system having a capacity of thirty-six simultaneous conversations. Technological developments are expected to result in the doubling of this capacity within the next few years.

The carrier
system of telephony

In the early 1900's, the message-carrying capacity of long-distance lines was increased by the use of "phantom" circuits, in which two pairs of wires are made to carry three calls simultaneously. Soon after, a system of multiplex telephony was developed to permit simultaneous conversations to be conducted over a single pair of wires. This system, first introduced commercially in the United States in 1918, is known as carrier telephony; it is based on the principle of modulation used for radio broadcasting (see Index, under Amplitude modulation).

Just as a sound wave may carry vibrations of many different frequencies at the same time, so an electrical circuit may carry a complex alternating current that is actually made up of many separate currents, each having a different frequency from all the rest.

In the carrier system, each of these different currents is composed of two parts: the carrier and the message. The message, of course, is the voice current from some subscriber's telephone transmitter. The carrier originates in an electronic oscillator (see Index); it is a current alternating at a particular high frequency, above the range of voice currents. In one arrangement the voice current is combined with the carrier in a device known as a modulator.

Voice currents from other phones can be transmitted on the same line, provided that each message is combined with a carrier of different frequency. Each frequency serves to identify the individual call it carries as it is transmitted together with others through a single cable. At the end of the line, a filtering device separates the calls according to the carrier frequencies and then sends each one of them along the proper route. Finally, before reaching the receiver at its destination, each call goes through a demodulator, which suppresses the carrier frequency, leaving only the voice current. Carrier telephony has played a key role in the striking advances in long distance communications of the last thirty years.

Microwave radio relay systems are an important postwar development in the field of carrier telephony. They supply a large number of telephone circuits for long-distance calls and the broad-frequency bands needed to transmit television programs. Radio relay systems consist of relay towers located within line-of-sight distances from each other. Radio waves at frequencies of several thousands of megacycles,* called microwaves, are sent from tower to tower. At each radio relay station, the signals are amplified and sent on to the next. The microwave system extensively used in the Bell System provides as

---

* A megacycle is a million cycles.

many as six or more broad-band communication channels in each direction. A pair of these channels going in opposite directions can carry as many as 600 conversations or two television programs.

The first radio relay system was built in 1947 between New York and Boston. By 1958, these systems provided more than 13,000,000 miles of telephone circuits or about one-quarter of the nation's long-distance telephone-circuit mileage. They also furnished 80 per cent of the channel mileage used in the country's television network, which extended to 550 stations in more than 360 cities and towns.

In 1957, the Bell System put the country's first commercial "over the horizon" microwave system in service between Cuba and the United States. The "over the horizon" system differs from conventional microwave installations in that the signals do not follow a "line-of-light" path. In a process called "tropospheric scatter propagation," a small fraction of the energy in the transmitted radio wave is deflected back to earth at points beyond the horizon. No intermediate stations are needed.

Carrier methods are used to divide the frequency band of a coaxial conductor into channels; each channel provides many more paths. Channels are separated by filters when they reach their destination. Repeaters amplify the signals at regular intervals. Eight coaxial conductors are contained in the coaxial cable most commonly used for land communication. Since each tube transmits in only one direction, four two-way systems can be operated in a single sheath.

The year 1964 marked the first commercial operation (on a very limited scale) of the videotelephone, or Picturephone. Service was established in three cities— New York, Washington and Chicago— and only in one place in each city. The videotelephone, combining television and telephone, makes it possible for the person at the telephone to see the person with whom he is talking. The desktop unit at which calls are made and received contains a television camera and a screen 5¾ inches high by 4⅜ inches wide.

See also Vol. 10, p. 287: "Telegraphy and Telephony."

Before the performance: spectators sitting around a Zeiss Planetarium installed in a large domed chamber at the Griffith Planetarium in Los Angeles, California. When the illumination in the chamber fades, the arching dome overhead will become a replica of the night skies.

Griffith Observatory

MAN-MADE SKIES

The Story of the Zeiss Planetarium

"NEVER has a means of entertainment been provided which is so instructive as this, never one which is so fascinating, never one which has such general appeal. It is a school, a theater, a cinema in one; a drama with the celestial bodies as actors." Such was the tribute paid by the renowned Swedish astronomer Elis Strömgren when he witnessed a performance of the Zeiss Planetarium at Munich, Germany, in the year 1924. Since that time millions of people have experienced the thrill that Strömgren described so eloquently.

In a planetarium chamber, the visitors attending a performance sit around a strange-looking instrument that stands more than a dozen feet high. Arching

over the whole room is a large hemispherical dome, which is generally from sixty-five to seventy-five feet in diameter.

At first the planetarium chamber is brilliantly lit; melodious strains of soft music fill the air. There is a stir among the members of the audience as the lecturer steps into the chamber. He takes his place at an elaborate console that contains the switches and the other controls for operating the huge instrument. The illumination in the chamber fades slowly until the audience can see only a faint glow extending around the horizon. The hemispherical dome has now become a counterpart of the night skies, studded with stars. The spectators forget that they are sitting in a closed room as they gaze upward.

The apparatus that provides this breath taking spectacle — the Zeiss Planetarium — was the creation of a famous German optical firm, the Zeiss Company. Shortly before the outbreak of World War I, Dr. Oskar von Müller, the director of the great technical museum in Munich, asked the Zeiss Company to design an indoor machine that would reproduce as realistically as possible the appearance of the night skies. In the first model developed by the Zeiss Company, the spectators were stationed within a large sphere with holes punched in it. These holes admitted light from a source outside the sphere and thus produced the illusion of stars. The sphere could be turned to reproduce the movement of the stars in the heavens.

All work on the planetarium stopped when World War I broke out in August 1914. After the war Dr. Walter Bauersfeld, of the Zeiss Company, designed a new kind of machine. In this, a fixed hemisphere replaced the movable sphere of

California Acad. of Sciences

the older model; the stars were projected on the inner side of the hemisphere from lantern-slide projectors set in the center. The first machine of this type was completed in 1924; it was installed on the roof of the Zeiss factory at Jena, and later was sent to Munich. This instrument and the next one that was built showed the sky only as it appears when seen from a single vantage point on the earth's surface. All the others that have been built by the Zeiss Company since that time are more versatile; they can reproduce the appearance of the sky as it can be seen from any place on the earth.

The total number of Zeiss Planetaria in the world is small; there are about thirty all told, and they are widely scattered. The United States has six large ones — Chicago's Adler Planetarium, opened in 1930; the Fels Planetarium, in Philadelphia (1933), the Hayden Planetarium, in New York (1935); the Griffith Planetarium, in Los Angeles (1935); the Buhl Planetarium, in Pittsburgh (1939); the Morehead Planetarium, in Chapel Hill, North Carolina (1949). The Morrison Planetarium, in San Francisco, is not a Zeiss instrument, but it is approximately equal in performance. A number of smaller planetaria have also been constructed.

As we pointed out, the Zeiss Planetarium reproduces the stars by means of a

How the night skies appear when "stars" are projected on the dome of the Morrison Planetarium, San Francisco.

series of lantern-slide projectors, or magic lanterns. Each of these contains a slide, showing a considerable number of stars. The projectors are so arranged that the pictures they flash on the hemispherical dome form an apparently continuous starry pattern.

For convenience, the sky is divided into two halves — northern and southern. Sixteen projectors are necessary to show the stars of each half. The sixteen of each half are set inside separate metal globes, so that only the lenses appear; they are fixed rigidly with respect to one another. The two globes, each containing sixteen projectors, are connected by a cylindrical framework; the entire instrument, therefore, forms a dumbbell-shaped mass. It is set upon a framework resting on the floor.

Each one of the projectors shows between 200 and 300 stars; the total for all the projectors is about 9,000. This represents the number of stars that can be seen by the unaided eye under the best conditions. Of course the observer cannot see all of these stars at once, since at any given moment half of them will be below the horizon. Besides, stars tend to fade as they come closer to the horizon, because of the greater thickness of air that their light must traverse. For this reason some of the fainter stars are invisible unless they stand high in the sky. At any one time, therefore, in a very clear and moonless night far away from any artificial lights, it is unlikely that you will be able to see as many as 3,000 stars with the naked eye. The heavens are filled with billions of other stars, but you can only see these with the aid of the telescope.

The stars appear to move westward in the night heavens as the hours pass. The dumbbell-shaped mass of the instrument is rotated on an axis to produce the effect of this movement. In nature, the westward movement of the stars is only apparent; what really happens is that the earth rotates on its axis in an easterly direction, while the stars remain relatively fixed in the heavens.

As seen from the earth, the stars all seem to move together in the heavens. But the sun follows its own route; so do the planets and the moon. Consequently each of these heavenly bodies must be provided with its own projector. These projectors are to be found in compartments, or cages, set within the cylindrical portion of the Zeiss instrument — the part that connects the two globes. There are projectors for only five of the planets — Mercury, Venus, Mars, Jupiter and Saturn. The other planets are not shown because in nature they are not plainly visible to the naked eye.

In the compartment, or cage, for the sun, the motion is simple. A large gear in the cage turns around once, while the instrument as a whole turns 365 times — once for each day in the year. The projector for the sun is attached to the gear; it causes a large bright disk to appear upon the dome. Actually there is a double projector in this case; two suns, matching perfectly, blend together on the dome. There are two reasons for this arrangement. For one thing, if there were only one sun, the projector might burn out in the course of a demonstration and the sun would disappear. As it is, since it is unlikely that both lamps will fail during a single demonstration, the lecturer can be reasonably

certain that the sun will continue to shine throughout the performance. Another reason for doubling is to prevent the "blinking" of the sun as the projector points directly at one of the struts or supports of the cage. One projector always shines between the struts when the other one is obstructed. There is also a double projector for each of the planets mentioned and the moon, and for the same reasons.

The two moon projectors are attached to a gear that makes one complete turn for each $27\frac{1}{2}$ turns of the instrument as a whole. That is because $27\frac{1}{2}$ days are required for the moon to come back to a given star after moving all the way around the earth. During this time, the sun has moved eastward against the background of the stars; the moon, therefore, requires something like two more days to catch up with the sun. That is why the period from one new moon to the next is about $29\frac{1}{2}$ days. Besides showing the movement of the moon among the stars, the moon projectors are provided with a complicated mechanism for producing the different lunar phases.

The planets Jupiter and Saturn are shown with the Zeiss Planetarium as they would appear in small telescopes — Saturn with its rings slightly indicated and Jupi-

American Museum-Hayden Planetarium

The Hayden Planetarium (above), in New York, was opened in the year 1935.

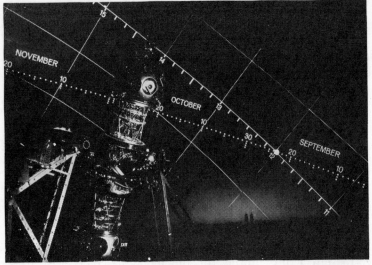

Right: planetarium cage, showing projectors for sun, moon and one planet. Four other planets are being projected from another cage.

Left: on the dark dome of the Hayden Planetarium, the sun's disk is shown crossing the celestial equator in the month of September.

Below: a model of the planet Saturn, with rings and satellites. It is on display in the solar system room of the Hayden Planetarium.

ter with dark bands across its middle — while Mars is shown in red color. This is done so that these planets will not be confused with one another or with the other two shown on the dome — Venus and Mercury.

The projectors for the sun, moon and planets are permanently set in place, and as long as none of the gears work loose from their shafts the motions of these bodies will be shown with considerable realism. The accuracy with which they are represented cannot compare with that which the astronomer can attain with his calculations; but, after all, such accuracy is not necessary, since the Zeiss Planetarium is intended merely to show the sky as the layman can see it.

The planetarium is provided with two motors to rotate it from east to west (or in the opposite direction) at two different speeds. The movements of the stars during a whole day may be shown either in about 10½ minutes or else in about 3½ minutes. There is a gear shift that will cause the stars to go through a day's movements in less than a minute; but the stars dart so rapidly across the dome in this case that most people who watch them feel uncomfortable. The gear shift for rapid star motion is seldom used in public demonstrations. It is particularly useful in teaching college classes, since in this case the lecturer is more interested in covering considerable ground than in presenting a finished performance.

The projectors for the sun, moon and planets can be operated while the stars are standing still. Three motors of different speeds are provided. One of these gives a year in about three minutes, another a year in one minute and the third one a year in about six seconds. These motors may be run forward or backward; they make it possible to go back through centuries of time or to race far forward into the future.

There are other projectors, not always shown in public demonstrations, but very important in setting the instrument. One of these — the cyclometer projector — is attached to the motors that take us swiftly through the years. This projector can indicate the year corresponding to a given sky pattern in much the same way as an automobile speedometer can tell us how far

North Star gradually descends in the skies; it disappears at last below the northern horizon when we cross the equator. As we continue southward, we see stars that never appear in the northern hemisphere.

Another motor spins the Zeiss instrument so as to show the changes that occur in the course of many thousands of years, as a result of the precession of the equinoxes (see Index). This motor can take us through more than 20,000 years in a single minute.

In almost every planetarium installation, the members of the staff have designed and built much additional equipment in order to show eclipses, displays of the northern and southern lights, meteors and meteor showers, beautiful sunset and sunrise colors and other interesting phenomena not displayed by the original instrument. There is a special comet projector, which shows a comet moving among the stars and changing its appearance as the tail first brightens and lengthens, then fades and shortens.

The dome of the planetarium chamber is generally of stainless steel; it has millions of holes in it to prevent echoes from developing. Aluminum and acoustic tile have also been used. A dome of steel or aluminum is best, because it becomes transparent when bright lights are turned on behind it; consequently, interesting effects and tableaux can be staged behind the dome for the benefit of the spectators.

Air conditioning machinery is necessary in the chamber, because it must be closed tight with double doors in order to bring about the degree of darkness that is required. There is a fine sound system to provide music before the demonstration and also at its close — at "sunrise." Sometimes transcribed remarks or special music form an important part of the presentation.

The Zeiss Planetarium is a constant source of inspiration to all who witness its performance. To quote Dr. Philip Fox, the first director of Chicago's Adler Planetarium, it represents "the heavens portrayed in great dignity and splendor, dynamic, inspiring, in a way that dispels the mystery but retains the majesty."

a car has traveled. By pressing a button at the console, the demonstrator can project on the dome, above his head, a number corresponding to a given year.

A special set of projectors shows the celestial equator, which is in the plane of the earth's equator. In addition, these projectors show the ecliptic, the sun's apparent annual path among the stars. At one end of the framework that supports the instrument there are two small spheres that project the celestial meridian. This is an imaginary line that splits the sky into eastern and western halves; it passes through the north and south points of the horizon and through the zenith, the point exactly overhead. Another projector is aimed directly at the demonstrator and is too faint to show on the wall behind him; hence only he can see it. It tells him at what latitude a given star grouping can be seen.

The east and west ends of the framework that supports the Zeiss instrument are joined by a horizontal axis. A motor can turn the entire instrument around this axis, in order to show the change in the appearance of the sky as we travel northward or southward along the surface of the earth at the speed of 5,000 miles per minute. As we go southward, the familiar

THE MIGHTY INSECT

A Small, Six-legged Competitor of Man

BY JOHN C. PALLISTER

THE insects are the most numerous, the most varied and among the most widespread of all animals. Already, something like a million species have been described and new ones are being discovered every year; there are probably more than two million in all. Insects live in almost every land area of the globe. They are found well up beyond the Arctic Circle, on high mountain peaks, in deep caves and in forbidding deserts, as well as in the areas, such as the tropics, where they particularly thrive. They are by no means restricted to the land. Some adult insects and many larvae dwell in lakes, ponds and streams; a few are to be found in or near brackish water and along the tidal limits; a very few live in the offshore waters of the ocean.

These widely distributed little creatures belong to the great phylum (primary biological division) of the arthropods, made up of segmented animals with jointed legs. This phylum includes such familiar animals as spiders, ticks, mites, centipedes, millepedes, scorpions, shrimps, crabs and lobsters.

The adult insect is a six-legged animal, which generally (though not always) has wings. It usually does not present a soft exterior of flesh and fat to a hostile world. Instead, most insects wear a kind of armor of stiff, leathery plates, joined by elastic connecting tissues. This armor serves as a skeleton and is called the exoskeleton (outer skeleton). Some insects, particularly the beetles, have extremely hard exoskeletons; at the other extreme, plant lice and certain other forms have very thin and fragile coverings.

The body of the insect is divided into three parts: the head, thorax and abdomen. The head is oval, or globular or simply roundish. It may be large in proportion to the body or very small. Except for a few primitive varieties, all insects are equipped with one pair of antennae, which arise from the front of the head, usually near the eyes; they function as organs of touch. The antennae of some insects also contain organs of smell; those of mosquitoes, some flies, some butterflies and some wasps are able to receive sound waves. Antennae show great

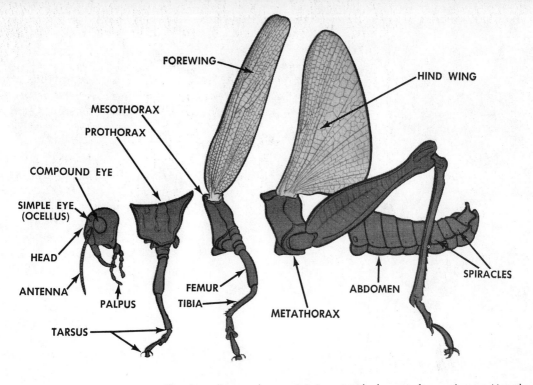

The above diagram shows certain important body parts of a grasshopper. Note the three divisions of the thorax—the prothorax, the mesothorax and the metathorax.

diversity in size, shape and structure; they may resemble threads, or strings of beads, or tiny combs, or feathers, or clubs or hammers, to list just a few forms.

Insect eyes are of two kinds, simple and compound. The compound eyes, often large and prominent, are composed of small hexagonal lenses. There are usually only a few lenses in the compound eye of an ant or other ground insect; there may be as many as 28,000 in the case of the dragonfly. The simple eyes, called ocelli, are very small; in adult insects, they are usually two or three in number and are placed near the compound eyes. Probably they permit the insect to distinguish between light and darkness. The immature insect usually has only simple eyes. Most adults have compound eyes; many have simple ones as well. A considerable number of insects, immature and adult, have no eyes at all.

Some insects bite and chew their food, which may be pretty tough material, such as wood. Others pierce plant leaves and tender stems and suck the juice; or they penetrate the skin of animals and suck the blood. An insect has three pairs of jaws. The mandibles, or true jaws, make up the first pair. In sucking insects, such as mosquitoes, the mandibles are fused together to form a needle-sharp piercing tube. Some male beetles and soldier ants have enormously enlarged mandibles that look and perform like claws; certain butterflies have no mandibles at all. Below the mandibles there is a second pair of jaws, the maxillae; these hold food, carry it to the mouth and chew it sideways instead of up and down. On the maxillae are a pair of feelers, called palpi, which may be quite long and conspicuous. The final pair of jaws is often fused together to form a lower lip; it too has palpi. Both sets of palpi are sensory organs, probably conveying sensations of taste and smell as well as of touch. Many insects have a kind of tongue; this may be short and fleshy, or it may be so long that when not in use it must be kept curled under the head like a spring.

Behind the head is the thorax, which supports the legs and wings. It is composed of three segments, each holding one pair of legs. Almost all insects have six true legs, and none has more than six. Some immature insects have no legs; the immature insects called caterpillars have three pairs of true thoracic legs and from two to ten other pairs on their abdomen. Certain adult forms use their two front legs for digging; others, for seizing their prey; still

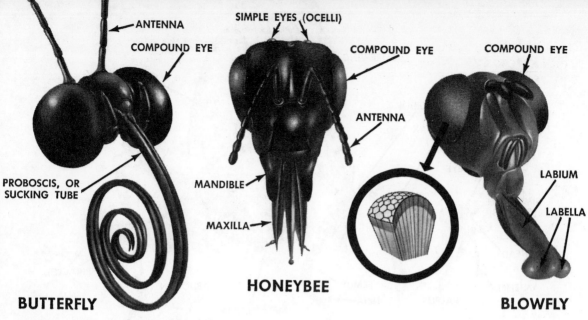

ANTENNA

COMPOUND EYE

SIMPLE EYES (OCELLI)

COMPOUND EYE

COMPOUND EYE

ANTENNA

PROBOSCIS, OR
SUCKING TUBE

MANDIBLE

MAXILLA

LABIUM

LABELLA

BUTTERFLY

HONEYBEE

BLOWFLY

Adapted from models in American Museum of Natural History

Insect heads. The mouth parts of the butterfly are used for sucking; those of
the honeybee for chewing; those of the blowfly for lapping. The inset shows the
arrangement of the hexagonal lenses that make up the compound eye of an insect.

others, for holding the female during mating. Insects that swim have paddlelike middle and hind legs. The hind legs of grasshoppers, fleas and other jumping insects are greatly enlarged. Some insects (including honeybees and houseflies) have a comblike structure on their front legs, which they use for cleaning their antennae. Usually insects move their legs in sets of three: the first and third legs on one side move with the second leg on the other.

Certain insects are wingless throughout their entire lives; others have but one pair of wings. The majority, however, have two pairs, one pair attached to the middle segment of the thorax and the other to the last segment. The second pair of flies' wings is represented by a pair of little stumps, called halteres; in effect, therefore, flies have but two wings. The forewings of beetles are stiffened and thickened into a shieldlike covering for the delicate rear wings. Insect wings are supported by a network of tubular veins. Wings may be smooth and transparent or covered lightly or heavily with hairs (fine or coarse) or with minute colored scales. The iridescent colors seen on some moth and butterfly wings are usually due to light diffracted by these scales.

The abdomen is usually the largest part of an insect's body. It is composed of a

series of nine to eleven ring-shaped segments; these may be closely jointed, making the abdomen stiff and rigid, or so loosely jointed that the insect is able to curve its abdomen up over its head. Commonly, the first segment is as broad or nearly as broad as the thorax to which it is attached. In wasps, ants and other "wasp-waisted" insects, the first and often the second and third segments are extremely narrow, while the rest of the abdomen is globular.

Many insects carry prominent appendages at the end of the abdomen. These may be a pair of long bristles, or tails, looking like antennae and serving much the same purpose; in the case of earwigs and japygids, the appendages consist of a pair of strong pincers at the end of the abdomen. Some females have a long ovipositor, or egg-laying tube, projecting from the tip of the abdomen. Female ants, wasps and bees use the ovipositor as a stinger.

Many insects wear odd or beautiful decorations, at whose purpose we can only guess. They may have horns, or spines or ridges on the back or head; hairs, stiff or silky, may cover them all over or in patches. On the wings of moths and butterflies the hairs are flat and scalelike. Insect colors are often striking. Certain colors — browns, blacks and yellows — are usually due to pigmentation, or coloring matter; metallic and

404

FOREWING

HOUSEFLY

WING

HIND WING

CECROPIA MOTH

UNDERWING

OUTER WING
(ELYTRUM)

LADYBIRD BEETLE

Insect wing types. In the ladybird beetle, the hard, shell-like outer wings, or elytra (singular: elytrum) serve as sheaths for the membranous underwings. The hind
wings of the housefly have been reduced to rodlike structures, known as halteres.

iridescent colors, to light diffraction from the surface structure; green and magenta, to both these factors.

An insect has no lungs. It takes air through openings along its sides into a system of air tubes, called tracheae, which spread throughout the body and wings. Aquatic insects breathe through tracheal gills, or they have chambers that they can fill with fresh air before they submerge. A simple pulsating tube, open at both ends, serves to keep the blood in motion throughout the body. In some insects pulsating sacs in the knee joints drive the blood through the legs. The blood is usually colorless or greenish; but some aquatic insects and some larvae have red blood.

The digestive system varies with the food habits of insects. Some take only liquid food. In those which eat solids, the food passes from the gullet into a storage chamber or crop; from there it goes into a kind of gizzard, where it is ground fine, and thence into the gut for digestion.

Special glands account for some of the extraordinary activities of insects. Caterpillars and all other insect larvae that spin silk are equipped with silk glands. The froth of spittle bugs is whipped up from a secretion that comes from a gland near the

Rear appendages of the May fly, earwig and honeybee. The "tail" of the May fly consists of long filaments. In the earwig, the rear appendages are forceplike; they serve as organs of defense or offense and sometimes aid in folding the wings. The sting of the honeybee work- er (always a female) is a modified egg-laying organ; it is withdrawn into the abdomen when not in use. Because of its barblike structure (see inset), it stays in the body of the foe that is stung. Consequently, the sting is torn off as the bee flies away; the latter soon dies.

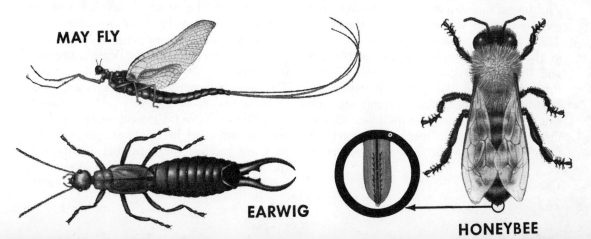

MAY FLY

EARWIG

HONEYBEE

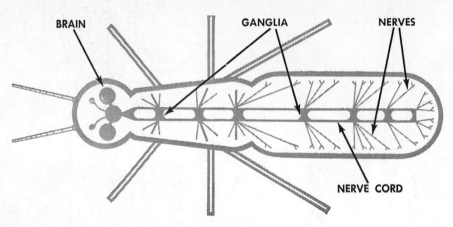

Highly simplified diagram of a typical insect's nervous system. From the brain, in the head, nerve cords extend to the end of the abdomen. There are a number of ganglia (that is, nerve centers) along the cords; nerves lead from the ganglia.

tip of the abdomen. Small glands provide certain insects with poisonous or ill-smelling liquids or gases with which they confound their enemies. Honeybees have wax glands. The glands of aphids, lac insects and most other members of the Homoptera * secrete waxy substances. The wings of some male butterflies have scent glands, which attract females.

Considering its size, an insect has an extremely large and complex nervous system. The nerve centers of the brain, in the head, control the eyes, the antennae and the mouth parts. Double nerve cords lead from the brain back to other nerve centers, each of which controls an adjacent part or function.

The sense of touch of insects is centered chiefly in their antennae; but many species have abdominal cerci, or bristles, which also react to touch. Caterpillars and many other larvae and some adults are equipped with sensitive hairs and spines.

Organs of smell are often found on the antennae; they sometimes occur on the hind legs, or the feet or some of the mouth parts. The insect can detect sounds through organs located in various parts of the body. These auditory organs are on the antennae of the true flies and of some butterflies and wasps. Katydids and crickets "hear" through so called "ears" on their front legs; grasshoppers, through structures on each side of the abdomen, near the base. Many insects have organs or specialized structures for producing sound. These are never in

* An order of insects; it is described later in this article.

the mouth or throat, but somewhere on the abdomen or legs.

All insects develop from eggs, which vary greatly in size and shape. Some are microscopic; others are balls an eighth of an inch in diameter or slender, cone-shaped structures a quarter of an inch long. In most species the female deposits her fertilized eggs singly or in groups or masses in or near the particular food that the young will eat — manure or the body of an insect or other animal. In some aphids and flies, the eggs hatch within the mother's body. Certain ants, bees, wasps and aphids produce a generation of perfectly formed adults from unfertilized eggs; this is called parthenogenesis. A generation produced in this way usually alternates with a generation of insects from fertilized eggs.

The number of eggs laid by female insects ranges from a few to many thousands. In general, the solitary insects that provide good protection for their eggs deposit a comparatively small number. Those that drop their eggs in exposed places — on leaves, or twigs or in the water, where the mortality will be great — may lay several hundred. Among the social bees, termites, ants and wasps, where large colonies are necessary, the queen may deposit several thousand eggs in a single day. Her eggs and young are cared for and fed by a special caste of adults.

The young of the noncolonizing species are not attended in this way; as soon as they are hatched they are able to care for themselves. Since the eggs were deposited in or near the food supply, the baby insect starts at once to feed on its immediate environment. Where eggs have been laid in masses, the first to hatch are quite likely to devour the later arrivals.

In the process of growth, from egg to adult, most insects pass through a series of drastic changes, called metamorphosis. In the case of many insects, there are four stages in this development: (1) the egg stage, which ends when the young insect, called the larva, emerges from the egg; (2) the larval stage, in which the insect feeds greedily and sheds its exoskeleton several times; (3) the pupal stage, a period of inactivity in which the body of the insect undergoes striking changes; (4) the adult stage. If insects go through all four stages, the metamorphosis is said to be complete. It is called incomplete if the pupal stage is omitted.

Various special names are applied to the larvae of insects. The young of grasshoppers, mantids, crickets, cockroaches, cicadas and others are often called nymphs;

young dragonflies, stone flies and May flies, which live under water, are known as naiads; the name "caterpillar" is given to the young of moths and butterflies. Other names applied to larvae are "maggots," "grubs" and "worms."

In the case of many species, the larval stage is the longest period of the insect's life. The periodical cicada spends either thirteen or seventeen years as a nymph underground. Many May flies live from three to five years as naiads and only a few hours or a few days as adults. Some wood-boring beetles are said to spend from twenty-five to thirty years as grubs within a tree trunk.

The larvae of the insects with complete metamorphosis bear no resemblance to the adults, as witness the caterpillars that become moths and butterflies, the maggots that become flies, the wireworms that grow to be click beetles. After undergoing a number of molts, the larvae are ready to enter upon the pupal stage. Those that have been dwelling underground or within a plant or animal will stay quietly in their quarters. Some of those that have been living in the open will surround themselves during this critical stage with a protective case; the cocoon of the silk-spinning moths is the best-known example.

The pupa, as the insect is called in the quiescent stage, undergoes a startling transformation. This may be completed within a

Insects show a wide range in size. To give some idea of this range, we show here three typical insects — the rhinoceros beetle, the housefly and the flea hopper, enlarged to twice their actual size. It should be pointed out that the rhinoceros beetle is not by any means the largest insect; nor is the flea hopper the smallest one.

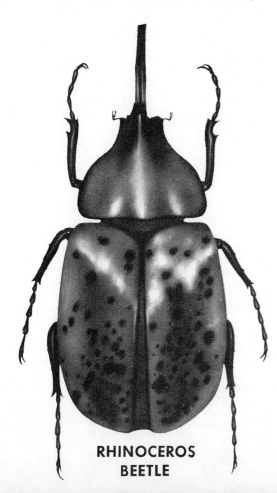

**RHINOCEROS
BEETLE**

HOUSEFLY

FLEA HOPPER

EGG, GREATLY ENLARGED

PUPA

LARVA (CATERPILLAR)

The metamorphosis of the monarch butterfly, shown above, is complete. It consists of four stages: the egg stage; the larval stage; the pupal stage; and the adult stage. The egg stage ends when the young insect, called a larva, emerges from the egg. In the larval stage, the larva, or caterpillar, feeds greedily, growing rapidly and molting. Finally it hangs head down from a supporting structure, such as a leaf or a twig, surrounds itself with a protective case and enters upon the pupal stage. As an inert pupa, the insect now undergoes some striking changes. Finally, the adult insect, or imago, emerges from the case and the pupal skin, and dries its wings.

few days, or it may take all winter. Finally, the adult insect breaks out of the pupal skin (and also the protective covering, if it had one) and dries its wings. The adult insect is called the imago; it will never change again nor will it ever increase in size.

The young of insects with incomplete metamorphosis, such as dragonflies, cicadas and grasshoppers, resemble the adult form somewhat but have no wings. Wing pads appear only after the larvae have molted several times. (Certain insects with incomplete metamorphosis, such as lice and camel crickets, have no wings as adults.) When the dragonfly naiad has reached its full growth, it comes out of the water in which it has dwelt onto some convenient plant stalk; the cicada nymph pushes out of the ground and climbs a few feet up a tree trunk; the grasshopper nymph stays where

it is. In each case, the hard exoskeleton splits down the back and a brand new creature emerges, with small damp wings. Soon the wings expand and dry, and the insect flies off.

Certain adult insects have just one important function—to reproduce; they mate, deposit eggs and die. A number of insects live only through the summer season; others survive the winter. Certain social insects may live for a few years.

Insects range in size from the $\frac{1}{125}$-inch-long fairy fly and the $\frac{1}{100}$-inch-long fungus beetle to the elephant beetle, which is as large as a man's fist, the stick insect, which may reach a length of thirteen inches, and the huge Atlas moth, with a wing expanse of ten and a half inches.

Even the individuals within a species may vary in color or size, sometimes enor-

408

EGGS

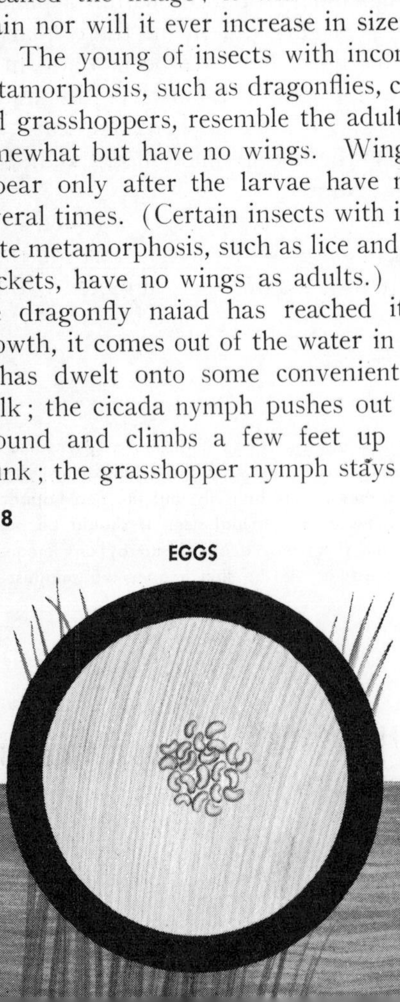

The metamorphosis of the dragon fly is incomplete, having only three stages: the egg, the nymph and the adult. The female lays eggs in or near water. The young insect that hatches from an egg is called a nymph, or naiad. It lives in the water, making its way along the bottom of the pond or stream and devouring insect larvae and other prey. It grows rapidly, molting several times. Finally, it crawls out of the water and onto a rock or plant stem. Undergoing a final molt, it becomes an adult dragonfly.

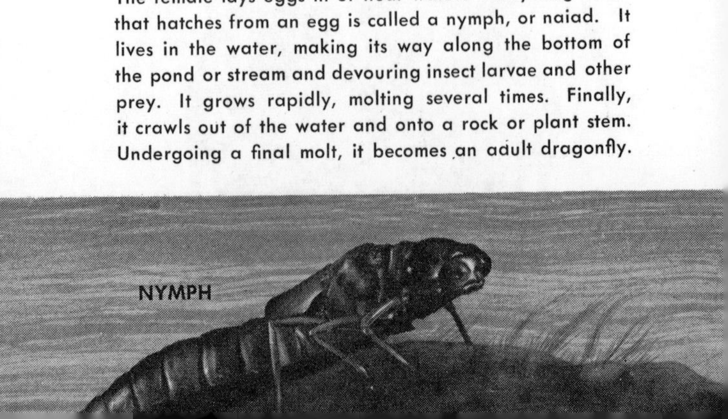

NYMPH

IMAGO (ADULT INSECT)

mously so. This phenomenon is called polymorphism; it occurs to a certain extent in most species. A mass of eggs of the tiger swallowtail butterfly may produce some females that are black and yellow like the males, and some that are dark gray and black. The spring, summer and fall broods of butterflies are likely to show differences in both color and size.

Variation within species reaches its maximum development among the social insects. All termites, all ants, a few families of wasps and a few families of bees live in highly organized communities, whose members are separated by physical differences into several types or castes, each with its own tasks. In general, each colony is founded by or around a queen mother, who is ordinarily much larger than the other members and who does nothing but lay eggs.

Besides the queen, there are the true males, the workers, the soldiers and, at times, the young queens. Generally, the ants have the most complicated social organization; they use several kinds of both workers and soldiers to maintain a colony. Bees and wasps get along with a simpler system of queen, males (or drones) and workers. Insect colonies range in size from hornet nests with a few dozen individuals to tropical ant and termite "cities," which have populations in the millions.

The great majority of insects are solitary; that is, they do not co-operate in forming nests, feeding the young or fighting, even though they may collect in masses, as the ladybirds do, or travel in great hordes as do the grasshoppers.

All insects have many enemies, big and small. Man wages unceasing warfare upon the species that infect him with disease, or that attack his crops and animals and goods or that annoy him with their stings and bites. Many species are the prey of other insects or of birds, snakes, spiders or fishes. Insects have developed a variety of defensive weapons against such enemies as these.

Stink glands, from which nauseating odors can be ejected, protect stinkbugs, bedbugs, many different beetles and some caterpillars from attack. Other insects discharge malodorous or poisonous fluids. The grasshopper covers his would-be captor with a brownish liquid called "tobacco juice"; the blister beetles, oil beetles and others discourage attack with caustic secretions. The hairs or bristles on many caterpillars irritate the skin, either through mere contact or because they carry poison from glands at their base.

It would be hard to imagine a method of camouflage that has not been used by some insect species or other. Ground insects and those that do not fly too far afield are likely to be colored in monochrome ("one-color") shades of brown, or green or gray, matching their backgrounds, or in mottled patterns that blend with sunlight and shadow. Others, whose activities might make them more noticeable, often wear brilliant or startling colors. This is supposed to warn that the insect carries stink fluids

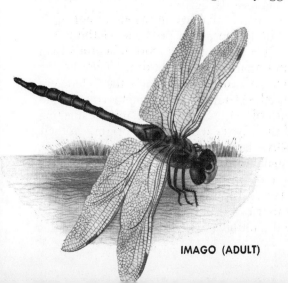

IMAGO (ADULT)

BUMBLEBEE   **ROBBER FLY**

MONARCH BUTTERFLY

VICEROY BUTTERFLY

Insect camouflage. The stingless robber fly looks like the bumblebee, which has
an effective stinging mechanism; hence it is shunned by enemies that otherwise
might devour it. The monarch butterfly is ill-tasting and hence is not molested
by birds and other prospective foes; the viceroy butterfly, which is palatable,
is shunned by the same foes because it looks so much like the monarch butterfly.

or is otherwise unappetizing. Sometimes
the conspicuous colorings of dangerous or
ill-tasting insects are mimicked by more
vulnerable species. The viceroy butterfly
apes the inedible monarch butterfly; the
harmless yellow and black syrphid fly resembles the wasp called the yellow jacket.

Since man is almost everywhere and
insects are almost everywhere on the land
areas of the earth, and since both eat all
kinds of food and use all kinds of materials
to build their homes, it is obvious that their
interests will often conflict. To be sure,
there are surprisingly few insect species
that are at any time dangerous to man's
health or possessions. It has been estimated
that less than one tenth of 1 per cent of all
the insects in the world have any harmful
relationship with man. But this relatively
small percentage takes a heavy toll in human health, lives and possessions.

Most of the insects that seriously affect man's health belong to the Diptera, or
true flies. Botflies, warble flies and some
other Diptera species are parasitic on man
and other mammals, spending all their larval life within the body of the host. The
common housefly spreads disease by walking first over germ-laden filth, and next
over the food or hands of the careless;
typhoid fever, dysentery and cholera have
been transmitted in this way. Insects that

feed on human or animal blood often carry
disease organisms in their salivary juices.
One kind of mosquito transmits malaria;
another, yellow fever; still others are vectors (carriers) of dengue, filariasis and
encephalitis. Tsetse flies carry the African
sleeping sickness; deer flies transmit tula-
remia. Fleas, lice and bedbugs carry typhus,
relapsing fever and one form of bubonic
plague.

Many insects irritate us without seriously disturbing our health. We are an-
noyed by the bites of mosquitoes, black flies,
horseflies and midges. The caterpillars of
the brown-tail moth are covered with bristles that sting like nettles. The stings of
bees, wasps and ants are often painful and
sometimes dangerous.

Insects that are injurious to our agricultural crops, food products, clothing and
wooden buildings are more numerous than
those that affect our health. They belong
to many orders, particularly the Coleoptera
(beetles) and the Lepidoptera (moths and
butterflies). Some of the most damaging
of these pests are of foreign origin. In their
native lands they do little or no damage,
usually because at home they have too many
or too formidable enemies to attain a destructive population. Brought to other
countries by accident, they are free to feed
and multiply on whatever crop is attractive

WALKING STICK

TREE HOPPER

Two more striking examples of insect camouflage. The walking stick, which may attain as much as a foot or two in length, looks so very much like a twig that it is almost impossible to recognize it as an insect until it starts to move. The small sucking insect known as the tree hopper is almost invisible, because of its coloration, against the background of the leaves and stems upon which it feeds.

to them. In the United States, the Hessian fly, the European corn borer, the codling moth, the gypsy moth, the brown-tail moth, the Mediterranean fruit fly and the Japanese beetle are prominent examples of insects that are relatively harmless at home.

Besides damaging crops by feeding on them, insects often transmit plant diseases. They may carry the spores of a destructive fungus on their feet or mouth parts from one plant to another; thus the engraver beetles carry the Dutch elm disease. They may harbor a plant virus through part of its development within their alimentary systems. Aphids, leafhoppers, and other plant-sucking insects transmit certain "blights" in this manner.

Man spends a great deal of time and money trying to defend himself from insects, and with only partial success. To keep out immigrant insects, of known destructiveness, governmental authorities establish quarantines; but their effectiveness is limited by the smallness and persistence of the incoming pests and the lawlessness, ignorance and carelessness of many people. Chemical warfare upon insect pests is waged with insecticides. Man also carries on biological warfare against the pests. The breeding places of the offending insects are destroyed. Patients suffering from diseases such as malaria and yellow fever are screened from insects that could transmit the diseases to other human victims. Entomologists (scientists who specialize in the study of insects) seek out the insect pests' natural enemies (which may be other insects, viruses, fungi or birds) and turn these enemies against the pests.

As we have pointed out, comparatively few species of insects are to be reckoned among our enemies. Certain species are directly beneficial to man. The honeybee supplies us with honey; the silkworm, with silk. One type of scale insect provides us with the dyestuff cochineal; another, with lac, from which the shellac of commerce is derived.

Insects benefit man indirectly in many ways. If they did not help to pollinate plants, we would be deprived of most of our fruit trees, our beans, peas and other legumes and thousands of other plants that are useful to us. Our fresh-water fish feed on insects; so do many of our game birds. Insects are also valuable as scavengers; they help to keep the earth reasonably unencumbered. It is true that they destroy some of our most cherished plants; but they also attack weeds. They are among our most effective allies in the war against insect pests. Above all, they play an important part in maintaining the balance of nature, upon which our very existence depends.

A survey of the world's insects

In classifying any living things, plant or animal, we put similar species in a single genus (plural: genera); similar genera, in a single family; similar families, in a single order; similar orders, in a single class. Insects form the class known as Insecta, which is composed of a number of orders. There has always been considerable disagreement among entomologists concerning the number, names and composition of these orders. For example, in some classifications, the order of the Orthoptera includes most or all of the groups that I have listed on this page as separate orders: the Grylloblattodea, the Blattaria, the Phasmida, the Mantodea and the Dermaptera.

Primitive insects of the first three orders

The first three orders are made up of primitive forms. They were probably the first insects to appear upon the earth and they now dwell in almost every land area. None of them have wings; the young differ from the adults chiefly in size.

Protura. The insects of this order were not recognized until 1907. They are whitish and from .5 millimeter to 2 millimeters (.02 to .08 inch) in size. They have no antennae, but use the first pair of legs as feelers. The number of abdominal segments increases with growth.

Thysanura: bristletails, silverfish, slickers. They range up to a half-inch in length. They have very long antennae and often three long tails, or cerci. Many of them look like small shrimps. Some are found in lichens, mosses and rotten wood; others, in books and under wallpaper. Some live in caves and are blind.

Collembola: springtails, snow fleas. Most species have a curved, taillike appendage that they use as a spring to propel themselves into the air. Some live in ant or termite nests and are blind. Most are dull-colored; but the snow-flea family (Poduridae), whose members often gather in masses on snow, has several brightly colored species.

Insects with incomplete metamorphosis

The insects of the orders from the Orthoptera through the Homoptera have incomplete metamorphosis; most have wings.

Orthoptera: locusts, grasshoppers, katydids, crickets, mole crickets. A large order of insects, most of them with hind legs developed for jumping. Locusts and grasshoppers sometimes migrate in hordes, devouring all vegetation as they pass. Mole crickets have powerful front feet, with which they dig their way underground.

Grylloblattodea: wingless, slender insects, usually less than an inch long and straw- or amber-colored. They were discovered in the present century.

Blattaria: cockroaches; mostly wide, flat insects with long legs. Not all have wings. A few species have spread all over the world, traveling with man. Cockroaches are scavengers, eating almost anything.

Phasmida: walking sticks, leaf insects. The bodies of walking sticks are modified to look like sticks or twigs. They are the longest of the insects, attaining a length of thirteen inches in Australia and New Zealand. The wings of the leaf insects closely resemble leaves in shape and color and even in veining; their legs are modified to look like leaf fragments. They are found in tropical Africa and in the East Indies. The leaf insects belong to the family Phyllidae.

Mantodea: the praying mantes, also known as preying mantes. These are big carnivorous insects. The wings are green or coppery in color; the front legs have been modified to seize and hold prey. They feed only on living creatures, usually insects. Females often devour their mates.

Dermaptera: earwigs. Small to medium-sized, brown or black insects, slightly resembling crickets. Their distinguishing feature is the pair of pincerlike forceps that adult insects carry at the tip of the abdomen. Earwigs are omnivorous, eating living and dead vegetation, insect larvae and each other. They were once thought to enter the human ear and bore into the brain.

Plecoptera: stone flies, salmon flies. Winged insects one-half to two and one-

INSECT
FARMERS,
SIGNALERS
AND BUILDERS

The social insects, including the ants and many of the bees and wasps, have a highly developed type of communal living. In each of their communities, the various activities that are carried on are destined for the good of the community as a whole rather than for the benefit of any individual living within it.

Among the most fascinating of these insect activities are herding and farming, signaling and building. In this color spread, we shall show some striking examples of each. We shall see certain ants "milking" herds of aphids, which they carefully protect from enemies; we shall see other ants preparing to grow crops of fungi, upon which they will later feed. We shall analyze the fascinating code of signals by which a bee arriving in a hive with a load of pollen can inform the other bees in the hive how far away the food source is and also in what direction it lies. (Only within the last decade or so have scientists learned the secret of the code.) Finally, we shall examine the building activities of certain wasps that construct their houses of paper; of others that build mud nests shaped like organ pipes; of still others that fashion nests consisting of beautifully rounded pots, complete with stoppers.

Ants "milking" their aphid herd. Aphids, or plant lice, are small insect pests, which secrete a sweetish liquid called honeydew from two small tubes near the tip of the abdomen. Upon being stroked gently by an ant's feelers, an aphid emits a drop of honeydew, which is lapped up by the ant. Ants that keep aphid herds often protect them from such aphid enemies as lady beetles and aphid lions. The ants of one species belonging to the genus *Lasius* store the eggs of the corn-root aphid in their underground nests. When the eggs hatch in the spring, the ants carry the little aphids to the roots of weeds, upon which they feed. As soon as corn is planted and sprouts, the ants move the aphids to the corn roots, which are the preferred food of this particular "cow" species. The aphids feed greedily on the corn roots, while the ants have their fill of honeydew.

The leaf-cutting ants, also known as parasol ants and fungus-growing ants (genus *Atta*) are skilled insect farmers. The workers snip off rounded pieces of leaves from appropriate trees. Then they make for the nest in a home-coming procession, each holding up a piece of leaf as if it were a parasol. The leaves are turned over to other workers, which chew them into a paste. This forms the "soil" on which the ants will grow a small fungus. The dung of certain caterpillars is spread over the "soil" as fertilizer. As the fungus grows, the ants keep snipping off the filaments of which the body of the plant consists. Finally, small white bodies, called bromatia, appear all over the fungus; it is these bodies that the ants eat. When a queen starts out on a mating flight, she carries a tiny pellet of fungus in a special pouch below her mouth. One of the first things she does after she has settled down in a new home is to plant the pellet in appropriate "soil."

The honeybee informs the other bees in the hive of the location of a food source by a series of signals, consisting of dance patterns. To indicate that the food is quite near at hand, it does a round dance on a vertical comb in the hive. It circles to the right and then to the left, again and again (A). This means that the food source is somewhere within a radius of a hundred yards. The bees that leave the hive in search of the food head in all directions but keep within a hundred yards of the hive.

If the food supply is more than a hundred yards distant, the bee does an abdomen-wagging dance (B). First, it makes a straight run up or down a comb, wagging its abdomen rapidly from side to side, and then circles to the left. Next, it makes another straight run, still wagging its abdomen, and circles to the right. The number of turns per minute that the bee makes in this dance tells how far away the food is: the fewer the number of turns per minute, the farther away the food is. Furthermore, the direction taken by the bee in making its straight run indicates in what direction the other bees are to go to find the food. The three drawings at the bottom of the page (C) show how this direction is indicated.

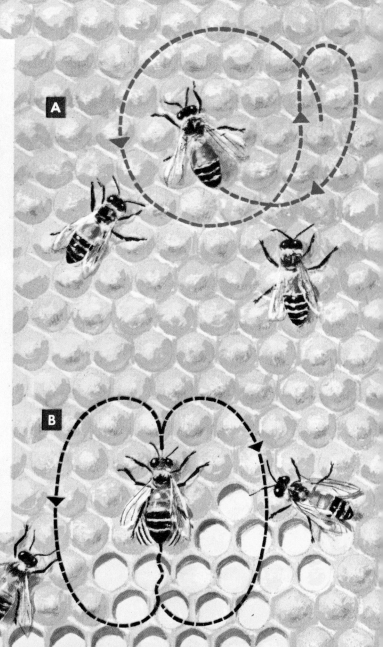

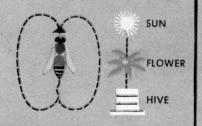

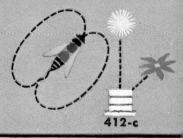

C   If the signaling bee heads directly upward during the straight part of its run, the food source is in the same direction as the sun.

SUN

FLOWER

HIVE

If the signaling bee heads directly downward during the straight part of its run, the food source is located directly away from the sun

If the bee heads upward and 45° to the right of vertical, this means that the food source is located at 45° to the right of the sun.

412-c

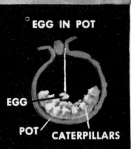

A

Wasps are accomplished builders. Papermaking wasps (A) construct their nests of paper; in fact, these insects were the first papermakers. They obtain wood fibers from dead trees or weathered posts or similar sources. Chewing the fiber and mixing it with their saliva, they form a pulp. The pulp is fashioned into the six-sided cells in which the young will be reared. When the pulp hardens, it makes a very tough paper. Some nests of the papermaking wasps, including the nests of bald-faced hornets and yellow jackets, are enclosed by several paper layers, with air spaces between layers.

The pipe-organ wasp (B) uses mud as its building material. It constructs a vertical tube of mud, with the opening at the lower end. The inner end of the tube is packed with food and provided with an egg; then it is sealed off. Another section is prepared in the same way, and this goes on until the tube is full. Then another tube is built beside the first one. The result is a series of tubes suggesting somewhat the pipes of an organ; hence the name of the insect.

B

The potter wasps build symmetrical pots out of mud on twigs. The pots have narrow necks and lips that flare out. The female wasp places paralyzed caterpillars in the completed nest. An egg is then suspended by a slender thread from the top, after which the opening of the pot is sealed. When the grub is hatched from the egg, it feeds on the caterpillars. Later, the grub becomes a pupa; the pupa develops into an imago, or adult insect, which bites its way out of the side of the nest.

EGG IN POT

EGG

POT   CATERPILLARS

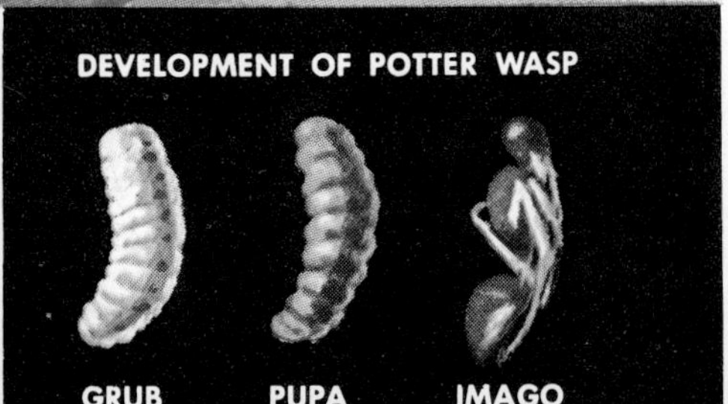

DEVELOPMENT OF POTTER WASP

GRUB   PUPA   IMAGO

half inches long, with soft, flattish bodies. They are usually dull brownish, greenish or yellowish, with long slender antennae and shorter tails, or cerci. Stone flies are found in rocky streams and deposit eggs in the water. The larvae live at the bottom of the streams; they eat other larvae and are themselves a food for fish.

Isoptera: termites, or white ants. Small, soft-bodied, pale-colored insects, living in colonies in wood and soil. Their complicated caste system includes winged, wingless and short-winged forms. Termites normally live in the soil or in dead trees and stumps; they also build their colonies in wooden foundations, buildings and fences. Tropical species construct elaborate nests, which may extend several feet above ground, or massive structures in the tree tops.

Embioptera: web-spinners. Small, slender insects with large heads and thread-like antennae. Males have two pairs of slender wings; females are wingless. They collect in large groups under small stones, debris and the tangled bases of grasses. During the spring rains, they build shining white webbed tunnels and awnings over the ground between their various retreats.

Corrodentia: psocids, book lice, bark lice. Very small, fragile insects; many are wingless. They live in straw, debris, fungi and cereal products. They eat the paste in wallpaper, the glue in books and the insects in museum collections.

Mallophaga: biting bird lice. Small, flattish, wingless insects, with short legs. They live on the hair, feathers and dried skin fragments of birds and mammals. Most of them move readily along the body of the host by means of claws; others cling to feathers or hairs with their jaws.

Anoplura: true lice, sucking lice. Minute, wingless insects, slender in form or oval or crablike. Their mouth parts are modified to pierce the skin of the host and suck the blood; their legs are fitted with claws for clinging to hairs. True lice are found wherever there are mammals. Those infesting man often carry and transmit such diseases as typhus and relapsing fever.

Ephemerida: May flies. Small to medium-sized, slender, soft-bodied insects. They usually have two pairs of wings, the hind pair being much smaller than the front pair. The adults never eat; they have weakly developed or no mouth parts. The larvae live in the water, emerging when they are ready to become adults. Some live only a few hours as adults; certain species may live as long as a week or two.

Odonata: damsel flies, dragonflies. Medium to large, slender insects, with two pairs of long, narrow, shining wings. They have large, mobile heads and very large, compound eyes. The dragonflies are often very large; they are able to catch most other insects on the wing. Damsel flies are smaller, more fragile and slower in flight. The Odonata spend their immature life of one to five years under water.

Thysanoptera: thrips. Minute, slender insects with sucking mouth parts, found on vegetation, particularly flowers, throughout the temperate and subtropical world. Many thrips transmit virus and fungus diseases to plants. They reproduce rapidly; there may be as many as nine generations in one year.

Hemiptera: true bugs, including stink-bugs, kissing bugs, bedbugs, lace bugs, pirate bugs, water striders, water scorpions, electric-light bugs (water bugs), back swimmers, water boatmen. Most true bugs have two pairs of wings; the base of the fore wings is hard and leathery, while the outer part is membranous. The Hemiptera range in size from the minute pirate bugs to the four-inch electric-light bugs. Most bugs are plant feeders. Some of them prey on insects and other animals: the assassin bugs capture bees and the pirate bugs destroy mites, thrips and aphids. The bedbugs are parasitic on man, birds and bats. There are many aquatic bugs.

Homoptera: cicadas, tree hoppers, spittle bugs, leafhoppers, psyllids, white flies, aphids (plant lice), scale insects, mealy bugs, lac insects, cochineal insects. It is very difficult to characterize these insects as a group. They vary widely in shape. The cicada looks vaguely like a cricket; certain scale insects suggest minute oyster shells, while others are like bits of fluff. The life histories of the Homoptera are just as diverse.

Insects with
complete metamorphosis

All the rest of the insect orders have complete metamorphosis, passing through four stages: eggs, larvae, pupae and adults.

Megaloptera: dobson flies, humpbacked flies. Adults are medium to large, with biting mouth parts, slender antennae and two pairs of wings, held rooflike or flat over the body. The larvae of the Megaloptera are aquatic.

Neuroptera: nerve-winged insects, lacewings, false mantids. Minute to medium-sized, fragile insects with biting mouth parts, large compound eyes, long, slender legs and two pairs of large, many-veined wings. In one family (Mantispidae) the adults resemble praying mantes. The larvae of one family are called ant lions because they prey on ants; they rest, half-buried at the bottom of small sandy pits, waiting for ants to tumble in. Neuroptera larvae spin silk cocoons in secluded places and here they pupate.

Mecoptera: scorpion flies. Small to medium-sized, extremely slender insects, with long heads and biting mouth parts. Some have two pairs of long, narrow wings; others have none. Scorpion-fly larvae are wormlike. Both larvae and adults are carnivorous.

Trichoptera: caddis flies, water moths. Small or medium-sized insects, with long, slender antennae, large compound eyes, husky legs and two pairs of wings lightly covered with hairs and scales. The larvae are aquatic, living in movable cases, which they construct out of bits of wood or pebbles, held together by silk. The adults live near water. Caddis worms are valued highly for bait.

Lepidoptera: moths, butterflies, skippers. Vary greatly in size; characterized by large wings and flat, overlapping scale-like hairs that cover the wings and bodies. The head is relatively small, the eyes are large. The antennae are slender and hooked or knobbed in the butterflies, and finely tapered or feathery in the moths. Butterflies are active during the day; most moths are active at night. Skippers are a kind of connecting link between the moths and butterflies. The larvae of the Lepidoptera are called caterpillars; they may be smooth, or hairy or spiny. The pupae of many species are protected by silken cocoons.

Coleoptera: beetles, weevils. A very large order of minute to large insects. The exoskeleton is tough and leathery; the fore wings, called elytra, are thick, stiff and shieldlike. The underwings are membranous; when in repose, they are folded under the elytra. The larvae are grublike. Several families of beetles, including the diving and whirligig varieties, are aquatic. Some beetles damage trees, crops, processed foods and woolens; others eat harmful insects, such as aphids and scales. Many of the beetles are scavengers.

Hymenoptera: ants, bees, wasps, gall-flies, chalcid flies, sawflies, braconids, ichneumons. Minute to medium-sized insects with mouth parts adapted for biting, or lapping or sucking. They are wingless, or have two pairs of relatively small wings, the fore pair being much larger usually than the hind pair. The females have a conspicuous ovipositor. This order contains all the social insects except the termites.

Diptera: flies, gnats, midges, mosquitoes and others. Minute to medium-sized insects, with sucking, piercing, lapping or functionless mouth parts. The hind wings are represented by a pair of small stumps, called halteres. There are some wingless species. The larvae of certain species live in decaying animal or vegetable matter and are called maggots; the larvae of mosquitoes and of some gnats and midges are aquatic. Some wingless and eyeless fly species live in the nests of ants or termites or in bee hives.

Siphonaptera: fleas, chigoes. Minute to small, wingless, vertically flattened, crawling and jumping insects, with piercing and sucking mouth parts. The head is small; the legs are long and stout. The adults live on the blood of birds and mammals. The wormlike, eyeless and legless larvae have biting mouth parts and feed on animal and vegetable debris. Some fleas infest man and his animals.

See also Vol. 10, p. 275: "Insects."

PLANTS AS STOREHOUSES

Reserve Materials Accumulated in
Seeds, Roots and Tubers

THE area from which the higher plants draw their food supply is limited, since these plants cannot move from one place to another. Food must be stored within the plant, therefore, to meet all the needs of the mature plant, as well as those of the embryo. The embryo must be nourished by such stored food during the crucial period of its early growth.

Within the seed coat, the embryo is surrounded by endosperm, or food-storage tissue. In many plants the embryonic leaves called cotyledons serve to absorb, digest and store food elements derived from the endosperm. The cotyledons form part of the embryo; there is also a radicle that will grow downward to become a root and the primary bud, or plumule, that will grow upward to become a true stem with green leaves. As long as the radicle and the plumule are enclosed within the seed coat, neither of them can perform any of the necessary functions of nourishment. It is the cotyledon leaf that must absorb, digest and store food contained in the endosperm that surrounds the embryo. In certain plants such as beans, peas, peanuts and pumpkins, the food from the endosperm is absorbed by the embryo before the seed leaves the parent plant. In other varieties such as corn, wheat and oats, the absorption of food does not take place until after the seed has been planted and can obtain water. Seeds of this type usually germinate slowly, because the embryo must absorb nourishment before beginning its growth. On the other hand, seeds of the former kind are able to germinate quickly, since the transfer of food has already taken place. When these seeds are mature, they consist only of embryos and seed coats. The vigorous stem is soon able to perform its functions.

The cotyledon food-producing tissues vary according to the type of plant. All angiosperms, or fruit and flower-bearing plants, may be classified as dicotyledons or as monocotyledons. In the first kind, two cotyledon leaves are enclosed within the seed coat, while the flower parts of the mature plant are in fours or fives and the outer leaves are net-veined. This group includes elms, maples, poplars, potatoes, roses and sunflowers — to mention a few. In the monocotyledon variety, one cotyledon leaf is present in the embryo, while the flower parts are in threes and the outer leaves are parallel-veined. Among this class are corn, oats, wheat, iris, daffodils and lilies. To distinguish between the two groups, the plant stem should be cut transversely, revealing the lateral cables which act as the plant's plumbing system and by means of which water travels up to the leaf and food travels down to the root. If these cables are bunched, the plant is a dicotyledon. If they are scattered, the plant is a monocotyledon.

As we have pointed out, the cotyledons make available the carbohydrates, fats and proteides that have been stored up in the endosperm for the embryo. When the seed germinates, the cotyledons sometimes become foliage for the newborn plant. In certain plants, such as castor beans, they persist for several weeks; they become green and capable of carrying on photosynthesis. The cotyledons of garden beans wither and fall off a few days after germination of the seed. In the case of some plants, the cotyledons, or seed leaves, remain underground as fleshy lobes.

THE WORLD'S GRANARY IN A GRAIN

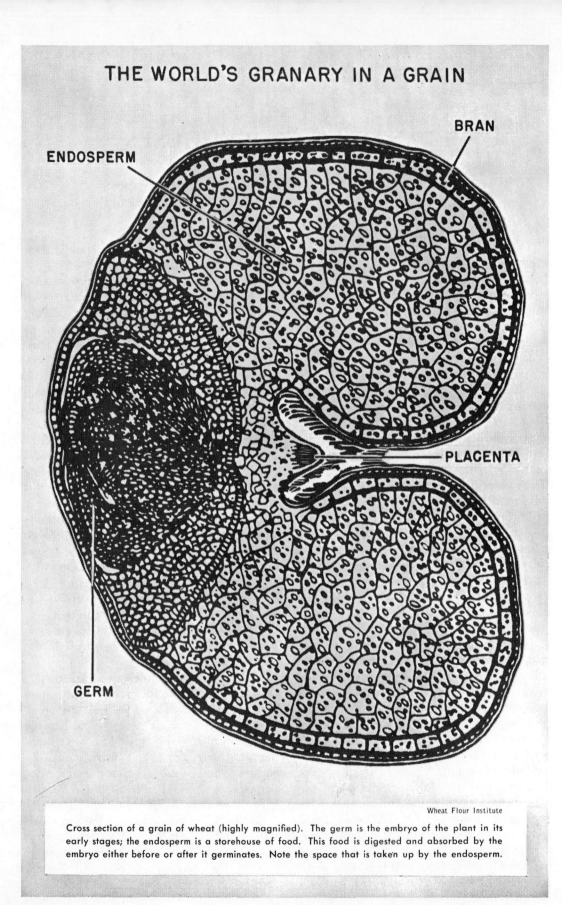

ENDOSPERM

BRAN

PLACENTA

GERM

Wheat Flour Institute

Cross section of a grain of wheat (highly magnified). The germ is the embryo of the plant in its early stages; the endosperm is a storehouse of food. This food is digested and absorbed by the embryo either before or after it germinates. Note the space that is taken up by the endosperm.

Let us return now to the endosperm in which food is stored for the embryo. This food serves two main purposes. It supplies the energy that the plant requires for the essential activities of life; it makes available the materials that the plant uses in the manufacture of its protoplasm. There are three kinds of foods in the endosperm: carbohydrates, fats and proteins. Carbohydrates and fats are fuel foods, which provide energy. Protein serves to a limited extent as a fuel but it is used mainly to build up protoplasm.

Energy released
through oxidation

Fuel foods release energy as the chemical process of oxidation — that is, combination with oxygen — takes place in plant cells. Oxygen drawn in from the air in the act of respiration (for plants breathe just as truly as animals do), is combined chemically with the carbon and hydrogen of food. The products of the reaction are carbon dioxide and water vapor, which are later given up during breathing. The release of energy as this all-important chemical reaction takes place suffices for all the needs of the plant.

The basic
food elements

Carbon, hydrogen and oxygen are basic elements in all three of the foods we mentioned above — carbohydrates, fats and proteins. As a matter of fact, carbohydrates and fats contain only carbon, hydrogen and oxygen. The name "carbohydrate" is derived from these three elements. "Carbo" stands for carbon *; the word "hydrate" (from the Greek *hydro,* meaning water) indicates the presence of the two elements that make up the water molecule — hydrogen and oxygen. Carbohydrates exist in several forms: sugars, cellulose and starches.

There are several kinds of sugars in plants. The sugar glucose, also known as grape sugar, has 6 atoms of oxygen, 12 atoms of hydrogen and 6 atoms of carbon

* Actually *carbo* is the Latin word for coal. Coal is made up mostly of carbon; the carbon percentage differs according to the kind of coal.

in its molecule. A sugar closely resembling glucose is fructose, whose molecule has the same number of carbon, hydrogen and oxygen atoms. It differs slightly from glucose; the atoms are arranged in a somewhat different geometric pattern.

Another sugar, sucrose (cane or beet sugar) has 12 atoms of carbon, 22 atoms of hydrogen and 11 atoms of oxygen in its molecule. Sucrose is the sugar we use to sweeten our coffee. In the molecule of maltose, we find the same number of carbon, hydrogen and oxygen atoms, but in a different geometric pattern. Thus, sucrose and maltose are related in the same way as glucose and fructose.

The molecules of the starches and cellulose are quite complex, containing many atoms. In both starch and cellulose, the atoms of carbon, hydrogen and oxygen are combined in the proportion of 6 to 10 to 5. Although the actual number of atoms varies, the proportion remains the same.

Fats have a
high energy content

The foods called fats release more energy than carbohydrates. The carbon and hydrogen content in a particular food determines its energy content. Since the plant gets its oxygen from the air, the presence of oxygen in the food is not really necessary. Therefore, a food with a higher proportion of carbon and hydrogen and a lower one of oxygen is much more valuable as a source of energy. Fats provide just such a food. To see how much more carbon and hydrogen atoms there are proportionately in each fat molecule, consider two typical fats, stearin and palmitin. The stearin molecule has 57 atoms of carbon, 110 atoms of hydrogen and only 6 atoms of oxygen. The molecule of palmitin also has only 6 atoms of oxygen; it has 51 atoms of carbon and 98 atoms of hydrogen. Fats occur in seeds chiefly in the form of oils, such as olive and linseed oil.

Proteins, as we have seen, serve chiefly to build protoplasm. The plant synthesizes proteins from elements found in the soil and the air and then assimilates them into its protoplasm. Proteins, like carbohydrates and fats, contain carbon, hydrogen and oxygen. In addition, they always contain nitrogen atoms and sometimes sulfur and phosphorus. Protein molecules are by far the most complex of all; they often consist of many thousands of atoms. The essential building blocks of proteins are the compounds known as amino acids and containing atoms of carbon, oxygen and hydrogen. (See Index, under Amino acids.) Many amino acids are combined to form the giant protein molecules found in protoplasm.

Animals are
dependent on plants

Plants are the only living things that can manufacture amino acids; animals cannot. Animals can rearrange protein to form their own protoplasm, but the basic amino acids must be provided for them by plants. Some animals eat plants and obtain their amino acids in that way; others devour other animals that have eaten plants. Thus the animal world is completely dependent on plants, for without them, they could not produce their protoplasm. For this reason, plants are sometimes called the connecting links between the inorganic world and the animal world.

Proteins are stored in the cells of the endosperm in little packages or bodies known as aleurone grains. Large numbers of these bodies may be found in the endosperm of such grains as corn and wheat and in other types of seeds such as beans, peas, soybeans and coffee.

Transportation and
germination of the seed

The embryo within the seed, then, has ample stores of food to sustain it after the seed is borne from the parent plant. In the article Seed and Fruit Dispersal, in Volume 5, we tell how the seed is transported by wind, water, animals or other agencies to a place where it comes to rest. If conditions are favorable, the seed will germinate and grow in the particular spot to which it has been carried.

Most seeds require a dormant period, or period of rest, before they germinate.

This period usually carries the seed through the winter so that it may begin its growth at the most favorable time of the year. The dormancy is usually caused by the fact that the seed coat is too tough for the oxygen and water, necessary for germination, to penetrate. However, after a winter of exposure to the elements, the seed coat becomes soft enough so that the seed can readily germinate.

The condition
of quiescence

There is also a condition known as quiescence in which a seed will not germinate. This is different from dormancy in that the seed appears to remain dormant long after it normally would have emerged from dormancy and germinated. Quiescence is caused by outside conditions which are unfavorable to germination. Extended cold or dry periods in the spring will cause a seed to go into quiescence. It will remain in this state until conditions become favorable for its germination. The seed can remain viable — that is, capable of development and growth — only for a limited period of time. This period varies from plant to plant.

Differences in the
time of germination

In the spring, water and oxygen enter through the newly softened seed coat and germination begins. Some seeds have already absorbed food from their storehouse before this time. Therefore they have already built up a store of energy for growth and they begin their development immediately. Beans, peas, peanuts and pumpkins are outstanding examples of this type. Others do not begin to use their endosperm until the spring. Plants of this kind, including corn, wheat and oats, generally take longer to germinate.

During the dormant period, the water content of the seed often drops to 4 or 5 per cent. The seed absorbs a great deal of water after germination begins. This serves several purposes. It further softens the seed coat so that the root and stem may grow out of it. The water also makes it possible for the physiological processes in the plant to go on. The food that is stored in the endosperm is in insoluble form. (See Index, under Solubility.) The cotyledon of the seed converts this food into a form that is soluble in water; the water then carries it throughout the embryo.

Soon the radicle, also called the hypocotyl, protrudes through the split in the seed coat and the first roots develop. These will aid in the absorbing of water necessary for the future growth of the plant. The plumule, or epicotyl, moves upward out of the seed coat. Soon it will go above the ground where it will develop leaves and begin to make its own food through the process of photosynthesis. (See Index, under Photosynthesis.) After that the plant is well on its way to maturity and self-sufficiency.

During the entire period of germination the plant is unable to manufacture its own food; it is entirely dependent upon the food contained in its endosperm storehouse. This food cannot be used by the plant until it has been digested.

The process of digestion

The digestion of food involves the breakdown of complex molecules into simple ones which can be easily utilized by the plant. This molecular breakdown is basically a chemical reaction. Scientists have brought about this reaction in the laboratory by using strong heat and powerful acids. In plants, the same end result — the breakdown of molecules — is achieved by means of certain chemical substances called enzymes. They serve as catalysts (see Index); they bring about the desired chemical reaction, remaining unchanged themselves and not being used up in any degree. A very small amount of enzymes can effect the breakdown of large amounts of carbohydrates and fats. It is not completely understood how enzymes work, but it is known that their presence is required in the reaction.

Enzymes are very specific as to just what substances they will affect. Because of this, the plant has almost as many enzymes as it has different kinds of food, for each enzyme will rarely digest more than one type of food. The enzymes that digest carbohydrates are known as carbohydrases. Amylase, or diastase, converts starch and dextrins to maltose. The maltose is then changed to glucose by the enzyme called maltase. Another sugar, known as sucrose, is changed into glucose by the enzyme sucrase. Cellulose changes to cellobiose under the influence of cellulase. Cellobiose in turn goes to glucose when acted on by cellobiase. Fats are acted on by lipases; proteins, by proteinases, and so on.

At first glance, the use of enzymes in digestion might seem to be a useless complication. Since the plant synthesizes its own carbohydrates, fats and proteins, why are these foods not manufactured in a form that could be made available without enzymes? If we consider the matter carefully, however, we find that the actual arrangement is a very useful one. It is distinctly advantageous to the plant to have its food in the form of complex molecules. Since these are highly concentrated, the plant can store much more food substance than would otherwise be possible. Enzymes are active agents in the storing process too. These amazing substances work both ways. They break the foods down when the plant needs them; they are also responsible for the building up of the molecules when the plant is storing food for future use.

Food storage in mature plants

The endosperm of seeds is not the only storehouse of food for plants. Food must also be stored in mature plants, even after they are able to manufacture their own carbohydrates, fats and proteins. There are several reasons why this is so.

The food supply of a plant varies during different parts of the year. The plant can make its own food only when there is available material for this purpose. Animals can migrate or look for food elsewhere; the plant cannot. It is rooted in one place and is dependent upon existing conditions in that place. The plant cannot make food without water and sunshine. During a period of drought, food production in the plant ceases because of lack of water. At night, the plant can make no food because there is no sunshine.

Annuals, biennials and perennials

Some plants, known as annuals, live only for one growing season. Many plants, however, live for two seasons (biennials) or for more than two seasons (perennials). These plants must store food for the periods between growing seasons.*

The mature plant, therefore, stores food in order to tide it over periods of nonproduction. The food is in compact form, as is the food in the endosperm of the seed. It may take the form of sugars, oils or starches.

A good example of sugar storage in the mature plant is offered by the familiar sugar cane. Large quantities of sugar in the form of sucrose are stored in the stem of this plant. Foods in the form of oils are stored in other plants, including cotton, flax and olives.

Roots as storehouses

The food stored in mature plants is most often in the form of starch, which is found in various parts of the plant. Biennials tend to store up starch in their roots. Such vegetables as carrots, beets and turnips are roots of biennial plants; they represent the food that the plant has accumulated for its own consumption. These roots, in addition to their starch content, also contain appreciable amounts of sugar. This accounts for the sweet taste of the carrot. Biennials such as those we have just named store up large quantities of food in their roots, which become fleshy and bulky. Some plants have been known to grow large-sized underground roots, which may weigh as much as fifty pounds each.

* In some cases there are no sharply defined growing seasons. Tropical plants may grow more or less steadily throughout the year.

In their second and final year of life, biennial plants live off the stored food accumulated during the first year while they concentrate their efforts on producing seeds for reproduction purposes. If we allow a carrot to remain in the soil after its first year of growth, we note that in the second year, instead of growing larger, the root actually shrinks and becomes shriveled up. This is because it is utilizing the food that it had produced during the first year of the plant

Bulbs store food between their layers

Another place that the plant may store its starch is between various layers. The onion is an excellent example. If one pulls off the skins of an onion one by one, he can see the soft, pulpy mass between them. This is true of all bulb-type plants. Other plants store quantities of starch in their stems. A rather unusual example of this is the sago palm. Under an outer covering of hard, dense wood is a mass of spongy material — the starch.

Food storage in tubers

Certain plants store starch in tubers. A tuber is really a swelling in an underground stem of a plant — a swelling in which starch accumulates in great amounts. A good example of a tuber is the vegetable called the Irish potato, which contains a large mass of stored starch. (The edible portion of the sweet potato, however, is the root of the plant.) The tuber has an additional function; its "eye" is actually the seed of the plant. The flesh of the tuber becomes the endosperm of the seed if the tuber is left in the soil. The sprouts utilize the food that has been stored so copiously in the tuber.

When we dine, then, on vegetables such as carrots, turnips and potatoes, and sweeten our beverages with sugar derived from sugar-cane stems, we are really partaking of foods that had been stored up for the use of the plants. These foods form a valuable part of the human diet.

See also Vol. 10, p. 272: "General Works."

LIVING ELECTRIC BATTERIES

Bioelectricity—the Electrical Activity of Living Matter

BY HELEN MERRICK

TELL a friend that his body is seething with electrical activity and he will probably smile in disbelief. For the word electricity generally calls to mind the house current that operates radios and washing machines or the terrific power of lightning strokes. But the flow of electric current and the flash of lightning are only two phases of a broad term, applying to numberless displays of force and energy. Some of these are mighty, others insignificant; some have to do with nonliving materials, others with life processes. All are based on the properties of certain atomic particles, which we shall discuss later in the chapter.

The electrical impulses in living things can be detected in various ways. Our own bodies can be made to generate a feeble electric current under certain circumstances. If two electrodes are placed in contact with the body at appropriate places and connected with a copper wire or other conductor outside the body, current will flow through the conductor — current whose pattern and strength can be accurately analyzed. Electrical activity in living things is called bioelectricity. (*Bios* is the Greek word for life.) Chemists, physicists and biologists have joined forces to investigate this fascinating field.

The first man, perhaps, to become aware of the electrical forces at work in the tissues of animals was the Italian physiologist Luigi Galvani (1737–98). Quite by accident he discovered that when a machine that produced static electricity was in operation, it brought about muscular contraction in the legs of freshly killed frogs. Later he found that when the frogs were hung on an iron railing by means of copper hooks, the muscles of their legs twitched. He came to the conclusion that this reaction was due to what he called "animal electricity." Galvani's ideas concerning this striking phenomenon were quite erroneous.

Influenced by the growing interest in electricity in the first half of the nineteenth century, scientists eagerly investigated the electrical activity of living things. In 1843 the German Emil Du Bois-Reymond discovered that injured nerve tissue is negative electrically compared to healthy tissue. Unfortunately he and the other investigators of the period were handicapped because their instruments were not nearly sensitive enough to analyze accurately the minute electric currents that were involved.

Early in the twentieth century Willem Einthoven, a Dutch scientist, contributed what is called a string galvanometer to the study of bioelectricity. The design of the instrument is based on the principle that a wire is magnetized when an electric current passes through it. The "string" in this apparatus is a very fine metal wire, which is stretched between the poles of a powerful horseshoe magnet. When a current flows through the string, it is pulled toward one of the poles. Strong lights are placed so that the string casts a shadow, which is magnified by a microscope and then thrown on either a screen or a moving photographic plate. Thus the record of a very weak current may be made. The string galvanometer is the basis of the electrocardiograph, by which the electrical impulses that accompany the beat of the heart are recorded. We shall discuss the electrocardiograph later on.

Another boon of tremendous importance in the study of bioelectricity was the invention of the modern vacuum, or electron, tube, which can amplify a weak current enormously. The vacuum tube is the heart of many bioelectric measuring instruments. The development of extraordinarily tiny electrodes has also helped researchers in bioelectricity.

All of these instruments measure the effects of unlike electric charges in the human body. What produces these charges in the first place? Our most useful starting point is the modern theory of atomic structure. According to this theory the atom has a nucleus, or core, made up of protons (each carrying a positive charge of electricity) and, in most cases, neutrons (which have no charge), packed tightly together. Whirling around the nucleus are one or more electrons (which carry negative charges), each moving in a distinct path. The electrons that maintain the same average distance from the nucleus are said to occupy the same shell. Some atoms have but a single shell; others have as many as seven.

Only the electrons in the outer shell of atoms are involved in chemical reactions, in which atoms combine with each other. They combine in several different ways. In some cases the atoms are joined together in a compound through electrical, or, as scientists would say, electrostatic, attraction. Ordinary salt (sodium chloride, NaCl) furnishes a good example of this kind of bond.

An atom of chlorine has seven electrons in its outer shell and has room for just one more; it is particularly likely to snap up any stray electron and thus fill up its quota of outer-shell electrons. On the other hand the sodium atom has only one electron in its outer shell, and this is easily lost. Consequently, when a chlorine atom reacts with a sodium atom, the chlorine atom captures the lone electron in the outer shell of the sodium atom.

Normally the chlorine atom has 17 protons (positive charges) and 17 electrons (negative charges), and therefore is neutral electrically. Once it has acquired an additional electron it has an excess negative charge of 1, which is indicated by a minus sign, thus: Cl^-. The sodium atom has 11 negative charges and 11 positive charges to begin with. When it loses an electron, it still has 11 positive charges but only 10 negative charges; it therefore acquires a single excess positive charge, indicated by a $+$ sign, thus: Na^+. Atoms (and compounds, too) that acquire an electrical charge, either positive or negative, are called ions.

The newly formed chlorine ions and sodium ions, having opposite electrical charges, are attracted to one another; they form a definite pattern in a sort of lattice called a crystal. (Below is shown a diagram of a crystal of common salt.) Since there are about as many sodium ions as chlorine ions in a salt crystal, the positive and negative charges balance each other, and as a consequence the crystal as a whole is neutral electrically.

But something strange happens to the salt crystal when it is dissolved in water. As they go into solution the ions in the crystal are separated from one another. Instead of being bound together through the force of electrostatic attraction, they become free ions moving every which way in the liquid. The creation of free ions of this kind is called ionization. Various substances, in solid, liquid and gaseous form undergo ionization. Water itself, though it is the most effective of all solvents, ionizes almost not at all; it has been estimated

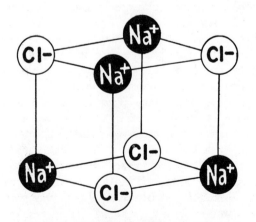

How the chlorine and sodium ions of salt are bound in a crystal lattice.

that only one molecule in every 555,000,-000 is broken up into ions.

Neither water nor common salt in its crystalline, or solid, form can conduct electricity to any appreciable extent; they are good insulators. But when the salt is dissolved in water and is ionized, the solution conducts electricity very well indeed. Any substance which, like common salt, becomes a conductor of electricity when it ionizes in water or some other liquid is called an electrolyte.

There are three kinds of electrolytes — acids, bases and salts. Acids — hydrochloric acid, sulfuric acid, acetic acid and the rest — all contain hydrogen. When an acid is dissolved in water, it yields positive hydrogen ions (H^+). It was formerly believed that these ions remained unchanged in solution. We now realize, however, that the newly created hydrogen ions combine with water molecules (H_2O) to form what are known as hydronium ions (H_3O^+). In chemical literature the hydronium ion is still called the hydrogen ion, indicated by the symbol H^+, and we shall so refer to it in the rest of this chapter. The greater the concentration of H^+ in a solution, the stronger the acid.

Bases — substances like caustic soda (sodium hydroxide), ammonium hydroxide and potassium hydroxide — always contain hydrogen and oxygen; when dissolved in water they yield negative ions, made up of oxygen and hydrogen bound together. These ions, called hydroxyls, have the symbol OH^-. The greater the concentration of OH^- in a given solution, the stronger the base is.

When an acid reacts with a base, they yield water and a salt. We may define a salt, therefore, as any substance besides water that results from the union of an acid and a base. Another definition of a salt is that it is a substance that does not produce either H^+ or OH^- when it ionizes. Sodium chloride, or common salt, is only one of many salts found in the home or used in industry; among the others are Epsom salts (magnesium sulfate), sal ammoniac (ammonium chloride) and potash alum (potassium aluminum sulfate).

The electric charges produced when electrolytes ionize are responsible for a vast number of chemical and physical phenomena. It is because of ionization that dry cells and storage batteries alike can generate electric current; the important industrial process of electrolysis is also based upon the activity of ions in solution. But we are particularly interested in this chapter in the effects of ionization in the body.

For one thing, ions are much more highly reactive than the original elements or compounds from which they are derived; they account for a vast number of essential chemical reactions in the body. Fortunately for us, our bodies abound in electrolytes — acids, bases and salts — and these substances can be readily ionized because bodily tissues are bathed in water, the most effective of all solvents. Much

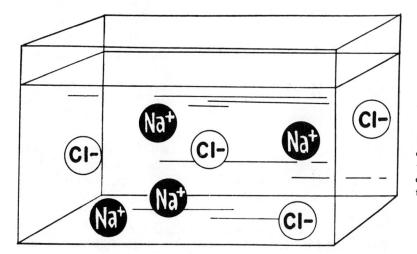

If the ions of a salt crystal go into solution, they are separated from one another; they become free ions.

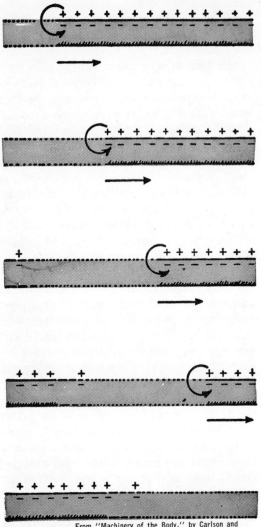

Transmission of an impulse along a nerve fiber, in five stages. As the membrane is penetrated (dotted area), positive and negative ions
come together and neutralize one another. Ions
from the adjoining section now make their way
through the neutral gap; another area becomes
permeable. Thus the impulse makes its way.

of the fluid in the cells — a large part of
the cells' content — is essentially water.

All living tissue contains hydrogen,
and the hydrogen ion (H^+) is necessary
for such activities as muscle contraction,
nerve impulses, digestion and respiration.
Measuring the H^+ content of electrolytic
solutions is standard procedure in much of
the work of the chemist and the physiologist. Here the symbol pH crops up. To
understand it, let us study pure water.

Though water ionizes very, very
slightly, it does contain .0000001 (or
1/10,000,000) gram of H^+ in one liter.
(One ounce equals 28.35 grams; a liter is
about a quart.) This also may be written as
10^{-7}. The minus 7 in this symbol is
called an exponent. The minus sign tells
us that our figure 1 is at the right of the
decimal point; the 7 tells us that it is seven
places to the right.

As pure water is practically neutral,
10^{-7} is taken as the dividing line between
acid and base solutions. To help make
his figuring easier, the scientist discards
everything but the exponent and adds the
symbol pH; it stands simply for "hydro-
gen-ion exponent" or acid-base balance.

The values of pH run from 0 to 14.
Less than 7 indicates an acid solution;
more than 7, a basic solution, also called
an alkaline solution. It should be noted
that a solution of, say, pH 5 (.00001) is
ten times as acid as one of pH 6 (.000001).
A solution of pH 11 (.00000000001) is
1,000 times as alkaline as one of pH 8
(.00000001). Normal human blood is
slightly on the alkaline side, with a pH of
7.35; normal saliva is slightly acid, with a
pH of 6.9.

In the human body, life seems to be
possible only within a very narrow pH
range. Yet acids and bases are constantly
being produced in various processes.
Some, of course, pass out as wastes. Nevertheless, excess amounts get into such
fluids as the blood. To offset their effects,
systems of buffers are present; they are so
called because they take up the shock of
the additional H^+ or OH^-. A buffer system consists of two parts — a weak acid
and a salt derived from that acid. Tissues
are so extremely sensitive to a change in pH
that the buffer is instantly fired into a chemical reaction by which the excess H^+ or
OH^- is removed.

From the fact that living cells are
bathed in electrolytic solutions, in which
ions are constantly being formed, it is
hardly surprising to find that the surfaces
of practically all cells have electric charges.
In fact, it was observed as long ago as
1860 that when an electric current is sent

through a suspension of living cells, they migrate toward the anode, the positive pole. So at least the cells used in this experiment apparently had a negative charge on the surface.

Most cells, of course, are much too tiny to be handled — even if they could be handled without killing them. Nevertheless, there are a few kinds of cells, such as the grape-size one of the giant squid, with which it is possible to measure the charges.

Cell surfaces are usually called plasma membranes. They may be actual membranes or very thin films, though in many cases no cell wall is visible even under the most powerful microscope. Only in plant tissues do most of the cells have real walls. In many kinds of animal cells the plasma membrane does not seem to be much more than a boundary, or interface, such as is formed when a drop of oil is suspended in water. Nonetheless, the plasma membrane acts as if it were semisolid.

Within the cell there seems to be a similar arrangement, with the nucleus in a kind of envelope. Besides this, fine particles of protein are suspended in the fluid contents of the cell. The proteins are not dissolved but are colloidal particles, evenly distributed in the fluid. Apparently they are held in place because they all have like electric charges and so repel one another. Protein is, as you know, the essential ingredient of protoplasm, the living matter of the cell.

If the cell is to be nourished and is to get rid of its wastes, food substances must pass in and waste products must pass out through the plasma membrane. At one time it was thought that the membrane has "pores," but this idea has been largely discarded. Passage through the membrane occurs only when the fluids on either side are unequal in concentration; that is, one side must have more dissolved or suspended matter in it than the other. By what is called the process of osmosis (see Index), the two fluids tend to become equal in concentration, with that of less concentration moving toward the other (though there is also a slower and less noticeable movement in the opposite direction).

The plasma membrane is not completely permeable (capable of being penetrated) but semipermeable. It will let some substances pass in or out and not others. In general, it tends to permit water, the solvent, to pass readily but is "selective" in regard to dissolved substances, or solutes. As we have seen, the solutes are composed of ions. Some ions appear to pass in and out much more rapidly than others and some seem to be blocked altogether. In any event, in living tissue a balance of ions on either side of the membrane is never reached. This would account for the difference in electric charges on the inner and outer side of the membrane — a potential difference, which would produce a current if an appropriate pathway were provided. A potential difference is created not only between negative and positive charges but also between charges that are negative and those that are less negative.

An explanation of nerve impulses

The idea of a membrane with different charges on either side is the basis for the most widely accepted explanation of nerve impulses. At rest the membrane of a nerve fiber is positively charged on the outside and negatively charged on the inside, which indicates that the membrane is keeping the ions on either side separated. Since no electrical activity is going on, we say that the area is inactive.

When a nerve impulse reaches any given place in the fiber it seems that the membrane is penetrated. The area then becomes active electrically; its negative and positive ions come together and neutralize one another. Through the neutral gap thus made, ions from the next not-yet-active place along the nerve fiber penetrate. This makes the outer surface of this second area permeable. It, in turn, affects a third place, still farther along the nerve fiber, and so on until the impulse completes its journey. Meanwhile the charges and membrane impermeability of the "rest" state are restored, after a brief interval, to each area in succession. The passage of the

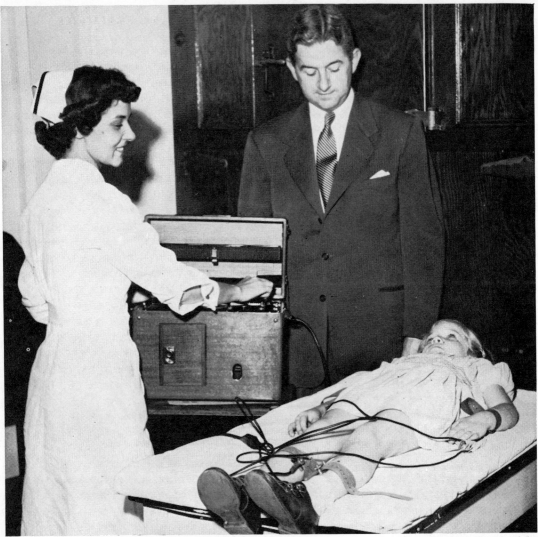

An electrocardiograph at work. The instrument picks up electrical impulses from the beating heart and records them on a moving strip of paper.

nerve impulse is often likened to a spark traveling along a fuse.

This idea of the nerve impulse would also explain the fact that injured nerve is negative because an injury would expose the inner side of the membrane, with its negatively charged ions.

As nerve tissue is rich in potassium, it is thought that potassium ions play an important part in the transmission of the nerve impulse. A complicated compound called acetylcholine that is produced by nerve tissue also enters the picture. Acetylcholine tends to neutralize charges and itself can generate negative electricity. As yet, however, scientists are not sure how the potassium ions and acetylcholine act.

Most of the work in bioelectricity thus far has been in the realm of pure research. Nonetheless, it already has at least two important applications in medicine. By recording the electric impulses generated by the brain and the heart it is possible to detect or pinpoint some disorders of these two important organs.

Of particular interest to the brain specialist are the waves generated by the cerebral cortex. This is the soft, rather thin mantle of folded gray matter that covers the two hemispheres of the cerebrum, much the largest part of the brain. We think and feel and have knowledge of the world about us because of the cerebral cortex. Into its texture are woven thousands of millions of nerve cells. By means of the fibers that extend from each one, the cells communicate with one another and with other areas of the brain and these, in turn, with the rest of the body. The vast number of connections thus made possible staggers the imagination.

Because it lies just beneath the top of the skull, the cortex is, of course, the most accessible part of the brain. So it is possible to get quite close to the cortex by attaching electrodes to the scalp. In some work on animals the brain itself is exposed (with the animal under anesthesia).

From the human cortex, three principal kinds of waves, or rhythms, may be detected. The alpha rhythm has a frequency, or vibration, of 8 to 12 cycles per second and a voltage of from 10 to 100 microvolts — millionths of a volt. It is picked up most easily from the occipital region (the lower back lobe) of the cerebrum — the center of vision — when a person is at rest. With mental effort the rhythm tends to disappear.

The beta rhythm is faster — 18 to 35 cycles per second — and is considered normal if the voltage does not rise above 50 microvolts. This rhythm seems to come most steadily from the frontal lobes and

to be related to the motor-sensory system. (Motor nerves carry messages from the brain to the muscles; sensory nerves carry messages from the sense organs to the brain.)

The delta rhythm is extremely slow, 6 cycles per second or less, and has a voltage of from 20 to 200 microvolts. It appears most often in normal sleep.

There are a few other types of rhythm: gamma, 40 to 50 cycles per second, which is quite rare and is recorded from frontal regions; theta, which is abnormal and has a frequency of 6 per second — it sometimes indicates the presence of a deep tumor; and a "spike," an abnormal sharp wave that lasts no longer than one-tenth of a second and is an indication of epilepsy.

The pattern of brain waves differs with each person. It requires an expert to interpret an electroencephalogram — as the record of the pattern is called. Even then it is used only in the light of other information to diagnose a brain disorder.

A vacuum-tube amplifier is used to magnify the weak brain waves. It may be harnessed in an electroencephalograph or in a cathode-ray oscillograph. The electroencephalograph ("encephalon" is the scientific word for "brain") is the usual

National Film Board

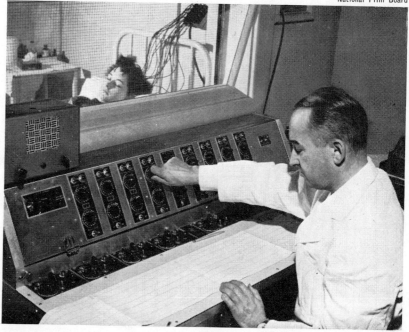

The electroencephalograph in this photo is often used to help diagnose mental illness.

instrument for examining the human brain. The scalp is moistened with a salt solution and electrodes are attached to it, painlessly. They pick up the faint electric signals, which are then relayed through amplifiers and magnified perhaps millions of times. The voltages pass to an electromagnet which, in turn, impels a pen to write the pattern on a moving tape.

In the cathode-ray oscillograph, the magnified voltage is directed against a beam of electrons moving in a cathode-ray tube. The beam is thrown on a fluorescent screen, where it appears as a quivering, luminous line. If the area of the brain being tested flares with increased electrical activity, the line pulses in rhythm with the variation in voltage. The length and height of the line's waves are measures of the electrical activity of the region.

The electrocardiograph
— a recording instrument

The electric impulses that accompany the beat of the heart — the contraction of heart muscles — are recorded by the electrocardiograph. As we indicated earlier, this instrument is a more complicated version of the string galvanometer.

Normally the heart beats about 70 times per minute so that one beat lasts only about 0.86 (6/7) of a second. Yet in that short space of time there is not one contraction but a series of contractions (systoles) and periods of relaxation (diastoles), which together are called the cardiac (heart) cycle. It begins in the right auricle, a little ahead of the left auricle. The auricular systole, by way of a bundle of tissues connecting auricles and ventricles, in turn stimulates the ventricles, which contract together. Each chamber relaxes immediately after its contraction is completed. Thus the auricles are relaxed at about the same instant that the ventricles begin to contract.

Just before each contraction in the cycle there is an electrical change (and probably other changes as well). Active muscle fibers (like nerves) become negative to inactive fibers. Thus the electrocardiograph records the potential differ-

ences set up by each contraction in the cardiac cycle.

The charges are comparatively strong and since the body's fluids are electrolytic solutions, the charges may be detected on the surface of the body by such a sensitive instrument as the electrocardiograph. Its electrodes are used in pairs and must be carefully placed so as to connect unlike charges. One may be placed on the hand and the other on the foot, for in the fraction of a second during which the upper part of the heart contracts, either hand will be more negative than either foot because the hands are closer to the active heart region.

The record, or electrocardiogram, of a healthy heart beat shows a low wave, P, at the beginning of the auricular systole. At the onset of the ventricular systole there is a high wave, QRS. A low wave, T, marks the end of the ventricular systole. Normally, the peak (R) of the highest wave has a value of from 0.70 to 1.80 millivolts — thousandths of a volt. Diseased heart conditions may be revealed by a departure from the normal pattern.

There are a few literally shocking exceptions to the rule of weak bioelectric potentials. These are some fish and related animals of which the best known is the electric eel of the Amazon and Orinoco rivers. It may be as much as 8 feet long and weigh from 40 to 50 pounds. Two-fifths of its body is occupied by an electric organ, with which the eel can defend itself or stun or kill prey. The organ is a mass of specialized muscle and the fish, as needed, can generate a current that may be as powerful as 600 volts. Successive waves of current travel from the front of the organ to the back at a rate of about 980 to 2,700 yards a second.

In this brief article we have been able to touch on only a few phases of bioelectricity. It is not only an enormously complicated science but one in which the unknown bulks much larger than the known. Certainly some of the deepest secrets of life lie hidden in it. But by the same token it offers a thrilling challenge to the imagination and zeal of the pioneer-scientist.